Integrating the Approaches
to Mental Disease

Integrating the Approaches
to
Mental Disease

• •

Two Conferences Held under the Auspices of the

Committee on Public Health

of The New York Academy of Medicine

• •

edited by
H. D. KRUSE, M.D.
EXECUTIVE SECRETARY, COMMITTEE ON PUBLIC HEALTH
THE NEW YORK ACADEMY OF MEDICINE, NEW YORK CITY

A HOEBER-HARPER BOOK

INTEGRATING THE APPROACHES TO MENTAL DISEASE

CONTENTS

first conference

CONTENTS

second conference

PARTICIPANTS

Franz Alexander, M.D., Chief of Staff, Psychiatric Department of Mt. Sinai Hospital, Los Angeles, California; Director of the Institute for Psychiatric and Psychosomatic Research, Mt. Sinai Hospital, Los Angeles, California

Carl A. L. Binger, M.D., Member of the Board of Consultation of the Massachusetts General Hospital, Harvard Medical School, Boston, Massachusetts; Editor-in-Chief, *Psychosomatic Medicine*

George H. Bishop, Ph.D., Professor of Neurophysiology, Department of Psychiatry and Neurology, Washington University School of Medicine, St. Louis, Missouri

Henry W. Brosin, M.D., Director, Western Psychiatric Institute and Clinic; Professor and Chairman of Department of Psychiatry, University of Pittsburgh School of Medicine, Pittsburgh, Pennsylvania

Oswaldo Camargo-Abib, M.D., Mental Hospital Advisor, National Service for Mental Diseases, Rio de Janeiro, Brazil

Norman A. Cameron, M.D., Ph.D., Professor of Psychiatry, Yale University School of Medicine, New Haven, Connecticut

Robert A. Cleghorn, M.D., Associate Professor of Psychiatry, Allan Memorial Institute of Psychiatry, McGill University, Montreal, P.Q., Canada

Stanley Cobb, M.D., D.Sc., Bullard Professor of Neuropathology (*Emeritus*), Harvard Medical School; Formerly, Psychiatrist-in-Chief, Massachusetts General Hospital, Boston, Massachusetts

H. Warren Dunham, Ph.D., Professor of Sociology, Wayne State University, Detroit, Michigan

Robert H. Felix, M.D., Director, National Institute of Mental Health, Bethesda, Maryland

Jacob E. Finesinger, M.D., Professor of Psychiatry, University of Maryland School of Medicine, Baltimore, Maryland

Thomas M. French, M.D., Director of Research, Institute for Psychoanalysis, Chicago, Illinois

Ralph W. Gerard, M.D., Ph.D., D.Sc., Professor of Neurophysiology, Mental Health Research Institute, University of Michigan, Ann Arbor, Michigan

Roy R. Grinker, M.D., Director, Institute for Psychosomatic and Psychiatric Research and Training, Michael Reese Hospital, Chicago, Illinois

G. Ronald Hargreaves, O.B.E., M.R.C.S., L.R.C.P., Professor and Head, Department of Psychiatry, The University of Leeds, Leeds, England

Harold E. Himwich, M.D., Director, Research Division, Galesburg State Research Hospital, Galesburg, Illinois; Professorial Lecturer of Physiology, University of Illinois College of Medicine, Chicago, Illinois

August B. Hollingshead, Ph.D., Professor of Sociology; Director, Program in Medical Sociology, Yale University, New Haven, Connecticut

*Hubert S. Howe, M.D., Formerly Clinical Professor of Neurology, College of Physicians and Surgeons, Columbia University, New York City

William A. Hunt, Ph.D., Professor of Psychology and Biological Sciences, Northwestern University, Evanston, Illinois

Herbert H. Jasper, Ph.D., M.D., Professor of Experimental Neurology, Montreal Neurological Institute, McGill University, Montreal, P.Q., Canada

H. E. King, Ph.D., Associate Professor of Psychiatry (Research Psychology), Tulane University School of Medicine, New Orleans, Louisiana

H. D. Kruse, M.D., Executive Secretary, Committee on Public Health, The New York Academy of Medicine, New York City

Lawrence S. Kubie, M.D., Clinical Professor of Psychiatry, Yale University School of Medicine, New Haven, Connecticut; Faculty, New York Psychoanalytic Institute, New York City; Lecturer, Department of Psychiatry, College of Physicians and Surgeons, Columbia University, New York City

Carney Landis, Ph.D., Sc.D., Professor of Psychology, Columbia University; Principal Research Psychologist, New York State Psychiatric Institute, New York City

Howard S. Liddell, Ph.D., Professor of Psychobiology; Director of Behavior Farm Laboratory, Cornell University, Ithaca, New York

* Deceased, February 4, 1957.

Theodore Lidz, M.D., Professor of Psychiatry and Psychiatrist-in-Chief, Yale University School of Medicine, New Haven, Connecticut

Erich Lindemann, M.D., Professor of Psychiatry and Head of the Department at the Massachusetts General Hospital, Harvard Medical School, Boston, Massachusetts

Donald B. Lindsley, Ph.D., Professor of Psychology, Departments of Psychology and Psychiatry, University of California at Los Angeles, Los Angeles, California

Fred A. Mettler, M.D., Ph.D., Sc.D., Professor of Anatomy, College of Physicians and Surgeons, Columbia University, New York City

Neal E. Miller, Ph.D., James Rowland Angell Professor of Psychology, Yale University, New Haven, Connecticut

Alfred Pope, M.D., Neuropathologist, McLean Hospital, Waverley, Massachusetts; Associate Professor of Neuropathology, Harvard Medical School, Boston, Massachusetts

J. H. Quastel, D.Sc., Ph.D., F.R.S., Director of McGill-Montreal General Hospital Research Institute; Professor of Biochemistry, McGill University, Montreal, P.Q., Canada

Frederick C. Redlich, M.D., Professor and Chairman, Department of Psychiatry, Yale University School of Medicine, New Haven, Connecticut

John R. Rees, M.D., Director, World Federation for Mental Health, London, England

*Thomas A. C. Rennie, M.D., Professor of Psychiatry (Social Psychiatry), Cornell University Medical College, New York City

Derek Richter, M.A., Ph.D., M.R.C.S., Director of Neuropsychiatric Research Centre, Whitchurch Hospital, Cardiff, Wales

David M. Schneider, Ph.D., Department of Anthropology, University of California, Berkeley, California

John P. Scott, Ph.D., Chairman, Division of Behavior Studies, Roscoe B. Jackson Memorial Laboratory, Bar Harbor, Maine

B. F. Skinner, Ph.D., Professor of Psychology, Harvard University, Cambridge, Massachusetts

* Deceased, May 21, 1956.

Eliot T. O. Slater, M.A., M.D., F.R.C.P., Physician in Psychological Medicine, National Hospital, Queen Square, London; Senior Lecturer on Psychiatric Genetics, Institute of Psychiatry, University of London, London, England

Richard L. Solomon, Ph.D., Associate Director, Laboratory of Social Relations, Harvard University, Cambridge, Massachusetts

Kenneth W. Spence, Ph.D., Professor of Psychology, State University of Iowa, Iowa City, Iowa

John P. Spiegel, M.D., Lecturer, Department of Social Relations, Harvard University, Cambridge, Massachusetts

George S. Stevenson, M.D., National and International Consultant, National Association for Mental Health, New York City

Erik Strömgren, M.D., Professor of Psychiatry, University of Aarhus, Risskov, Denmark

Robert J. Weil, M.D., Assistant Professor, Department of Psychiatry, Dalhousie University, Halifax, Nova Scotia, Canada

John C. Whitehorn, M.D., Henry Phipps Professor of Psychiatry, The Johns Hopkins School of Medicine, Baltimore, Maryland

Eric D. Wittkower, M.D., L.R.C.P., L.R.C.S., L.R.F.P.S., C.S.P.Q., Associate Professor of Psychiatry, McGill University, Montreal, P.Q., Canada

PREFACE

Integrating the Approaches to Mental Disease comprises the transactions of two conferences held under the auspices of the Committee on Public Health of The New York Academy of Medicine. Their broad aim was to afford an opportunity to a group of experts who hold different views on the causality, pathogenesis, and therapy of mental disease to come together, to engage in cross-exposition, and to plan research in common.

What was the situation that occasioned the desirability for such a meeting? No one single concept of causality of mental disease is regarded as all-embracing and is accepted universally. Rather, a multiplicity of diverse viewpoints prevails. In considering the different schools of thought on the causality of psychiatric disorders, it is convenient to classify them in four major categories: (1) organic, (2) experimental psychological, (3) psychodynamic, and (4) psychosocial. Each approach, however, is not an indivisible unit. Rather, each has divisions; some have subdivisions. For example, the organic view includes genetics, embryology, histology, biochemistry, physiology, pharmacology, and pathology. Within these special fields, there is subdivision; e.g., neurophysiology, endocrinology, nutrition. Nevertheless, four main schools of thought may be recognized, each with its own approach to the causality of mental disease.

Each of these four groups has its own distinctive methodology, vocabulary, and doctrine. To the others the methods of each are unfamiliar, the language strange, and the concepts esoteric. It is not surprising that this situation has created a barrier to communication among the four groups. Certainly it has done little to encourage investigators to venture beyond their own borders. In a milieu of provincialism, each

group has a nodding acquaintance rather than familiarity with the others. Yet, all are part of the large heterogeneous company serving under one banner in quest of revealing the same shrouding and baffling mystery. This insular grouping is an obstacle to progress in the search for understanding what leads to mental disease.

How did this situation come about? It is a phenomenon not peculiar to mental disease. It is more conspicuous there because of the complex nature of the subject. Segmentation was a natural step in the growth and advance of medical and biological knowledge; indeed, it is a developmental characteristic of science. A challenging problem may have so many pieces that division of labor in the approach becomes a necessity. This practice is readily recognizable under its common name of specialization. Fragmentation is an ineluctable procedure in the acquisition of new facts. Admittedly in concentrating on a small sector, an investigator accumulates a large body of essential information about it. But this plan has its losses as well as its gains. Fragmentation brings a restricted objective and approach. Breadth gives way to depth. Too often, in consequence, for the worker on one piece, there is separation and isolation from the other pieces with a lost sense of relationship; furthermore, preoccupation with one piece tends to lead to disregard of the whole. Intent upon a narrow vista, the specialist may thereby neglect the scanning sweep and panorama in full perspective. Ever-luring analysis leads away from synthesis. As a net effect there is too little organization and integration of new knowledge from all sources. What has occurred in other areas of science is strikingly exemplified in the diverse independent approaches to mental disease.

Without derogation of the analytical

process, what is also needed is breadth in knowledge and view for relating and organizing parts and for comprehending the whole. Synthesis is as important as analysis. Indeed, essential and indispensable as is the analytical approach, integration of the parts and reconstitution are frequently the ultimate goal. Surely there is a place for totality in planning and interpreting, in linking concepts, and in applying prevention and therapy.

To articulate and array the various branches so that they may function as a unit: that is the task. The first obvious step is to bring about mutual understanding. Each must know the language, methods, content, and concepts of the other domains if all are to be related and joined. That is the basis for a multispecialized approach.

Clear as is the grand strategy, the tactical maneuvers are not easily executed. The usual opportunities and occasions for mutual imparting of information, to say nothing of cross-fertilization, have not come into being. No single journal covers all the aspects. The observations, data, and conclusions of the various approaches are not to be found collected within one cover; instead, even in the literature of one country, they are scattered in a number of different journals. There is no permanent over-all organization cutting across conceptual and disciplinary lines to provide a common meeting ground at regular intervals over a sustained period. So, against this background, to meet a manifest need, the Conferences were arranged as a rallying point for the diverse groups.

Specifically the aims of the Conferences were:

1. To re-examine the thesis of each approach. Its fundamental principles and basic supporting evidence should be classified into three categories: (1) what is demonstrable and certain; (2) what is logical, probable, and presumptive; and (3) what is possible.
2. To relate, organize, integrate, and unify what is known within each approach. Each needs to interrelate its own segments and to constitute the parts into a whole.
3. To take a look at the whole and to attempt to relate, organize, integrate, and unify the various conceptual groups. There is a need to explore and search for interrelations and for a larger concept that encompasses all approaches.
4. To denote in this quest what is found to be untenable, overlapping, or unknown.
5. To encourage research with broad objectives for integration of the subject and with joint application of methods, technics, and procedures from the various conceptual schools and specialties.

Admittedly these were high and ambitious aims; nevertheless the results were most encouraging. It was not to be expected that two meetings would produce the solution to mental disease, neatly packaged for immediate use. The Conferences were convened in full awareness that the reach would probably exceed the grasp; at this moment the reach is an important movement. Actually there were obvious and substantial gains. For diverse groups to assemble and consider the problem as an essential initial action was in itself an achievement. Even to criticize one another's approaches more knowingly must be counted an advance. Above all, there was earnest effort toward the objective of coming into a relationship. Here was an occasion when specialists of different persuasions, skills, and vocabularies meeting together attempted to plan a combined, unified approach—that was an important step forward.

This is a book for all, whatever their special field, who are interested in mental disease or engaged in investigating the antecedents conducing to it, who seek a panoramic view of this area with its vast, complex constellation of influences, who wish to observe specialists attempting to design a plan for uniting different divisions into a joint enterprise, a multidisciplinary approach, and who want to know the difficulties and obstacles, surmountable for the most part, that are encountered in the endeavor.

To the participants in the Conferences who are the real authors of this book, the

Editor once again would express his deepest gratitude. Whatever measure of merit is accorded this book, it should be attributed wholly and unqualifiedly to them.

It is a pleasure to express my appreciation to the Rockefeller Brothers Fund for its generous support of the enterprise.

I desire also to record my thanks to Mrs. Thelma Pierce Anderson for her indefatigable assistance in the preparation of this work.

H. D. K.

New York

INTRODUCTION

Presented in the First Conference are the principles and underlying evidence of the four major approaches to mental disease. In addition, within each school of thought, individual differences and nuances in interpretation are brought out for the sake of completeness. After pointing out the landmarks of each domain and imparting the characterizing theories and salient underlying observations, representatives engaged in the search for areas of interagreement. This step was preparatory to entering upon zones of interdoctrinal unacceptance. In this latter area, issues were raised, not to accentuate or magnify them, but to settle them. It was recognized that they must be resolved if there is to be a harmonious larger whole.

After this exploration of the extent of acceptance of each other's concepts and principles and of the points still at issue, the evidence of interrelation between doctrines was marshaled to indicate the basis for integration and the amount of data available for it. The final topic in the First Conference has to do with the next steps for further interrelation and integration. It may be clearly seen that none of the schools of thought believes it alone has or can provide the complete answer to the problem of mental disease. To the proposition that there is a place for investigative projects designed with a combined approach is given implied assent. Further on a practical plane, the deliberations reach a point of considering the *modus operandi* of multidisciplinary research on mental disorders.

As the First Conference drew to a close, it became apparent that not all points at issue had been aired during the allotted period, that they were coming out into the open belatedly when integration was the item of business, that the crisis which was to be expected as a natural antecedent of resolution was brewing, but that neither the crisis nor the resolution would be reached before the termination of the session. Another conference was therefore scheduled so that the process might run its course.

The Second Conference, the transactions of which comprise the latter part of this book, was similar in the main to the first but had modifications in both plan and content. Also several new participants were in attendance, and a new group of exponents set forth the positions of the four schools. Interestingly enough, as might be expected, these expositions were quite different from the first. It is evident that two scientists, though similarly oriented, do not advance the thesis of their position identically.

As a means of inducing the frankest exchange of views, four different teams, each comprising one representative from each approach, met in advance of the plenary session to discuss respectively the items on the agenda: areas of acceptance; areas of unacceptance; clinical principles in the practice of psychiatry, their clarification, validation, or refutation; and an outline of decisive studies with an interdisciplinary approach on causation of mental disease.

In the transactions of both the team meetings and the plenary session, it developed that the four doctrinal approaches constituted a spectrum in the following sequence: organic, experimental psychological, psychodynamic, and psychosocial. Each was found to have its own frame of reference, vocabulary, and methodology. Surprising but comprehensible was the development that the two schools of thought which were farthest apart manifested the fewest points of unacceptance. Between them prevailed a spirit of mutual respect born of unfamiliarity. The organic and the experimental psychological schools showed a mutual understanding and rapport on a different basis, similarity in methodology. For still different reasons, the psychodynamic and the psychosocial disciplines displayed a close relationship. In points of issue the lines were drawn between the psychodynamic versus the organic and experimental psychological. Difficulties in communication and differences in methodology were the outstanding reasons.

The sessions reached their climax in an attempt to design a study with an interdisciplinary approach. Then it was manifest that on a theoretical level there was much tolerance on all sides, but that differences developed rapidly in concrete situations. Thus the transactions clearly reveal the basis of difficulties of mutual understanding and of planning a combined research project by the four approaches. At the same time it is highly encouraging to observe that these difficulties are not an insuperable obstacle. In the concluding chapters may be observed the degree to which the various conferees achieved a "convergence of viewpoint."

The concept of etiology as embraced by modern psychiatry differs from the simple cause and effect system of traditional medicine. It subscribes to a "field theory" hypothesis in which the interactions and transactions of multiple factors eventuate in degrees of health or sickness.

—National Advisory Mental Health Council,
EVALUATION IN MENTAL HEALTH, 1955

first CONFERENCE

chapter *1*

The Organic Position
on Etiology

RALPH W. GERARD

• •

Some four years ago in this city I had the pleasure of giving the Menas Gregory Lecture in which I said:

Avoid the disaster and confusion that results from the careless admixture of different levels of discourse. Mind does not act on matter, nor matter on mind. There are only an antecedent mind-body state and a consequent mind-body state, whether mental or physical aspect chances to present more acutely . . . This can all be given point at a favorite level of argument, as to the cause or genesis of psychoses. The constitutionalists and the organicists and environmentalists and mentalists too often are quarreling with each other as to which of them has *the* cause. Now it is obviously useful to find out that schizophrenics have abnormal capillaries in their fingers, that they had abnormal experiences in their childhood, and that they have abnormal individuals as parents or sibs; but one does not exclude the other and no one of them can possibly be the whole story.

That statement indicates my own predilection toward an eclectic viewpoint in this area. Indeed, it was only under masterly pressure that I was persuaded to present to you the organic biological viewpoint. So perhaps I can borrow from what most of the people in this room have said at one time or another and try to make a story from that viewpoint.

Perhaps even with an eclectic orientation there is some justification for now stressing the biological viewpoint. Somewhere or other Freud wrote, "I have not emphasized the biological factors in mental disease because others have done so sufficiently." As the result of his own work in the interim the other factors have been emphasized with sufficient vigor and generousness so that perhaps it is not amiss to call attention again to some of the biological factors.

I take it that our objective in this Conference is to attempt to define more sharply and collectively our concepts, to see clearly areas of definite agreement or disagreement, and so, if possible, to bring into focus opportunities for further research. That this is necessary certainly needs no documentation; for I cannot help recalling a presentation just last week by a dynamic psychiatrist on the problem of pain. In his presentation there was not a single word about afferent impulses or an actual peripheral lesion, or what he was talking about, phantom limb pain. Some of the biologically minded people present were very much disturbed by the entire consideration of pain in terms of personality constellations. Actually, of course, he had not mentioned the peripheral factors because, as he said later, he had taken them for granted.

But it remained true that the biologists were talking one language and the analyst was talking another; and there was no attempt whatsoever to translate them. This I submit is a rather dangerous schizophrenic situation in the area with which we are concerned.

Let me remind you, perhaps too categorically, of some of the relations that are true biologically. I would say first that the biological, clinical, and psychological evidence justifies the belief that the various types of insanity are true disease entities or groups of entities. The general incidence, I understand, of schizophrenia and the manic-depressive state tends to be alike throughout the world—even though Dr. Cobb has pointed out that the state line between New Hampshire and Vermont makes a tremendous difference in the "incidence" of involutional psychoses! The records of a number of families obtained in the East in the first decade of this century and those of their descendants in recent years have been studied. The families have been traced around the country and it turns out that those which had members receiving the diagnosis of schizophrenia in 1910 continue to have members with the same diagnosis in 1950, and similarly in respect to manic-depressive psychosis, although entirely different people made the diagnoses under apparently quite different detailed criteria.

It has been suggested that each of the diseases, schizophrenia and cyclothymia, may itself not be a nosological entity but be composed of several subdivisions. Various tests have been applied singly to groups of schizophrenics, each test to a different group. The fact that the results show a division on a two-to-one basis so frequently— for example, two-thirds react to ACTH, one-third does not; two-thirds have an abnormal sugar tolerance or insulin tolerance curve, one-third does not; two-thirds react one way to the mecholyl blood pressure tests, one-third another way—is not conclusive evidence that schizophrenia is not a clinical entity. What should be done is to apply all these tests to the same group of individuals. If it should turn out that the same individuals fall into the same groups on different

tests, that should be practically conclusive evidence for a real nosological difference. So far as I know it has not been done; it cries to be carried out.

This procedure was successfully used in studies on hypnosis. When a battery of tests was applied to a population group comprising both hypnotizable and nonhypnotizable persons, no differences were revealed. But it was noticed that the hypnotizable persons could be further divided into two separate subgroups on the basis of their response to the galvanic skin resistance; and finally, for the whole sample of the population, three clearly definable subgroups were established. One was normal and two were hypnotizable, each differing from "normal" in opposite ways.

Secondly, brain pathology, structural or dynamic, may or may not have been found —there is rather sharp disagreement among the experts—in the histological area. Some say that visible pathology is present in 50 per cent of the schizophrenics; others, that none is to be seen at all. No enzyme abnormality in the cortex as yet has been found. Certainly one can get severe symptoms with very insignificant lesions or with no demonstrable lesion of any kind; and, conversely, one can have very severe lesions with no demonstrable symptomatology. The organicists interpret this situation to mean merely that investigators have not found the lesion or have not examined carefully enough for the behavioral defect, as the case may be. Hence, more and more tests are developed in the search for differences in behavior. But there are certainly such sudden changes in the behavior of an individual that they could not reasonably be related to an equally sudden change in the material substrate of behavior. For example, there is the sudden shift in the schizophrenic during a few minutes, from clarity to confusion, with an attendant increase in heart rate.

As the third major point, there are biochemical and physiological abnormalities in schizophrenics. In mentioning some of them I would be inclined myself to agree with Pierre Janet who said, "The chemist will solve dementia praecox." The response to the Quick hippuric acid test, for example, is significant. This procedure tests the ability of the body to change benzoic acid into hippuric acid by coupling it with glycine. If a disturbance in this ability is present, it apparently is due to inability to mobilize glycine, not to interference in the coupling. The test is dramatically positive when symptoms are acute; it fades out in the remissions. Of course, this reminds us of the reverse finding of the increased hippuric acid in the urine in anxiety states. Similarly, the Felix test reveals disturbances in amino acid metabolism. Specifically, it discloses an inability of the body to handle p-oxy-phenylpyruvic acid, a compound related to tyrosine. These results in turn make one think of oligophrenic phenylketonuria, in which there is a twentyfold increase in the blood glycine. All of these phenomena suggest a disturbance in amino acid metabolism. So much on the amino acid side.

On the carbohydrate side the story, of course, is old and well known. The results of the glucose tolerance, the Exton and Rose, and the insulin tolerance tests, the presence of anti-insulin factors in the urine in schizophrenics, are all perfectly well known and perhaps related to insulin shock therapy. The best biochemical evidence today is to the effect that the extra energy used by the nervous system under stimulation in convulsions is a noncarbohydrate fuel. The idea that carbohydrate is the sole source of brain metabolism has become a dogma, but it is not correct.

There is evidence which, if correct, would suggest that schizophrenia cannot be solely and perhaps not even primarily a disease of the nervous system. Two lines of evidence prompt the inference of an abnormal metabolism of the red blood corpuscles in schizophrenics: one, Weil-Malherbe finds that the erythrocytes of schizophrenic persons have greater ability to counteract the antihexokinase action of brain, a very important phenomenon; the other, Dr. Boszermeny-Nagy, my colleague, seems to be finding evidence of an abnormal glycolytic process in the red blood corpuscles of schizophrenics. Funkenstein and his colleagues have noted differences in the reactivity of the ortho- and parasympathetic systems in schizophrenics, and others have found differences in stress reaction of the autonomic system and in the reaction of the adrenal cortex to ACTH or of the target organs to cortisone. These and such phenomena as the behavioral disturbances in pernicious anemia and athiaminosis indicate that neurological symptoms may originate from disturbances primarily outside the central nervous system.

The fourth source of support for the biological position is the evidence from the genetic approach, particularly the well-known experiments of Kallmann. The expectancy rate of schizophrenia in the general population, based on figures from surveys, has never exceeded 1 to 2 per cent. The expectancy of schizophrenia in schizophrenic families is nearly 10 per cent; of manic-depressive psychosis in those families, essentially 0. Conversely, in manic-depressive families the expectancy rate of manic-depressive psychosis is 21 per cent. When consanguinity is taken into account, the tremendously impressive expectancy figures for schizophrenia and manic-depressive psychosis, respectively, in half-siblings are 7 and 17 per cent; in full siblings, 14 and 23 per cent; in dizygotic twins, 14 and 26 per cent, and in monozygotic twins, 86 and 96 per cent. I do not see how one can possibly throw out these figures on the basis of an even greater similarity of environment for identical twins than for fraternal twins; they are undoubtedly true in view of the sharp differences in the types of psychoses. It might be interesting to compare these figures with those from some comparable studies not involving mental pathology; for example, the work on intelligence in twins by Newman, Freeman and Holzinger.[*] They recorded the difference in IQ between paired individuals for those raised together and those raised apart, respectively: for orphan pairs, 18 and 18; for full sibs, 14.5 and 15.5, not much different; for monozygotic twins, the difference drops to 5.9 together and 7.7 apart. In the well-known studies on musical virtuosity, it was shown that superiority appears in the great ones always before six years of age. Over two-thirds of the parents of these individuals have shown outstanding talent in music. These are familiar matters. The genetic evidence seems to be reasonably impressive although I am not qualified to evaluate it: Schizophrenia apparently passes as a recessive factor; manic-depression as a dominant.

Fifthly, the finding that psychoses may be induced by drugs, for which I suggest the name, psychosomimetic, is a major piece of evidence that there is an organic element in mental disorders. Mescaline can reproduce much of the symptomatology of schizophrenia. Whether the manifestations are identical or not I do not know; but the drug produces its effects much more easily in schizophrenics than in normals. Schizophrenics who have been treated by psychosurgery and have lost their symptoms will have these symptoms recur, the same ones, under the action of mescaline, although they are likely to be less vigorous. Mescaline, Amytal, lysergic acid, given to the same individual, produce different constellations of symptoms; that is, they can produce different psychoses in the same person. We know something about the biochemical action of these agents. Mescaline interferes with some oxidations; lysergic acid seems to interfere with phosphoglucomutase in relation to oxidation and glycolysis of carbohydrates; Amytal decouples oxidative phosphorylations. It is therefore highly suggestive that different biochemical actions on the brain by different agents produce different constellations of mental disturbance.

Finally, the favorable response of psychotic persons to chemical and physical therapy is another strong argument for the existence of an organic element in mental disease. The measure of success with insulin, Metrazol, and electric stimulation need not here be detailed. Then there is the record of the deteriorated schizophrenic patient who has paid no attention to anything for years and who becomes *en rapport* with his surroundings in a few minutes upon administration of carbon dioxide, even giving detailed reports of what was happening when he apparently was unable to respond. Further evidence comes from the recovery of paretics under treatment with malaria or penicillin.

In concluding I should like to say that I personally feel that in the mental diseases, the psychoses specifically, we are dealing with violins of which the construction, tuning, and playing are bad. In the research program that I would envisage—and I am sure none of this is really original—if we can identify the population, that is the nosological delimitation of the disease, define the type and range of individual variation, develop adequate criteria for change in mental state and performance, and then go on to identify and quantify the etiological factors involved, locate them as to time when they act—for that is not often remembered and their effect might be quite different whether they act early or late—then when all of that is done, we will be prepared to face in detail the questions of the precise mechanisms from the environment through the mind, the nervous system, and the soma, and of the way in which the causal relations run.

chapter 2

The Experimental Psychological Position on Etiology

CARNEY LANDIS

• •

That part of knowledge which deals with the behavior and mental experience of the individual is called psychology. When knowledge concerning behavior and mental experience is organized according to certain principles, it is called the science of psychology; and when the systematization meets still more rigorous criteria, we arrive at the scientific discipline known as experimental psychology.

Everyman (spelled with a capital *E*) thinks that he knows what psychology is and almost Everyman considers himself a good psychologist. Everyman understands (or thinks he does) most other people's actions and thoughts. Everyman can explain (more or less adequately) his own behavior. Everyman feels that if he exerted himself sufficiently, he probably could control other people's behavior; and although he has his doubts as to whether he can control other people's thinking, he is always willing to try.

Everyman suspects Psychologists (spelled with a capital *P*). Everyman is unsure whether these professional practitioners are really better Psychologists than he, or whether they are charlatans. Many of the positive statements made by Psychologists seem to Everyman to be an odd mixture of the obvious plus topics best not mentioned in polite society; and many of the negative statements of the Psychologists seem to Everyman to be fatuous denials of ordinary common sense.

Every now and then Everyman meets, or is told about, behavior or experience of some individual which seems to him to be most unusual or peculiar. This behavior or conversation is so foreign to Everyman's ideas of common sense and appropriate behavior that he calls the person crazy. On such occasions Everyman is willing to listen somewhat skeptically to the learned explanations given by Psychologists. It also happens in the life of Everyman that at times he cannot understand or control his own thoughts or behavior. He accounts for such aberrations by saying he has had spells when he is "out of his mind" or that he was so upset that he thought he would go crazy.

Hence, although Everyman does understand most people (and himself) most of the time, it does occasionally happen that he is baffled and astonished by behavior and experience which are unusual and abnormal. Much of this astonishing behavior is today designated as mental disease. The mission of the present Conference is to review the thinking now current as to the causes, explanations, and next steps toward better understanding of these unusual conditions, most of which are truly inexplicable.

Psychology is systematic scientific knowledge concerning the entirety of the behavior and mental life of mankind. The guiding ideas in the organization of all science are classification, cause, probability, and prediction. The ways in which Everyman characterizes and classifies unusual and abnormal people are descriptive but not systematic. To say that a person is insane, crazy, out-of-his-mind, nervous, queer, mad, cracked, unbalanced, idiotic, or half-witted does not lead to any better understanding of the abnormality. At the present time such peculiar people are usually classified into five groups.

1. The psychotics are those who exhibit marked deviations from normal behavior. These individuals are said by the medical profession to be suffering from some form of mental disease, while by the legal profession they are designated as insane. These persons exhibit peculiar behavior and gross disorders of their mental life, which are often so severe that they may endanger their own existence and well-being, as well as that of their fellows.

2. The neurotics are those persons who are troubled but not legally insane, and who are said by the medical profession to be suffering from one or another mental disease, disorders which are milder than are the psychoses. Neurotics are usually able to carry on their daily lives after a fashion, although with nowhere near the efficiency which might be expected of them were they not preoccupied with morbid fears, anxieties, compulsions, and obsessions.

3. Next, there is a borderline group of persons who feel that their usual response to the demands of everyday life are unsatisfactory. They are neither insane nor suffering from a mental disease. Such individuals complain of feelings of inferiority, feelings of discrimination, jealousy, unwarranted suspicion, overenthusiasm, exaggerated emotional reactions, mild depressions, chronic unreasonable irritability, or violent likes and dislikes. Generally, these borderline persons are problems to themselves and only secondarily are they problems to society.

4. The sociopaths (or psychopathic personalities) are not, as a rule, mentally or physically ill or insane, but their behavior is socially disturbing and socially inadequate. This group includes delinquents, criminals, some alcoholics, the moral imbeciles, and certain of those said to be sexually abnormal. They are social problems, but are usually not problems to themselves.

5. Finally there are the aments who, from a very early age, lack the ability to acquire knowledge or to profit from experience and training. These persons we term mentally deficient or feeble-minded.

These five groups include the majority of human beings who are called "abnormal" and whose behavior and experience puzzle Everyman. And at this point Everyman includes all scientists as well as all Psychologists.

By way of illustration, suppose that any of us knew five hundred persons. Among that five hundred there would probably be fifteen or twenty who are considered abnormal. Of these, three or four would be feeble-minded, three or four would be criminal or delinquent, three or four would be psychotic, while the remaining six or seven would be neurotic or borderline persons.

The five-group everyday classification is based on a mixture of criteria referable to the law, medicine, sociology, and psychology. This classification is relatively unsatisfactory for the further aims of any one of these disciplines. It does illustrate the point that no single or small number of etiological explanations will suffice for all of mental disease and disorder.

Having stated these dimensions of the problem, it is next in order to outline certain of the principles and concepts used in experimental psychology. The basic postulate of the experimental psychologist is that man is a biological organism, and that his behavior and mental life must be explained by means of concepts which are concordant with those of the biological sciences. We start then with the human organism which is capable of physiological and of psychological modes of operation. When we advance from simple description of psychological phenomena to their causes and explanations, we find—just as was found with the physiological operations of breathing, contracting, conducting, or digesting—that the agencies considered basic to psychological events are all bodily. It has not been found basically necessary to assume either conscious or unconscious agents, or energy. Although many psychologists do utilize concepts involving mental or psychogenic causes, it is usually acknowledged that these terms are used as a matter of convenience, and that consciousness or unconsciousness are functions wholly sustained by bodily mechanisms.

If we actually observe the human organism as it functionally operates in planning, doubting, believing, perceiving, emoting, or thinking, we may conceive that the government, control, and effective operation rest with three interacting sources; namely, extraorganic factors, the state of the organism, and the historical residues. (The word "government" as used here denotes that which others have termed purpose, drive, dynamics of mind, or springs of human activity.)

Extraorganic factors as determinants of behavior are of many sorts and occur in many different temporal relationships. Although the living body is a relatively independent physical system, maintaining through its life-span its integrity of being and of activity, its course is variously shaped and partially governed from the outside. Extraorganic or environmental government is not of itself a sufficient source of all behavior determination. It is self-evident that the output and outcome of action depend quite as much on the immediate status of the organism as they do on the action of extraorganic components.

To say that the state of the organism is a determinant of many physiological events has become trite, while the converse of this statement frequently has been overlooked. For example, to mention the effect of ideas on digestion, or of emotion on circulation, is commonplace. Only recently has psychosomatic medicine started to consider the effect of indigestion on hating, or of high blood pressure on remembering. It must also be borne in mind that any theory of psychology or of psychopathology must stay within the boundaries imposed by the anatomy and physiology of the human organism. For example, no amount of psychological theorizing can surmount the functional limitations imposed by an as yet undeveloped brain and nervous system of the newborn infant.

The third category of governing determinants is constituted by the historical residues or memory traces, and habitual modes of behavior. These residues represent those factors and occasions from the organism's past which are effective at the present. A clear acknowledgment of the role of an organism's history in governing and misgoverning is of value in distinguishing the biological and the biographical pasts of the organism. Either or both the biological and biographical pasts are effective in the present and future organic control, a control which affects both physiological and psychological functions.

This organizational scheme is more or less implicit in the thinking of most of present-day academic psychologists (with the exception of those psychologists who call themselves behaviorists or operationalists). The experimental psychologist who subscribes to this scheme usually proceeds to organize the evidence which he will regard as relevant to causation or etiology of mental disease in terms of three further concepts; namely, constitution, maturation, and growth-through-exercise.

Constitution is the resultant of the interaction of heredity and the extraorganic and historical residues, that is the environment since conception. The hereditary pattern of psychobiological organization was determined at the instant of conception, or perhaps one should say that it was determined by biochemical patterns present in the sperm and ovum. In certain respects the maturation of this patterned organism is an automatic process in the sense that a chemical reaction is automatic. Coordinate with maturation is growth-through-exercise. The present status of an individual, either healthy or diseased, can be related to the interaction of constitution, maturation, and growth-through-exercise.

Examples of such action and interaction with respect to psychopathological conditions may aid in clarifying this formulation. The interaction of heredity and maturation is shown in Huntington's chorea. This disease depends on a definite Mendelian genetic dominant determinant which has in one family been traced over a period of three hundred years through twelve successive generations. The disease usually has its onset between thirty-five and forty years of age with mental and physical abnormalities which become apparent without recognizable preformation or provocation. There is first a gradual onset of jerky, uncoordinated, choretic movements, together with an increasing irritability, excitability, quick-temperedness, and a lack of self-control. This is followed by disorders in judgment, failure of insight, various personality deviations, and finally a very marked or a complete mental deterioration. This mental disease constitutes an example of the interaction of heredity and maturation without evidence of influence of extraorganic factors, historical residues, or growth-through-exercise.

The interaction of extraorganic factors, hereditary determinants, and growth-through-exercise is illustrated by the mental disorder known as combat neurosis. Soldiers subjected to the stress of prolonged front line combat frequently emerge suffering from uncontrollable anxiety, hysteria, or profound depression. Sargant and Slater [6] found that over half of these combat neurosis patients had records of neuro-psychiatric disorders occurring in their immediate families. Combat neurosis may be said to occur in those individuals in whom heredity provides the potentiality while the extraorganic stress and threat of life provoke and precipitate the disorder. Seemingly, maturation plays little or no role in this condition.

Delirium tremens presents a psychopathological condition which may be said to depend on extraorganic factors, maturation, and exercise, with little or no evidence of an hereditary determinant. Ordinarily delirium tremens occurs in persons who are of normal, healthy family stock. These individuals have an extraordinarily high tolerance for alcohol and have drunk heavily for many years without marked ill effect. Finally and frequently an injury or physical illness lowers resistance, so that the ingestion

of alcohol precipitates the violent psychotic reactions of delirium tremens. The experience itself is so frightening that, as a rule, the patient remains dry for some months following such an episode. If he returns to heavy drinking, he is very apt to experience another attack. In other words, the process of maturation and exercise has brought his constitution to the point where overindulgence in alcohol produces a specific psychotic state.

Returning now to the viewpoint of the experimental psychologist with respect to the etiology of mental disease, it is apparent that he has organized his thinking in terms of predisposition (which depends on the interaction of heredity, maturation, and exercise), preformation (which depends on the gradual development in the direction of a particular deviation), and on provocation (that is, the precipitating incident or stress).

Having thus defined the position and certain of the concepts utilized by the experimental psychologist, an example of a psychopathological condition may be selected and considered from this viewpoint.

An outstanding psychopathological experience or symptom is that of hallucination, which is an organized perceptual experience without known or definable external stimulation. Hallucinations do not seem to be chance events. They have many systematic, but peculiar, referent conditions. Hallucinations occur as organized perceptions in any sense modality or combination of modalities. They are not jumbles of noise or flashes of light but are, for example, auditory perceptions of meaningful spoken words or messages made by a definitely seen person. Hallucinations are almost always said to be unpleasant experiences which carry with them an irresistible emotional content. They cannot voluntarily be started, stopped, changed, or modified. They are personalized and usually externalized, that is, the voices, visions, or odors are outside the person having the experience, or if inside, are not part of himself. To the hallucinator these experiences are as real as any reality he has ever experienced; the experience intrudes; the experience cannot be ignored.

Hallucinations occur during the course

of many varieties of mental and neurological diseases. Occasionally they may occur in otherwise normal persons, particularly during toxic or febrile illness and in exhaustion states. They are sometimes unilateral. Auditory hallucinations have been reported in persons who have been deaf from childhood. They may be induced by drugs such as mescaline, cocaine, or hashish.

Several years ago, Klüver [3], from the standpoint of the experimental psychologist, reviewed some part of the literature on hallucinations, combining with this review the report of some of his experiments with self-induced mescaline hallucinations. In mescaline hallucinations, Klüver distinguished hallucinatory constants referable to three perceptual levels; namely, the level of form constants; the level of alterations in the number, size, and shape of visual perceptions; and the level of changes in the spatial and temporal relations of the material. These levels were not unique for hallucination but occur in other, and normal, visual experience. On the basis of such evidence, Klüver concluded that hallucinations produced in mescaline intoxication are distortions of ordinary visual experience, and that they may be very close and possibly identical in form and content to the hallucinations of schizophrenic patients. Some patients who have recovered from schizophrenia and have been given mescaline for experimental purposes have said that the hallucinatory process is quite similar in either condition.

Equally significant with the origin of this experience is the question of content of hallucinations. The similarity of hallucinations to dreams during sleep is obvious. Vivid imagery and emotion are not uncommon during our dreams. It is not uncommon on awakening to find that we have been crying, laughing, or sweating. But hallucinations are much more than vivid daydreams. A daydream can be stopped or started, its dreamlike quality is comprehended as such, so that the dreamer, not the dream, is the master. Many dreams seem to have a symbolic quality; they may be considered as the living out in imagery of the repressed or forgotten wishes of the dreamer. It is not uncommon for theorists to attempt to find a communality of symbolism in dreams and in hallucinations. For example, if a childless woman has an hallucination of many babies, such an hallucinatory experience could be interpreted as a projection of her emotional wishes. But when the same woman first sees a single chair, and then suddenly sees a row of chairs, it would not seem likely that repressed emotional factors were responsible for the multiplicity. Any object, event, or idea may have a historical residue of emotional significance. A patient with a crippled arm saw in his hallucinations persons around him who were also crippled, while a blind patient saw heads with empty eye sockets. That a particular object should appear in hallucination connected with some emotional need seems no more significant than the fact that our ordinary perception of actual objects may be modified in meaning by the attendant conditions during which we see these objects.

The topic of hallucination has been considered at some length since it illustrates something of the procedure and approach of the experimental psychologist. There is still no answer from any source as to the basis or meaning (if any) of hallucinatory experience; but experimental psychology has a definite position to take in the organization of such knowledge as is available.

This brings me to a brief survey of the position of the experimental psychologist with respect to the central problem of psychiatry; namely, schizophrenia. The findings of the medical geneticists, particularly those of Kallmann [2], indicate that in certain family stocks, this disease occurs much more frequently than chance would provide. The family history studies and the collection of life histories of identical twins where one or both were suffering from this condition have demonstrated beyond the benefit of doubt the importance of hereditary predisposition. Since the disease is extremely rare before age fifteen, there must be a large maturational factor acting together with heredity in the predisposition. There is very little acceptable controlled scientific information available concerning the preformative extraorganic or historical residue circumstances which may be related to schizophrenia. One can say that if a certain family stock is free from the predisposition for schizophrenia, no member of the family will develop the disorder no matter what circumstances occur. In a family stock in which there are a fair number of relatives with schizophrenia, one can predict that if sufficient preformative circumstances (not further defined) have occurred, the disease *may* result. The psychological description of the behavior of these individuals in terms of narcissism, repression, and regression is of small value to the experimental psychologist in his speculations as to the etiology of the disease process or to the psychological experience of the schizophrenic patient. If, on the other hand, one considers the almost omnipresent experience of hallucinations which most schizophrenic patients report, one can understand something of the immediate basis of their peculiar behavior. These hallucinations commonly are of the auditory variety and are experienced as outside voices or thoughts forced upon the patient. Frequently the voices or thoughts purport to be of some divine or evil agency. The patient must, in some fashion, integrate this experience into all of the rest of his everyday life. In attempting to do this he may build delusional systems, he may retreat into a state of mutism, or he may show catatonic symptoms. Associated with the hallucinations are the experiences of acute but vague and unreasonable fears together with transient physical pains. This fear and pain, added to the disorders of his perceptual world, seem a sufficient basis for the peculiar schizophrenic apathy and emotional outbursts.

The experimental psychologist would summarize his approach somewhat as follows. This disorder occurs only in those individuals with an hereditary predisposition and whose developmental maturation has progressed to or beyond adolescence. Little is known concerning the nature of the preformative circumstances. The provoking extraorganic conditions are so diverse that one suspects that they may be irrelevant. The peculiarities of the psychotic behavior are understandable in terms of an organism reacting as best it can to the usual percep-

tual and emotional elements of hallucination, fear, and pain.

In concluding, be it noted that I have already emphasized the fact that Everyman considers himself a Psychologist—as indeed, in a sense, he is. It has been urged by some critics that experimental psychology has the greatest treasury of negative knowledge of any of the scientific disciplines. Perhaps it has. Many experiments have been carefully done and recorded showing the fallacy of beliefs commonly called "common-sense psychology" both by the man-on-the-street or by other scientists. To cite a few random examples: It has been shown that one cannot judge character, personality, or success in business from a photograph; that one cannot cause another to turn around by staring at the back of his neck; that very high intelligence—genius—is not associated with insanity or a frail physique; or that surgical excision of frontal lobe tissue does not result in loss of intelligence, as measured by objective tests. In order to acquire valid positive knowledge it is first necessary to test whether or not "common-sense" knowledge is true or untrue. In spite of the necessity of testing the validity of common-sense knowledge at every step of the way, the experimental psychologist has made many positive contributions to knowledge concerning the etiology of mental disease, and he may be expected to continue to do so.

In summary the position of the experimental psychologist with respect to the etiology of mental disease is this: There is and should be as much legitimate speculation as possible when any person or group of persons is confronted with an unsolved problem. *The etiology of mental disease is an unsolved problem.* The methods and approach, the concepts and the skills of the experimental psychologist are such that he may be said to have as much—or as little— to contribute as any other relevant scientific discipline. Today many problems of this sort are attacked by research teams. The experimental psychologist has a place on research teams whose goal is the solution of the problem of the etiology of mental disease.

The experimental psychologist has developed, utilized, and passed on to science in general, including medical science, methods, procedures and findings which grew out of the viewpoint of scientific psychology. There is no official dogma or party-line in scientific psychology. There is only the same basic attitude that characterizes any true scientist; namely, the careful collection of factual evidence from the maximum number of observations which may be afforded by opportunity. This collection is followed by legitimate generalizations, conceptualizations, and evaluations which any qualified expert can make—the whole being presented as the best judgment possible at the moment, and that judgment being as little tinged with dogma and bias as is humanly possible.

REFERENCES

1. BENTLEY, M. "General and Experimental Psychology," Chap. 15 in *The Problem of Mental Disorder,* M. Bentley and E. V. Cowdry (Eds.). New York: McGraw-Hill, 1934.

2. KALLMANN, F. J. *Heredity in Health and Mental Disorder.* New York: W. W. Norton, 1953.

3. KLÜVER, H. "Mechanisms of Hallucination," Chap. 10 in *Studies in Personality,* Q. McNamar and M. A. Merrill (Eds.). New York: McGraw-Hill, 1942.

4. LANDIS, C. A modern dynamic psychology, J. Comp. & Physiol. Psychol., 1947, 40: 135–141.

5. LANDIS, C., and BOLLES, M. M. *Textbook of Abnormal Psychology* (Rev. Ed.). New York: Macmillan, 1950.

6. SARGANT, W., and SLATER, E. Acute war neuroses. Lancet, 1940, 2: 1–2.

chapter **3**

The Psychodynamic Position on Etiology

LAWRENCE S. KUBIE

• •

INTRODUCTION

The purpose of this Conference is to reduce to their essentials the divergences among certain viewpoints on the psychogenesis and psychodynamics of mental disease. The assumption is implicit that these viewpoints are conflicting or at least alternative approaches. If this is so, then to reconcile them or to clarify the issues between them would serve a useful purpose; but we cannot attempt this without first eliminating those tacit premises which are misleading and invalid. For instance, the over-all title might be understood to mean that mental diseases are all one, which is patently untrue. Moreover the topic which was assigned to me seems to imply that it is possible to be clear about the forces which play a role in the genesis and shaping of mental disease, without first clarifying the dynamics of normal psychological functions from which disturbed functions deviate. Yet we have no right to assume that mental disease and normal psychological function have unrelated etiologies and dynamics. The issue is whether health and illness are wholly different states or bands on a continuous spectrum. Their paths must diverge at some point, of course, but it makes both a practical and a theoretical difference whether this divergence occurs early or late in the evolution of illness out of health.

Therefore it seems to me that for the sake of clarity we must begin our discussion of the specific topic of this symposium by describing the genesis of psychological processes in general, deferring until later a consideration of the forces (physiological, psychological, and cultural) which determine how behavior acquires the varied attributes of illness.

Such an inquiry demands a logical formulation of concepts and theories based on careful observations of natural phenomena. Knowledge never grows by logical steps but rather by comparing contrasting types of experience. The easily perceived phenomena of pathology sensitize our perceptions of the subtler variations of normality. This has been true in physiology, as it is proving to be true in psychology. Yet this perceptual expedient has the result of exaggerating to us the significance of the differences between the pastel hues of the normal and the more blatant colors of pathology; and as a consequence of this learning device, we come to regard the two as having no relation one to the other. This has misled scientific psychology and psychiatry, as it has misled popular psychologizing, into an understandable but nonetheless fallacious tendency to exaggerate both the qualitative and quantitative differences between sickness and health. That is to say, the melodramatic and tragic consequences of mental illness have given rise to the popular, self-protective assumption that mental illness is something "alien" (to wit, the term "alienist"). Scientific thought has been led into similar fallacies by its need for sharp contrasts to illuminate its perceptions. Therefore layman and scientist alike have failed to appreciate that that which is common to mental health and illness is at least as important as that which differentiates them. Even Freud in his early days thought that psychoanalysis was a technic for the study of illness alone, and would shed no light on normal personality, a view which he soon abandoned. I would not like to see this Conference strengthen this antique fallacy of lay and scientific thought.

I. THE PHILOSOPHICAL BASIS FOR OUR CONSIDERATION

Any consideration of dynamic interactions on the level of psychological experience stirs a venerable philosophical conundrum out of Rip Van Winkle slumbers. Fortunately, although the problem is ancient, I have the temerity to believe that it can be resolved simply; and without wasting too many words, it may clarify later discussions to dispose of this pseudo-philosophical issue at the start.

The idea that sequences of psychological events can exert dynamic influences on one another seems at first thought to do violence to all scientific concepts of the world, and to the laws governing the conservation of mass and energy. Yet this need not worry us. There is no difficulty in understanding in physical terms how perceptual stimuli which arise from *immediate* occurrences initiate chain reactions in the central nervous system, and thereby influence the psychological expressions of central activity, because such perceptual units initiate the immediate discharge and transmission of energetic processes, however small.*

Furthermore, once these processes are launched in the nervous system, they can continue in transmutable forms even for years, and in this sense can be "stored." Thereafter, any symbol which represents past, or spatially distant, or even future perceptual events acts on the nervous apparatus as a coded signal which can trigger off or redirect or redistribute these energetic processes. Therefore it is merely using a legitimate verbal shorthand to talk of cause and effect on a psychological level. This is a semantic economy, and does no violence to our basic concepts of the physical world.

From this we may generalize and say that it is the coded signal (i.e., the symbolic process) which enables one group of psychological states to cause alterations in other psychological states. It may seem strange that we even stop to explain this, since its occurrence is an elementary fact of human experience. If it did not happen, our past could never influence our present or future, nor could there be any communication on any level of psychological interaction. If it were not true, no mere event could have a lasting influence on anyone. Yet we know that the thoughts and feelings of today are integral with those of tomorrow; and that words, expressions and gestures, and events communicate with one another, so to speak. We also know that

* I would emphasize the fact that I use the term "energetic processes" vaguely on purpose, because I do not wish to imply that variations in quanta of energy are the only adequate and necessary way of explaining variations in psychological processes. In a personal communication Warren McCulloch has rightly pointed out that this aspect of psychoanalytic theory derives from Bruecke and Johannes Müller, whereas the current trend in theory is to look upon the nervous system rather as a center for the handling of information by means of coded signals. If this is true, then it follows that as long as minimal energy requirements of the brain are met, both the total quanta and the variations in this quanta may be insignificant in magnitude. McCulloch argues furthermore that the energy requirements of the central nervous system may be derived from general metabolism, and not generated specifically within the nervous system. For these reasons McCulloch challenges the use of quantitative concepts in Freudian theory as having been appropriate early in the century but as leading us now "to nothing but confusion." [See also Kubie, 14.]

my symbolic activities, acting as perceivable signals, are incorporated into the psychological processes and ultimately into the personalities of other human beings, whose symbolic responses in turn and in the same way become incorporated into mine. Thereby comparable sequences are initiated within each of us. Once my own symbolic processes have occurred, they become events to me quite as potent as are the symbolic attitudes, expressions, gestures, and acts of a friend or stranger. In short, the symbolic process, which is that which stamps the human race with its uniqueness, and the extraordinary development of which distinguishes man from even the highest primate, is also the mechanism by which all psychological interactions and

est challenge that medicine faces today; because if this did not happen, there could be neither the neurosis nor the psychosis *as we know it in the human being* [Kubie, 18]. (See Figure 1.)

At the same time the symbolic representation of remote events binds widely separated times and far places into one immediate interacting psychological continuum. This is one of its several essential functions; and whereas on conscious levels, and in lesser degree on preconscious levels, we can sharply distinguish the past from the present, and the near from the far, on the more obscure levels of dynamic unconscious processes, near and far, past, present, and future all fuse into a continuum so complete that differentiation among them

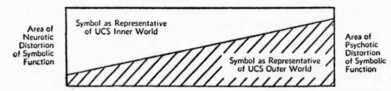

Fig. 1. The continuous spectrum which represents the relative roles of symbols derives from interoceptive and exteroceptive experience in the neurotic and psychotic processes. (*Courtesy,* Stanford University Press.)

interrelatings occur both within and between individuals. It is the mechanism by means of which internal psychological events are capable of having psychological and also psychosomatic consequences. The symbolic process is not only the instrument for communicating signals, information, and interactions; it is also the instrument by which experience on the psychological level can be translated into somatic changes, and conversely, somatic experience into psychological change. It is the source of our greatest creative power, but also the source of our greatest vulnerability [16, 19].

Evidently then, the symbol is the psychophysiological implement, an understanding of which is essential for an explanation both of normal and of pathological human psychological function. It is the key concept in psychodynamics and psychogenesis, whether of normal or sick activity. That from earliest childhood the symbolic process can go off its rails is perhaps the great-

is lost. This was first described clinically by Freud [2]. More recently it was demonstrated experimentally by Penfield [22].

We can summarize this salute to an ancient philosophical dilemma by stating that in the study of dynamic interrelations on the level of psychological experience, no assumptions which violate basic scientific concepts of the world are needed, since by means of symbols, acting as coded signals, effective and sustained interactions can occur among sequences of psychological experiences, with a binding of time and space and with effective storing of "energetic" processes (v.s.).

To this we must then add two additional working hypotheses:

1. Such dynamic interactions occur whether the symbolic representation of events takes place on conscious, preconscious, or unconscious levels. It should no longer be necessary either to illustrate or to prove this statement to any audience which

is informed about the elementary data of clinical psychology, both normal and pathological. Any such group will be familiar with the phenomena of automatic recording and reproducing of events of which we are unaware at the time; the automatic execution while in states of posthypnotic suggestion of orders which were received under hypnosis; the phenomena of multiple personalities; and other examples of the segregation and compartmentalization of the processes of awareness.

2. Dynamic interactions among psychological processes can occur both within each system and between the three systems. That is to say recognizable interactions occur not only among conscious psychological processes, but also between conscious and preconscious, between conscious and unconscious, and between unconscious and preconscious, in all of which the symbolic process is operative.

The figurative word "level" as applied to these three forms of psychological activity, is deceptively graphic, but aggravates our proneness to the fallacy of treating abstractions as though they were concrete realities. The term "compartments" has equal disadvantages. Although worn as smooth as old coins, neither has become incapable of harm. Many theoreticians take these figures of speech literally, and attach subconcepts to them, which in turn are treated as equally concrete realities. This is reminiscent of the early stages in the evolution of bacteriological concepts of immune bodies, or the hematologists' concepts of clotting substances and mechanisms. Freud's stricter concept of three systems—systems CS, PCS and UCS—is conceptually clearer, is relatively free of the danger of turning words into anthropomorphic entities, and has richer connotations for an understanding of the psychodynamics of health and illness.

It will be helpful to visualize the interrelationships among these three systems as a triangle with conscious, preconscious, and unconscious functions at its three corners, and arrows pointing in all directions among the three (Figure 2).

It is probably true, however, that in their actual operations temporary alliances form among pairs of systems, alliances which de-

termine the basic characteristics of different psychological states. This hypothesis is illustrated diagrammatically in Figure 2. I present this hypothetical possibility not as an explanation, but as a description of the varied alignments among three systems which can play a significant role in determining some of the characteristics of various psychological processes. The diagrams

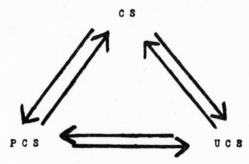

Fig. 2. The dynamic interplay among conscious (CS), preconscious (PCS), and unconscious (UCS) processes.

represent a hypothetical description, not an explanatory hypothesis (Figure 3).

Thus, in the "normal" waking state the conscious and preconscious systems would seem to cooperate closely in dominating over the unconscious system. The same may be true in well-integrated creative processes but with greater preponderance of preconscious functions. In more dissociated creative processes, in the dreams of sleep, in hypnosis the PCS may dominate over both CS and UCS forces; whereas in delirious states, in drug-induced dissociations, and in neuroses and psychoses, preconscious and unconscious processes may be in close alliance, with the preponderance shifting from preconscious to unconscious processes. Thus, such varied phenomena as sleep, hypnosis, dream states, delirium, drug effects, and neurotic illnesses can be characterized in terms of their positions on a continuous spectrum (Figure 3), the position depending upon which alliance is preponderant, that between the systems CS-PCS or between the PCS-UCS. One might wonder whether the CS > PCS > UCS hierarchy obtains at the normal waking end of the scale; the PCS > CS > UCS in many intermediate normal creative states; a PCS > UCS > CS hierarchy in more dissociated conditions; and an UCS > PCS > CS in states of frank illness.

In connection with these possible permutations and combinations one fact should be emphasized, if only because it usually is overlooked; namely, that we know more the open (whether as symptoms or in other forms), either we become aware at once that something unanticipated has erupted into the stream of conscious experience, or else those symptomatic distortions occur which led to the development of the whole psychoanalytic method. Strictly speaking then, psychoanalysis cannot claim to be a

"NORMAL" WAKING STATES
"NORMAL" CREATIVE PROCESSES
}

CS – PCS

UCS

{ ALLIANCE BETWEEN CS + PCS PROCESSES DOMINANT OVER UCS PROCESSES

"NORMAL" DISSOCIATED STATES (e.g.: SLEEP, DREAMS and HYPNOSIS) DISSOCIATED CREATIVE PROCESSES
}

PCS

CS   UCS

{ PCS PROCESSES DOMINANT OVER BOTH CS and UCS PROCESSES

DELIRIOUS STATES (DRUGS, TOXIC, etc.)
NEUROSES PSYCHOSES
}

PCS – UCS

CS

{ ALLIANCE BETWEEN PCS + UCS PROCESSES DOMINANT OVER CS PROCESSES

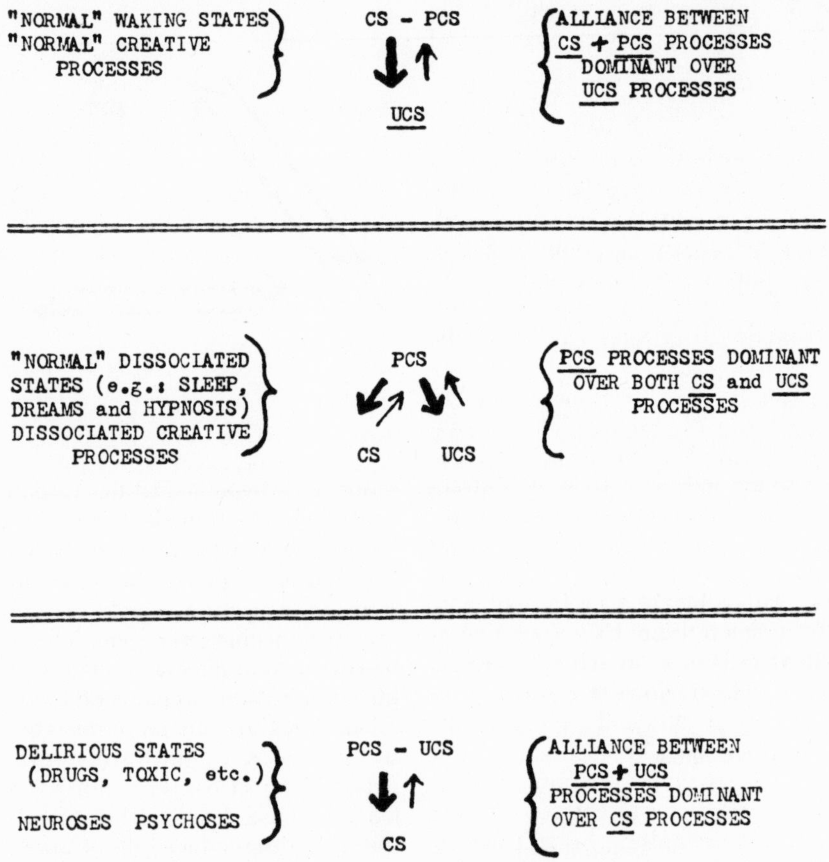

FIG. 3. The hypothetical relationship of CS, PCS, and UCS processes in normality, creativity, and psychopathology.

about the influence of unconscious on conscious processes (and perhaps of preconscious on conscious processes) than we know about the impact of preconscious or conscious processes on those which are unconscious [cf. Hixon Fund Lectures, 17, p. 94]. This strange fact is due to the inescapable technical difficulties which hamper the study of the influence of conscious (or preconscious) on unconscious processes. When unconscious processes break out into technic for the direct examination of the system UCS itself, but rather of its impact upon the systems PCS and CS. It is from the observable resultant distortions of CS and PCS processes that we derive and construct our conclusions about the system UCS. Thus conscious and preconscious processes provide their own direct registration of the fact that unconscious processes have been significantly operative. On the other hand, when the preponderant influence is in the opposite direction, i.e., when conscious and/or preconscious processes influence unconscious processes, the effects disappear behind the iron curtain which segregates the system UCS, making it inaccessible to direct self-inspection. Therefore, the influence of the systems CS and PCS on the system UCS can be investigated only by methods which are even more indirect, i.e., through secondary boomerang effects on CS and PCS activities from changes induced in the UCS. Precise clinical or experimental approaches to this problem have not yet been designed, and the lack of validated technics for the direct exploration of the system UCS itself circumscribes our knowledge of these dynamic interactions and places sharp limitations on our knowledge of the processes both of psychogenesis and of psychotherapy. Yet precisely because our knowledge in the one direction (i.e., UCS to CS) is greater than our knowledge in the other direction (i.e., CS to UCS), we know a little more about psychogenesis than we do about psychotherapy. Furthermore, this is one of the basic reasons why we still know so little about how insight actually operates in the processes of psychotherapy.

II. THE TRANSMUTATION OF ORGANIC PROCESSES INTO LEVELS OF BEHAVIOR FOR AN ENTIRE ORGANISM

By steps which we are about to outline briefly, local biophysical and biochemical processes in the fluids of the body and in its organized cells, tissues, and organs become compounded into the requirements of the body-as-a-whole for chemical and energy interchanges with its environment. Beginning with elementary instinctual acts, these requirements are expressed in a hierarchy of patterned behavior, through a series of instinctual derivatives and affects, and thence in higher levels of symbolic psychological activities, including the ultimate and challenging phenomena of the variations of awareness and self-awareness. It is this transmutation of local molecular chemistry into the highest levels of symbolic behavior which is the foundation for our consideration of the role of individual psychological processes and experiences in the genesis of psychological health and illness.

On another occasion I described in detail the steps in this process of transmutation [15]. There I pointed out that under conditions of free activity no biochemical process moves simultaneously in one direction throughout all tissues and organs. While some tissues are undergoing oxidation, others are in process of reduction. While some are taking up water, others are giving up water. While some are increasing their metabolic rates, others are decelerating. Thus, the state of so-called rest is actually a state of unstable dynamic equilibrium, in which the pluses and the minuses are approximately balanced, with the result that the needs of the body-as-a-whole to interchange with its environment approximate a minimal basal rate.

The same study then pointed out that when we consider the body's interchanges with its environment, we must consider separately its intake and output. On the *intake* side, restriction or *deprivation* imposes a uniformity of direction on the biochemical processes within the body. This uniformity develops only gradually, and at different rates for different tissues, for different vital chemical processes, and under different circumstances. Thus, oxygen deprivation causes all tissues to go into a state of oxygen debt in a matter of seconds. Water deprivation causes all tissues to need water in hours or days. Food deprivation causes all tissues to need food in days and weeks. In each case as deprivation intervenes, those biochemical processes which had previously been in a state of random flux become synchronized; and this synchronization of vital biochemistry creates a uniform need throughout the body-as-a-whole for interchange with the outer world, the "non-I" world. This constitutes the biochemical substrate of what becomes on psychological levels an "appetite." Without such synchronization there could be no such thing as a biogenetic appetite.

On the *output* side, synchronization of biochemistry and physiology is imposed by *accumulation*, whether this is the accumulation in the tissue fluids or blood stream of hydrogen ions, lactic acid, or CO_2, or the accumulation of fluid itself or of waste matter in specialized transporting systems, receptacles, and excretory organs. Again this occurs at different rates for different chemical processes and different organs, depending on the chemistry itself, storage capacity, etc. Thus, with significantly variable time lags, *deprivation* on the intake side and *accumulation* on the output side synchronize molecular, cellular, and tissue processes to form the biochemical and physiological substrate of the psychological appetites.

In that study it was also shown that the length of the time interval between the intake and the output phases of any bodily biochemical system has psychological implications. The longer this interval, the greater is the opportunity for the development of psychological complications, and more specifically, for the development of compulsive and phobic mechanisms.

Moreover, in the translation of molecular and tissue chemistry into body needs and appetites, two further processes are significant for psychodynamics and psychogenesis:

1. *Anticipatory mechanisms*—Sensitive psychophysiological warning mechanisms in local tissues trigger off both the intake and the output appetites long *before synchronization occurs throughout the whole body,* thus protecting tissues in general from the damage which would result from repeated deprivations or accumulations. Thus we experience local warning signals of thirst and hunger *before* any actual tissue deprivation or need has occurred. These anticipatory mechanisms become the object of complex emotional and symbolic investments; and here again, time intervals become important. The longer the time interval between the action of the trigger mechanisms and the physical state of synchronization, the greater becomes the complexity of this psychological superstructure [cf. 15, esp. pp. 19–24]. On the intake side these warning mechanisms which are built on deprivation are in turn closely linked to fear, both normal and neurotic. On the output side the warning mechanisms built around accumulation and discharge are

more directly linked to compulsive phenomena.

2. *Compulsive overdrives and phobic inhibitions*—As a consequence of these widely variable time lags, i.e., between the intake and output phases of different basic biochemical processes in the body, and also between deprivation or accumulation on the one hand and on the other the occurrence of synchronization of tissue chemistry, and finally through the operation of the anticipatory mechanisms which ward off total deprivation and overaccumulation or overdistension, every biogenetic need becomes a nucleus around which cluster primary psychological forces, which are in essence either compulsive or phobic or both. These are the primary compulsive and phobic phenomena of human psychopathology; and because of them, the psychological "appetites" which the human being experiences subjectively are only in small part biogenetic. To a larger degree they are an outcome of the continuous interplay between the compulsive and phobic components in the psychological superstructure which is built around the biogenetic core. (I believe that when we realize the full significance of this universal interplay of balanced compulsive and phobic processes around an instinctual core, we may discover that we no longer need a libido theory of special psychic energies. If I am correct in this guess, then the libido concept may prove to be not only superfluous but actually an impediment to clear theoretical and experimental work.)

In the meantime, a psychological tool is lacking which is urgently needed for accurate scientific work; namely, a measuring device by means of which to determine to what degree any expression of need or craving is biogenetic (i.e., expressing the algebraic summation of the underlying biochemical processes) and to what extent it is psychogenetic in origin (i.e., expressing the algebraic summation of superimposed primary compulsive and phobic processes). At present we have to be content with a few pragmatic indicators which are far from quantitatively precise or adequate.

This issue is so fundamental to an understanding of the combined interplay of bio-genetic and psychological forces in the determination of human behavior that I will quote from a previous discussion of the topic [Hixon Fund Lectures, 17, pp. 100–101]:

Thus, even so primitive a body need as breathing can be overdriven by compulsive psychological superstructures or inhibited by phobic mechanisms. *In man, therefore, the amount of instinctual activity in which he indulges never measures directly or alone the underlying biochemical requirements which it may seem to serve. Indeed in human life the biochemical function of any biogenetic act is almost incidental to its psychological function.* To what extent this is true for the lower animals we do not know. It may be a peculiarity of the human being alone. Certainly it is a major source of many of our neurotic troubles. One of the more familiar examples of this is the compulsive overeating of many adolescents, and the reverse of the same medal is the child who develops what is called "anorexia nervosa" and refuses food even to the point of death. Quite frequently the same child passes through the compulsive phase into the anorexic stage, but the caloric requirements of the body are no greater in one phase than in the other. The same phenomenon is observed in anyone who passes through a period of compulsive sexual hyperactivity (so-called "nymphomania" or "satyriasis") into psychic impotence or psychic frigidity. The study of such patients indicates that in the first phase an obsessional-compulsive overdrive has taken hold of a pattern of activity which originally served a biochemical or instinctual body requirement, and that in the second a phobic inhibitory mechanism has taken hold of this same biogenetic activity. The fact that this can happen to man is one of the numerous special disadvantages of being a member of the human race, because it seems to be more or less peculiar to us that our biological requirements are so highly sensitive to the influence of the conscious and especially unconscious components of our psychological apparatus.

This subjugation of the simple body-need by complex superimposed psychological necessities occurs because in the human being the act of gratifying a biological necessity becomes in itself a form of unconscious symbolic behavior, a language which is used for manifold unconscious purposes. This is why the biochemical kernel of any act which, superficially regarded, seems to serve biological needs may actually play only a small part in determining the act. To the extent to which such behavior pursues symbolic gratifications, it can never reach its goals, and consequently becomes insatiable. Therefore, we must constantly ask ourselves how much of any pattern of behavior is organically determined and how much of it is the result of the interaction of these complex superimposed psychological forces.

This issue was first raised some years ago by Bertram D. Lewin and myself in our published discussion of a paper by Hoskins [12], and later in my paper on "Instincts and Homeostasis" [15]. I cannot here go into all aspects of this basic and intricate issue; but I hope that the discussion has made it clear that this is another area where we need instruments which we now lack, instruments which would enable us to make quantitative estimates of two interacting and concurrent components in the determination of behavior, i.e., the biochemical and the unconscious psychological ingredient in instinctual acts. Let me emphasize the analytic position that in human beings there is no action which can be called "pure instinct" in the sense of being solely an expression of a biochemical necessity alone, and also no action which can be said to be solely psychological, in the sense of being devoid of the influence of biochemical necessities. Furthermore, psychoanalysis indicates that on different occasions even in the same man, any act (breathing, eating, drinking, or sex) can be determined by quite different constellations of influences. With appropriate instruments we could place any particular act at the proper point on a scale, at one end of which would be the theoretically pure instinct and at the other end the theoretically pure psychological motivation (neither of which occurs in pure culture in nature), with every admixture of the two falling between. Once again this is best illustrated by our familiar diagram (Figure 4).

These basic considerations should make it self-evident that quite apart from variations in psycho-cultural forces, complex distortions will form around sexual functions with greater constancy than around the biochemical processes which have to do with the intake and output of food and fluid, and more constantly around food and fluid than about respiratory function.

These considerations are complicated, but they are essential for an understanding of psychodynamics in general and of psychogenesis of illness in particular. Time limits me to emphasizing the fact that the aggregation of compulsive and phobic mechanisms around the biochemical genetic core of instinctual processes, which is universal in the ontogeny of man, is also the critical initiating step in the genesis of psychopathology. Let me repeat this: Our vital body chemistry and the needs which it creates for continuous or intermittent interchanges with the environment become the center of symbolic compulsive and phobic pressures. This fact is the critical initial

to form abstract concepts of them; (c) the ability to represent such abstractions by means of symbols (coded signals); (d) the development of repressive and segregating and economizing forces which compartmentalize the stream of psychological processes into the conscious, preconscious, and unconscious systems. In the latter instance the repressive processes dominate, with the result that the symbol and its affects are so segregated from their original connections as to render all original connections both unconscious and inaccessible. Together this constitutes the universal "neurotic poten-

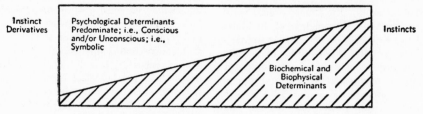

Fig. 4. Under different circumstances, any act can fall at different points on this scale. Respiratory functions tend in general to operate at one end and sex at the other, with the other body needs distributed approximately in the following order: respiratory, water intake, food intake, water output, food output, sleep, general activity, sex. (*Courtesy*, Stanford University Press.)

and universal step in the psychogenesis of neurosis. Its fate in any individual depends upon both how and when it occurs, and how its consequences vary with the age at which it crystallizes, how the balance shifts between obsessional compulsive overdrives and phobic inhibitions, a phenomenon which is masked under the classical but unanalyzed term "fixation."

In another communication [16] I assembled all of those universal elements in human development which together constitute the soil out of which the human neurosis develops. I called them "The Neurotic Potential" which is both ubiquitous and indigenous to human psychology. In essence this consists of (a) the distorting influence of early compulsive and phobic processes which form around the biogenetic core of body needs, to create those complex derivatives which we call "instincts"; (b) the early development of the ability to condense varied concrete experiences and then

tial" which is inherent in physiologically and psychologically "normal" human development, even apart from any complicating intrusion of cultural forces.

The role of culture and of variations in the impact of individual phylogenetic and ontogenetic experiences must be studied and evaluated in terms of their impact on the neurotic process as this begins to evolve out of the universal neurotic potential, whether the evolution is toward the development of a neurotic character structure or toward the precipitation of a clinically manifest neurotic state. This will be considered more fully in the next section.

III. PSYCHODYNAMICS AND PSYCHOGENESIS OF MENTAL ILLNESS

In view of the continuum between psychological health and illness, the psychogenesis of illness is in general a function of the forces which cause manifest illness to evolve out of the neurotic potential which is latent in all human nature. These forces will cause first a gradual development of a neurotic process out of the ubiquitous latent potential and then the precipitation of an overt clinical illness out of the veiled neurotic process [16]. (A full understanding of these forces would include also the dynamics of their resolution, whether spontaneous or induced.) In this sequence of events organic, cultural, and psychological forces play continuously interesting roles. Therefore there cannot be independent "schools" (e.g., organic, psychodynamic, psychosocial, and experimental) except insofar as they represent differences in emphases, interests, and investigative tools. They are interdependent and converging approaches to the explanation of psychological events.

Each of us was asked to represent one of these "schools," to re-examine that school's fundamental principles, its certain evidence, its assumptions, and that which it holds possible. A more realistic general question would be to ask: How early in any chain of linked causes does each of these forces first play a significant role; and how does each variable—organic, cultural and individual—influence (1) the laying down of the neurotic potential; (2) the evolution of the neurotic process out of the underlying potential; and (3) the crystallization of the neurotic state. For instance, these forces would influence (1) the age at which the compulsive and phobic superstructure first begins to form around one or another of the body's biogenetic needs; (2) the age at which a child first becomes able to form abstract concepts, and then to give condensed symbolic representation to these primitive abstractions; (3) the age at which it first becomes possible for an individual to obscure or distort the relationship between the symbolic representatives of experience and either the underlying abstractions or the relevant emotions; (4) the age at which either organic variables or individual experiences first establish a central emotional position for a personality, i.e., an emotional position to which that individual always tends to return throughout his life.

Many organic variables are conceivable which can influence these fundamental events in the story of the neurosis. Together they are the constitutional component which Freud emphasized consistently. As examples, and in addition to more familiar hypotheses about glandular factors, growth factors, etc., are such things as the proneness of any individual to forming reverberating circuits in the CNS, as for example through some anomaly in the balanced action of the two hemispheres, or else through some idiosyncrasy in the relative durations of conduction times and refractory periods, etc. Presumably these will be operative recurrently from earliest development throughout life, influencing both the initial steps and the ultimate fate of each component in the neurotic potential.

The influence of individual life experiences must be broken down in the same way, whether we deal with early separations from a parent, early pain, early illness, early threats, early seduction, early immobilization. How early must these operate and how long at each age period, if their effects are to become persistent, whether by determining primitive central affective positions or by fixing the evolution of patterns of instinctual expression into stereotyped forms of compulsive overdrive or phobic obstruction, or through early distortions in the normal unrolling of symbolic functions.

Similarly the influence of psychocultural variants must be considered in terms of the same basic units of the neurotic process. How do varying patterns of family relationships influence the development of fixed points in the affective balance, the development of fixed overemphases on instinctual derivatives, the warping of the symbolic process by the early unleashing of repressing forces, the consequent development of early symptom structures, etc. The cultural anthropologist and the sociologist have not yet considered the problem in these basic terms. They have given us no evidence as to whether cultural forces influence either the neurotic potential or the primary steps in the development of the neurotic process. Without realizing it they have concerned themselves solely with the more obvious role of psychocultural forces in determining the price we pay for our neuroses once they are established, and in general in shaping all the secondary and tertiary manifestations of the neurotic process.

This fact is self-evident; yet it may be helpful to illustrate it briefly. The price we pay for our neuroses is determined largely by the conditions under which we live, and the relationship of these circumstances to the specific forms of the neuroses. A man with a height phobia or a man with a claustrophobia may live on the open prairies without evident symptoms and with relative comfort. But the one could not be a structural steel worker, nor the other a miner, without being precipitated into a major neurotic or even psychotic break. Cultural forces also influence the ultimate form of the neurosis by determining how early in the neurotic process help will be sought or made available [Redlich, *et al.*, 23]. This in turn influences the later course of the neurosis, in part determining whether or not it will stabilize or decompensate into psychotic illness. Let me repeat, however, that such data offer no evidence on the more basic question of the extent to which cultural differences play a role in determining the neurotic potential itself or in initiating or shaping the original neurotic process. In spite of glib assertions and claims, it remains undetermined whether or not such a primary relationship exists.

In all of these problems the contribution of the experimental psychologist has consisted largely of studies of conditioning and learning, studies of the child's acquisition of the ability to serve himself and to assert himself, or of his competitive adequacy in neuromuscular skills and coordination, or of his ability to acquire and use the symbolic tools for communicating and understanding and learning. None of this constitutes a separate school of thought concerning the origins of illness, but rather an array of technics for understanding certain fragments of the equipment with which the individual attempts to master all aspects of human development, including the consequences of his evolving and inescapable neurotic process.

The nature of the experimental neurosis, so-called, has been called into question so often that the argument need not be repeated here [13, 16, 20]. The core of the question is whether there can be a neurosis comparable to the human neurosis in any animal form in which the symbolic functions are primitive, and whether the persistent emotional disturbances which can readily be induced in laboratory animals are equivalent to the human neurotic process as such or merely to the emotional disturbances which regularly accompany human neuroses.

I hope that these general considerations will clear the ground for a return to a consideration of more basic aspects of the psychodynamic position. I must first avoid one other possible misunderstanding by excluding arbitrarily all so-called organic mental illnesses: i.e., those in which an individual is altered by the intrusion of some organic agent. This may be an infection, an injury, a tumor, an intoxicant, or a biochemical change within the body (such as a spontaneous hypoglycemia, Addison's disease, an allergy of the central nervous system, a severe jaundice), any of which may distort psychological functions. I must limit my discussion to illnesses which evolve without such extraneous accidents since these lie outside of the domain of possible psychogenesis.

Yet in order to clarify an important later distinction, it is necessary to point out that concomitant psychodynamic forces are always at work in such organogenic illness, but not as fundamental causes. Without them the patient would be ill nonetheless, although there would be differences in the details of his symptomatology. Thus, the *content* of a delirium will always be determined in large measure, as is the content of any dream state, not by intoxication or injury but by a patient's previous life-history, both remote and recent, and by the pressure of his conscious, preconscious, and unconscious needs and conflicts. For instance, a childless woman who longed for children underwent a necessary hysterectomy. During the course of a postoperative infection she then became delirious. In the hallucinatory fantasies of her delirium she experienced the gratification of her yearnings by acting out the care of the twins she imagined that she had had. Obviously the *content* of her delirium was psychodynamic in origin, although the delirious state itself had an organic etiology. This daily experience is even easier to recognize in organic psychoses than in dreams. It is not so easy to recognize in the neuroses, where the boundary between content and cause may become blurred. This should warn us not to confuse the *content* or the *meaning* of an illness with the cause of that illness [Whitehorn, 24]. This fundamental distinction is frequently forgotten; I will return to it in closing. First, however, let me itemize a few of the areas of legitimate agreement and also of disagreement among the so-called "schools" of psychodynamic emphasis.

A. Areas of General Agreement

Among those who explore psychodynamic forces and processes there are, of

namic patterns which interact by means of those coded signals which constitute the symbolic process.

3. The symbolic process operates on three levels of *systems* of psychological organization; to wit, conscious, preconscious, and unconscious. These always operate concurrently in varying relations to one another. The relative roles of conscious, preconscious, and unconscious forces determine whether the resulting behavior will be flexibly adaptable and satiable, whether it can learn and change, or whether it is to become rigid, insatiable, unadaptable, stereotyped, repetitious; i.e., sick (Figures 5 and 6).

4. Two major areas of conflict in human life are interwoven and interrelated and are found in all known societies of man: namely, conflicts over sex and conflicts over

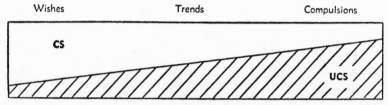

FIG. 5. Every human thought or feeling or act or pattern of living falls somewhere along such a diagram as this. The technical and quantitative problem is to determine where. It will be noted that the diagram indicates that there are no acts in which UCS processes play no role, and none which are devoid of CS determinants. If this is true, then in all probability the ends of the scale are theoretical abstractions. (*Courtesy,* Stanford University Press.)

course, varying emphases, but more important areas of general agreement, plus some persistently nagging unsolved problems, many of which were discussed recently in the Hixon Fund Lectures [17] and again at the celebration of the Twentieth Anniversary of the Chicago Psychoanalytic Institute [19].

Let me state what I believe to be the areas on which most workers in the psychodynamic field will be in general agreement.

1. All psychological processes ultimately derive from the organization of biogenetic levels. (The steps by which this basic derivation occurs have been described.)

2. There is a compartmentalization of psychological processes into various dy-

aggression. Variations in culture produce variations in the specific patterns of these conflicts; but no society is known in which either is wholly devoid of conflict whether on conscious, preconscious, and/or unconscious levels. For instance, cultural patterns will make differences in the attitudes of individuals at various ages toward rage, killing, fear of bodily injury, death, accident, suicide, and the supernatural. Consequently, cultural variants must play a contributory role in determining to what extent the individual will live out the expression of such universal conflicts predominantly on conscious, preconscious, or unconscious levels. Similarly, such cultural influences as family taboos, body taboos, attitudes toward the

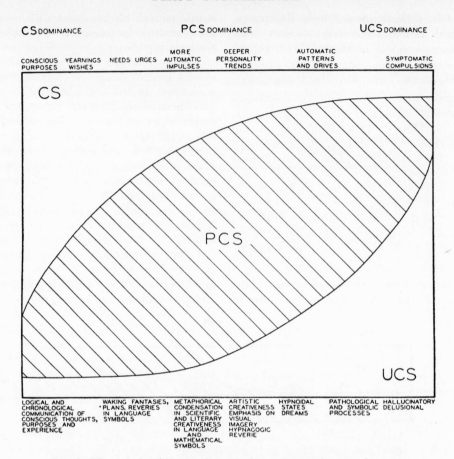

CS DOMINANCE   PCS DOMINANCE   UCS DOMINANCE

CONSCIOUS YEARNINGS NEEDS URGES MORE DEEPER AUTOMATIC
PURPOSES WISHES AUTOMATIC PERSONALITY PATTERNS SYMPTOMATIC
IMPULSES TRENDS AND DRIVES COMPULSIONS

CS

PCS

UCS

LOGICAL AND WAKING FANTASIES, METAPHORICAL ARTISTIC HYPNOIDAL PATHOLOGICAL HALLUCINATORY
CHRONOLOGICAL PLANS, REVERIES CONDENSATION CREATIVENESS STATES AND SYMBOLIC DELUSIONAL
COMMUNICATION OF IN LANGUAGE IN SCIENTIFIC EMPHASIS ON DREAMS PROCESSES
CONSCIOUS THOUGHTS, SYMBOLS AND LITERARY VISUAL
PURPOSES AND CREATIVENESS IMAGERY
EXPERIENCE IN LANGUAGE HYPNAGOGIC
AND REVERIE
MATHEMATICAL
SYMBOLS

Fig. 6. The relationships of the conscious, preconscious, and unconscious systems to each other are represented crudely by the two diagrams in Figures 5 and 6. One is purposefully simplified by the omission of PCS symbolic functions. The other represents hypothetical relationships in something approximating their full complexities. The shapes of these curves, their points of origins and insertion, the areas they subtend are all purely hypothetical. Even the assumption that their interrelationships can be expressed in quantitative terms is only a working hypothesis. Therefore the diagram is not to be taken literally. It is designed rather to illustrate complex interrelationships, as they may be assumed to occur in nature; i.e., in Human Nature, in which the concurrent action of preconscious processes frees our psychic apparatus, and more specifically our symbolic processes, from rigid anchorage. At the conscious end of the diagram this anchorage is to fixed and literal relationships to external realities. At the unconscious end of the diagram there is, if anything, an even more rigid anchorage to unreality; i.e., because unconscious symbolic relationships predominate and are unmodifiable by experience as long as they remain unconscious. The essential, flexible, and creative contribution which is made to our psychic processes by the concurrent play of preconscious processes is illustrated. The diagram has an unavoidable complexity, reminiscent of the nomograms with which the late Dr. L. J. Henderson used to represent the concurrent changes of the mutually interdependent constituents of the blood stream.

body in general, toward body differences, toward genital differences, toward body products and dirt in general, the accepted mythology of the body, the mythology of birth, illness, death and the supernatural, and the mythology of sexual experience— all help to determine the acceptable attitudes toward sex at various age levels of individual development, and whether in any particular culture the individual's conflicts over sex will be dealt with in the full light of consciousness, in the dimmer preconscious zone, or to what extent they are behind the iron curtain of the unconscious. Here again, however, no culture is known which is totally devoid of conflict in this area; because where there is no conflict, cultural taboos and preferences cannot come into existence. Thus, there is a circular interaction between *culture* and *conflict*.

5. Certain perplexing facts seem to indicate that some conflicts persist even in spite of wide ranges of cultural differences, and also in spite of presumptive genetic or hereditary influences. Thus there is the ultimate conundrum of why and how it happens that in spite of the fact that the human race has been divided into two sexes for quite a long time, each new generation still rejects this fact as unacceptable, each individual rejecting both his own anatomy and that of the opposite sex. A similar perplexing conundrum confronts us in relation to our conflicts over age and size. How does it happen that we have not inherited an acceptance of childhood and its limitations as to size, strength, independence, etc.?

Around these persisting perplexities heated feelings tend to cluster, which unfortunately give rise more to confused and unnecessary arguments than to investigations.

6. There is substantial agreement that where conflicts are lived out on unconscious levels they remain nonetheless dynamic and highly charged (whence the phrase the "dynamic unconscious") and are transmuted into many indirect and disguised forms of symbolic expression. Some of these forms of expression may be socially creative, even though they may be destructive to the individual and his family, as with compulsive overwork for example, or compulsive philanthropy. Some are protective toward society even as they injure the individual, as with the individual who unconsciously is a potential murderer and develops a paralyzed arm, or a potential rapist who becomes impotent. Contrariwise, the indirect expressions of an unconscious conflict can be "creative" for the individual though destructive socially, as with a Hitler, or in certain forms of modern art and literature. In general terms one may say that conflicts which are handled on a preponderantly unconscious level may be represented symbolically in powerful and persistent personality traits, in socially constructive or socially destructive forces, or in those segregated symbolic forms which constitute the clinical entities of neurotic and psychotic symptomatology.

7. Finally, it may be safe to say that there is fairly general agreement that in the exploration of psychodynamic relations certain basic technical procedures are essential: (*a*) As in all science, there must be an observational situation which is fairly constant; i.e., a situation in which extraneous and adventitious variables are kept to a minimum. (*b*) There must be a situation in which the variables introduced by the unconscious processes of the observer are kept out of the picture as far as possible, so as to focus the study on one unconscious at a time; to wit, that of the subject under observation. (*c*) There must be a technic for a more or less random sampling of the data to be studied. (In science, where it is impossible to examine all, we are forced to sample; and whenever we sample, that sample must attempt to be both random and statistically adequate.) (*d*) There must be a continuous study and control of the distortions of data introduced by the interplay of affective forces between observer and observed, on conscious, preconscious, and unconscious levels. (*e*) Finally, in this *relatively* constant situation, in which we struggle to secure random samples of human psychological behavior, we introduce a controlled variable, which in this case is the nonaffective interpretation. The technic which approximates these essential scientific

standards most closely in the study of psychodynamic relationships is that of formal psychoanalysis [Kubie, 19].

On these matters there will be essential agreement among informed representatives from all schools of psychodynamic thought.

B. Areas of Disagreement

There are also legitimate and important areas of disagreement; but popular attention tends to turn toward those less substantial disagreements which have arisen out of uninformed thinking, historical naïveté, and premature claims of therapeutic innovations. Especially on these last an eager and angry public seizes with avidity. Consequently, many old and discarded formulations keep reappearing under new names, disguised as new theoretical or technical innovations.

1. Not all, but much of Jung, Rank, Adler, Horney and Rado, and some of Freud himself fall into this category. During the initial phase of the struggle between Adler and Freud there was the quite one-sided emphasis which Adler laid on the conflict over aggression and power, at a time when Freud was emphasizing the inextricable interlinking of sex and aggression in the derivation of the neuroses. I will dismiss in an equally summary fashion the ancient struggle between Freud and Jung, where the issue was between a mystical as opposed to a biological approach [cf. Glover, 4]. Horney and Klein swing between an overemphasis on earliest infancy and an overemphasis on the present. None of these goes to the heart of any basic issues with which we are concerned here today.

2. The struggle over variations in therapeutic technics takes us into fields in which it would not be profitable or possible to go on this occasion. Some are matters of great moment. Others are insignificant details. In essence, one can say that any technic which meets the fundamental requirements which I have already outlined is a valid technic for the exploration of psychodynamic relationships: viz., it must establish and preserve the constancy of the situation in which the data are evoked, and also the constancy of the listening post; it must

scrupulously limit the intrusion of the observer's psychological processes (so as to protect the exploratory process as far as possible from contamination from the observer's unconscious); it must make use of our only technic for random sampling of psychological activity (namely, the technic of free association); and it must continuously note and counteract the influence of the conscious and unconscious affective interplay between observer and observed. These constitute the essential matrix into which a calculated and controlled variable is introduced in the form of a nonaffective interpretation. By whatever name one calls it, these are the essentials for any technic of psychodynamic exploration which is worthy of serious scientific consideration. Details as to posture, frequency, duration, etc., and many others besides, are trivia which do not need to concern us.

3. Another important area of disagreement concerns the role of early instinctual problems, how they arise, how persistent their influence is, to what extent individuals become fixed at a certain point in instinctual development, and the subsequent fate of early instinctual fixations if they occur. These are all legitimate objects of inquiry, but hardly constitute divergent schools of passionate faith. It is unfortunate that there has been more claim and counterclaim than objective investigation in this area, resulting in two schools which in reality should supplement each other: the so-called "biogenetic" school, as opposed to a "cultural" school. The distinction is as unreal as the old battle between heredity and environment, as I hope to demonstrate in the final section of this paper.

4. Related to this area of instinctual problems is the still unsolved question of the influence of relatively isolated early traumatic experiences or stresses, and the role of such experiences, both in the genesis of the neurosis and in its alleviation.

5. In turn this question of early traumatic experiences is interwoven with the problem of the so-called "structure" of the personality, and the question of which aspects of the personality become organized into independent dynamic units. Man has long thought of himself as tripartite: i.e.,

as a thinking, feeling, and acting animal, or as an animal who has ideals and a conscience on the one hand, basal or carnal impulses on the other, but also a *will*, or at least an executive capacity to plan and to serve himself and his environment by implementing his purposes. Putting this venerable tripartite view of man into new terms (id, ego, and superego) does not add to our knowledge, except insofar as the new words help us to remember that there are conscious, preconscious, and unconscious components in each of these three aspects of man, and that consequently there are both voluntary and involuntary automatic components in all three. Such a structuring of the personality touches the issue of psychodynamics when we ask whether the ego, id, and superego are more or less autonomous units, each commanding its own needs and defenses. This is a matter of fundamental moment in current theory: i.e., whether the metapsychological concepts (as they are called in psychoanalysis) are useful solely as descriptive units or also as explanatory entities as well [cf. Hartmann, Kris, Loewenstein, 5, 6, 7, 11].

6. This tripartite personality structure links to a basic issue; to wit, how can we use the concepts of force and energy legitimately in the effort to explain the interplay of psychological events in the human being in terms of quantitative variables. Here I must refer you to earlier discussions of this issue [14, 17]. In any congeries of multiple variable forces it is extremely difficult to determine which is the effective quantitative variable which has produced some specific effect. In psychological matters it is often hard to decide what is an indicator of a quantitative change of any kind. For instance, how do we ascertain the *strength* of a compulsion? If a man washes his hands a thousand times a day is his compulsion "stronger" than that of a man who washes his hands a hundred times a day? Or if two men have hand-washing compulsions which lead each to wash his hands a hundred times a day, then if one washes for one minute each time and other for five, is the latter's compulsion five times as *strong* as the former's? One could multiply these examples many times. This problem must be solved before we can confidently assign quantity values to underlying processes as an explanation of dynamic interrelations on the psychological level [Kubie, 14] (See Figure 6.)

7. This problem of the measurement of the multiple forces in turn is relevant to the problem of how to estimate the role of instincts. This has already been discussed at length. We know that in man the biogenetic core of every instinct becomes the center of a tornado of compulsive and phobic processes. Man never serves his biological needs alone. Whatever he does in the service of his biological needs is at the same time serving concurrent supercharging (compulsive) and braking (phobic) forces. How then can we determine the relative roles of the underlying biogenetic forces in energizing the final behavior and the roles of these superimposed concomitant psychological pressures? Freud's initial assumption [3] was that all differences in behavior reflected differences in the individual's constitutional biogenetic instinctual heredity. Clinical experience and closer observation of the data have proved that it is not that simple [cf. Lewin and Kubie, 12]. Yet we remain without technical devices by which to isolate or measure these two concurrent groups of forces. Therefore, in heated arguments about this issue people express not their knowledge but their biases.

IV. THE GENESIS OF AWARENESS

Logically our next topic should be the genesis of states of awareness and their modulations. This would carry us back dangerously close to those philosophical issues from which I had hoped to escape through my earlier comments. Perhaps we can economize time by referring to the famous essay "Does Consciousness Exist?" from William James's *Essays in Radical Empiricism* [10], and to *The Concept of Consciousness* and *The Freudian Wish* by E. B. Holt [8, 9] and finally to the transactions of the Laurentian Conference which was held in the summer of 1953 on neurophysiological contributions to our understanding of states of consciousness [1].

The general argument concerning the psychogenesis of awareness can be boiled down to four general propositions, which I will not try to develop in full:

1. Awareness (consciousness) is an abstraction, and as such it is not an object of scientific inquiry.

2. On the other hand, awareness or consciousness of a concrete thing is a concrete psychophysiological experience which can be investigated.

3. Concrete awareness is an extension of the processes of sensory perception, to include simultaneous interwoven perceptions of the self and of the non-self.

4. In turn these perceptions are represented through the symbolic process by coded signals of both the inner and outer world; and as with the symbolic representation of all perceptual processes, whether internal or external, they operate on conscious, preconscious, or unconscious levels.

The ontogeny of the processes of awareness is a matter for microscopic genetic studies, since a fuller understanding of how awareness becomes compartmentalized is essential for our ultimate understanding of the psychogenesis of illness. It would be premature to attempt to specify its details at this time.

V. THE CONCEPTS OF CAUSE, CONTENT, AND MEANING

A. Description vs. Explanation

The relationship of cause, content, and meaning, and the relationship between description and explanation are interwoven issues in the understanding of psychodynamics and psychogenesis. Probably in no science, and certainly not in psychology, is there ever a single cause. There may be one highly important variable among many; and there may be one final trigger; but causal processes consist rather of sequences of events, linked in circular or reverberating relationships. Thus, every psychological event is part of a cybernetic constellation, each event tending to alter the symbolic representatives of past experiences, while at the same time altering the orientation of the individual toward both current and future experiences. Therefore, while each psychological representative of the past is a product of the past, it is also a force which can be said to alter the *symbolic* past, the

perceptual present, and the *real* future. These circular relationships add to the difficulties of distinguishing between description and explanation in psychological matters.

In every branch of science, natural phenomena are described predominantly in terms of their own level. Thus one describes the behavior of water in terms of water molecules; and in so doing, one explains the impact of water as water on the future. Thus a full description of water's present is explanatory for water's future behavior, at least in large part. But to *explain* the present behavior of water itself requires that water must be reduced to its preceding components, that is, to an understanding of the forces which were set in motion and stabilized by the interactions between hydrogen and oxygen in certain quantities and arranged in certain spatial patterns, and with certain electrical charges. In the same way, if we are to go beyond the *description* of sequences of behavior to an *explanation* of behavior, we are forced to reduce behavior to its components. On the behavioral level, microscopic description is adequate for explanation of future consequences; but explanation of current behavior requires an equally minute description of its antecedent components. Sometimes this is spoken of disparagingly as the "reductive tendency" in psychodynamic or psychoanalytic explanations; but the use of the word as an epithet is unwarranted. All scientific explanations require "reduction" in this sense. This is a further reason why any controversy between culture and nurture or between culture and biogenesis is naïve, whether we are dealing with the phenomena of heredity or of psychoanalytic theory.

In psychoanalysis, however, there has been another tendency, the validity of which should be reconsidered carefully. This is the assumption that if we can redescribe conscious phenomena in terms of preconscious and/or unconscious processes, such a redescription constitutes a full explanation. Undoubtedly this adds a description of an additional group of important and relevant determining forces; but the description of the role of these additional systems of awareness does not alone constitute a total explanation, although they make vital additions to the data which we need in our attempts to explain behavior.

B. Cause, Content, and Meaning

Any dynamic sequence of psychological events is a chain reaction, each link a part of a closed series of reverberating, feedback symbolic relationships [Macy *Transactions*, 21]. Among the interrelating elements of this chain reaction, any event may play roles on a psychological level which are at the same time or alternately characterized by cause (genetic), content (continuing and sustaining the process), and/or meaning. As Whitehorn has pointed out [24], of the three terms the latter is the most inclusive. Clearly, to explain any pattern of behavior, we need to know several things:

1. The forces (genetic) which shared in starting it and shaping it.

2. The nature of the continuing dynamic forces which keep it going. These may or may not be identical with the originating or genetic forces. They constitute part of the content of the state, yet they are not purely inert. Consider, for instance, the childless, delirious woman, who after a hysterectomy acted the care of the twins whose birth and presence she hallucinated. Her subsequent feelings and behavior were markedly influenced for many months by the content of that delirium. The same thing is true of the content of any neurosis. Indeed *the entire structure and history of a life* may be determined in large part by the relatively accidental specific content of an early period of neurotic illness; a content which is itself a product of past processes and a link in a chain of processes with far-reaching secondary and tertiary consequences.

3. The resolving forces which terminate the ultimate pattern of illness or alter its shape.

It is only when we understand the interplay of all of these forces that we can claim to understand the *meaning* of behavior in its fullest sense. Furthermore *meaningfulness* implies meaning in at least four directions:

1. There is the meaningfulness to the patient himself. Superficially this comprises the patient's own explanations of his conscious purposes and behavior. These may be merely his rationalizations, in part or in whole; i.e., those partial truths which are acceptable or gratifying to the patient, but which obscure and evade all less palatable truths, which in turn may constitute either a peripheral fringe of additional purposes (i.e., preconscious in nature), and/or an array of concurrent, deeply concealed and inaccessibly unconscious purposes. The latter are often erroneously spoken of as the "real" purposes, as though the *unconscious alone* constituted a more "real" or more adequate explanation of behavior than the conscious or preconscious. Actually, of course, the "real" purpose must always represent the algebraic sum of all three systems; and purposes, whether CS, PCS, or UCS, or all combined, do not constitute the total explanation of behavior (cf. Figure 5 above).

2. Concurrently, to the patient's family and friends and society the same patterns of behavior will mean largely, and yet not exclusively, the *consequences* of the patient's behavior and of his total life pattern; i.e., its consequences to himself, to his family, and to society as a whole. This too is part of the *meaning* of behavior; and in understanding the meaning of behavior, the observer first becomes aware of these consequences and then usually tries to make the patient aware of those to which he may be shutting his eyes. Thereby he attempts to bring together those divergent *meanings,* which are the meaning to the patient of his behavior, in contrast to its meaning to others. It is obvious, of course, that many of a patient's rationalizations have it as their unconscious purpose to hide from the realization and acknowledgment of these very consequences.

3. Third, there is the meaningfulness to the observer, whose own conscious, preconscious, and unconscious processes are stirred by that which he observes. The observer cannot understand behavior fully until he understands its meaning on all three levels (conscious, preconscious, and unconscious) to all participants: i.e., to the patient himself, to the patient's environment, and to the observer.

As therapists, we must consider how far to go beyond this in each individual case: i.e., in our efforts to communicate to the patient our own deepening insights into his behavior. Theoretically the inclusive goal of therapy is to communicate to the patient every insight which anyone gains into all of these meanings. The practical strategic goal is to share with the patient as full an understanding of the various levels and directions of meaning as that patient can use flexibly and constructively. This requires that we deal effectively with the fearful and guilty reluctance which every patient feels toward such searching self-knowledge, and with all of his active defenses and resistances, conscious, preconscious, and/or unconscious. Without this, a permanent gap will remain between our vision of the truth about a patient and his self-protective view of himself. In the effort to communicate this to the patient himself it is critical that we not allow such interpretations of meanings to be caught up in the web of a patient's own neurotically conditioned thinking, thus merely feeding new symptoms to an old neurosis—a goal which is easy to formulate but far from easy always to attain.

4. Finally there is a meaning which includes the ways in which recurrent patterns of behavior fit into the total scheme of a personality and of a life, under the influence of component forces which are so conflicting and so contradictory as to render the resultant behavior purposeless, from any logical, sensible, creative viewpoint. Its meaning becomes meaningless. It creates only destruction and self-destruction. Its outcome is illness. From the point of view of understanding the role of psychogenetic forces in psychological illness, this is perhaps the most important meaning of all: and here *meaning* approaches closest to *cause* [cf. Whitehorn, 24].

Thus *meaning* entails certain causative or genetic implications, partial explanations of the content of illness and of their consequences to the patient and to others, plus an understanding of continuing forces. Depending upon the viewpoint from which they are approached and the purpose for which they are to be used, these together may be said to make up what Whitehorn calls "meaning" in psychodynamic interpretations.

VI. SUMMARY

I will not attempt to summarize in detail this diffuse presentation; but it may be worth while to pick out a few items for special emphasis, and as points of departure for future inquiries.

There has been a central emphasis on the importance of circular interactions in all psychological descriptions and explanations: (a) those which focus around biochemical body needs, (b) those arising from affective variables, (c) circular relationships around symbolic variables, and (d) the ultimate circular relationships among intrapsychic, psychosocial, and cultural variables.

Another basic assumption is that there is a neurotic potential which is intrinsic to human psychology, quite apart from cultural variables. The threshold of this potential, however, and the age at which it becomes fully operative is profoundly influenced by organic variables and individual experiences; but whether cultural variables influence the neurotic potential has not yet been established.

Out of the neurotic potential evolves the neurotic process. This also is ubiquitous, although frequently it is completely masked; and it evolves under the influence of organic and cultural variables, as well as individual life experiences, and to a degree which increases with each year of life.

Finally, out of the neurotic process a state of clinical illness can precipitate, whether as neurosis or psychosis. It is the expression of a decompensation in the neurotic process. This decompensation occurs under an even more preponderant influence of cultural and individual stresses.

Perhaps the fact that the investigation of these interrelating forces has not been carried on precisely in terms of their impact on these three phases of the neurotic process is what has left the whole problem in a state of confusion and controversy for so long a time.*

* Figures 1, 4, 5, are reproduced from the Hixon Fund Lectures [17] with the permission of the publishers, the Stanford Univ. Press.

REFERENCES

1. COUNCIL for INTERNATIONAL ORGANIZATION OF MEDICAL SCIENCES. *Transactions,* Conference on the Electric Activity of the Cortex as Affected by the Brain Stem Reticular System in Relation to States of Consciousness, Ste. Marguerite, Quebec, Canada, Aug. 23–27, 1953.

2. FREUD, S. The Unconscious (1915). *Collected Papers,* London: Hogarth Press, 1925, 4: 98–137.

3. ——— *Three Contributions to the Theory of Sex* (4th Edition). New York and Washington: Nervous and Mental Disease Publishing Co., 1930.

4. GLOVER, EDWARD. *Freud or Jung.* New York: W. W. Norton, 1950. p. 207.

5. HARTMANN, H., KRIS, E., and LOEWENSTEIN, R. M. Comments on the formation of psychic structure. In: Psychoanalytic Study of the Child, 1946, 2: 11–38.

6. HARTMANN, H. Psychoanalysis and developmental psychology. In: Psychoanalytic Study of the Child, New York: International Universities Press, 1950, 5: 7–17.

7. ——— Comments on the psychoanalytic theory of the ego. In: Psychoanalytic Study of the Child, New York: International Universities Press, 1950, 5: 74.

8. HOLT, EDWIN B. *The Concept of Consciousness.* New York: Macmillan, 1914. p. 343.

9. ——— *The Freudian Wish.* New York: Holt, 1915. p. 212.

10. JAMES, WILLIAM. *Essays in Radical Empiricism.* New York: Longmans, Green, 1912. p. 283, and especially Chap. 1, "Does Consciousness Exist?" pp. 1–39.

11. KRIS, E. Notes on the development and on some current problems of psychoanalytic child psychology. In: Psychoanalytic Study of the Child, 1949, 5: 24–46.

12. KUBIE, L. S., and LEWIN, B. D. Footnotes to article by R. G. Hoskins. "An Endocrine Approach to Psychodynamics." Psychoanalyt. Quart., Jan. 1936, 5: 87–107.

13. KUBIE, L. S. The experimental induction of neurotic reactions in man. Yale J. Biol. & Med., May 1939, 5: 541–545.

14. ——— The fallacious use of quantitative concepts in dynamic psychology. Psychoanalyt. Quart., 1947, 16:: 507–518.

15. ——— Instincts and homeostasis. Psychosom. Med., Jan.–Feb. 1948, 10: 15–30. (Reprinted in *The Yearbook of Psychoanalysis,* Vol. 5, pp. 157–188.)

16. ——— The neurotic potential, the neurotic process, and the neurotic state. U.S. Armed Forces M. J. Jan. 1951, 2: 1–12.

17. ——— "Problems and Techniques of Psychoanalytic Validation and Progress," pp. 46–124, chapter in: *Hixon Fund Lectures on the Scientific Status of Psychoanalysis,* (March–May 1950). Stanford, Calif.: Stanford Univ. Press, 1952.

18. ——— The distortion of the symbolic process in neurosis and psychosis. J. Amer. Psychoanal. Ass., Jan. 1953, 1: 59–86.

19. ——— "Psychoanalysis as a basic science," from *20 Years of Psychoanalysis, a Symposium,* Franz Alexander, M.D., and Helen Ross, (Eds.). New York: W. W. Norton, 1953. pp. 120–145.

20. ——— The fundamental nature of the distinction between normality and neurosis. Psychoanalyt. Quart., 1954, 23: 167–205.

21. THE JOSIAH MACY, JR. FOUNDATION. *Transactions,* Conferences on Cybernetics, 1949–1953. New York: 1950–1955.

22. PENFIELD, W. Memory mechanisms. A.M.A. Arch. Neurol. & Psychiatr., Feb. 1952, 67: 178–198.

23. REDLICH, F. C., HOLLINGSHEAD, A. B., ROBERTS, B. H., ROBINSON, H. A., FRIEDMAN, L. Z., MYERS, J. K. Social structure and psychiatric disorders. Am. J. Psychiat., April 1953, 109: 729–734.

24. WHITEHORN, JOHN C. The concepts of "meaning" and "cause" in psychodynamics. Am. J. Psychiat., Nov. 1947, 104: 289–292.

chapter 4

The Psychosocial Position
on Etiology

ERICH LINDEMANN

• •

There has been for many decades, especially in German philosophical thinking, a strong tendency to split man into two kinds of being: one kind who is a biological, physiological entity, and can be explained in scientific terms after the pattern of physics and chemistry; and another kind of man who is essentially oriented toward goals, ideals, strivings, and who primarily has to be *understood* rather than to be explained. An important exponent of this view was Carl Jaspers in Heidelberg; I became acquainted with him there some years ago and I am probably still influenced by his teaching. I believe that a person presenting the psychosocial point of view is likely to be oriented in the second direction.

I should explain, by the way, that I am not a professional social scientist. I wish I were; for starting at the age of almost fifty to acquire knowledge in social science is not an easy matter. Hence, I am talking more as a clinician than as a social scientist.

There is no argument with the position that all human beings become sick by virtue of their emotional and physiological organization and the functional limits inherent in it. However, it is important to keep in mind that one not only can view a sick person as a defective machine but also

can see in his behavior evidence of an adaptive process.

It is clear from the work of Head and Goldstein that even a large portion of neurological disease is to be understood not as brain damage alone but as an adaptive process to this damage. The actual symptomatology is a secondary elaboration of biologic damage. This process of adaptation, repair, whatever one would like to call it, leads straight to the problem of human beings as goal-directed personalities, as individuals who have to satisfy needs, and what is more important, who have to fit their need satisfaction into a system of related need satisfactions of others.

People concerned with social factors in the causation of mental disease are likely to make a number of basic assumptions. The essential situation is this: Instead of being focused primarily on an individual, the social psychiatrist is concerned with a togetherness, or an aggregate of people, or a social system. What happens in an individual is seen as the resultant of processes not only within but also around him. His behavior is adaptive or nonadaptive to an external situation; therefore, the way his partners in the social system adapt at this time is also important. So, the social scientist would be somewhat uncomfortable with the nosological concept of an illness as expounded by the biologist: that there are schizophrenics and manic-depressives, people who are victims of a disease entity irrespective of the social system in which they develop. Social scientists are likely to prefer to say that they are dealing with variants of deviant behavior, trying to determine the degree of deviance from the accepted norm of behavior for a certain social context in a variety of terms. They are very much interested in how the controls of behavior or conduct will limit behavior under ordinary circumstances to only a special permissible range and in those social factors which might make for a change in the range of behavior for one or many people at a given time.

Out of this approach grows another notion related to nosological entities: that behavior variations are seen on a continuum from mild changes to more severe changes. I think that Dr. Kubie implied that notion, too, although he did not say it specifically. These variations in behavior may be due partly to biological factors. There might be some abrupt breaks in that continuum and there might be clusters of deviant behavior. But the clusters might not exclusively be determined by biological factors. There might be powerful societal factors making for the recurrence of behavior clusters to be considered as deviant.

Another position which is certainly current in the psychosocial field sees what we call illness as an ultimate solution of an adjustment problem in preference to some other solution. They believe that it would be useful from the societal point of view to compare the rates of mental illness, delinquency, disordered peoples in general hospitals, and individuals who have a performance deficit on the basis of a neurosis. They might regard as conceivable that one form of adjustment to a societal problem might be shifted into another adjustment, the one bearing the label "illness" and the other bearing the label "court case" or "a very successful fellow indeed." These equivalents, as we like to call them, are all seen as forms of deviance, perhaps "deviant behavior."

In the social system it is recognized that the role which a person assumes for a given period of time has certain features which make this role considerably more acceptable than other roles. Talcott Parsons has taken great pains to describe what he calls the sick role vis-à-vis the well role: to describe the important features of the sick role in society which permits one to give up for a while in one's expected performance of duties; which gives one access to a special form of intimacy with a doctor, making it possible to have a restricted acquaintance for a limited time by contract with a trusted person; and which makes it possible to receive a variety of satisfactions of the nature usually permitted only earlier in life—dependency, passivity, nurturing care by nurses.

From these considerations it follows that there might be motivations and constellations in society which would be just as pathogenic as biological factors may be. Many people like to point, for instance, to the insurance arrangement of compensation for accidents as a factor related to increase in certain types of sickness, for instance, traumatic neurosis.

Another axiom of the social scientist, perhaps a variant of what I said, states that there is a continuum of steps which leads from the neurosis to the psychosis and toward the psychosomatic disorders. You all remember Alan Gregg's interest in it when he raised the question: What is the relative frequency of psychosomatic disorders in mental disorders? It has turned out to be a rather complicated issue, on which the books are not yet closed. By and large, the trend seems to indicate that there are some rather low counts of certain psychosomatic disorders in mental hospitals. That finding leads to the following line of reasoning: The social system might be regarded as the primary concern and the sick or other deviant people as casualties of something in this society, whatever it may be. A study might be undertaken into the articulation of an individual with the setting of other human beings in which he is operating. So the individual personality versus the social system and the community and its needs for deviant people might be discussed.

Investigators subscribing to the psycho-social position would be interested in problems of distribution of disturbances in society; in variations from culture to culture, from different societies at different levels. Dr. Dunham, with Dr. Ferris, really opened this field when he demonstrated in his study in Chicago that the metropolitan cities have special areas which are particularly prone to have found in them individuals with certain kinds of mental disorder. What order for the moment does not concern us. Mark Shaw was similarly concerned with problems of delinquency that might arise in certain areas. The problem was: Are there certain characteristic geographic areas in the context of a society which are likely to be the locus for the occurrence of illnesses? That question is in contrast with the statement that certain illnesses are evenly distributed all over the world. In metropolitan areas they certainly are not. Then too, a number of projects are trying to work out with some precision the various kinds of recurrence and various rates of illness in relation to the nature of the community context.

As for convergence which appears in the theme of the Conference, the psychosocial field might not converge from social types to biological science but it is converging from social science to epidemiology. This field is becoming very well developed in its knowledge of rates for other acute and chronic disease and co-occurrence of certain variables which can be easily assessed. We are quite honest in saying that we are barely beginning even to understand what we are doing. Recent discussion about When is a case, a case? points out the great difficulty. Dr. Redlich, who has pushed ahead in New Haven in this area, has been relating his observations to problems of class structure. He has been wise to relate his observations on social characteristics not to disease as such but to people who have had psychiatric care. Perhaps differences may be found among the kind of people who have felt the need of going to a psychiatrist.

In respect to individual deviants, Gruenberg has been interested in one aspect of the community, which is often designated as community tolerance. Deviant people may or may not be accepted. They may be "extruded" by the community or they may be kept in circulation. The factors operating probably vary from community to community. Tolerance seems to vary highly from ethnic to ethnic group, for instance, Italians being more tolerant of older people than are Yankees.

Assuming for the moment an average rate of decay of the vascular system, perhaps decay of the cellular structure of the brain, Gruenberg raised the question whether there may be less likelihood of brain impairment, deterioration, and inability to perform as usual among people in a tolerant than in another society. The related problem with which we are faced is: Are there community or social features which might provide for some deviant behavior as a solution of a societal problem?

Society is involved in the care of the sick by other than medical personnel. That is perfectly obvious. When we, at the Massachusetts General Hospital, started to study bereaved people, it became perfectly clear that most of them are seen by clergymen and funeral directors, not doctors. It was evident that the whole group of individuals who temporarily were severely disturbed were not consulting doctors but were turning to their clergymen. When we really looked at these persons, we found that there was a whole set of reactions which might well be described as psychotic behavior. But for us and the clergymen this was not deviant behavior because we thought that it was proper under the circumstances to be so disturbed. So the social judgment concerning a given form of behavior in terms of societal circumstances is one factor, first of all, in determining whether or not a type of behavior is being considered as a case of illness.

Further, if a succession of bereaved people are observed, a variety of reactions are noted, all to the same crisis which we described as a cessation of interaction between two individuals in a social system. Patterns were seen which Freud first mentioned and which we continue to call "grief work"; they comprise a sequence of psychological operations. These we see as forms of adaptive behavior. These operations may be so intense that for the onlooker they appear as impairment of function; indeed, with this preoccupation, the persons are impaired in the pursuit of happiness and performance, as compared with what other people might expect of them.

We might mention especially the process in which a review of shared past experiences brings forth the mourning response. However, there are individuals, who, instead of exhibiting normal grieving, display an adaptive response which may very well be maladaptive responses of various forms. There may also be peculiar things happening to the image of the deceased. He may not be remembered. The process of adapting to the crisis in this social relationship, where now one person is missing, might operate in such a way that the survivor makes desperate efforts to reinstate the deceased person, to deny the loss. This may appear as acquisition of the symptoms which were previously witnessed in the deceased. It may appear as an acquisition of his personality traits. Then it may be concluded that a mental disease really has developed because now the survivor feels as though he is two instead of one; temporarily one loses one's identity. Thus, in sequence to a purely social event, with a change in context of human relations, there may be found going on a process which at times appears as an illness.

With this example as a starting point, it might be said that social crises, such as disaster, bereavement, the appearance of the newborn child (the arrival of a new person in the woman's life), marriage, role transitions such as are found in passing from pre-puberty to puberty, from the home into the nursery school, might be situations in which a variety of adaptive processes might be noticed as behavior changes with different degrees of deviance from the accepted norm for that particular section of society. It depends very considerably upon a given society whether a person with behavioral changes under such circumstances would be referred to an inquiring public health officer or to a sociologist or to a doctor as a case of illness.

The processes which we have considered fall to a large extent into the area of dynamic psychiatry. But they raise another issue. They raise the problem of well or not-so-well being of an individual and well or not-well being of that context of human relationships, the social system, of which this particular individual is only one part. The processes which might not be so conspicuous in the other members of this group might nevertheless lend additional understanding for the problem of an individual with conspicuous processes who knocks at the door of the psychiatrist.

Some individuals in the fields of anthropology and sociology who have been very much interested in the nature of social systems and cultures are concerned with the way in which a society arranges to facilitate adaptive responses. In the times of crisis, in the times of bereavement, different societies operate in different ways. Funeral practices have been studied in great detail since Malinowski. It is quite obvious that the group behavior of some societies at the time of a severe bereavement may indeed have the features of highly abnormal behavior, certainly when seen with Western eyes. Vis-à-vis the deceased, there are very primitive types of behavior, such as aggressive outbursts. The problem becomes whether these types of behavior have clinical equivalents; namely, whether there are societal processes which have to be viewed in terms of what is healthy and what is abnormal in a universal sense. Then it might be said that some of these operations spare, and others might be contributory to, individual casualties. Accordingly, the phenomena of rituals of various kinds in different types of society and the various forces reflected in such ritual become subjects of importance. Kluckhohn has been interested in witchcraft among the Navaho. He raised the question whether labeling a person as a deviant and subjecting him to death or some similar punishment is related, as are some other casualties, to societal needs. If so, it should be demonstrable that the rate of accusing people of being deviants, for example, witches, would change with different pressures, ecological or otherwise, on the society. He believes that he has evidence on that point. He believes that there are marked fluctuations in the rate of witchcraft accusations depending upon outside pressure upon the Navahos.

Other situations involving not only individuals but societal forces which might be pathogenic and based on society structure are worth looking for. For each society has ecological needs, a role distribution, a hierarchy, various cultural values and shared goals, and it enforces conformity with these values. It might even be said that societies may in a certain sense need various rates of casualties. If the focus is directed upon families and upon the context of human relationships in hospitals, run by nurses, supervised by doctors, and handled by aides, it may be asked whether or not the context of the human beings in the family or their temporary context in the hospital have features of a sick-making quality which serve to foster that kind of adjustment which deserves the designation as sick. For example, the studies of Stanton and Schwartz at Chestnut Lodge and of Caudill at New Haven in mental hospitals show a strikingly high relationship between the well-being of patients and fluctuations in agreement and disagreement and channels of communication among the caretaking staff. Family studies on parents and siblings, just beginning to be made, are systematically designed to appraise possible pathogenic roles in which members may earn their well-being at the expense of the symptomatology of the "sick person." They may be useful with a very practical problem just now beginning to receive attention: the return of the mentally sick population into the community for "rehabilitation." In sum, it may be concluded that by its organization and orientation, whatever else society is, it probably is one of the potent factors in determining rates of breakdowns or casualties.

I have really been spelling out what Dr. Kubie touched upon under the head of "culture," when he said that we all agree that culture, biology, and dynamic processes are related. It is quite true. I fully agree. There are, however, some points at which sociologists feel that they might improve on traditional psychoanalytic theory of causation of neurosis and psychosis, and they are particularly concerned with certain phases of personality development.

Talcott Parsons has taken issue with the Freudian formulaton of the development of the superego or the development of the internalization of all those controls of conduct which the growing child experiences on the part of his parents. In the whole problem of dealing with mental illness as a casualty of the societal process itself, this would probably be a nuclear point for investigation. Inasmuch as a psychoanalyst might readily say, "My job in the neurosis is to decrease the severity of the superego," it should also be understood that by implication he is trying to reduce the impact of the internalized constellation of coercive forces which are still binding this individual. That brings us to a whole area of problems too vast to be discussed here, the problem of social learning. In the area of learning theory as related to neuroses and psychoses, David Levy has pointed out succinctly that we ought to distinguish in emotional disorders two kinds of relationships: one in which an overwhelming emotional trauma has caused a block for further learning; the other, in which a chain of traumatic experiences leads to another kind of impairment which has been described as an impoverishment of the personality in terms of the acquisition of social skills. Both kinds of personality structures might represent very different predispositions to succumb at the occasion of precipitating events.

It is also important to remember that even severely impoverished people, so far as social skills are concerned, may find themselves in highly rewarded places in the social context even though they have a very limited capacity for rewarding human re-relationships.

Next to be considered is the problem of acquisition of social skills and the capacity for relatedness, the latter being quite clearly one aspect of social systems; namely, individual encumbrance in roles. There has been much discussion about Bowlby's work which showed that separation from the mother at critical periods of life development may be followed, perhaps, not by schizophrenia or any of those nosological boxes, but by a disturbance of relatedness. Bowlby used the word "affectlessness" for some of these people who in some areas have no regard for the rules of conduct laid down and cannot relate themselves in a constructive way to others.

The question then arises whether social

events, pure and simple, might in most, if not all, individuals, particularly in susceptible individuals who face a situation of risk such as separation from a caretaking, maternal person at a critical time, be producing a severe handicap of subsequent relatedness and subsequent learning capacity, leading to a kind of impairment of function on a social basis which would parallel impairment on the basis of reduction in available biological machinery. The details of that process are very exciting objects for further research.

In this area there is a parallel in animal sociology. Lorenz, Tinbergen, and in this country, Scott at Bar Harbor have been conducting a systematic inquiry about the earliest period of social behavior in dogs, birds, and fish. Liddell has worked with later phases of social learning in sheep and pigs as well as dogs. He has pointed out vigorously that animals who in adult life are impaired in certain behavior segments may have special problems in their social relationship to their caretaker. I can give only a hint in this direction today.

To conclude, in presenting this discourse, I have attempted to advance the proposition that there are certain factors in societal context and in the social system context which may be highly significant in determining rates and patterns of emotional disorders. Anybody who overlooks them will do so at his peril.

DISCUSSION

STRÖMGREN: I should like to say a few words in connection with Dr. Lindemann's presentation. Surveys to determine the incidences of mental disorders in different populations are, of course, absolutely necessary for psychosocial studies. Several such studies have been conducted and some far-reaching conclusions have been drawn from anthropological materials. Inasmuch as such material is very small and the nature of the samples is unknown, perhaps containing instances of inbreeding, we cannot draw many conclusions and generalizations from them.

There are, on the other hand, some investigations on primitive populations which seem to be extremely useful. I am thinking especially of one study conducted in Kenya by F. C. Carothers [1]. It was made on a very sizable sample by a very competent psychiatrist, who knows not only statistics but also the population which he was surveying; for he had been living for a long time in Kenya as the superintendent of a mental hospital. He found that the prevalence of psychosis was very low there and he thought that it must be correlated with the special culture in which people live in a state of security and need no anxiety. He ventured the opinion that if they should come in contact with other cultures, the prevalence of mental disorder would rise.

I was so very much impressed with this survey that I have mentioned it several times in lectures as a good example of such studies. After some time I got some pertinent information from a Danish farmer who had lived for some years in Kenya. He told me about the treatment of the mentally abnormal persons in the interior of Kenya. They were treated humanely. But if there came to be too many mentally disturbed persons, the tribe would take an excursion for some days through the jungle and would travel at a speed that was beyond the ability of those who were mentally or physically disabled. They would be left in the jungle when the tribe would go home. Or the tribe would take a trip up to the mountains where there seemed to be a peculiar risk for the mentally disabled to drop down the sides. All these practices would influence the prevalence of mental disorders in such a population to a degree which would make it very difficult to draw any conclusions as to the influence of the culture of the people on the incidence of the disorders. This example illustrates the difficulties to be expected when such investigations are attempted.

When the investigations which seem to be reliable are checked, it is amazing to find that in respect to the incidence of the major psychoses such as schizophrenia, manic-depression, and insanity, there seems to be very little difference among the different populations.

It is necessary that many investigations be conducted with the same methods on the incidence of mental disorders in different cultures. Of course, I think that rates of admission do not reflect the true incidences; for admission rates are very much influenced by the policies of the different hospitals. It would be wise to have international cooperation committees, comprising investigators from different countries and of different viewpoints, to work together to conduct surveys in a quite uniform way. These surveys should distinguish between the social and nonsocial casualties, for there is not a natural continuum between these two groups. It would be important to classify the different categories of mental disorders: firstly, cases existing in all kinds of cultures and always giving social problems; secondly, cases existing in all kinds of cultures but giving problems only in some kinds of cultures; and then thirdly, cases existing only in some kinds of cultures. Such investigations should be a highly productive way to estimate the influence of the culture on the incidence of mental disorder.

There are other areas in mental disease in which cooperation among research workers of different viewpoints would be fruitful. I may only mention the instances in which organic brain damage and psychodynamic factors jointly have influence. Attempted suicide by hanging is an example. After the attempt the patient is unconscious; later he awakens with amnesia which is caused by the physical insult. Still later it turns out that the content of the amnesia is determined systematically by the conflicts of the patient. During the first days or weeks after the attempt, he will usually be in an euphoric state, and only those things which are in accordance with his mood will be able to come into his consciousness. After some time his mood may change into a more or less depressed state; then again he may remember the conflicts and the amnesia may disappear completely. Inasmuch as everybody must agree that psychogenic and physical factors are both important in such cases, investigators with different viewpoints on mental disease will be able to cooperate in studying them. None will say that such a case belongs only to the organic group or to the psychogenic group.

The same possibilities for cooperation may be found in twin-studies. I would like to direct attention to the recent studies of Dr. Eliot Slater [2] in this field. There is a misconception in some minds that only those who are interested solely in genetics study twins. Actually twin-studies provide perhaps the most reliable method for determining the extent of the influence which *environment* exerts, all differences between uniovular twins necessarily being of exogenous origin. Here, then, is an excellent field of activity for the joint efforts of "geneticists" and "environmentalists." I should like to illustrate this by means of one of Slater's cases, "Gladys" and "Linda" [2, p. 351 ff.]. In middle life Gladys developed a depressive neurosis with hysterical traits, leading her into a chronic state of social parasitism, "hospitalism." As the environmental circumstances preceding her illness were not convincingly pathogenic, it would, in search for the etiology, be natural to concentrate on the fact that the history of Gladys' childhood comprised some environmental adversities and a number of neurotic traits in her personality. But then we have the control: Linda had the same environment, and she, too, had neurotic symptoms as a child, in spite of which she remained completely well-adapted all her life. We learn, then, that neither the genetic background nor the childhood environment of Gladys could be sufficient cause for her illness. This fact leads us to concentrate our diagnostic (and therapeutic) efforts on the point of Gladys' life-curve where it begins to deviate from Linda's.

The developmental history of any personality, normal or abnormal, may be described as a succession of "conflicts" or reactions to "stress." Twin-studies are a good tool for discriminating such adversities that are *really* pathogenic.

REFERENCES

1. CAROTHERS, F. C. A study of mental derangement in Africans. J. Ment. Sc., 1947, 93: 548.
2. SLATER, ELIOT. *Psychotic and Neurotic Illnesses in Twins.* London: Her Majesty's Stationery Office, 1953.

chapter 5

Areas of Interdoctrinal Acceptance

• •

An Organicist Speaks

ELIOT SLATER

The problem we are called on to consider is the major contemporary problem of psychiatry. There are dangers that psychiatrists may split into mutually irreconcilable schools, unable to understand each other's languages. We must build a synthesis; and although in our several parties we are working on separate parts of the building, we should be aware of the ground plan, in which space is allotted to the other fellow, whose work will eventually join up with ours. From this point of view, the detail of the other fellow's work will be of no great interest or importance to us, but the skeleton on which his superstructure is raised will be vitally important, as it will have to interlock with our own.

Looking at psychiatry from the organic point of view, which I take to include also the genetic viewpoint, I think that the modern organicist is fully aware of the limitations of his field and the insufficiency of his methods. He knows that his work must be complemented from other sides. He has discovered, for instance, that a particular genic mutation provides the predisposition for the disease we call Huntington's chorea, after the American discoverer who found it

in certain families living on Long Island a century or so ago. But the geneticist is quite unable to say what it is that makes the condition appear early in life in some cases, while in others the onset is retarded to the presenium, why some people who are gene carriers never develop the condition at all, why in some cases the disorder leads to gross abnormalities of behavior, sexual misdemeanors, and the like, while in others there is only a flat dementia. The organicist knows that there are some forms of depression which have a specific genetical basis; that in other cases what matters most is a structural lesion of the brain; and in yet others it is the psychodynamic causes which predominate. In any particular case his methods will probably be sufficient to elucidate only part of the story. The coordinated use of other technics will be needed to understand the case in all its complexity. When we are called on to deal with the individual patient, we must try to decide how far causative factors of all these and many other kinds are involved. This brings me to the importance of diagnosis.

It is sometimes maintained [2] that if

41

organic disease of the brain is present there is always a degree of intellectual defect. I do not believe this is true. Certainly many lobotomised patients show no degree of intellectual defect which can be detected clinically or measured psychometrically. Their predominant defects may be shown in the temperamental field, along lines which we are accustomed to classify as neurotic or psychopathic. There is no single psychological symptom, of which I am aware, which cannot be caused by an organic or by a psychodynamic factor. The deviation of personality in the direction of irritability and aggressiveness will be associated here with a train of frustrating circumstances, there with an old brain contusion, and in a third case with a temporal lobe epilepsy. But for purposes of prognosis and treatment it will be of paramount importance to decide whether or not there is an epilepsy, whether or not a history of a knock on the head meant that the patient has had a cerebral contusion, whether or not the frustrating circumstances, which can no doubt be found in his life, are to be regarded as the predominant cause. Our means of reaching such a decision will be provided by clinical tools, psychometric, physiological, psychosocial, and not least by the tools of descriptive psychiatry and the phenomenological approach which are today so much out of fashion.

Once we have allocated a patient to a particular diagnostic group, we do not pretend to ourselves that we know all we need to know about him. But we have simplified our problems. We have reached the point where certain lines of inquiry and certain practical procedures are in the center of our field of attention, and others have passed into the periphery, or have been left behind. If we discover that a mentally ill man, however adequate the psychodynamic factors which could explain his illness may be, has many cells in his cerebrospinal fluid, a positive Wassermann, and a paretic gold curve, then the first thing we shall do is to give him penicillin. Whether or not he is to have psychotherapy has become a secondary issue.

When we come to the problems of classification in psychiatry, the same concepts will continue to provide a useful guide. Causes of a particular kind are of greater frequency and importance in some conditions than in others. In the genetic field this is particularly obvious. In my own investigations on twins [4], the genetic factor was found to be much more important in the schizophrenic psychoses than in the field of neurotic disturbances and behavior disorders. In close agreement with the findings of Kallmann [1], three out of every four pairs of uniovular twins were adjudged as concordant in respect to schizophrenia. But only one out of four were concordant in respect to neurosis. Among the schizophrenics, binovular twins were no more alike than one might expect ordinary sibs to be; in the neurotic group there were pairs of binovular twins who took very similar delinquent or aberrant paths despite large differences in intellectual and temperamental make-up, owing to the fact that they shared a bad environment and disturbed home life. This does not mean that in the schizophrenics the genetic factor was the only one that mattered; after all, one in four of those who had the necessary genetic equipment never fell ill and must have been protected from the environmental side. There were also often large differences in age of onset. In one uniovular pair, for instance, one twin started on a slow progressive hebephrenic deterioration at the age of sixteen, while the other fell ill with a more stormy paranoid psychosis at forty-nine, having, as far as we could tell, been quite normal until then. If we could discover what exactly were the environmental differences between two such individuals, we would be a long step toward finding reliable methods of treatment.

In the neurotic group it is easier to tell what are the decisive psychodynamic factors than in the psychotic group. Let me instance one pair, a uniovular pair of boys. They were of good intelligence, and in addition had some artistic abilities in painting, modeling, music, and writing. One of the two was of a slightly more passive but steadier personality, made nothing of his little talent, and settled down contentedly to the humdrum life of a commercial traveler. The other twin, the leader of the pair, was ill content with life as a city clerk, changed from job to job, but wrote stories and succeeded in selling some of them so as to make a worth-while addition to his income. He fell in with a Bohemian set and eventually married a girl who was even less emotionally stable than he was. There were frequent quarrels and threats of violence and of suicide; and eventually on the part of our twin, a hysterical fugue which landed him in a psychiatric clinic. In such cases as this we see a chain reaction between constitution and environment which leads to a decisive departure from the normal. The causative factors are laid out, as if on a dissecting dish: genetic constitution, results of early environment and the psychological inter-twin relationship, and even sheer for-tuitous accident in the form of the marriage lottery.

I hope I have said enough to show that, from the organic point of view, there are wide areas where we are ready for interdoctrinal acceptance. I do not anticipate that there is cause for any very hot disputes between the organic and the psychometric schools. What I am hoping for is that those who approach psychiatry from the psychodynamic and the psychosocial angles will concede that we on the organic side have some glimmer of the light that illumines their paths, that we too can contribute something useful to the structure of psychiatric theory. A recent paper by Sandor Rado [3], which I have had the privilege of reading in manuscript, gives me hope that that may be so.

REFERENCES

1. KALLMANN, F. J. *Heredity in Health and Mental Disorder*. New York: W. W. Norton, 1953.
2. LIDZ, T. "Some Remarks Concerning the Differentiation of Organic from So-called 'Functional' Psychoses," in *The Biology of Mental Health and Disease*. New York: P. B. Hoeber, 1952, p. 322.
3. RADO, S. Dynamics and classification of disordered behaviour. Am. J. Psychiat., 1953, 110: 406–416.
4. SLATER, E. *Psychotic and Neurotic Illnesses in Twins*. London: Her Majesty's Stationery Office, 1953.

A Psychologist Speaks

NEAL E. MILLER

From the preceding papers it is already obvious that the four main approaches to the causation of mental disease—the Organic, the Psychodynamic, the Psychological, and the Psychosocial—are not mutually exclusive alternatives; no single one is sufficient, all are necessary. Furthermore, each approach is not unitary, but within itself includes a number of diverse causal factors. For example, the organic approach includes such diverse factors as genetic determinants, toxic agents, and brain injuries.

The relative importance of a given approach depends upon the range through which its causal factors are varied in the particular sample of cases being studied.

For example, if we are dealing with extreme differences in hereditary strain or with the presence or absence of a severe head injury, the importance of organic factors will be emphasized. On the other hand, we might be dealing with an unusually homogeneous group of men carefully selected for the absence of any organic, psychodynamic, or social defects to go on a crucial military mission. If some of these men had an easy time while others were subjected to great extremes of psychological stress, the situational variable would be the most important determinant of who developed a combat neurosis. Therefore the degree of emphasis which a given approach receives depends upon the type of cases the investigator selects. It is no accident that more of those who emphasize the organic view are working in mental hospitals, while more of those who emphasize the psychodynamic view are in private practice. Some of our failures to achieve wider interdoctrinal acceptance may be due to the fact that we are dealing with different, selected groups of cases.

Next, I believe we will all agree that none of the causal factors emphasized by the four different approaches operates in complete isolation from the others; they all interact. This interaction of the factors has one particularly significant result. It means that the practical importance of a particular factor is determined, not only by the degree to which it is varied in a particular sample of cases, but also by the means for controlling it which are available at a given moment in history. For example, in the past, the organic defect of congenital deafness was a catastrophic handicap because it completely cut off the afflicted person from speech—the chief means of social communication. At that time the organic defect of congenital deafness was widely believed to include a general deficit in intellect and personality. However, with the development of psychological and educational technics for teaching deaf people sign language, lip reading, and even speech, this organic defect became much less important; the marked intellectual deficits and personality deviations disappeared. The invention of new psychological technics dramatically changed the significance of an organic defect! Similarly, fundamental advances in psychodynamics could radically widen the range of cases susceptible to psychotherapy.

The history of diabetes illustrates a change in the opposite direction. Formerly this disease could be controlled only by the environmental means of reducing carbohydrates in the diet. With the discovery of the metabolic processes involved and the development of insulin, an organic type of treatment became more important and environmental control over the diet could be relaxed. Similarly, radical new developments in our understanding of the anat-omy, physiology, or pharmacology of the nervous system could greatly increase the importance of organic types of treatment of mental disease.

Furthermore, we all know that the best results can sometimes be secured by various combinations of technics. For example, in World War II the organic technic of drugs was used to make men with combat neuroses more susceptible to psychotherapy, and their psychosocial situation was also changed by assigning them to noncombat duty.

The acceptance of the foregoing points is a valuable and significant sign of progress. But it is only a beginning. Actually we have not gone very far when we say that all of these factors interact and are important. The real problem is exactly how they achieve their effects. This problem remains largely unsolved. The next task which lies before us is to work out step by step the mechanisms by which each of the factors interacts with the others and makes its contribution. For example, we need to understand the mechanism by which a genetic factor interacts with the environment to produce a personality defect. What are the differences between a bright and a stupid person? How do children learn to discriminate fantasy from reality? How does sleep facilitate dreams? How do drugs produce hallucinations? How do neurological or hormonal changes produce their effects on personality? How do psychological stresses produce psychosomatic effects? I believe we are beginning to accumulate the theoretical ideas and research technics to start learning the detailed answers to such questions.

As a point of departure for further detailed research, I would like to suggest in a general way how the factors emphasized by the various approaches are interrelated. The organic foundation determines such things as the repertoire of innate responses which are available, the initial dominance of different responses, the innate strengths of various drives, the sensitivity to different stimuli, and the ability to withstand various types of pain and stress. We need to understand the mechanisms of each of these factors in much more detail.

In most aspects of behavior that are distinctively human, including the neurosis, the innate, organic factors are profoundly modified by learning. To the extent that abnormal behavior is acquired, it must either follow laws of learning that have already been discovered by the experimental psychologist or new laws of learning which have not yet been discovered. In either event, a study of the acquisition and cure of neuroses as instances of learning should be profitable. John Dollard and I have attempted to take the first steps in this direction in our book *Personality and Psychotherapy* [1]. Two useful hypotheses are that some neurotic symptoms are rewarded by temporary reductions in drives such as fear and guilt, and that others are direct physiological reactions to high levels of drive produced by conflicts that prevent drive reduction.

Human learning occurs under social conditions; in general, the psychologist studies the *laws* of learning and the sociologist and social anthropologist supplies essential information about the social *conditions* of human learning. In order to understand behavior, one must know both the laws and the conditions. Again we need to work out the details step by step. For example, exactly how is the superego learned during the socialization of the child?

The psychodynamic clinician has a peculiarly favorable opportunity to observe his patients struggling to learn how to adjust to their organic drives under the conditions of our society. He can supply the physiologist, psychologist, and sociologist with leads to fruitful research problems and can be helped by knowledge from each of these fields.

In conclusion, let me underline Lindemann's excellent point, which is not widely enough appreciated, that sociological factors are extremely important. To give an example, the social workers in a certain agency believed that all unmarried mothers must have an abnormal Oedipus complex and be acting out aggression against the family. These social workers were not enough aware of the striking differences between their own middle-class mores and those of their clients' lower social class. For a middle-class social worker to have an illegitimate child would represent a marked deviation from her parental training and social group; it would terrifically punish her family. Thus one might well look for some deep psychodynamic factors. But the majority of the unmarried mothers came from a lower social group in which the sexual taboos were not nearly as strict. They had not been deviating widely from the mores of their group. Having an illegitimate child may have been merely a matter of ignorance and bad luck.

REFERENCE

1. DOLLARD, J., and MILLER, N. E. *Personality and Psychotherapy*. New York: McGraw-Hill, 1950, p. 488.

A Psychodynamicist Speaks

FRANZ ALEXANDER

Although they often are proposed in a polemic manner, the four points of view do not necessarily represent controversial but rather complementary positions. My contention is that the controversies over them are largely artificial and are based on a confusion concerning the epistemological issues.

In order to evaluate them, the problem of etiology must be scrutinized from the point of view of epistemology. So I will try to submit an epistemological analysis, but you will find it will be a skeleton more than a full exposition. The flesh and blood must be, indeed already is, being added.

First of all, the concept of mental disturbance must be defined. The several schools of etiological thought all agree that mental disturbance is a special case of dysfunction within the human organism, manifesting itself in a disturbed relation to the environment, particularly to the human environment. The etiological problem consists in describing those factors—we call them variables—which are pertinent in bringing about such disturbed function.

For the sake of logical consistency I shall reduce the four positions to three and speak of a biological, a psychobiological, and a sociological position because both the psychodynamic and experimental psychological are the same although they may use different concepts and tools.

According to the biological position, the dysfunction called mental disease is the result of disturbed functioning of the central nervous system which is brought about either by some kind of a pathological process within the nervous system itself or by some disturbance of other organ systems, for example, the endocrine glands or the liver, in other words, by some change in body physiology. No matter what the specific nature of these changes is, they are the results of heredity or toxic influences, or the aging process, or of still-to-be-defined extraneous influences upon the body.

For the psychodynamic position, mental disease is a dysfunction affecting the organism's relation to its environment as the result of psychological experiences which occur primarily in the early part of the postnatal development. Both the psychological theory and biological view assume that certain still undefined hereditary factors predispose individuals to react to early and late experiences in a pathological manner. But, the psychological concept can be reduced in most general terms to the statement that interpersonal experiences of certain kinds in predisposed persons are the primary cause of mental disturbances. The hereditary and the postnatal factors represent a complementary series. The greater the hereditary factor, the less interpersonal conflict is necessary to bring about mental disturbances.

The sociological position maintains that the causative psychological factors can be understood only in the total social configuration in which an individual exists. Ex-periences which may be traumatic in one social setting may be favorable or neutral in another. Obviously this position also considers the etiological factors psychological in nature, but views them from the total social configuration in which the individual is born, reared, and functions.

As stated before, these three views are not contradictory but complementary. All schools of thought would agree with the biological position that mental disturbances take place in an organism and therefore necessarily follow the general principles governing organic processes. In other words, the psychological processes are functions of the highest coordinating centers of the organisms and theoretically could be described, if adequate knowledge were available, in neurological terms. Furthermore, everybody would agree that organic processes within the organism have an influence on psychological events. Influences such as alcohol and deterioration of cerebral blood supply in old age may be the cause of mental dysfunction. On the other hand, all three views, including the biological, concur in that interpersonal influences, through the mediation of the nervous system, may introduce psychopathological processes.

The psychodynamic position maintains, in addition, that the influences arising in interpersonal contacts are the most common factors in mental disturbances and can be best studied in terms of psychology. The question is not what they are—they are, of course, biologic processes—but how can they be studied? The psychodynamic position considers the interaction with the human environment as one of the most fundamental and at the same time most complex functions of the mental system. It further maintains that even when a more advanced knowledge of neurophysiology will be available, a knowledge which will make it possible to describe all psychological functions in the terms of neurophysiology, the nature of the disturbing external stimuli arising in interpersonal contacts will be adequately described only in psychological terms. Physiology therefore cannot fully displace the psychological approach. It is thinkable that with advanced knowledge, the physiological processes involved, for example, those in sibling rivalry, will be described in physiological terms; yet the family situation itself can be understood only in psychological terms.

If this epistemological position is adequate, it follows that the physiological and psychological approaches to etiology are not antagonistic but complementary. Whatever takes place in the organism itself, potentially can be described and understood in physiological terms. The nature of the interpersonal configuration, however, has meaning only in psychological and sociological terms.

We turn now to the agreements and controversies between the psychodynamic and sociological points of view. Some anthropologists have contended that Freud attached too much importance to biological factors in the causation of mental disturbances and neglected the sociological influences. Actually, however, Freud recognized and described in detail the influence of the social environment upon personality development and its disturbances in his concept of superego formation. According to his view, the superego is the result of the internalization of parental attitudes within the child personality. The parental attitudes themselves represent the prevailing code of the society. It is true that Freud was concerned, not with the varieties of superego formation in different societies, but exclusively with personality development in his own culture.

Anthropological studies of normal and disturbed personality development in different cultures have already contributed to a better understanding of the causation of mental disturbances. For example, these studies have put the Freudian emphasis on sexual etiology of neuroses in proper perspective. The importance of the sexual factor is specific for the Victorian era in which the sexual drives were drastically curbed by the prevailing cultural attitude which was transmitted to the child through parental influence. As for mental diseases during this era characterized by extreme repression of sexual impulses, this social attitude was undoubtedly a major etiological factor. Anthropology today has already demonstrated that in different cultures different impulses become vulnerable spots according to the restrictions which the specific ethics of the society imposes upon them. Only the historical, sociological, and anthropological approach will be able to account for differences which exist among cultures regarding parental and child-rearing attitudes, the various technics of child care, and the prevailing emotional climate in the family. All these are determined by the total social configuration which is the result of historical development, but also, of course, of the individual personalities of the parents.

While the individual approach to mental disease describes the disturbances arising from emotional experiences in the family, the sociological approach takes a step further and tries to answer the question of how the emotional climate of the family and specific principles of child rearing are determined by the culture as a whole. It is often held that therapeutic skill is enhanced by knowing more about the cultural determinants of parental attitudes. This view is erroneous because an understanding of each case requires the intimate knowledge of the specific parental attitudes in that instance, regardless of whether such an attitude may be common in one culture and a rare deviation in another. The cultural approach can only explain the frequency of certain types of conflict situations, but never an individual case. I expect that during the course of this discussion I shall have an opportunity to illustrate this point with concrete examples; namely, how the sociological point of view may lead, not to increasing therapeutic skill, but to the contrary. This is not true for etiological research. I refer only to the understanding of individual patients. A patient may have a crazy father, whether he is Japanese or a Westerner.

The integration of the three points of view can be schematically described as follows: Every individual represents a complex biological system; he is born into a family and is exposed to specific influences. Every family is a constituent part of a larger system, a given culture. The comprehensive understanding of mental diseases requires the study of the interaction of these three systems: the biological system, which is exposed to interpersonal influences within the family, which are themselves determined by the culture at large. The biological approach deals with what takes place in the smallest unit of this system, the individual; the psychodynamic approach deals with the influences of the immediate environment of the family; and the sociological approach studies the influence of the largest system of the society upon the family. Why the family is what it is can only be understood by considering it as part of the total culture configuration. These approaches are of necessity overlapping. This explains the confusion in the roles of the physiologist, the psychiatrist, the psychologist, and the anthropologist.

Frequent types of trespassing are the psychologizing biologist, and the anthropologizing psychodynamicist. Thus, for example, some cultural anthropologists influenced by the psychodynamic considerations have focused their attention almost entirely on the psychodynamic problem of the parent-child relationship and have neglected what should be their specific contribution, the understanding of the prevailing parental attitudes as the result of sociological and historical factors. No matter how valuable such contributions from anthropologists may be, one cannot help asking: If they focus their attention on the psychodynamic problems of personality development, who then should deal with the problem of how parental attitudes came about and are determined by different forms of social structure and history?

This epistemological analysis shows that we deal with three, not opposing etiological theories, but complementary approaches to the total problem. None of these approaches can replace the other, and only in collaboration with each other can they achieve a comprehensive answer to the problem of how and why an individual—a person who is born with an individual hereditary equipment, who grows up in a specific family, which itself is the product of a specific culture—becomes mentally disturbed.

A Psychosociologist Speaks

THOMAS A. C. RENNIE

I find that I have no real difficulty in accepting the four positions which have been so ably propounded. For psychiatry is that branch of medicine which conceives of and concerns itself with the whole man. Certainly it holds that man cannot be fragmented except for purposes of highly specific researches which allow one or another aspect of the wholeness to be approached. But it should always be remembered that it is only an aspect which is under investigation and that the whole remains. So I can see no way that in the study of man we can ignore any of the four positions which have been presented.

Historically, I think, the study of man by psychiatrists has passed through a phase in which there was very much interest in genetic or constitutional determinants. This is extremely difficult material to subject to scientific study; nonetheless, I think that it would be foolish to discard it just because it presents complex procedural problems. It is known that a very considerable percentage of patients admitted to a psychiatric hospital, for whatever reason, will show significant abnormalities of electroencephalographic findings which are difficult to conceive of as being experience-determined. It would be foolish also, I think, to ignore completely the studies on identical twins who were separated at birth, raised in utterly different environments, and finally developed relatively the same kind of psychopathological conditions. None of us would quibble about the acceptance of these constitutional differences; hence, there is an area not too adequately explored as yet which cannot be left out of our conception of man.

Currently I find that psychiatry is caught in a wave of extreme enthusiasm for the study of the individual psychodynamic processes. This has been most fruitful. It has led us very far along the way of a pragmatic understanding of man's behavior. This too is an area extremely difficult of reduction to the rigid scientific experimental method of understanding. Psychodynamics is so popular at the moment that it is practically impossible to get some resident psychiatrists today to give consideration to anything else in the study of man. They are fascinated by it to the point that if their senior associates try to teach them what happens to an organism under the impact of severe induced hypoglycemia, they do not even want to hear about it.

I find myself perhaps most interested in the presentation of the psychosocial position because, I think, it spells out some new frontiers of scientific and research interest in the function of man. Admittedly man is a biographic creature. His biography starts at the moment of birth and it is not over until the time he dies. In his exposition of the psychodynamic position Dr. Kubie asked: At what time period can psychodynamic or experiential influences so disrupt the organism as to constitute sickness? He knows very well the answer. It can happen in the first three days of life, as Ribble* has shown. It can happen in the first month of life, as demonstrated by Dr. Leo Kanner† in autistic children. Presumably by some kind of experience-determined reaction, a one-month-old infant can be set off the track of any possible normal adaptation. I believe this to be essentially an experience-derived imbalance. But every man has a unique biography. He has the unique biography not only because his own experiences are highly unique but also because he derives the components and elements of his

personality from a unique setting. That setting is the family, and every family, just as every man, is unique and different. The development of a family might even be compared to the biography of a person. The family has a beginning, a growth, a life, and a dissolution. Within the family there is a kind of prevailing homeostasis; every member is so integrated with all others that the impact of something befalling one is inevitably going to affect every other member in it. We know that psychoneuroses tend to occur in clusters within families. We also know that emotional disturbances very commonly occur in families which also have a high incidence of physical and organic illnesses. So to neglect the enormous impact of the family, which no one with a psychodynamic approach would do, would of course be an obvious mistake.

The conception of the individual as a functioning person is now being expanded to that of an individual arising and growing within a highly unique social and cultural milieu. All cultures as well are highly individual. It is surprising to find that at this late date there are perhaps no more than a dozen or at most two dozen major research attempts in this area in psychiatry to scrutinize seriously the impact of the culture and its environment on what happens to persons. I am speaking now not just about the epidemiological approach. I am talking not of the counting of the numbers and kinds of disturbances in a given community situation. I am talking about a more basic attempt to search out certain etiological factors within the social environment itself. For I think we could state as a hypothesis that mental disorder does not occur at random in our society. It occurs in particular areas, in particular concentrations, with particular colorings dependent upon certain elements in the society itself. These elements can be spelled out in various ways: differences in sex, socioeconomic status, and ethnic background. All these things constitute the highly unique and highly specific milieu of the individual within his family context. Differences in child-rearing practices, differences in attitude about health and illness and food-intake and so on, all are of vital importance

---

* Ribble, M. A. "Anxiety in Infants and Its Disorganizing Effects," in *Modern Trends in Child Psychiatry*. N. D. C. Lewis and B. L. Pacella (Eds.). New York: International Universities Press, 1945. pp. 11–25.

† Kanner, L. *Child Psychiatry*, Springfield, Ill., C. C Thomas, 1948. p. 716.

as part of the total constellation which we are trying to study.

It was well over thirty years ago that Adolf Meyer* once and for all did away, I thought, with any dichotomy about psychologizing versus biologizing or physiologizing. This he did through his concept of the psychobiologic man and by his insistence that this unit was inseparable, indivisible, and functioned always as a totality in which every element, including his physiochemical, hormonal, endocrinological, organic, and others entered into every single interaction of that human being's life.

To this concept of psychobiologic man we might well add the concept of "psycho-bio-social" man. If this is accepted as a legitimate domain of medical study of man, then I see no difficulty whatever in reconciling all points of view.

DISCUSSION

Cobb: I wonder whether the genetic point of view is accepted as much as we think it is. It is an area with much solid evidence supporting it, thanks to Dr. Slater and other workers; and this evidence is overwhelmingly acceptable to most of us. Yet I have noted in staff meetings that if I pick up a lead in the heredity of the patient and try to follow and develop that point, the whole group of students and assistants exhibit resistance and I am shut out. They are not interested in genetics. They regard it as something immoral because it is not ameliorable, not improvable by medical measures. Hence, it is not acceptable. This is a peculiar attitude about genetics nowadays among the students and young physicians.

I am very much pleased that Dr. Miller brought in the god of luck because I think that we psychiatrists are often prone to believe that there is an explanation and a meaning to all events. There is such a thing as hard luck.

Dr. Miller's question "What are the steps?" appeals to me. In the relating of one field to the other we will have to give up our infatuation with a naïve psycho-

dynamics which is interested in only the first step and the last step and leaps over all the others. The real job is to learn patiently all the steps of the processes.

Gerard: I would like to indicate some points on which I believe that we can properly assume all schools of thought will be in agreement.

First of all, I take it that we will all agree that the mind is related to the brain, and that even though we may use different languages when speaking biologically or in mental science, in principle the languages are translatable.

Secondly, I think that we will all agree in principle that there are multiple factors in the causation of mental disease. There are factors of heredity, of prenatal life, of early life experience, and of the current life situation. I would also suppose that the biologically-minded would even accept, as another term, the future goals toward which a person is operating.

Thirdly, I take it that we would all agree that the most important symptomatology, the presenting disturbances in mental diseases that concern us most, is at the interpersonal level. The relation of the individual to other persons (or to culture) is disturbed; the symptoms are social symptoms. Incidentally in that connection, as Appel, Stevenson, Wortis, and others have pointed out, the results of therapy in a great variety, if not in all types, of mental disease are sufficiently alike in their quantitative successes to suggest that some very deeply common factor may be underlying all the various particularities. Since in nearly all treatments, whether they are called psychotherapies or not, there is a strong interpersonal relation between the patient and the therapist, and since, as we have just agreed, the problem is one of interpersonal relations, and since all these therapies do involve the giving of some attention to the patient, an interpersonal relation may be underlying many of the successes. In fact, it is reminiscent of the Hawthorne experiment* in which performance of a group of workers improved with

---

* Winters, Eunice E. (Gen'l Ed.) *The Collected Papers of Adolf Meyer.* Baltimore: The Johns Hopkins Press, 1950, vols. 1–4.

* Roethlisberger, F. J. *Management and Morale.* Cambridge: Harvard University Press, 1941.

each change in light intensity. Not light but attention given the workers boosted the group morale and output. In connection with group psychiatry, Ruesch uttered a statement, which I have rather liked, concerning sufferers of mental disease: "By the group they have broken; by the group shall they be healed." But of course I would quickly add to what I have said so far that when one has a clear knowledge of the causes of a mental disturbance, as in pellagra for instance, and administers the specific or rational therapy, the "cures" have a higher per cent and tend to be permanent.

the dividing line comes is not clear; somewhere beyond early experience I would suppose. The interaction of units does include the notion of goals, which is quite acceptable to the organic position. This has further meaning. Man in his own right is a complete system, or org, or entity, with certain psychological and neurological factors involved in it; and man is also a penultimate unit in a larger system, or org, or epiorganism, or society. I am quite certain that it is valid and highly useful to take the basic problems of interaction among units in a larger system, whether molecules in a cell, cells in the organism, or organisms

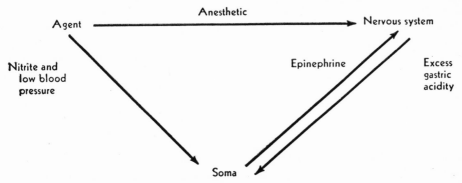

FIG. 1. Diagram indicating the mechanism of factors impinging upon the organism.

A fourth point on which I suppose we would be in agreement is that there is a mechanism involved. There is an initial precipitating factor, an environmental factor. Let us think of it as hitting the organism from the outside or inside. There are several possibilities: it might act directly upon the nervous system; it might act on the soma, and so on the nervous system; it might act on the nervous system, and so on the soma. (Figure 1.) As long as we think of all of these possibilities I think that there will be no problem of agreement; disagreement will come at the level of details.

We have all indicated a whole spectrum of causes, from the completely genetic factors to completely social ones. I think it is rather meaningful to break these into two major categories: those factors which involve the unit and those factors which involve the interaction of units. Just when

in a group, and deal with the problems of unity and interrelation from that point of view. So that if one thinks of a society as merely a larger type of biological organism, the problems of the interactions of men do not put them out of the realm of a strictly biological approach.

Incidentally, I have always liked to think of culture as simply the *milieu intérieur* of the epiorganism. It plays exactly the same role in the interrelation of men in the community as do the blood, fluids, etc., for the interrelation of cells in their community in multicellular organisms. If you try to define what constitutes the aging process, for example, you get yourself into a beautiful circuit. It is because the cells are older that they are turning out substances into the body fluids which make them act older; and the body fluids have substances in them which make the cells act older. So it goes round and round.

JASPER: It seems to me that the concept presented by Dr. Alexander is the growing informed attitude of anybody interested in the brain and its mechanisms. There is no such thing as an either/or. If an investigator studying the cellular chemistry of the brain or studying the responses of single brain cells wants to relate this information to the mental life of an individual, he naturally has to incorporate into his thinking the fields that are usually classified as psychological and sociological. But the division lines, I think, are very artificial. As a biologist, one must also be a psychologist and sociologist; for these points of view are not separate, isolated doctrines any more.

chapter 6

Areas of Interdoctrinal Unacceptance

• •

An Organicist Speaks

HERBERT H. JASPER

The points of view already expressed in this Conference have shown that in the minds of the most mature and able men working in fields related to problems of mental health and disease, there are no areas of complete unacceptance. No one would deny that cultural and social factors are important in determining behavior and the mental life or mental disorder in man. Neither can anyone deny the importance of brain which is interposed between the stimulus patterns of our environment and the resulting thought and behavior. Even those of us most preoccupied with psychodynamic processes in behavior are ready to accept the importance of cerebral structures and circuits as determinants of behavior when we are faced with an organic psychosis secondary to brain tumor. We are also ready to accept the importance of neurochemical factors, even at the molecular level, when we witness the profound mental disorders produced by minute quantities of such substances as lysergic acid. No longer do we maintain an attitude of conflict between these areas; rather we struggle in the attempt to incorporate all these concepts, insofar as we can, into our thinking.

The question is not one of acceptance or unacceptance of doctrines. The question is as to the relative emphasis placed by different groups of workers upon one or another of the multiple factors whose interaction results in those rather poorly defined entities, mental health or mental disease. The field of emphasis may be due not to the force of facts which everyone must accept, but due to the type of training and experience obtained by a given worker. The lack of agreement also does not apply to clearly defined diseases for which definite causes have been established, but to the ill-defined, vaguely understood, mental disorders which may have varied descriptions and multiple causes, some more or less primary and others merely precipitating. It is in this area that we encounter differences in terminology and in ways of thinking about the problems of human behavior which tend to isolate one group of workers from another.

I have listed a series of terms and expressions which are sources of difficulty to the scientist who approaches the problems of human behavior from the biological, neurophysiological, and neurochemical points of view. I am sure that this is not an area of unacceptance. It is not that the neurophysiologists do not accept these terms;

53

rather, they do not know what to do with them. Some examples are as follows:

Functional vs. organic
Biological vs. psychological
Unconscious vs. conscious or subconscious
Ego, id, and superego functions
Psychological forces
Repressive forces
Psychosocial forces
Chain reactions of symbolic forces
Interplay and feedback of symbolic processes

These are very familiar terms to all of us. Most of them have been familiar to me for about twenty-five years, since I first approached problems of mental health and disease from the point of view of a student of sociology and classical as well as "dynamic" psychology. After years of struggling with these conceptions I turned to experimental psychology, and then to neurophysiology in the attempt to find more objective methods of attack, retaining the conviction that only by a more objective and scientific approach would we make real progress in the understanding of mental disease.

Let us examine first the often used and misused distinction between "functional" and "organic." For the biologist such distinctions have no real meaning. An organism is organic. It functions in response to stimulation, and the stimulus response may be called a functional disorder or a function of the organism. But, except for this type of relationship, a function without the organism or a functional situation has no meaning to a neurophysiologist.

Because a psychosis seems to be precipitated by stimulus patterns in the environment of an individual which cause severe emotional trauma, does the brain cease to be the "organ" of the mind? Is it not the "organic" changes in the brain which have retained the response patterns developed from early childhood which determine the "traumatic" character of the immediately precipitating experience, not to mention predisposition of genetic origin for which there is growing evidence? Neurophysiology

is a "functional" science. The successful use of such neurophysiological methods as electroconvulsive therapy only serves to emphasize the role that neurophysiological methods and concepts should play in the future study of disturbed brain function labeled psychotic, a disturbance which must always be considered both "functional" and "organic."

Similar problems arise with the terms "biological vs. psychological." If this is only the old mind-body problem in a new guise, we cannot, of course, hope for a solution. The scientific approach to the study of human behavior requires a more pragmatic point of view, a psychophysical parallelism being the closest approach to a satisfactory working hypothesis. The extensive development of psychosomatic medicine, with, we hope, an increasing emphasis also on somatopsychic medicine, is the evident answer to this apparent dilemma in our thinking.

The terms "conscious" as opposed to "unconscious" or "subconscious" mental processes have been largely abandoned by psychologists attempting to develop a more objective and experimental science of behavior. They remain, however, at the very core of "psychodynamic" theory. To quote from Franz Alexander [1]: "The dynamic principles established by the psychoanalytic method are valid in themselves and independent of the generalizations and speculations concerning the ultimate nature of psychological forces." The neurophysiologist cannot in the foreseeable future shed much light on the "ultimate nature of psychological forces," but he may be able to shed some light on the brain mechanisms underlying them. Recently developed conceptions and technics are beginning to give approaches from the laboratory point of view to the problems of consciousness and unconscious states. But do we all really understand each other? Is the unconscious of the psychodynamicist the unconscious that the organicist recognizes in stupor and coma? They are the same words, but they do not mean the same to the two schools. But if a neurophysiologist is supposed to be able to contribute to the understanding of brain mechanisms which in the distant future should throw light on mental disorders, we have to begin to speak the same language, at least to understand each other.

"Psychological forces," "repressive forces," "psychosocial forces," and then the wonderful expressions "chain reaction of symbolic forces," "interplay and feedback of symbolic processes"—these terms present difficulties to the neurophysiologist. How can he handle them? For example, how can an organicist, accustomed to working on the detailed anatomy, structure, function, and neurophysiological mechanisms of the brain deal with a concept such as psychological interaction? How can he bring it into the laboratory? I am prepared to accept all the terms; for I am sure that they must mean something. So if I may call this an area of difficulty, not unacceptance, I should like to ask: What can I do with these terms and conceptions?

Are the concepts which have been found so useful in the development of this "dynamic science" of human behavior, which has had such a profound influence upon present-day culture, to remain ignored and forever beyond the scope of neurophysiological study? The problem of brain mechanisms underlying conscious behavior has already been attacked by several competent neurophysiologists and was the subject of a week's conference at Ste. Marguerite, Quebec, under the auspices of the International Council for the Organization of Medical Sciences. However, it is doubtful that many of the intricacies of psychoanalytical theory can ever approach the degree of objective validity and clarity, even as descriptive terms, of sufficient precision for an attempt to undertake a neurophysiological investigation of their underlying mechanisms in the brain. Here we have a world of discourse claiming the status of a complete science of the mind, which has had a profound influence upon romantic literature and sociophilosophic thinking about human behavior, but whose concepts cannot be used by workers attempting to investigate mechanisms of brain function. Is this only a question of means of intercommunication, or has it a more fundamental significance?

Certainly no one in the present group can be classed with those psychiatrists referred to in a classical remark of Dr. Gerard, who once stated that insofar as many psychiatrists are concerned, the skull might as well be filled with cotton wadding. We all admit the importance of brain determinants of behavior—but once admitted, a purely "mental science" is developed which cannot be related in any specific manner to mechanism of brain function. This I present as a major problem of interdisciplinary cooperation which may merit discussion in this distinguished gathering.

REFERENCE

1. ALEXANDER, FRANZ. *Dynamic Psychiatry.* Chicago: Univ. Chicago Press, 1952, p. 9.

A Psychologist Speaks

WILLIAM A. HUNT

So far the Conference has involved itself largely with abstract, theoretical matters with little consideration and evaluation of concrete research findings. I feel we need more consideration of such evidence if we are to come to any profitable conclusions. Let me illustrate by introducing one such bit of evidence concerning etiology that has bothered me for the last three years. I have been associated with a study of men in the U.S. Navy in which we have followed over 30,000 men through their combat histories. We can work out nice curves for the incidence of psychoneurosis as a function of length of service, and the curve is positively accelerated. In any selected group, as the length of service increases the incidence of psychoneuroses increases. To me this is the way in which a disorder that is largely environmental or at least heavily influenced by environment should act. We have never been able to get a similar function for psychosis. The rate here seems to be constant, and not dependent upon length of service.

In my opinion it is not possible to have any extensive unacceptance if such scientific data are under consideration. In such an instance we are dealing with evidence; and if it is valid evidence, we have to accept it. We run into areas of unacceptance only when we allow ourselves to be diverted from the objective evidence.

There are some areas of apparent acceptance where I feel our agreement is more apparent than real, where our words are speaking louder than our actions. One is the idea of multicausality. I do not see how we can avoid accepting it. Everybody who has spoken thus far has accepted it. Yet I would like to ask my psychiatric colleagues: If we are in agreement about multicausality, where can I send a patient to get this multidimensional treatment? The apparent discrepancy here disturbs me.

Of course, in accepting multicausality we still must realize that no man can do two or three things at once. He has to stick to the thing in which he is most interested and which he can best do. This is where relative emphasis in research comes in. But too often we forget that this specialization on our part also entails the obligation of not only allowing but actually encouraging the other fellow to do the things that we are neglecting and that would not otherwise be done.

Another such area is our agreement that the phenomena which we are studying are amenable to orderly scientific investigation. We all pay constant lip service to this, but we often fail to realize that the technics of scientific investigation include not only the beautiful objectivity of the Skinner Box but also the beautiful flexibility and subjectivity of the psychiatric interview. They are both amenable to scientific utilization.

Finally, I think we should realize that our data and technics with which we obtain, analyze and study them, and the interpretations which we draw from them, are in great part a function of human beings. We, as scientists, are a sample of human beings. We project our personalities into our work just as other men do. Many of the areas of unacceptance that develop in science arise from a confusion between the objective realities of the problem and the subjective peculiarities of the investigator.

A Psychodynamicist Speaks

THEODORE LIDZ

It is my task by assignment to help sow controversy with a few well-chosen words. I hope that they will neither loose the tumult of Babel, nor, on the other hand, just foster tolerance or compromise, because we are here to attempt to define our theses and antitheses as a necessary step toward some sort of resolution.

As has been pointed out, many areas of seeming disagreement are rather differing approaches to the study of human behavior, or explorations of different segments of the territory, or reflections of emphasis on different facets of the same problem. However, there are conceptualizations which are mutually exclusive and which lead investigators away from one another and indicate a faulty grasp of fundamental issues by some of us, or by all of us. I think that this is what we are trying to define.

A major effort of the scientist is to simplify. The achievement of scientific laws usually accomplishes simplification that permits understanding of seemingly random and complex phenomena. Such simplification is achieved through inclusion and recognition of the complexity rather than through limitation of consideration to a fragment of the field because it can be encompassed. What I imply and will be attempting to say is that many areas of disagreement concerning the study of human behavior arise from a lack of willingness to deal with its inordinate complexity. To simplify, to make measurable, to explain through animal analogy, to derive motivation from basic drives, to study societal differences while neglecting the human constants, are all acceptable approaches; but unless the limitations are remembered, unless studied in relation to the total field, they can lead, and have led, to schemata that may be fascinating but which have little pertinence to our problem.

In the service of brevity, the organic frame of reference of the neurologizing type can serve as foil for my argument, though actually today's presentation of experimental psychology might serve better. Stated briefly and all too simply, it expresses or harbors the concept that human behavior eventually can be understood and studied in terms of neuronal activity, and that abnormal behavior reflects disordered structure or disordered impulses through the nervous system.

As a specific example which has been mentioned, one might take the efforts to understand schizophrenic reactions as deriving from brain lesions or from disordered metabolism affecting the central nervous system. The disagreement with this argument concerns both factual and conceptual matters. Behavioral disorders which can clearly be related to brain damage or impaired metabolic functioning of the central nervous system include degradation of symbolic functioning along with any distortions of symbolic activity. Capacity for mentation is lowered. The mechanisms requisite for thinking are broken or disorganized. In functional disorders, tentatively including schizophrenia, there is no satisfactory evidence that the mental capacities are limited or disturbed by faults in the apparatus. The equating of defects in ability to think abstractly, as encountered in the organic syndromes, with the distortions in the highly abstract thinking of schizophrenic patients, provides an unnecessary source of confusion. In other types of disorganiza-tions due to brain damage, such as psychomotor epilepsy, a focus of abnormal irritability temporarily dominates the integration of activity and sets up episodes of automatic behavior which are quite different from the behavioral abnormalities with which we are concerned in schizophrenia.

Perhaps we have been so caught up in the need to negate the mind-body dichotomy that we have too readily gone on to consider the potentiality that mental activity can be understood in terms of physiologic functioning. The objection that I make has to do with the assumption that matters pertaining to symbolic activity and emotions, including communication, thought, and the role that symbolic activity can play in the regulation or disruption of physiologic functioning, can be understood in terms of neuronal activity because they require a certain organization of the brain and transpire over neuronal pathways. The sense or nonsense of a radio broadcast is not to be found in the transmitter, nor understood through analysis of the electronic patterns being emitted.

Perhaps we can utilize Dr. Gerard's comment about the violin and the structure of the wood, which I think has something to do with Dr. Jasper's questions about nomenclature. The violinmaker is concerned with the wood and the structure of the violin, but I do not think that one can, or would wish to try to, describe the sonata played on the violin in terms of the structure of the violin, the type of wood in it, or even the vibrations of the violin as analyzed by some mechanical apparatus. It is necessary for us to consider the unique manner in which the human brain permits adaptability, remembering that man is not just another animal but that he can greatly modify nature in the service of his adaptation. Inborn reflex patterns appear to have been diminished to the minimum necessary to assure survival. Needs or drives give impetus but little direction. The way of living must be learned and is adjustable to the physical and interpersonal environment in which the individual develops. Human development is not simply an unfolding of a genic inheritance in a beneficent environment. It also involves growing into an interpersonal environment which it assimilates as it develops. Without such assimilation of human ways, institutions, sentiments, the infant cannot become a person and cannot survive. I am reminding that the human is heir to a dual heritage: the genic endowment of the race and the individual ancestors; and also a cultural heritage which is transmitted extra-biologically and, to a large extent, by the family, which is charged, usually without knowing it, with preparing the child for maturation which will permit him to live in the broader extra-familial society in which he happens to be born. The interplay between the two inheritances is so intimate that they are inseparable, and one cannot be understood without the other.

The human attribute which permits this type of adaptability—the unique structure of the brain that permits language, symbolism, and conscious and unconscious mentation—so complicates human motivation that animal experiments with motivation are of very limited pertinence. Merely to indicate the complexity, I mention that selective recall can bring any segment of the individual's past, as well as anything learned about the past, into decision, and that which cannot be recalled can exert its influence as powerfully. But the human is not motivated by current needs, nor by the past alone, for he can project the past through the present to hypothesize the future. Nor may we forget that the history of humanity indicates that man's knowledge includes awareness that death is his ultimate end, and that efforts to come to terms

with this end has influenced motivation profoundly. Finally, the human being does not live alone, and we can readily realize that his motivations are not to be found within his body alone but require an understanding of his relationships with others.

There are, of course, areas of psychiatry which are most appropriately studied primarily through scrutiny of the central nervous system, or of the metabolic processes. Endless lessons can be derived from animal experimentation or from experiments in conditioning or learning theory, from intercultural or intracultural studies. However, it seems to me that the problems of psychiatry proper are those which arise because the infant, born with limitless potentialities but with little inborn patterning, must find his identity and his way to maturity by assimilating his cultural milieu as well as his physical environment, and find his way through life despite conflicting motivations and countless interpersonal stresses. We may wish to deal with these matters in other terms or in another frame of reference and conceivably it may be possible to do so; but if these are the problems, they are most aptly studied in terms of problems of human organisms living in an interpersonal environment.

What I find doctrinally unacceptable is that type of simplification that seeks to solve the problems of human behavior by confining attention to a segment of the field and often either explicitly or implicitly hopes to avoid the complex problems that arise in considering human living.

A Psychosociologist Speaks

H. WARREN DUNHAM

It does not seem feasible to me to consider our areas of interdoctrinal disagreement without considering certain implications in the task. First, I am constrained to suggest that the emphasis on and the detailed statements of the various viewpoints

bearing on the etiology of mental disease, while in all probability they will lead to some stimulating discussion, will not tend to increase the mutual acceptance of the various viewpoints among those listening to these papers, especially among those listeners who have worked exclusively within the theory encompassed by a particular viewpoint. What I am indicating here, of course, is that the differences between the viewpoints tend to be minimized when we center discussion on a particular problem area and face the necessity of formulating hypotheses, examining data, and arriving at agreement concerning essential concepts. In other words, when we act in our roles as scientists, we begin to see one another's problems; when we act the role of teachers of our pet theories, we tend to become more welded to our respective doctrines.

Secondly, while the various viewpoints have been most ably presented, one cannot help noting that the emphases which were stressed in a viewpoint are at least partially the function of the orientation of a particular scientist. That is to say, there are various theoretical orientations among scientists who think of themselves as social psychologists, clinical psychologists, and the like. In fact, if the statement of the position is not in a pure form but tends toward an eclectic viewpoint—favored recently by certain psychologists as the better taking-off point for the clinical psychologist [1]— then the areas of agreement or disagreement will not emerge in any clear fashion but are likely to be vague, indefinite, and incomplete. I should hasten to add that I do not regard this situation as undesirable; rather it is inevitable in the present state of our knowledge not only with regard to the etiology of mental disease but also with regard to our attempt to formulate more general laws of human behavior. From the standpoint of the methodology of science itself, which lies behind all the viewpoints, our theory will always have a tentative and incomplete character to it.

Finally, our task also seems to imply that these four positions have worked out theoretical frameworks which have approximately the same quality of completeness. This does not seem to me to be very valid, for actually the organic and psychoanalytic positions have more complete theoretical formulations than do the other two. In fact, it seems difficult to present any psychosocial positions which provide a theoretical explanation for the etiology of mental disease

except in the most broad and general terms.

Before considering some of the areas of unacceptance among these different viewpoints, I wish to reaffirm my belief that a more desirable knowledge of the etiology of mental disease which should be useful for both therapeutic and preventative purposes will not come through any one-sided attack upon the many problems with which we are confronted in this area. Indeed, as we well know, these problems often cannot be attacked from any one viewpoint, and to ignore this consideration might prove disastrous in the long run to our aims.

There is a certain value here in pointing to those elements that represent the data or observations implied by these various viewpoints. The organicist has the bones, cellular tissue, blood circulation, and glandular secretions which make up the physical character of the organism. He can objectify these things and examine them directly. For the psychoanalyst, data consists of a postulated biological energy plus certain free-floating mental reproductions of the person. These data have a high degree of subjectivity and gain their significance through the framework of psychoanalytic theory. Overtly all we can see are certain types of behavior, verbal and motor, from which inferences are made about the way the person tends to manage certain of his problems or from which we infer meanings of which the person himself is unaware. The psychologist takes as his data human behavior, responses and external influences (stimuli), all of which, in order to be scientific, he attempts to observe under highly controlled conditions. The psychologist has further attempted to develop measuring instruments which will objectify those entities such as intelligence, personality traits, attitudes, and the like, which are subjective but which, if they are to be manipulated in accordance with scientific canons, must be objectified. Again, in an extreme form the sociologist has taken as his chief source of data, group structure and process or the abstracting of those common elements in behavior which go to make up the nonmaterial group culture. He may study these entities as things in themselves; but when he deals with any problem of human behavior, he must show how these forms become incorporated into the human psyche to emerge as various action patterns, either socially acceptable or socially unacceptable.

In general, the problem which we face is to determine or rather to formulate explanations concerning the manner in which these elements constituting the data of the various approaches become interlaced in such a fashion in the person that they appear to competent observers as different types of mental or behavioral symptoms or even as acceptable so-called normal behavior. The usual method for accomplishing this task in science is to set up theoretical models in an area of reality, to derive hypotheses from these models which can be tested by reference to indicated observations, and then to make the observations in some systematic and controlled manner which will establish the validity of the hypotheses. Our results thus serve to provide us with a certain tentative assurance of the soundness of our model, or else they cast a certain doubt upon its validity. Now, in the behavioral sciences we are faced with difficulties which I believe are more a function of our immaturity than, as some persons have held, of the complexity of our data. The difficulties are inherent in the inadequacy of our models, the loose quality of our hypotheses, the shortcomings in the representativeness, adequacy, and reliability of our observations, and the flaws in the reasonableness of our inferences.

Let us turn now to consider some of the areas of disagreement or unacceptance among the various viewpoints with which we are concerned. It seems to me that most of our differences stem from the following: our lack of awareness of the significance of certain factors, the narrow focus or range of some of our theoretical models, our inability to objectify certain concepts utilized in constructing our theoretical models, and finally different conceptions as to the nature of man.

When I state that one of our differences appears to center around different conceptions as to the nature of man, I might illustrate my contention with reference to the outmoded doctrine of instincts. Forty years ago the theory of instincts was widely ac-

cepted both by most psychologists and by most sociologists. As certain evidence from non-Western cultures began to accumulate and as the logical fallacies of the theory were revealed, it ceased to have any scientific authority as an explanation for human behavior. And yet in the orthodox statement of psychoanalytic theory the notion of instinct still survives as a biologically based impulse seeking satisfactions in objects found in the body of the child or later perhaps in some external objects. The great difficulties which face the person in terms of obtaining "normal satisfactions of the sexual instinct" are seen in the restrictions imposed by immediate conditions or the more permanent social institutions. If one takes away this postulation of the sexual instinct with its subconsequent stages of development, much of the framework of psychoanalytic theory would be undermined. In thus making central the achieving of expression of the sexual instinct, psychoanalytic theory tends to overlook the phenomena of learning, the impact of institutions and social catastrophies, and the immediate situations as they arise in the experience of the person and affect and influence many aspects of his behavior. The overlooking of learning is illustrated in the psychoanalytic notion that the mother's breast is the first object of sexual desire in the child without facing the question as to how a child could ever find its mother's breast if he was not first presented with the object.

To the extent that the psychologist tends to overlook Morgan's famous canon that an action should never be interpreted in terms of a higher psychical faculty if it can be interpreted in terms of a lower one, and hence draw conclusions about man's behavior from experiments with animals, he is operating with a different conception about man's nature than that held by sociologists who would emphasize that conclusions about human behavior must be based on experiments and observations with man himself. To be sure, not all make this error, but to the extent that they seek for basic laws of learning which apply to animals and humans alike, they seem to hold a different conception of man than does the sociologist or social psychologist. For as Hilgard remarks facetiously, "Who ever heard of animals getting together and writing a constitution to govern themselves?"

We have referred to the narrow focus or range of some of the viewpoints which we are examining. All of the viewpoints, it seems to me, must plead guilty here, for in their pure statement they all represent extreme forms of determinism in explaining man's behavior. It seems to me just as erroneous to think of culture as determining every aspect of human behavior as it is to think of organic and physiological changes in the organisms as deterministic of man's mental life. In the mental diseases certain mental symptoms, such as in general paralysis, can be laid at the door of a specific bacterial infection which causes brain damage. It does not necessarily follow, however, that similar symptoms which are observed in the absence of this specific infection are to be explained in terms of some as yet undiscovered infection. This reasoning frequently ignores the logical principle that comparable effects may have different causes. The environment by the organicist is frequently seen in all too simple a guise, largely as a source of bacterial infections, while the complexity of the social world, which is the central psychosocial fact for man, is largely overlooked in its function of forming the intricate content and structure of the mental life and of overt behavior. The often repeated notion that what currently passes under the label of schizophrenia may be in fact two or more different disorders points to the necessity to be on our guard before adopting completely any specific theoretical position.

What I have said with respect to those who adhere to the organic position can be just as easily applied to those investigators who hold an extreme sociological position. Such a view, as in the case of the other positions, can only provide a narrow focus which overlooks the constitutional and behavioral factors as sources of data relevant to certain mental health problems. One must admit immediately that within this framework there is almost no theoretical model which offers an explanation for any specific type of mental disturbance, although there are numerous theories for explaining nonconforming behavior as depicted in statistical distributions. There is a certain social psychological model involved in viewing not only the social actions as goal-oriented behavior but also the emotional consequences which follow the blockage of on-going social acts. However, this model is of such a general character that it has failed to date in suggesting any explanatory hypotheses for mental disorder which can be subjected to satisfactory tests, although it has hypothesized certain generalized personality reactions. Then, too, those sociological theories which attempt to deal with the evolution and functioning of sociocultural systems, while they have provided certain correlations between aspects of the social environment and certain mental diseases, have not succeeded in showing the manner in which these social environmental elements become so distorted and twisted within the experience of persons that they can appear as specific mental symptoms with the appropriate behavior manifestations. The careful observation and analysis of certain social situations of disorganization have been suggestive of certain hypotheses as denoted by the marginal man or minority group position concepts but have not succeeded in showing why some persons seem to become "infected" with the disorganized situation and others do not.

In a similar vein, one might point to the observations of some cultural anthropologists that some cultures provide more channels for the acceptance of the deviate than does our own. This may be so and may mean that certain behavior which passes for mental disturbance in our culture may not be so defined in another, but it does not explain the behavior in question. Even if hallucinations are found to be acceptable in a culture, we still would want to understand them as part of so-called normal behavior. While it may be eventually possible to make some mentally disturbed persons more comfortable in our culture, we cannot take a chance on letting them run our machines. The tolerance of any culture for various mental symptoms or behavioral deviations would seem to be negatively correlated with its technological complexity.

All of our viewpoints, as we have indicated, are likely to overlook factors which may be relevant to a given problem. The completeness in form of the theory encompassed by the psychodynamic position illustrates this matter nicely. Perhaps when a more adequate theory emerges to explain human personality and human behavior in both normal and abnormal forms, the greatest deficiency of the psychodynamic position will be seen in the fact that its theory has a significance for only certain types of cases. What I am saying is that behavior cannot be universally interpreted as manifestations of unconscious needs or as having meanings which are deeply embedded in the psyche, but that much of human behavior in actuality is to be seen in terms of the immediate situation or even as a manifestation of custom. In most kinds of deviant behavior there are always, it seems to me, at least two possibilities. The behavior in question may be an irrational manifestation of some deep-seated conflict having its genesis in the early developmental years, or it may be an accepted, appropriate response to an immediate situation. It is the prevailing tendency of this position to slough off these possibilities.

Again, certain psychological positions which place primary emphasis on the early childhood experiences as accounting for adult personality and behavior would appear to overlook the fact that human personality is dynamic, and that while early childhood experiences may carry much weight, there are experiences which the person is having all the time which we must look to and examine carefully if human personality is to be completely understood. Failures in adolescence may be just as crucial as failures in childhood with regard to a specific item of behavior. This also emphasizes the point that in our efforts to build a theoretical knowledge about human personality and behavior, it is necessary to examine all areas of experience including the sexual.

These considerations inferentially stress that the current affection noted in certain psychiatric circles for making secure the mother-child bond appears to emphasize that normality will flow only from what is natural. And yet the very core of our culture, which is constantly developing and expanding, is that man replaces what is biologically natural with what is natural in a cultural sense. One does not look far for illustrations. We cook our food, an unnatural activity, and usher our children into the world not in a condition of nature but in a condition of culture. The concern for getting at the early familial experiences and child-rearing practices in the life of the child is, no doubt, relevant to the analysis of the emergence of human personality, but the significance of these things cannot be seen so readily if the family of the child is not seen as a specimen of a cultural series. In other words it is the atypical family discipline, as Kardiner puts it, that is significant if we are to develop a knowledge concerning certain personality disturbances which the adult person may manifest. The family discipline may be brutal or soft, rigid or permissive, lovable or hateful; in fact, whatever the discipline, the important factor is not likely to be whether or not it occurs in a particular family, but whether its occurrence in a family makes the family significantly different in its particular milieu. And one might add that in our modern urban world the situation is an increasingly complex one because we have lost our traditions in these matters, relegating them to the experts and mass media.

As an aside, I should explain that I prepared my remarks in advance; and that I composed them as though there were a much greater disagreement in the several positions than there apparently is, as judged from the comments that have been made so far. But in view of the moderation and reasonableness exhibited here by the exponents of other approaches, some of my statements are in consequence not completely appropriate. Specifically, I might say that my very brief comments about psychoanalysis are certainly not at all appropriate to Dr. Alexander's stand. For I have spoken of psychoanalysis, like the other positions, primarily from its orthodox view; whereas I find myself much in agreement with what Dr. Alexander had to say.

In summary, in these remarks I have attempted to argue the following: First, each theoretical position which we have considered has a too narrow range for encompassing a valid scientific explanation for the etiology of the great variety of mental and behavioristic disorders. Second, each of the theoretical positions will have a certain significance with reference to certain categories of these disorders when we know what these categories are. And finally, it is necessary to be vigilant in revising any given theoretical position when its hypotheses cannot be supported by available evidence. In doing these things we may approach, in accordance with the canons of science, an adequate but tentative theory for explaining mental disturbances and behavior disorders in man for our time.

REFERENCE

1. SHAFFER, G. WILSON, and LAZARUS, R. S. *Fundamental Concepts of Clinical Psychology.* New York: McGraw-Hill, 1952.

chapter *7*

Further Interdoctrinal Differences

◆ ◆

WHITEHORN: I am distressed at the miscarriage of a very interesting and possibly sometimes useful metaphor that people with different backgrounds and training have difficulties in communication because they do not speak the same language. I think that is an interesting metaphor, but I have real concern lest it lead us into difficulties here.

There has been some loose talk to the effect that the operations of the neurophysiologist or biochemist and the operations of the psychoanalyst or psychotherapist could somehow be translated into a language which all would immediately then understand, each in terms of his own experience. This I think is an extremely deceptive metaphor, and I should say it is the principal reason why Dr. Jasper's question cannot be answered. He lists terms which he has heard discussed; then he asks how these can be translated into terms which the laboratory man can use in his laboratory experiments. I think the reason why this is a foolish question is that these words refer to different kinds of experiences. The experiential referents are quite different. So it is foolish to think they can be translated. If one is to understand what the other fellow is talking about, it is necessary to understand in some measure the experiences on which his remarks are based. Some of this can be crude experience. Some of it can be imaginative. But it gets us nowhere

to ask for a transduction, so to speak, of one person's thinking in the terms of the other person's operations.

I myself have had a certain experience in two fields of work, in chemistry and psychiatry. Several others here have, too. The differences in my experiences in the two fields are reflected to some extent in my difficulties with the German language. I read chemical German with much more facility than I read psychiatric German. This difference might be explained by the way in which these articles are written. One kind might be more readily readable than the other. But, I think, another explanation is the general orientation to and the time spent in that particular part of the German language. That has a lot to do with whether one handles one or the other with greater facility. Similarly, the biochemist or psychoanalyst finds the language of his specialty simple or difficult depending on how much experience he has had in the field.

I felt very bad that Dr. Jasper asked this question. I thought to myself, "Now this Conference is really not only useless but pernicious if it makes so wise a man ask so foolish a question. Are we not in some danger of getting a kind of pious sham under way here which will do us more harm than good?" I thought, therefore, that it might be of some use to raise this important practical question: How does the laboratory man, preoccupied with a certain technic,

64

come to have any basis of mutual respect, some kind of understanding and working arrangement with a man who operates with quite different ideas, quite different experiences, quite different referents? The answer as I see it is: They work together. They eat together. They communicate in a certain freedom, away from the obsessions of their professional tasks, then sometimes cross these barriers, and come to an appreciation of the task that the other fellow is doing in the terms in which the other fellow is doing it. Out of such communications they reach much more practical and effective operating relationships than if formal attempts were made to translate one set of doctrines into terms suitable for another set of doctrines.

In particular it seems to me useful to point up that the psychotherapist or psychoanalyst, or some combination of types, spends a very large part of his time making inferences about people's motives. The laboratory worker does not especially bring this angle into consideration. He has no special reason to be concerned about the motives of the molecules. Hence, motivational understanding of behavior is one of these areas where I think the attempt to translate bodily from one body of experience to another and on formulation to another runs into very serious difficulties.

GERARD: I think that there is one very real difference between the biological and the psycho- or sociodynamic type of explanation. I will state it bluntly to make the issue very clear. In the history of physiology or biology there was a long phase during which we were discovering the phenomena that were important, that we had to explain, that we could very well understand in terms of purpose or teleology. There was nothing reprehensible in using the forward-looking explanatory approach; indeed, we had to do it. For instance, we stated that the respiration increases with exercise *because* the body cells need more oxygen. That is a perfectly good "explanation." It is expressed in terms of the action of a vital force from some source. Now as long as we were in that strictly forward-looking teleological phase of explanation, we were perhaps making progress in clarifying the phenomena with which we had to deal. But we were making no progress in understanding them, in getting at mechanisms; these come only through a true causal understanding working forward in time. And, as I once said, "Mechanism adds utility to purpose."

So I suggest that when we talk today of psychological forces or repressive forces, we are simply recognizing the fact that, at the psychological and sociological level, we are at the descriptive phase of identifying our phenomena, of giving teleological descriptions. There is nothing wrong about that whatsoever. But we will really not gain control until we can get down to the basic processes, just as physiology and biology got nowhere until they began to penetrate beneath the strictly physiological explanations to the physicochemical mechanisms that underlie those phenomena. So I submit that the organic approach at least has this possibility of merit, that as fast as we are able to enter into that level of discourse, just so fast will we really have a mechanism that we can understand, handle experimentally, manipulate, and predict with. Then we will really know what we are talking about.

It is apparent that the languages of the several schools are different. But they are translatable, if by that is meant that the phenomena at the social or mental realms of interaction are reducible in principle, if not yet in practice, to the phenomena of biology and through that to physics and chemistry. I believe that those taking the organic position would insist that this is so: that reductionism is possible, that the same basic scientific approaches and methodology that work in the organic will work in the mental area. Some of the non-organicists will certainly not accept this stand.

I would therefore like to make perfectly clear what I mean by the position of the reductionist.

Particular sciences differ from one another enormously in detail. The units of concern, the concepts which prove useful, the methods of study are, in practice at least, fairly unique for each area. A good yardstick for yards is likely to be a poor one for health. The method of breeding in biology is as different from that of timing in physics as is the mental test or sociological questionnaire from breeding. Even if all could be accurately measured, the "pointer readings" would still be vastly different for volts, vitality, and values. Further, at present the degree of quantification, of logical compulsion of available evidence, and of predictive assurance varies greatly from segment to segment. Yet within the proper scope of science these particularities are secondary and might with sufficient knowledge, reduce to continuities."*

So the reductionist position, I would say, is the biological one.

Despite mutual expressions of agreement in the abstract, there will still be disagreement and uncertainty over working out the pathway and mechanism in any particular case. To this statement, "There is no twisted thought without a twisted molecule," I suppose that all organicists would say *yes* and some of the non-organicists would say *no*. There are some difficulties in getting together on these matters. We pay lip service, all of us, to the kind of agreement that I have indicated, and even recognize some of the disagreements when we are formally put to do it. But in practice most of us find it extraordinarily difficult to think and talk in the different languages. We relapse into the one that is familiar to us. Students who have received very advanced training in neurophysiology or other neurobiological subjects, gone into psychiatry, become analysts or practitioners of some other branch, fail from then on to think in biological terms in the great majority of cases.

Having considered language, definition, and reductionism, I now move on to other points of dissent. When we move on from agreeing that multiple factors are involved and start giving quantitative statements as to the magnitude of these factors, there is likely to be very great disagreement. The meaningful question, which mostly is not asked, is a quantitative one: "Within the permissible limits of variation of the hereditary factors and of the environmental factors, what is the correlation between hereditary variance and the variance of the somatic character in the organism and between the environmental variants and the variants

* Gerard, R. W., "The Scope of Science," Scientific Monthly, 1947, 64: 496.

of this character?" If the phraseology of this question sounds complicated, I think that the gist of it is clear enough. It is merely saying that in each particular instance the question has to be asked and answered experimentally. One cannot make an over-all statement that environment is important or that heredity is important. Within the permissible limits of variation, that would hold true in all instances. But their relative quantitative weighting and their range can certainly be all the way from 1 to 99 per cent. I would like to remind my clinical friends that although sex is completely determined by hereditary factors, the X and Y chromosomes, it is also completely determined by environment; the ratio can be changed from 0 to 100 per cent female by varying the salt solution in which fertilized frogs' eggs develop. So both influences may operate.

It is not always easy to look at a given set of facts and interpret them correctly. I am reminded, for example, of the old views of paresis. Not too many decades ago it was attributed to emotional strain and stress. Evidence for this view was the very high incidence among the soldiers of Napoleon's army, who were certainly under severe strain, contrasted with the very low incidence among the peasants of France, who presumably led nice placid lives. The discovery of Treponema pallidum and its spread explained the facts rather differently.

Then, of course, the basic difficulty, I think, is that in mental disease we are concerned with a very fine discrimination in a narrow range of total performance. Interpersonal relations constitute a small part of an octave of the total spectrum of behavior, just as the light octave is a small part of the spectrum of electromagnetic radiation; but it happens to be the part with which we are most intensely concerned. Since we as human beings depend upon light in most of our ordinary relations to the external world, we tend to examine this part of the spectrum under oil immersion or, in electrophysiological terms, we look at the sweep of the cathode tube spread out on a "pedestal." It is as though one were concerned, at the sociological level, with the classification of fingerprints for identification of individuals; whereas the biologist is still busy declaring that there are ten fingers, a covering skin that can be described, and an epidermis on the skin. True, there are ridges on the epidermis, but he has not yet paid much attention to them. It is the very small differences in performance and behavior that make tremendous differences in how we feel about whether an individual is well or not. I would like to continue to emphasize this point with one more comparison.

The difference between an Amati violin and a Montgomery Ward specimen is, I am sure, much less than the difference between any violin and anything else; just as there is less difference between a man and a woman than between humans and anything else. In the violin the materials that went into it may be regarded as heredity; the shaping of it, as prenatal development; the tuning, that is, the tension of the strings, as past experience of a functional kind; and the cracks, nicks, or bangs, as past experiences that left morphological traces. The player might be likened primarily to environment playing upon it; but noise or a sympathetic vibration also produces its effects. All the foregoing factors have to be reasonably right for the violin to yield good music. Superior music cannot be extracted from a violin that has not been made right, or is not in good tuning, or is not in the hands of a competent player. Parenthetically, I would like to point out the main reason that I introduced this figure. If one looks for traces of the past in the tuning or for bad experience as a basis for bad tuning of the instrument, one does not apply an anatomical test, as looking at a string under a microscope, but a physiological test, plucking it and listening.

Lastly, a point on which there might be some difference concerns the area of interpersonal relations in the social domain. It would apply to the specific comparisons or extrapolations made between the biological and the social. I have in mind here the biologist who has been inclined to view a society as a type of epiorganism and finds that he can think in the area of social science with some success by using biological knowledge and relationships.

BISHOP: It does not bother me that the physiologist attaches a meaning to a word and that the psychiatrist uses the same word for another meaning. That is the way we coin words. We take a word out of one context and give it a new meaning in another. That is perfectly proper. However, what I do want to be sure of is that I know in terms of nerve physiology what the psychiatrist means by depression. During a depressed mental state what is happening to the neurons which I study? What happens in terms of mental behavior? If we both know what we mean by the same words in the terms of both disciplines, then we can begin to correlate.

BROSIN: I am surprised that, in the extremely able statements of positions, two very well-known conceptual devices were not employed. The first one is the levels of organization propounded by J. H. Woodger, Joseph Needham, and notably by Ralph Gerard. The latter hinted at it in his use of the tadpole as an example. Perhaps he will help me in my dilemma. It is easy for purposes of teaching, however oversimplified, to diagram, perhaps even to describe, a molecule in which the organization is relatively well understood; then to proceed to the level of the neuronal network with its added complexities and independent sphere of activity; to advance next to the psychological level with its new variables and new levels of activity; and finally to reach the social organization above that. It seems to me that there has not been as much use made of this concept as might be. Dr. Gerard will speak of it as being an oversimplified concept that is worth while in an elucidation of how interdisciplinary activities are related in a living person, without the fragmentation we have been trying to avoid. Why cannot we just speak of a living man instead of a psychobiosocial, or whatever, man?

The second of the teaching examples that might be relevant—I am sure it is well known to all of you as a classic issue—comes from the field of physics, where scientists have had several hundred years of experience in trying to find some solution to the problem of the irreconcilable—not in opinions, but in experiments. The most notable example of such a contradiction is the one between the Newtonian demonstration of the corpuscular theory and the Huygens' demonstration of the wave theory, which can be handled mathematically. It took a couple of hundred years of controversy, during which people hated each other thoroughly, until a highly improbable solution was reached in the form of the quantum theory. But for our problem I do not expect the emergence of a highly improbable solution that can reconcile an entirely different model brain with a model of mind assumed by present methods. We need an entirely new quantitative mathematics, perhaps other than the usual Euclidean logic—a new notation to describe the problems with which we are dealing in all of their dimensions.

GERARD: I was really using the concept of levels throughout, without mentioning them quite so explicitly. This was involved, for example, in the point of whether we would or would not agree on reductionism. I do not myself see that the issue before us is one of two sharp irreconcilable positions; they are neither sharp nor irreconcilable. What I have heard so far from the other schools of thought is, except for one statement, compatible with what I have said. Dr. Alexander said that certain things could be understood only in psychological terms. If he means that they could be understood best, or most easily, or most meaningfully at this time, I would not disagree, but *only* implies nonreductionism, and that I cannot accept.

BROSIN: May I use a very homely example, which may be out of place in so sophisticated a group, but it works well with freshmen medical students? A child is crying and implacable in its grief for a number of days. In an attempt to relieve the incident, all the physical and chemical processes of the tears may be very carefully measured, and the decision may be reached that because of the urgency and surrounding concomitants of the situation, medical treatment may be used and the tears dried with atropine. Or one could come to the conclusion that since these tears come from glands, one may remove the glands and

thereby stop this very unhappy process. But it is simpler to discover that there is the problem of meaning and value—that the child has lost a favorite doll—and to replace this object, and thereby solve the problem at the level of psychology and interactionism. I have real trouble with reductionism in the terms of meaning and value at the level of psychology, as opposed to, let us say, an entirely different but legitimate universe of discourse that can be explained in terms of molecular activity.

GERARD: I would put the matter this way: For the foreseeable future it is going to be incomparably more convenient and meaningful to operate at the level of sociological problems and interpretations, or psychological problems and interpretations. It may be necessary forever—a dangerous word to use—to do so when one is dealing with the individual case. For, as soon as one limits consideration to dealing with a specific situation, to concrete particular action such as a physician ministering to a patient, large, important, and valuable elements of art are introduced and, thank heavens, they are there to use. But, when trying to explain, rationalize, give meaning to, interpret, in the scientific mode, the investigator deals with the class. At this level, I am confident that reduction will come, although this is faith in the sense of confidence based on past experience.

ALEXANDER: Since I am also in a conciliatory mood, I really would not stand up to discuss this question in itself. But I think that there are other considerations. I will use a very simple example. Gastric secretion can be studied only in physiological terms insofar as the local process is concerned. Psychological technics or concepts cannot be used to measure the secretion of hydrochloric acid. This is a physiological process; the symbolic system does not enter into it. But then the question is asked: What stimulates the stomach secretion? The parasympathetic nerves. This is still neurophysiology. Then one asks what stimulates the parasympathetic system? Now comes the psychoanalyst who tells of nostalgic feelings that stimulate the parasympathetic nervous system.

GERARD: That is where you introduce a gremlin, feelings do not stimulate neurones.

ALEXANDER: It is observed that the secretion decreases when the nostalgic mood wanes. Nostalgic mood cannot be studied neurophysiologically today. But let us go a little farther. Nostalgia can be studied in psychological terms. Maybe sometime you will be able to describe it in neurophysiologic terms, the type of process which takes place in the central nervous system when a person feels nostalgic. Let us take another example. A young boy in a family competes with his older brother because the mother prefers the latter, and the younger boy wants to be equally strong and good in order to be equally loved by his mother. This whole constellation cannot be studied by a physiological approach because the tools of physiology are not adjusted to this kind of phenomena. This family constellation can be studied only in terms of interpersonal relationship, that is to say, of psychology. True, if I say that cells can be studied only with the microscope, you may answer: *Today* only with the microscope, tomorrow maybe with an improved optical apparatus. I insist upon only one point: The technic must be adjusted to the object of your investigation. Let us take a sociological example. Suppose the proposition is advanced that in a particular country mothers try to harden their children in early life in a Spartan fashion because the nation is very young. This statement, whether true or not, is sociological. It cannot be arrived at, proved, or challenged with the technics of physiology. It must be studied with the technics of sociology.

SKINNER: I would like to comment on Dr. Brosin's suggestion that physics might teach us something about technic in deciding whether we really are talking about the same subject matter. Also I would like to mention the general procedure of analysis which Bridgman did not, but which some of his associates did, call operationism. In the physical sciences it works out very well. What is meant by a concept, and what are the processes which permit a concept to be formulated and dealt with?

If we are going to find out what the neurologist is studying, whether it is the same thing as what the psychoanalyst is studying, whether both call it the same thing or not, the first step would be to analyze the operations which stand between the investigator and the subject matter. I do not think that the neurologist is in a particularly good position to say that he has analyzed his subject matter. On the other hand, the analyst has set up a system of concepts which certainly are not directly related to the data of observation. For example, let us consider the process of inhibition in these two fields. We give one name to several processes on the assumption that they may be the same. The physiologist would have to state what he does to observe inhibition or what effect it has on his observing instruments or on him. The analyst who happens to use that term would also have to analyze his operations. If they turn out to be the same, then there is some reason to suppose that the same kind of datum has been observed. If they do not turn out to be the same, then probably it would be best to give different names to the two processes.

I think that we have protested altogether too much today that we are harmonious. I am quite sure that there is a very strong residual dualism pervading this room, and to assert that mind is only something which the brain does or secretes is no resolution of that dualistic paradox. I should like very much to believe that there is something more than the mere assertion that the two things are the same. I should like to see an effort to show that the several methods eventually reduce to the same method and therefore must be impinging upon the same subject matter.

MILLER: All of us will agree, I believe, with Dr. Skinner's main point, that we would eliminate much controversy and confusion if we sharpened up our operational definitions. We would also agree that the use of the same word, "inhibition," by the physiologist and psychoanalyst does not necessarily mean that they are studying the same process. I want to disagree, however, with his apparent implication that two processes are similar *only* when the operations of observation are the same. The physicists use a number of quite different operations for measuring temperature: reading the height of a column of mercury, reading the dial of an electric meter attached to a thermocouple, measuring the resistance of a thermistor, or observing the spectrum of a flame or a star. Though these operations are quite different, the results of one can be predicted within limits from another; and they yield a common body of laws. In this case, the most parsimonious way of making orderly sense out of a large number of separate interrelationships is via a single concept, namely, temperature. I believe that the same procedure should be applied to our problems. In addition to clarifying our operational definitions, we must pay attention to the matrix of functional interrelationships, or in other words, laws. If two differently observed phenomena follow exactly the same set of laws, it is economical to assume that some similar process is involved. Operational definitions alone are not enough; we must select those concepts which enable us to formulate the most generally useful set of laws.

SKINNER: I think that the physicist would not assert that because two indicators behave in the same way when the same known data are applied, the same thing is being measured. I am talking in the sense of a concept, not a field of force. As for the latter, there are different ways of detecting the presence of a field of force. These must then be reconciled with each other; but, eventually, there is no such thing as the field. It proves to be a convenient verbal device. If you believe in the field as such, that assumption may temporarily give you some advantages. But in the long run it is better not to take it too seriously. The same thing is true in the case of measures of time or space. These things must all work together eventually if the concept is to be regarded as the same in all fields.

ALEXANDER: I was very glad to hear about evidence because I am also a stickler for evidence, which is so very difficult to get in our field. Just because I am so strongly for evidence, Dr. French and I have been engaged during the past four years in trying to find evidence for the validity of clinical observations which we are subjectively convinced are absolutely correct. Yet we do not yet have satisfactory objective evidence. I have great doubt that statistical observations constitute evidence. For example, the statement that the incidence of neuroses increases during military service is very interesting but we do not know what it means. Maybe it is the diet. From statistical correlations many conclusions can be drawn. Dr. Hunt contrasts neuroses with psychoses in which this type of correlation is not found. We do not know from this statistical fact alone whether it represents a relevant correlation. That the incidence of psychoses is independent of the length of service does not mean that environment is not a relevant etiological factor. It might be that very early influences in childhood are significant. These early influences are universally present, but possibly only constitutionally predisposed individuals respond to them with psychosis. We cannot exclude the influence of early family difficulties because we have never investigated systematically their effect. Dr. Lidz tells me that he is doing just that. Maybe he will furnish real evidence.

May I say one more word to illustrate how statistical evidence may be deceptive or meaningless. There is a positive correlation between the number of blond people in Italy and their being engaged in industry. That is a very startling correlation: more blond people in industry than in agriculture. Does it mean that blondness predisposes a person to going into industry? If you know that the industries are concentrated in an area where more blond people are living, in northern Italy but not in southern Italy, the answer becomes simple. From such a statistical correlation you may assume some unknown relationship between blondness and predisposition for industrial work.

I do not consider that statistical evidence is evidence until we know what it means. Mostly we do not know what it means. A correlation might be secondary or tertiary. Therefore, I still prefer the so-called "subjective" psychiatric interview to counting the correlated frequency of so-called "facts."

HUNT: Would you follow that through and say that you would not care for statistical evidence in the field of drugs?

ALEXANDER: Yes.

HUNT: You would treat a patient with drugs without any statistical evidence?

ALEXANDER: Statistics must have all the controls. You may harm a specific patient with a drug which helps many others if you do not know the mechanics of its effect. Without all possible controls, statistics are meaningless if you do not understand the processes involved.

HUNT: Since I admit that the results in our Navy study are not conclusive evidence, tell me what is wrong, what you have that is better. Unless you stop saying that statistical evidence is meaningless, there will be a nice big area of unacceptance between us.

ALEXANDER: Statistical evidence is valuable if it follows the basic principle of statistics; namely, that similar things must be counted, and that things that do not belong together should not be lumped together. Most statisticians in the social and sociological sciences do not know what they count; therefore, the statistics in these fields are usually meaningless.

MILLER: He is against poor statistics.

HUNT: In short, he is for his statistics and against my statistics.

ALEXANDER: I think statistics are very important. But they are meaningless until we know the how and why. Alone they are never enough.

HUNT: I would like to add one thing more, if I may. I have been engaged for about eight years in applying statistical treatment to psychiatric data. I would like to say that apparently the statistics are "good" because I have been emotionally pleased at the way they have confirmed certain clinical assumptions.

COBB: This is an area, I think, where before we go on, we should define what we mean by statistical evidence. After all, one case is one case, two cases are two, and three are three. Is there any line where we begin to speak of statistical evidence? If so, where is it?

HUNT: This is a flexible situation, Dr. Cobb. If you want to prove a point, you accept the 5 per cent level of significance; and if you do not want to prove the point, you accept the 1 per cent level. I still think that the trouble is not with the statistics, but with the people using them. Sometimes I have a feeling that the clinical disciplines are a little afraid that if they approach science, they will get into something that they cannot handle, and that the results will be disastrous. Actually, I believe, their fears are misplaced. I do not see how psychiatry could have survived all these years on a scientifically invalid basis. I feel that when problems in that field are given proper treatment, the answers will come out; and they will not be answers that discredit clinical psychiatry.

But I can get thoroughly upset by the assertion that statistics are not a way to approach this problem. Dr. Alexander uses statistics. When Dr. Brosin mentioned a girl, he was using them; for he was counting. True, he started with unity, a single phenomenon. I would have preferred that he cited observations on three or four girls. I think that all psychiatrists are using statistics.

BROSIN: What I have to say is commonplace but I think it may help to explain why clinicians often have, let us say, a cautious and skeptical attitude about application of statistics. In the past, clinicians have suffered all too often from what Dr. Miller mentioned as bad statistics. Further, I would say that personal derogation has caused thin-skinned clinicians to rather resent the status to which statisticians in the past, not at present, have elevated themselves, in which they were the repository of all research method and all proper design of research. In that design, anything that did not follow the tenets of R. A. Fisher was not science.

Let me detail this point. I remember that in 1933 we were reading about how unscientific projective technics were. A couple of years ago, Lee Cronbach* of Illinois wrote an admirable essay describing the

* CRONBACH, LEE J. Statistical methods applied to Rorschach scores: A review, Psychol. Bull., 1949, 46: 393–429.

need for a different, more flexible kind of statistics that can deal with multiple variables, and asking for statisticians to cease decrying such projective technics as the Rorschach. Now statisticians are seeing that multiple variables, when dealt with properly in clusters, are highly meaningful in the clinical material. Dr. Thurstone has been, I think, an extremely good teacher on this subject for many years.

HUNT: I think this is an area of difficulty that lies between Dr. Alexander and myself. I think he has been led into overstating his attitude towards statistics, and I have probably overstated mine. There is nothing wrong with statistics per se. It is obvious that the data on blonds and industrial employment which he cited were not properly interpreted.

FRENCH: There is a problem about which there is a great deal of disagreement that should be mentioned at this point: it is the matter of the role of interpretation in psychodynamics. My own feeling, which I think is shared by many, but not by all, is that no really significant data with regard to the two most important variables in human behavior are possible without interpretation. What a person does can be observed, but then the most significant things are what he wants (his motives) and what he knows about how to get what he wants. Neither of those are matters of direct observation. Extremely strict application of the operational principle, I think, is impossible unless a system is evolved to interpret from directly observed data to the only quantities that are really significant. This question of how to interpret is of such importance that it should be discussed at great length. It is an approach to interpretation that perhaps would lead, I hope, to similar results from a number of interpretations. If each discipline would apply this approach, observations could perhaps be converted to their true and fundamental meaning.

SKINNER: I think that it is not possible to have interpretations that can be distinguished from scientific analysis and are said not to be subject to research. Perhaps it is a little rash at this point to talk about

repression of impulses or memories. What is an impulse? What is a memory? What observations do you make when you assert that there has been a memory or impulse? What are the actual things that you observe from which you conclude that one of these has been repressed? What is the Iron Curtain? I am not going to give up on that. If there is anything in the Iron Curtain, its effect must be on our observations. By appealing to our observations, I think that we can take the problem out of the realm of metaphor.

FRENCH: I am sorry that you chose the subject of repression; for I think that it is a special case. The basic problem of interpretation is to find the motivation. Perhaps I can go into what is the principle of interpretation although it is one that arouses many objections; nevertheless, it seems to me that it is the only possible one. It is based upon a person's behavior that can be observed and a common sense knowledge of human nature. The situation in which the person finds himself is observed, and it is then fitted into a context that makes sense in terms of what is known about human nature. You may say that what we know about human nature may be wrong. All right, it may be wrong. But then some more data are obtained, and the same methods are applied. Fortunately, when common sense is wrong, it is wrong in many, many different ways; and the more data that are applied to it, the more reliable it becomes. This is a procedure that does not satisfy the demands for a complete description of what is done. But I think that this subject cannot be fathomed without this sort of procedure.

SKINNER: I am sure that you can proceed that way usefully, but I still take issue with your statement. I do not want to give up trying for an operational definition of all concepts, such as those, for example, which come out of psychoanalysis.

RICHTER: I have a rather elementary question that I would like to ask Dr. Lidz. I feel that there is general agreement about the multifactorial nature of the causes of mental illness, and it is not difficult to make formal agreement with that viewpoint, especially in a discussion of this kind. But still, I find that there are real differences of emphasis, differences which would find expression in practical problems, as for example, in the treatment of a patient, or in deciding how the training of students should be carried out, or again how funds for research should be allotted. Those underlying differences are surely there, and I feel that it would be a pity to gloss over them too much by agreeing in a merely formal way.

In the account that Dr. Kubie gave us of the range of relations from the lowest organic level, leading up to the psychological and sociological factors at the higher levels, we have the picture of a system of organizational levels. Is it wrong to ask, then, at what level are the etiological factors most important in giving rise to any particular psychiatric condition? Surely the factors at one level are likely to be more important than those at another in any particular type of mental illness.

As I see it, we have a number of separate diagnostic categories in mental illness associated with etiological factors at different levels. We may attribute a particular form of mental illness to specific social, psychological, or organic factors, but I do not see any possibility of *proving* that they are causally related. Nevertheless, one can establish a *probability* that a factor is causally related, and the only way that I can see for establishing that etiological relationship is on a statistical basis, with a sufficient number of properly controlled cases. The classical example is general paresis, which at one time was supposed to be psychogenic in origin; and then as a result of the discovery of Wassermann's reaction and carefully controlled experiments, it was established with a high degree of probability that the spirochete was more important than the psychogenic factors in this disease. In other conditions which we have been discussing, more particularly those attributed to social factors, we are given a whole variety of possible causes. I would like to ask: Are there statistics available that can answer the question of how important these different etiological factors are in relation to the psychiatric conditions that we have been discussing? Etiology is a statistical concept, and without figures our ideas about etiology are likely to be vague.

Lidz: The remark that Dr. Richter makes on a practical level reminds me of something which Dr. Cobb and others have said: that the student today wants to talk only about psychodynamics. This is not purely accidental or cultural at the moment. This is a practical matter. Most of the students that we now have became interested in psychiatry during the war or shortly after the war; they saw what many other people saw, that the organically trained psychiatrist and even the Continental psychiatrist, trained in a kind of organic tradition, was of very little use in the treatment of most patients.

I had a visit from a professor of medicine from Munich yesterday, who pointed out that the psychiatrists in Germany are not interested in neuroses at all because the organic orientation led them in a totally different direction. I suppose that the real question that many of us are thinking about, and perhaps arguing about because we do not know the answer, has to do with schizophrenia. Statistics have been cited that show that schizophrenia is in part connected to hereditary or constitutional factors. This is, of course, not the whole answer to the question. Although I think that I might be going a little too far, I want to point out again that if leprosy is studied epidemiologically, a very strong apparent hereditary trend is found. The infant has to be separated from the parents at a very early age not to be in danger of contracting leprosy, very much as in tuberculosis. Some very strange phenomena are recounted. In countries where the head of the infant is shaved at birth, leprosy is apt to appear on the top of the head. These are very difficult manifestations to explain.

I have been told that because the investigators in some studies have been impressed by the familial influences, that is the interpersonal influences, of schizophrenia, they have neglected heredity. I do not think that is the case. It is a pragmatic matter to some extent. The interpersonal influences require exploration at the present time, for they have been neglected in the past.

The other part of the argument has to do with how we conceptualize the nature of schizophrenia. If it is conceived to be a deteriorating illness with clearly defined limits, it might be concluded that this disease must be somehow determined constitutionally or by some metabolic defect. But if, as frequently happens today, schizophrenic patients are studied in an environment where a fair number of schizophrenic patients go into remission (I hate to say "recovery"—a schizophrenic one day and not a schizophrenic the next) one begins to doubt that it is so clearly an entity. When one broadens the spectrum even further, the question focuses on not only where the normals and the neurotics merge, but also where the normal and schizophrenic diverge. So, many of us think it is tactical or pragmatic to try another approach; and the evidence seems to lead in this direction as clearly or more clearly than toward the constitutional or hereditary approach.

chapter 8

Evidence of Interrelation among Doctrines

• •

From the Organic Approach

HAROLD E. HIMWICH

If we consider the manner in which we have been working in the past, I would say there is no evidence of interrelations between doctrines. Each group goes along on its own way, influenced little or not at all by the others. But the schism goes even deeper than the divergence of doctrines because the very technics employed are entirely different. Most investigators have been using technics with results that could be applied only to their own theoretical viewpoint. If we wish to limit our discussion to two schools, the organicists and the psychoanalysts, we find a large number of individuals employing exclusively either one methodology or the other, using either the more exact technics of physiology, biochemistry, and biophysics in their studies of patients or the more subjective methods of psychoanalysis.

It is true that we are beginning to see some investigators who are employing technics stemming from both viewpoints. A few individuals with strong psychological orientation are, nevertheless, making quantitative measurements of functional changes in their patients. This, in my opinion, is a step forward. Though the facts are gathered by both methods, they are still evaluated on

a basis of different theoretical standards. The strict division is not breached. They do not exert a mutual influence upon each other. Still to be awaited are the benefits of the fertilization which might accrue as a result of the crossing of the two doctrines. If we assume, and I see no reason why we should not, that each doctrine contains a portion of the truth, then it should be valuable to combine them in one way or another.

Though I know of few such combined studies, it is possible to let one's imagination loose and suggest certain possible modes of attack. In the insulin hypoglycemia treatment of schizophrenia we observe a series of release phenomena, release from the constraints usually applied to the activities of the patient. The behavioral changes of insulin hypoglycemia arrange themselves in five symptom-complexes. The first group indicates a growing depression of cortical functions with alterations in vision, audition, motor coordination, and understanding. Somnolence deepens and finally the patient loses contact with the environment.

The second series of signs is the kind that would be expected if the patient were decorticated and the subcortical structures permitted to express their patterns of activity uninfluenced by the coordinating effects of the cortex. The motor phenomena observed during the second stage of insulin hypoglycemia are reminiscent of those observed in a newborn infant, who may be regarded largely as having a nonfunctional cortex. Primitive movements of many types are seen: forced grasping, forced sucking, as well as motor restlessness. At this time the sympathetic branch of the autonomic system is the preponderating one, and signs usually associated with sham rage are seen: flushing of the face, dilation of the pupils, acceleration of the heart, and elevation of the blood pressure. In a similar fashion the response to tactile and painful stimuli is exaggerated and poorly coordinated in the absence of cortical modulation.

The third series of signs is similar to those observed in a patient with a supracellar cyst separating the midbrain from the more cephalad structures. Prominent are torsion spasms and tonic spasms. The latter especially reproduce the pictures of high decerebrations, seen in patients with such a lesion, with flexion of the arms and extension of the torso and legs.

With a still lower section, just above the medulla, the classical signs of Sherrington's decerebration are evoked: tonic extension spasms. These signs of the fourth stage of insulin hypoglycemia are characterized by extension of the arms, the back, and the legs.

Finally, in deepest hypoglycemia the vital medullary centers are released, as if by a section just above them. The preponderantly parasympathetic pattern discloses itself with pinpoint pupils, slow pulse, shallow respiration, and pallor.

In this treatment we witness the release of mechanisms which with a normal level of blood sugar are able to express themselves only with the permission, as it were, of more cephalad structures and under their inhibitory and facilitatory coordination.

An analogy is seen between the release of subcortical mechanisms of the hypoglycemic treatment and the catharsis which is associated with a successful analytic treatment. If it could be proved that the beneficial effects which are sometimes obtained by hypoglycemia are due to a release of pent-up and repressed material, we might see a crossing of doctrinal alignments.

Another possible investigation of this type would be to determine whether an oral drive is associated with enzymatic changes in the gastrointestinal tract, for example, strong oral dependency occurring in an individual with hyperactive gastrointestinal functions. It is true, however, that psychosomatic studies of this type have begun to appear recently.

As a result of such investigations we might see the beginnings of a common basis for two apparently divergent doctrines. In these early stages of the development of the science of psychiatry, in contrast to the art of psychiatry, we cannot hope to explain the various details of a psychotic reaction by such combined studies. But even a first step in that direction whereby a broad and general agreement could be reached on an experimental basis would be a most welcome turn of events.

From the Psychological Approach

HOWARD S. LIDDELL

A few specific examples of behavior from our studies of conditioning in sheep and goat give evidence, I believe, of interrelation between doctrines. These examples have been chosen to illustrate the influence of "traces" or "traumatic memories" on the animal's present behavior.

Those who represent the organic position or the experimental psychological position will speak of traces while the representatives of the psychodynamic position will prefer the concept of traumatic memories.

One of our goats, trained for several months in the laboratory, was observed as it wandered about the barnyard. A new electric fence had been installed and the goat shortly approached this unfamiliar strand of wire. It hesitantly touched the wire with its muzzle and instantly wheeled and dashed away. But after a few steps it wheeled again, faced the electrified wire, and precisely flexed its *right* foreleg.

The casual observer would be at a loss to account for this unfamiliar or peculiar instance of goat behavior. However, the circumstances of the animal's training make its precise but bizarre reaction to the unexpected shock on its muzzle more understandable.

It had been trained in the laboratory for several months according to the following regimen. For an hour each day, while the goat was confined by a restraining harness and ten electrodes were attached to the right foreleg, a buzzer was sounded for ten seconds, followed immediately by a mild electric shock to the foreleg. Forty of these buzzer signals, spaced a minute apart, were given at each session.

If the goat kept its foreleg flexed until the buzzer stopped, it received no shock. It learned very soon to avoid the shocks and, indeed, had not received a single shock for several weeks. However, its prompt and precise flexion at the sound of the buzzer continued without lapse.

Now, in the barnyard, the novel experience of electric shock on the muzzle promptly released the inappropriate behavior of running from the fence, wheeling, and *then* making the avoidance response— a most unrealistic reaction to a situation meaning danger.

During the past two years further observations have indicated that this goat has developed a definite and chronic emotional disorder (which is all that is meant by the unhappy term "experimental neurosis"). Except for the dramatic episode of its unrealistic reaction to danger just mentioned, a visitor unfamiliar with the history of this animal's behavior would fail to note any striking peculiarities setting it apart from our other goats. However, we accidentally discovered that its pattern of emergency reaction to danger had become highly simplified and stereotyped. We no longer give shocks no matter what the animal does during the test period; and although the buzzer signal has now been repeated more than two thousand times at irregular intervals and for as long as a minute and a half, the goat still continues to maintain flexion of its right foreleg as long as the buzzer is sounding. It will not, or cannot, take a chance. When the buzzer sounds for a minute or more, the goat shows evidence of pronounced fatigue. Tremor of the flexed leg and gradual sinking of the forefoot toward the floor will be corrected by a sudden, forceful flexion just before the foot touches the floor. Moreover, all sudden stimuli, such as turning on lights, starting a movie camera, tapping the goat's side lightly with a wooden rod, instantly evoke a brisk and maintained flexion. Sometimes the animal suddenly and spontaneously assumes the flexed position of the foreleg in the absence of any observable change in its laboratory environment. All alarms are now channeled through the right foreleg.

What keeps this simple and stereotyped avoidance response going when there is no longer anything in the animal's real situation to be avoided? It seems to us that this is fundamentally the same question which the psychiatrist faces in combating his neurotic patient's phobias. There seems to be no reason why the operation of "traumatic memories" may not be inferred in both cases.

I. Arthur Mirsky* has recently been investigating these stereotyped avoidance responses in rat and monkey. As in the goat, they continue of their own momentum in the absence of all shocks. Further, he finds that they may be terminated by administration of ACTH or cortisone.

Several years ago we published definite evidence that the emotionally disturbed sheep takes its worries home to the barn at night. When a sheep is subjected to the

* Mirsky, I. A., Miller, R., and Stein, M. Relation of adrenocortical and adaptive behavior. Psychosom. Med., 1953, 15: 574–588.

monotony of a rigid time schedule of ten-second conditioned signals spaced six minutes apart and this schedule is followed day after day, a severe emotional upset is precipitated and becomes chronic. The animal exhibits diffuse agitation in the laboratory with frequent and vivid startle reactions, labored breathing, and rapid irregular pulse. Even weeks or months after all tests have been discontinued, the animal exhibits its perturbation in the barn at night. With the aid of a long-distance stethoscope the observer, in a shed outside the barn, can listen to the heart sounds of both normal and neurotic sheep. When the flock is resting quietly in the barn, the normal sheep's heart beats slowly and regularly. By contrast, the neurotic sheep's heart may be beating twice as fast with wide fluctuations of rate, with frequent premature beats, and with abrupt acceleration in response to a lamb's bleating and so on. When placed on a long recording platform within sight of other sheep, the disturbed animal, unlike the normal one, continues its nervous pacing back and forth on the platform during the dark hours; this behavior suggests that its traumatic memories (or worries) have led to insomnia.

The examples just cited from our own research could be multiplied many times. I have reviewed them here because it is the purpose of this symposium to strive for the convergence and even coalescence of viewpoints on the etiology of mental disease.

Those of us who investigate animal behavior with medical intent have been frustrated for many years by habitual attitudes of "interdoctrinal unacceptance." For example, the statement is repeatedly made that the so-called experimental neurosis in animals can have little or no bearing upon human mental disorder. This, it is said, is because the animal's emotional disorder is situational. It originates in the laboratory and appears only when the animal is returned to the laboratory situation or fears that it may be, actual published evidence such as reviewed above notwithstanding. Thus, "interdoctrinal unacceptance" irradiates to embrace "factual unacceptance"; and that, we would all agree, is going too far.

From their beginings, the two traditions of research originating in the classical studies of Cannon and Freud have converged upon the same fundamental problem; namely, the functional significance of emotion. This physiological tradition and this psychodynamic tradition will eventually coalesce in spite of the well-known inertia and conservatism of thinking peculiar to the sciences. The merger will be hastened, I believe, when it is recognized that between the organic position and the psychodynamic position there is another distinct viewpoint—the behavioral or psychobiological position. Those of us who adhere to this position and who have persevered in the study of the animal's chronic emotional disorders brought on by the stresses of conditioning can contribute to an understanding of the functional significance of emotion. We can certainly do so when it is clearly recognized that a division of labor is not only desirable but necessary in attacking our common problem of emotion. This division of labor is based upon the well-established zoological principle of homology. The sheep's foreleg and the human hand and arm are homologous structures serving diverse purposes. The sheep's foreleg is one member of a locomotor quartet and that is all. The human upper extremity is capable of incredible feats of manipulative skill. Why should we expect the sheep to learn to play the piano? But the sheep's "locomotor" brain and man's "manipulative" brain are driven to action by the same primitive, neurohumoral "emotional" or emergency machine.

If symbolizing derives from manipulating, we cannot expect the sheep's simple but chronic emotional disorder to reveal evidences of distorted symbolism or of the operation of a "primary process" as in human psychoneurosis. But evidences of emotional disability obtained from sheep undergoing the long-continued stress of conditioning and from soldiers subjected to the long-continued hazards of the combat situation reveal the same basic patterns of alarm behavior as revealed in posture, movement, and organ dysfunction.

In conclusion, our work is providing evidence in support of the psychosocial position. Two examples: A lamb three weeks of age is brought into a bare laboratory room ten feet square. I now lead my class of four students into the room and line them up against the wall. The lamb remains in a far corner and stares intently at us. It attempts to escape if we approach. The twin of this lamb is now brought into the adjoining room and the class files in as before, lining up against the wall—but instantly this lamb runs to us and tries to wedge itself between our legs or as close to us as it can get. This lamb had been removed from its mother at birth and raised by bottle-feeding.

From the Psychodynamic Approach

NORMAN A. CAMERON

Although I am committed by the program to agreement, I find that this casts me in an unfamiliar role. Yesterday the conciliatory statements seemed at times to set up reverberating circuits, even to the extent that we kept on saying the same things in different words. So I am going to preface conciliation with a good deal of criticism; and I shall mention names because this will help crystallize my material around the previous discussants and give it context.

First, there is Dr. Gerard's statement that the biologists and the psychodynamicists seem to be speaking two different languages. I think he said the biologists were speaking English, and the psychodynamicists Hungarian. There is an implication in this statement that the psychoanalysts are speaking a foreign language known to very few Americans. I do not think this is the major issue. The really important difference is that we are not speaking about the same or interchangeable things. The languages of physiology and of psychodynamics, whatever we call them, are not even close enough together to be made in any way equivalent. Yet I am sure that they are both biology.

Any contrast between biology and psychodynamics is artificial. Psychodynamics is a biological as well as a behavioral science. But a contrast between physiology and psychodynamics is not artificial at the moment. For in psychodynamics and physiology we get different results, which are differently expressed, because we are dealing with different materials, by different operations, and under different conditions. At the present time, there seems to be no point in trying to avoid these differences or in attempting what would be a premature resolution of them.

Dr. Jasper gave a straightforward list of words commonly used in psychodynamics which the neurophysiologist does not understand and does not know how to employ. The neurophysiologist clearly wants to understand them. But he does not know what to do with these words for a good reason. It is that they do not say anything about what he, as a neurophysiologist, is doing or is directly interested in.

It is understandable that many psychodynamic words and concepts mean practically nothing to a neurophysiologist. Even the word "couch," as used in therapy, does not really mean anything significant to a neurophysiologist, unless he has had experience with the couch as a means of psychodynamic investigation. Certainly he can see it, talk about it, read about it, and see cartoons of it; but he will not understand it.

The same is true of "unconscious." Without some experience in this area, under the conditions which open unconscious processes to investigation, the neurophysiologist cannot possibly understand what "unconscious" means. Similarly, he will have no real comprehension of such processes and terms as "free association," "manifest dream," and "dream interpretation." They do not belong to his context. My advice to the neurophysiologist who does not know what to do with psychodynamic terms is to leave them alone. He will not be able to learn their meaning by consulting a dictionary, any more than a psychologist can learn neurophysiology out of a dictionary.

There are many words in neurophysiology which are useless and meaningless to a psychodynamicist. Let me start with the word "neuron." This word is useless in psychodynamics, not because it is not a good word, not because it does not have a vast background of careful scientific research, but for the simple reason that it has nothing to say to the psychodynamicist about the things in which he is interested and with which he works. The same could be said for words like "commissure," "tract," "decussation," and a thousand others.

Of course every man trained in medicine has some understanding of these terms. He cannot have done work in neuroanatomy, neuropathology, and clinical neurology without knowing them. But the point is that these words in a study, let us say, of motivational dynamics in a clinical setting have no meaning and no usefulness. Some day perhaps they may; but today they have no application in psychodynamics. They are definable in their own context; but that context is not the one in which we work.

Now I see nothing evil in this situation at all, nor in the sharp differences of attitude among us. One of the things we have lacked so far in these discussions has been some straightforward expression of antagonism. We feel it. The sweetness and light here is to some extent a consequence of the fact that we are not talking about the same things. We have not as yet come close together in our thinking; we are not likely to; and we are trying hard to deny it. The time seems to be nowhere near when neurophysiologists will be ready to deal with psychodynamic problems, or when psychodynamicists will be ready to deal with neurophysiological problems.

I do not see how anyone can expect a Conference such as this to function in diffusing information among us to the point where we can all go away in two days, or in twenty days, with unanimity of experience, understanding, and terminology. At our present stage, the neurophysiologists should go on developing their exceedingly interesting and remarkably useful concepts, in their own area, by their own methods, and with their own materials. The psychodynamicists should do the same in theirs. As these two fields grow closer together—for they must eventually—the time will one day be ripe for doing the sort of thing that we have been trying to do here prematurely.

But there is an aspect of this "growing closer" which is usually neglected. This aspect is the growth of neurophysiology toward psychodynamics. It is more often assumed than not that psychodynamics will become really scientific when it is reduced to nervous system function. That is a mistake. The materials of psychodynamics begin with direct, expert observation, as all science must. The sort of behavior we are engaged in here and now—our interpersonal relationships, the interaction within this group, your reactions to what I am saying, and my reactions to your manner of listening—these are the fundamental behavioral manifestations from which all studies of live human beings must start.

The concepts and methods we derive from these first observations must always take physiological findings and postulates into account; but physiological concepts need just as much to take seriously into account what we are finding and postulating. *Rapprochement* is a two-way proposition. Whether or not we are speaking Hungarian, what we are now able to say about the dynamics of unconscious motivation, as one example, is well within the understanding of our cousins in neurophysiology.

Besides the reductionism which Dr. Gerard has espoused, we should be thinking also of a reductionism in the opposite direction. Let me take physics as an extreme example. It is conceivable that a system of physical postulates can be worked out so as to be of immediate use to human beings devoted to the study of human beings. Such an oriented system could then be brought into harmony with basic concepts of physiology, just as physiological concepts need ultimately to be in harmony with those of psychodynamics. It is true that all of us here are interested in reducing the immense complexity of surface behavior down to simple and specific abstractions. But these abstractions have also to be regulated by these very complexities that we observe—see, hear, feel, interact with, record, and measure—on the surfaces of behavior.

Another important source of unnecessary friction arises from the dogma, implied by earlier discussants, that science belongs in the laboratory. If we cannot bring psychodynamics into the laboratory, it is no science. To me this sounds as illogical as to say that if you cannot get an elephant into Skinner's box, you can say nothing scientific about an elephant.

The statement that we cannot get psychodynamics into the laboratory is largely true; but the conclusion that therefore its contributions are unscientific is not. All of us know that much unscientific work is done in laboratories, and much scientific work is done out of them. I need only cite Schneirla's* work on ants, carried out now over a period of twenty-five years, which has produced highly scientific contributions. Most of his studies were carried out in the field; they could not have been made accurately in a laboratory. In a later phase, many of Schneirla's conclusions may be tested under laboratory conditions; but the most significant work has already been done in the field.

We in psychodynamics are engaged in comparable work. In the present phase we are studying our material under the freest possible conditions, within four walls, it is true, but without instrumentation. To force our material into a conventional laboratory at this phase would be to produce a mock-up of scientific procedure. We cannot evade that first great phase in every young science, the phase of careful observation. Galileo's revolutionary concepts were not hatched in a highly organized laboratory. Neither were Darwin's. Neither were Freud's.

These three men demonstrated something we all know, and all at times forget: that you have to study phenomena where you can find them, and not where they disappear. Science is a matter of how you do things and what you can say about them. The "how you do it" is not necessarily most scientific when it is most fragmented. You certainly cannot fragment the material of psychodynamics without destroying the phenomena you are trying to investigate.

Now a word about teleology. Earlier in my own career I used to thunder against teleology; now I find myself ready to speak in its defense. There is a great deal of confusion about this word, a confusion of meaning and context. The teleology which Dr. Gerard rightly boasts as having been eliminated from physiology is not at all the teleology which he complains about as surviving in psychodynamics. The teleology of current purposive behavioral science is simply a recognition that there is a beginning and an end to human action, to planning and execution; that the end envisaged may have a significant effect upon the course and outcome of action; and that these relationships can be formulated in useful ways. It says that all significant human action is goal-directed.

Let the behavior of physiologists themselves be our example. The physiologist is determining and shaping his behavior today by what he imagines will happen in his field next week, month, year, or decade; and he knows it. He may not want to call this teleology, but I do. The mere words "experiment," "project," "program," envisage some goal or purpose. They are never aimless. They include behavior which is determined by a projected, predicted future.

None of us is so naïve as to imagine that something which is not happening and has not happened is pulling us toward it—if we include present imagining as a present happening. But we all know that in our biological organizations it is possible for us to project from the present on to an imaginary future, and then bring the actual future more or less in line with the imagined one. The goal is there, in some representative form, in all significant human activity as the activity goes ahead. This is all that the teleology in psychodynamics and in neurophysiology amounts to.

And now, at last, I come to convergence in scientific thinking. The preamble has

---

* Schneirla, T. C. Learning and orientation in ants. Com. Psych. Monog., 1929, vol. 6, no. 4 (Serial No. 30). 143 pp.

been long, and this part will have to be correspondingly short. Historically, one of the most interesting examples of convergence is a favorite with Talcott Parsons: the concept of the internalization of one's culture. Freud and Durkheim, working in different countries, on different materials, by different methods, developed essentially the same conception without any communications between them.

There are many places in America where serious attempts at convergence are now being made—with neurophysiology, psychiatry, psychodynamics, and psychology contributing diverse backgrounds, methods, and data. The behavioral studies at McGill exemplify this trend. At Chicago there has long been interaction between physiological and psychological disciplines at experimental, observational, and doctrinal levels. And there are many other instances.

For the remainder of my discussion, I am going to focus on a topic I was specifically asked to include: the controversial area of doctrinal convergence. Are there signs of doctrinal convergence in the field of psychodynamics? I think there are. Perhaps the most significant one is the move on the part of social scientists, now well renamed "behavioral" scientists, to seek firsthand experience in psychodynamics. This seems to be a nationwide trend, small in numbers but significant in scope. The trend seems to have originated in a wholly unplanned way from a recognition by individual behavioral scientists that this firsthand experience is essential to the work they are doing. They are getting it in the only way one can, within the framework of psychoanalysis, and they are influencing psychodynamics in turn because their own fields of expertness border upon the domains of psychoanalysis. Again we see an example of mutual induction.

What is the reason for this trend? Taking American psychology as a representative of behavioral science, during the past three decades there has been a rapid and massive growth of interest in motivation—in the study of drives, needs, and goals, and of interest and attitude. There is even some revival of instinct concepts in relation to behavior.

Studies in perception seem nowadays to be promoting a healthy doctrinal convergence; for example, the gradual interpenetration of perceptual and personality concepts. The work of Witkin *et al.* is only one case in point. Here is a group of psychologists who started out studying what looked like a problem in pure perception in a very restricted laboratory setting. But as time went on, they found their results forcing them more and more to take account of broader questions concerning the personality organization of the people they were observing—the only source of their perceptual data. What began as a very limited "pure psychology" approach has expanded into a study of the general orientation of each individual subject to his world.

This expansion came, not from the ambitions of the experimenters, but from the sober recognition that personality variables were involved which the original strict experimental design did not envisage. The results of the early experimentation pushed the program increasingly toward psychodynamic considerations until these proved an inescapable part of the program. Naturally, these behavioral scientists had to be ready and able to see where their material was leading them, and courageous enough to strike out along the new trail. Similar trends are common in sociology and anthropology; Dr. Dunham has already made this clear.

Psychoanalysis, the ultimate in psychodynamics, is rapidly moving in directions which bring it into closer and closer contact with certain branches of psychology. The growth of ego psychology, for example, brings to the psychologist something which he can easily understand and immediately use. So there is a reciprocal movement, unplanned, to some extent haphazard, but making each discipline noticeably more like the other.

One of the speakers here stated that psychoanalysts are interested only in tracing things back to archaic processes in infancy and early childhood. Nothing could be further from the truth. Certainly analysts are deeply interested in infancy and childhood. What behavioral scientist is not? But they are at least equally concerned with what goes on in their patients today, what this has to do with yesterday and last week, and what this may mean for tomorrow and six months from now. Whether or not this material happens to be infantile, it is also contemporary. The psychologist makes an important discovery for himself when he realizes that psychoanalysis, too, investigates the everyday life of ordinary human beings.

There is a perceptibly growing interest on the part of many psychoanalysts in putting some of their motivational hypotheses to the test, insofar as these deal with normal adults, children, and infants. Here is an area of potential contact which both analysts and psychologists can be expected to cultivate further. They share many facilities and utilities which may gradually transform what are now adjacent suburban developments into something approaching a common scientific community.

In general, it is the younger men in the behavioral sciences—in which I am here including psychoanalysis and psychiatry—who tend more and more to look upon one another as colleagues. There is not mass movement in this direction; but one witnesses examples of it wherever the old defensiveness has been worked through, or has not had a chance to develop. And it is for the most part among the younger men that one sees behavioral scientists seeking to round out their training with psychodynamic experience, and people with a background in behavioral science and medicine entering upon a career in psychoanalysis. These persons in themselves constitute doctrinal convergence.

chapter 9

Searching for Common Ground

◆ ◆

LINDSLEY: There is something paradoxical in what Dr. Cameron has said. In the first place, he asserted that we are all animals, which was a contradiction of what someone had previously implied, that the humans were perhaps set apart from the lower animal forms. But what seemed somewhat paradoxical to me was that after having made this statement, he then said that perhaps we are dealing with two universes: one represented by the biological scientist, including perhaps the experimental psychologist; the other, by those looking at the psychodynamic and sociodynamic point of view. It did not seem to me that it was so much a matter of looking at different universes. We do have something in common; namely, the language of behavior. It is common to all of us, whether we are dealing with cells, aggregations of cells, organs, or even organisms themselves. We are dealing with groups, and the language of behavior of these individuals or groups is perhaps the same.

It seems to me that there is a different universe of discourse, but not a different universe in terms of the actual problems, or separate matters that we are concerned with. If one looks at behavior as seen in an infant, there are certain things on which we can agree. One is that the wellsprings of behavior are perhaps determined by certain physiological, biochemical needs of the tissues of the organism, not yet well controlled or integrated by its developing nervous system. I do not think that any of us would contradict that point of view. We speak of those tissue needs as primary needs or the beginning of what we call primary drive states. Then moving along the line of development as maturation proceeds, we see evidence that these primary needs are converted or modified in terms of secondary acquired needs or drives. Eventually also the social, emotional, and cultural factors begin to come in. Thus, what we start out with initially is some kind of primary value; then the primary aspect begins to take on multiple characteristics. I think that it is at that point that we begin to get confused, not only in terms of our viewpoint but in terms of our terminology.

Certainly the psychologist does not, at the present time at least, deal very much with the term "instinct." We talk about "primary drives"; we talk about "patterns of behavior." As we proceed along further it becomes a matter of the introduction of maturation and learning; then we speak of secondary drives and eventually motivation, when goals are brought into the picture. But I am not sure that the psychodynamic point of view does follow along this developmental line of thinking. I surmise that there has been a point of view or conceptual system which has been built up more in retrospect than in the forward, developmentally determined progression.

My final point does not deal so much with the matter of interrelationship among disciplines as it does with the philosophy of the approach to mental disease. Naturally in biological sciences and in experimental psychology there has been a tendency to deal with the single-variable type of approach. When there are other variables in operation, the attempt is made to control them so that the single variable or primary variable may be studied for its influence or effect. As we proceed toward increasing complexity of the stimulus pattern and increasing complexity of behavior itself, we obviously get into the area of multiple variables. I think it is at this point that we not only become confused about what we are going to call behavior or call the situations which provoked it, but also get into difficulty in terms of the methods.

We have already discussed whether statistics or some other method should be used. Actually in sociology and other sciences we now have a number of ways of dealing with variant factors. We can deal with groups. We have factor analysis; and so if we cannot hold a particular variable constant, at least we can balance it out in the design of our experiment. I am wondering to what extent, in terms of the philosophy of approach to mental disease, we have not neglected this factor. As I look at the various studies that have been reported, I find instances in which the investigator has taken a single technic or a single variable and attempted to find out whether that gave a certain result in schizophrenia, psychoneuroses, using a nosological classification as one of the parameters on which to conduct this experiment. I have often thought that perhaps we would be better off if we took as our starting point, not a conceptual system determined in that way, but rather the objective measures which we had reason to believe were appropriate to be applied to the problems with which we were dealing. Then we might apply them to the heterogeneous body of patients, let us say, and find those particular objective measures which gave us differences among the population with which we were dealing. Then we could always return to other considerations. We would not have to throw out symptoms or clinical findings. By returning to them, we could re-evaluate at a subsequent time.

CAMERON: I am willing to accept Dr. Lindsley's correction with respect to the "universe of discourse." What I was trying to differentiate was this: In physiology, and to some extent in physiological psychology, there are certain materials and methods which we are able to handle well at their own level. But there are other materials being studied in clinical settings which cannot make contact with these physiological levels of abstraction.

This does not mean a dichotomy into two different worlds. It means only that there are two different kinds of activities going on in two different fields from which at present two different sets of data are being obtained. I hope that one day these may establish functional contact. I do not believe that either will simply be reduced to the other.

I agree also that we are dealing with what William James called "the sheet of experience," rather than with separate little abstractions. What we have often managed to do with our various instruments is to abstract, and appear to isolate, things which are actually not isolable.

Much of what we have been discussing as a "heirarchy of sciences"—for example, physics, biology, psychology—is actually only an *historical* and *academic* hierarchy. There are the historically old sciences, dealing with impersonal things; then the sciences dealing with life, but still at an impersonal level; and nowadays the inclusion of things more and more personal. Perhaps it is this personal intrusion which arouses a certain degree of enmity in those who prefer the impersonal. At any rate, I do not believe that these academic hierarchies really represent anything really independent or immutable.

RICHTER: I propose to say something about brain metabolism; but first I would like to say a little bit about the background, the thoughts that led to this experimental work.

It seems to me when a patient who is mentally ill and behaving irrationally is seen for the first time, the first thing that comes into the mind of the observer is: What is the cause of this? What is leading to this irrational behavior and thought? Clearly we must accept the view that many causes are playing a part; and we can run through the whole gamut, the sociological, psychological, and possibly physical. But I believe that one is entitled to take the matter a little bit further than that and ask: Is there any primary cause? Is there any "most important" cause for the irrational behavior of this patient? In trying to analyze the problem, it may be asked what is meant by primary or "most important" cause. It seems to me that the answer might well be: a cause that, if removed, results in the patient's improving. In fact, it suggests the thought of treatment. I feel it very difficult to dissociate etiology and treatment. That may be because I myself happen to have been brought up by an old school clinician who held that it was nonsense to talk about etiology without considering treatment at the same time. At all events, there is some real basis for linking those two items together in our minds.

If we agree that there are many different levels at which this "most important" cause may act, ranging from the sociological right down to the lower levels of molecular activity, then these lower levels, the metabolic processes and the physical causes, are surely a legitimate subject for investigation. If we are looking for more definite evidence to go on, I think that some evidence is already accumulating.

GPI (general paralysis of the insane) was one of the first of the mental diseases in which a definite organic or physical cause was established. More recently there is the work on phenylketonuria, a metabolic disturbance with which irrational behavior is associated in a very high proportion of cases. In arteriosclerotic conditions, a physical cause seems to be the basis. The acute toxic psychoses and a number of nutritional disorders with psychiatric manifestations, e.g., pellagra, B_1 avitaminosis, are linked with metabolic factors. The psychic disturbances accompanying a proportion of cerebral tumors, and the epileptogenic foci with evidence of related metabolic disturbance due to enzyme abnormalities belong in the organic category. This list seems to be steadily growing, and it does justify the approach which seeks to find out more about the metabolism of the brain in the hope of bringing new evidence into the field.

If irrational behavior is consistently found to be associated with some physical or metabolic factor, one is justified in concluding that the two are related. In view of the impressive evidence just cited, we might expect to find an enormous drive of research at present on brain metabolism, going on in many places, and resulting in a great deal of knowledge about brain metabolism. But the actual truth is that we know extremely little. We are still right at the beginning, asking the most elementary questions. For example: How active is the protein metabolism of the brain? There is nobody who can give a decent answer to that question or to other similar questions about the lipid metabolism of the brain at the present time. These processes simply have not been investigated. Yet, they are practical questions that could be answered. This seems to be a line that should be pursued.

One of the most striking points that has come out of research in this field is the revelation of the enormous metabolic activity of the brain. Folch calculated recently that in the young child more than half of the heat production of the body is due to the brain. That tremendous metabolic activity of the brain has not been generally appreciated. The figures are clear, but the reason for this prodigious activity is still obscure. No one can yet explain why this enormous metabolic activity goes on.

Such a situation raises the further question: Where should we start in the investigation of brain metabolism? What are the kinds of problems that are most likely to yield useful answers? One of the most promising leads is from evidence now coming out on the distribution of biochemical substances, enzymes and other substances, throughout the brain. It is only about a decade ago that people were thinking of the brain as a fairly homogeneous kind of tissue, in which one part might be biochemically much the same as another. But in the last few years it has become abundantly clear that there are enormous differences in the biochemical make-up of the various layers and parts of the cortex, and in the various ganglia. The different anatomical regions are not only specialized in their physiological functions but also in their biochemical characteristics as well. Here a really vast field for investigation has opened up. There are many possible methods of approach, but I think that histochemical methods may be chiefly used.

Another question that seems to come closer perhaps to the topics which we have been discussing is: What are the changes in the metabolites in the brain with different kinds of activity? If a patient suddenly changes from a quiescent, dormant state into one of emotional activity, what is happening to the chemical compounds in his brain? Are there any tangible biochemical correlates? Clearly for many reasons it is difficult to investigate this point in human beings; but I will mention briefly one line of approach that has been productive. One experimental approach with animals is to take a series of them in different states of functional activity—some anesthetized, some convulsed, some excited, and some asleep—and to compare the concentrations of metabolites in their brains. That procedure has been followed in studies on a series of young rats. By dropping the animals into liquid air, freezing them at once in a few seconds, and fixing the biochemical changes in the brain, postmortem changes can be largely avoided. Comparison of a series of animals by this procedure showed striking differences in the various metabolites.

Perhaps I should mention how these different physiological states were produced in the animals. Proceeding from anesthetized animals at one end of the scale to convulsed at the other end gives a fair range of functional activity. It is easy enough to excite young rats; it is easy to frighten them by shaking them or by putting them in strange surroundings. They defecate, micturate, and they behave as if excited or alarmed. Although I hesitate to apply the word "emotion" or terms with human connotation to these animals, they behave in a way that indicates that they are not in their normal mental state. The sleeping series presented more difficulty at the first; for although young rats were watched for a long time, it was found that they will not easily go to sleep. But if they are put in strong sunlight under comfortable condi-

tions, they will go off to sleep of their own accord in the daytime. Thus a suitable cage may be rigged up with artificial sunlight and a liquid air vessel immediately below; in a fraction of a second the rats may be brought into the liquid air and the changes in their brains fixed. There is one minor point of distinction. Animals are apt to doze at times rather than sleep. But there is a slight difference in that a dozing animal, if alerted in the slightest way, will immediately open its eyes and respond; whereas animals in deep sleep keep their eyes closed for quite an appreciable time if touched or roused by sound. Animals examined in these various states showed significant metabolic differences in their brains.

The metabolites that could be examined are vast in number. I do not know how many hundreds or thousands of biochemical substances there are in the brain, but they comprise an immense field for investigation. The most obvious substances to study at first, the most elementary compounds like lactic acid and acetylcholine, have shown significant changes with activity. Similarly, the changes in the phosphate esters and in a number of other related substances indicate that when the brain is more active, there is a greater utilization of glucose. However, the changes are apparently not limited to these labile metabolites, like lactic acid and acetylcholine; for there is evidence that the more permanent substances in the cells, like the phospholipids (which may be more relevant to the changes in the mental patient) are also affected by the state of functional activity of the brain.

It is clear by obtaining correlates between biochemical factors and behavior we are never going to explain that behavior in biochemical terms. In my opinion, there is no point in attempting to give an acceptable explanation for activity at a high functional level in terms of activity at a low level; but I still feel that it is of value to obtain these associations. After all, it is known that a schizophrenic psychosis can easily be precipitated by an emotional upset. It may therefore be asked if the changes occurring in the brain in emotional upsets were known, whether that information would not help toward understanding what is happening in the precipitation of a psychosis. It seems, therefore, that a further knowledge of the metabolic processes occurring in the brain would help. If metabolic defects were found (and it would not be surprising if quite striking defects were found, say the absence of certain enzymes in some patients), this information would surely help in suggesting what could be done in the way of treatment. Just as the discovery of insulin deficiency in a diabetic has helped in the treatment of diabetes, surely in the same way the discovery of deficiencies in a brain enzyme, shall we say, might also lead to a rational line of treatment in the mental patient. What will be discovered is by no means certain, but the area does seem to be worth investigating.

To return for a moment to the topic with which I started: When confronted with a patient who is behaving irrationally, the psychiatrist can possibly put him into some diagnostic category and find various etiological factors associated with this diagnostic category. But I feel that in every instance the evidence for drawing any conclusions about the etiology must be based on numbers of patients and derived by a statistical method. Statistical analysis is a most valuable tool.

I think that Dr. Alexander was a little critical of the use of statistics, and I agree that his attitude is fully justified. Surely it is a healthy attitude to mistrust statistics. But, on the other hand, I feel that we are not justified in throwing out the whole lot just because some figures derived by statistics are not the finally accepted values. After all, the history of every science has shown that at the start people tried to get approximate figures. The earlier figures for mortality rates were long and violently challenged; and gradually, by criticizing and getting new statistics, we were able to get more reliable figures. Even measurements like atomic weights, which are also statistical figures, were at the start far out. After critical discussion more reliable values were gradually obtained. I think too that some of the new statistical methods that have recently come into use have greatly improved the situation.

Statistics can also be of practical value in psychiatry. As an example may I cite an incident in one of the provincial mental hospitals in England, where conditions had been the same for a very long time and everybody had been happy with them until one day somebody started to look into the figures showing how many of the senile group of patients were getting out of the hospital and going back into normal life. That was a most uncomfortable thing for anybody to do. But it brought about the realization that their figures were not as good as those elsewhere; that something must be done about them; and that active treatment should be given to a number of the senile patients. In fact it was found that quite a considerable number of these senile patients, mainly by shock therapy but also by other methods, could be released from the hospital and sent back into their homes. That incident is only one very elementary example of the value of the statistical approach. One of the most encouraging things about this Conference has been the way in which psychiatrists coming from many different centers have shown a tendency to think in quantitative terms and to obtain statistics. If this trend continues, it will help those of us who have been brought up in a more severely scientific tradition to understand better those who are working at the other extreme in the psychoanalytical field.

WHITEHORN: I thought that Dr. Richter was also going to pull together the beginning and the end of his remarks. I would like to do that myself in some small measure. He spoke of the intimate relationship between concepts of etiology and of therapy; I could mention a personal experience that has some bearing on that. At the beginning of my scientific studies in the field of psychiatry I was impressed with the probable importance of the knowledge about emotional processes, thinking that they might have something to do with the etiology of mental diseases. After a considerable number of years of working around in this field, I became more and more impressed with the certainty that emotional processes had a tremendous lot to do with the way people got well from mental illnesses. This conclusion leads back to a consideration of what this association might have to do with the etiology.

We have had here an illustration of the capacity of some comments about statistics to arouse emotional processes. Dr. Richter referred to another instance where it operated in a hospital to raise a good deal of concern about what was happening to the senile person. So perhaps for the purpose of this Conference, this arousal of emotional effects by discussion of statistical technic may be just a shot in the arm which we need.

KUBIE: I would like briefly to discuss Dr. Liddell's sheep. I do not maintain that because there are certain fundamental differences between the disturbances induced in the sheep and human neuroses, the two have no relationship. About this relationship, however, the data presented this morning puzzled me and seemed to raise critical questions. I would like to know how such a sheep ever knows when his ordeal is over. We cannot tell him. In fact his experience with man-the-scientist would inevitably engender distrust both of man and of the passage of time itself. A hundred times the sheep must have reached the point of feeling, "Well now, that is that," only to have the vexing process start up all over again. Let us imagine a child in a dentist's chair, a child who could not be reached by speech, perhaps because, like the sheep, he was deaf-mute. Suppose that the dentist drilled on a nerve in this child a fixed number of times a day, then stopped, and then started up again repeatedly; and that this went on over a long period of time. In the course of time, like the sheep, that child would go into a chronic state of wariness, avoidance, and "abwehr." Indeed, not to do so would be abnormal, perhaps feeble-minded. Maybe Dr. Liddell is asking his sheep to be too feeble-minded if he expects them not to develop a disturbance. Is this a neurosis in our usual sense? Or again, how does the sheep react to the unmeasured passage of time? Even in human beings we do not know much about the effect of time on the highest levels of our own functioning. How long is *long* for a sheep? How long is "long enough" to resolve these disturbances? Today we are seeing old people, even in their eighties, who are still dealing with the emotional problems of their nursery years with a vivid immediacy "as though it happened yesterday." I could give many examples of this because longevity is giving us a new laboratory in which to work. If that is true for the human after the passage of years of time, what is really "long enough" for the sheep? Those questions do not dispose of the problem which Dr. Liddell's work poses. But they puzzle me as I attempt to interpret his data.

We have been skirting one topic and then fleeing away from it. I think that we have done this because of a confusion about which of our psychodynamic and psychoanalytic concepts are purely descriptive, and which characterize operative and forceful processes? If we review the history of psychoanalytic theory, we see that Freud thought at first solely in terms of instincts and social restrictions. Then he conceived of "erogenous zones" and of a censor. Then he broadened the idea of erogenous zones to the libido concept, and to his concept of the controlling and guiding forces added the concept of ego ideals, and then a superego. Along the way came transference forces and resisting forces; and then the tripartite divisions into id, ego, and superego, cathexis, countercathexis. Thus gradually there was a multiplication of forceful concepts with obvious overlapping and reduplications. Evidently we must do a lot of weeding in our garden before we can ask the neurophysiologist to help us to understand which are the operative forces. This is where we still fail you in our own formulations of psychodynamic relations. This problem has been worrying me for years; and I have not been able to formulate it clearly enough to satisfy myself, much less anyone else.

I agree, of course, that we need greater clarity in understanding what we mean by "unconscious." There is a basic difference between the psychosomatic connotation and total incapacity to function with the awareness, such as we see in coma, stupor, and organic brain changes. But assuming that the capacity for awareness is intact, then we still have variations and compartmentalizations of awareness to formulate and explain; and about these we must ask the neurophysiologists to help us to understand the physiological mechanisms which mediate the deviant processes of awareness, whether we call these mechanisms repression, dissociation, or by any other name. In addressing our challenge to these colleagues, we must avoid using different names for approximately the same or identical states and processes. If we ask them to explore the processes by which compartmentalization of our conscious processes occur, we must characterize for them with greater precision the different kinds of compartmentalization of awareness which can occur. We ask them to study with us the processes of waking and sleeping, the intermediate states between waking and sleeping, hypnagogic states, hypnoidal states, and the various forms of automatism, etc. I mention these only as examples of areas in which coordinated investigations are possible even today between strictly analytical concepts, psychodynamics, neurophysiology, and experimental psychology.

QUASTEL: I think it worth while recalling and emphasizing again that the psychological effects of certain physical-chemical environmental changes may be very similar to those found in a variety of cases of mental disorders. For example, the effects of exposure to low pressure oxygen, oxygen at high altitudes, have been amply described by Barcroft, McFarland, and many others. The experiences of pilots at high altitudes are well known; their reactions have been tested quantitatively. The pilots were shown how erratic they actually were under hypoxic conditions when they themselves felt that they were perfectly fit. The abnormal effects in behavior of all forms, and various phases, of narcosis, the visual hallucinations due to drugs like mescal, the catatonic effects of bulbocapnine, all these are well known. They should be more closely studied in as quantitative and varied a manner as possible so that they may be better related to the biochemical and physiological effects of these substances on the central nervous system. Possibly then certain fairly clear-cut correlations or associations would be observable.

It is equally important to have more knowledge of biochemical and physiological changes occurring, let us say, during sleep or during such a mental disturbance as in narcosis, for these changes in the entire organism may differ markedly from the specific effects of drugs themselves on the nervous centers that are affected. It is equally important also, it seems to me, to discover all data bearing on the changed physical conditions in the body when it is in an abnormal psychological state, however this state may be brought about. A knowledge of the biochemical and physiological consequences of administration of chemical and physical stimuli, when considered in conjunction with the changes in mental behavior, should help us in the study of mental disorders.

I agree that work of this nature will require further refinement of technic than we now have so that there will be a more detailed exploration of body changes in the nervous system and elsewhere in the body. Already the advent of radioactive isotopes is proving of considerable help in this connection. The fact that a given stimulus may affect one person more than another in certain cases indicates an underlying difference in physiological make-up which may be due to an inheritance factor. If so, it is our job to reveal it. Increasing knowledge of the role of endocrines, of the effects of the various nutritional factors on metabolism, of changed chemical effects both in the central nervous system and other organs is quite indispensable in such work. I cannot see how it is possible to make headway in the study and treatment of mental disorders without more detailed knowledge of the chemical and physical changes in the body that must accompany them. One affects the other, and a study of one is a study of half, or less than half, of the whole. I would like to ask to what use, from the investigative point of view, are we putting our new knowledge of the effects of modern therapy such as prolonged narcosis, insulin shock, or electric shock treatments? However empirical these forms of therapy are, they bring about remarkable changes and remissions in the psychoses. There must be many changes in all levels in the central nervous system from a biochemical standpoint. A very detailed investigation of all these chemical and physiological changes seems to be quite necessary; for, in such changes, I think, must lie a clue to the origin of the mental disorders.

LIDDELL: Dr. Kubie raised the question of a sheep's knowing what time it is. This is a very interesting question because a sheep and man are both mammals. We have a special sensory nerve impulse velocity spectrum of fibers. There must be other determinable time constants at the behavioral level. For example, once when Dr. George Daniels was visiting my experimental farm, I put a demonstration sheep through a battery of tests of its conditioning skills, metronome rates, and tactile spots. When we demonstrated this or that signal, the sheep gave this or that response. As Dr. Daniels and I talked on, the "therapeutic hour" went by. At that point the sheep had had enough; all his differentiations disappeared and he just would not work any more. Dr. Daniels was reminded that sometimes in the analytic hour he would be getting such very good material that he would decide to pursue his advantage and keep the session going a little longer, but then would lose ground. I believe that even in the original experiments in Pavlov's laboratory, the experimental session for the dog was about an hour. With our sheep it is optimal at fifty minutes or an hour, and apparently so it is with people in the psychotherapeutic situation. So after all we can have a common measure with respect to time.

FRENCH: I would like to talk about some of the methodological problems that result from the fact that behavior is goal-directed. There can be no question about the fact that we have come to this Conference. We came here. We intended to come here. We bought tickets and did all the various things which were subordinated to the goal of getting here. Numerous examples could be given, even below consciously goal-directed behavior. An animal looks for food. Then there is the regulatory principle in biology: Certain lower animals will regrow a limb that they had. That is obviously a goal-directed process. But the next question that immediately arises, if you try to deal with the matter scientifically, is: How are you going to check conclusions about an animal's goals or a person's goals? How do you know whether you are right if you infer that a person has a particular goal? The problem becomes particularly difficult because not every person or animal that tries to reach a goal will succeed in reaching it. How do you know whether an animal is blocked in reaching that goal that you think it is trying to achieve, for how do you know that it was really striving toward that goal?

These questions raise some difficult methodological problems. I think perhaps most of the controversial feelings today among the different sciences that deal with behavior are traceable to different kinds of reactions to this methodological problem. Of course, when modern biology methods started—and biology was the first realm of science that presented us with this problem—the notion of teleology was dominant. Assertions were made without any thought of verification. The idea that conclusions should be checked was a new one that was necessary if the science of biology was to develop. The answer that used to be given, "Why, God intended it so-and-so, God's purpose was such-and-such," had a theological connotation. Actually the only answer that could have been made at that time was to ignore the problem altogether. Let's forget about the problems of ultimate purpose, forget about them entirely and devote ourselves to things that can be investigated in terms of a mechanistic frame of reference. A past cause gives rise to a present effect. Now, of course, that conception has been extremely fruitful; it has limited the area of investigation. But after all we cannot investigate everything at once anyhow, and science has concentrated its attention on things that could be investigated in terms of strictly mechanistic concepts.

A psychiatrist dealing with patients and trying to think, trying really to understand what he is doing, cannot ignore the notion that behavior is goal-directed. It is goal-directed. And a psychiatrist dealing practically with patients has to take that fact into account. A research psychiatrist is in a better position; he can confine himself to other problems. But if the psychiatrist deals with patients, he has to find out their motives. If he does not find out what their motives are—and by motives I mean goals —he cannot understand what they are doing. I suppose that Freud was the one who first really systematically accepted this challenge of trying to understand the goals and the motives that activate people. A dream was a wish fulfillment. In other words, it had that goal-directed striving.

Here another problem emerges. Many of the concepts—I think that this is particularly true of the psychoanalytic concepts of the drives—are very difficult to translate back to actual behavior. By that I mean that it is difficult to test how one knows that a person is behaving in response to a definite stimulus. What meaning, what definite factual concept, what practical clinical test can you give to the statement about what is happening to the libido? Many in the field, not the psychoanalysts but the non-psychoanalysts, have become critical of the methodology of inferences about the goals of behavior. When we say that a dream means a certain thing or expresses a particular wish, how do we know that? How can we prove it? These questions were passed over at first. It was said that a person just has the wish and that is all there is to it.

There are two possible and necessary orientations that we have to make to meet this challenge. The first is the problem of technic and interpretation. In my opinion we never will get a really fundamental understanding of behavior so long as we evade this problem. The challenge is being met now in some circles by people who are not faced with clinical responsibilities. This approach, in my opinion, is not without its use. It is valuable. Let us see what we can find out without recognizing that behavior is goal-directed. I think that has been essentially the point of difference between Dr. Skinner and myself. If the investigator is not a psychiatrist and does not have the responsibility for dealing with patients, all he can find out is by technics that escape this elusive concept of a wish or a motive or a goal. Whatever he can discover is all to the good, but not all of us can do that. Instead of trying to get away from interpretive technics, we have got to refine our

methods in order to make more explicit our means of making and checking interpretations. Hence, my first thesis is that no real understanding of a person's behavior is possible without determining his goals.

The second problem—and this gets down deeper—is strictly a methodological problem. As soon as we frankly recognize the goal-directed character of behavior, we have another problem as to the content of our science. That is: What is the mechanism of goal-directed behavior? We have to try to bridge the gap between mechanism and goal-direction. We have a number of habits that interfere with this problem. We have the habit of being contented with our explanation when we have found the goals for the patient's behavior. My second thesis is that having found the patient's goals, the analyst still has an equally, perhaps an even more, difficult task. He must study the scientific and interpretive thinking that is involved in really understanding people. For more and more he has to focus his attention on the problem: What is the mechanism by which behavior is goal-directed?

Two tasks lie ahead of us. One is the task of refining our technics of interpretations and checking interpretations; the other is the problem, the deeper scientific problem, of working out the mechanisms which make goal-directed behavior possible. These two tasks should, I think, lead to the ultimate synthesis of the two types of approaches: the mechanistic approach, which is viewed as the ultimate goal of science; and the interpretive approach, which is first a matter of understanding a person's behavior and his goals.

LIDZ: I should like to disagree momentarily with Dr. French for purposes of clarification, though basically there is no real disagreement. He started talking about teleological problems, then came around to motivation and goal-direction. He pointed out that unless we know what the motivation is, we cannot get very far in understanding our patients. In my opinion, the problem we have with a patient is not just in learning his motivation, but more often in trying to find out why his motivation is not clear to him. The question often is: How does the animal in Dr. Liddell's experiments or how does the human patient know what his goal should be? He gets caught up in not knowing what his goal should be. I think that part of the therapeutic problem is to try to help him by understanding basic motivations, and to arrive at a goal, or even goals, that he can then pursue.

The question has already been raised of what we can learn from therapy in this direction. It has been commented that all sorts of therapy seem to produce statistically about the same results. I do not know whether these statistics are valid. In any event, enlightenment concerning motivation enters into all kinds of psychotherapy. In some forms of psychiatric therapy on an advisory level, the psychiatrist sits down with the patient and clarifies motivation. The same is often true, though less apparent, of the analyst in the analytic situation. There are many things that may play a part, but often enough I think the analyst becomes a superego figure that permits certain types of motivation that the original figures did not seem to allow. We might perhaps say that after shock therapy the patient does not always care what his motivation should be. At least some of the more complex divergences between motivations are wiped out and everything can move along at a more simplified level.

To a great extent for a large part of the population, the role in society determines motivation, and surely society often gives or helps to give people the purpose of their lives. This concept has some importance. One of the critical factors in analytic thinking and theory is that basic drives, physiologic urges, can not concur with the societal motivations. That is to say: If the society was too restrictive or the figures in the society that counted were too restrictive, the person could not have a single useful motivation. This leads to one type of split in goals.

We should think of these things particularly in relation to this Conference. It has been said that we are in a schizoid state, and many of us are uncomfortable here in our professional or our scientific capacities for just this sort of reason. It may be the reason why many of us came here. We may like what we are doing; but we cannot always be really putting our hearts and souls

into it because we are not sure that the goals that we are pursuing are the ones that are ultimately going to lead to the places that we want to reach. Therefore, we are assembled here for the purpose of seeing whether we can get our goals sufficiently unified to go about our tasks with a better feeling. I think that if we arrived at an agreement concerning the way psychiatric research should be done, all of us would go back home to our specific areas of interest and know just what we were going to do and be quite contented about it.

I think that one of the confusions that has come about in psychiatric research or behavioral research in general has been the tacit assumption that the homeostatic forces that restore the patient to equilibrium are the same sorts of physiological homeostasis that are familiar in internal medicine and physiology; that is, that the body will restore itself over a period of time because of the physiologic setup of the organism. This concept has, of course, oriented a great deal of psychiatric research in just that direction of studying the physiological homeostatic mechanisms. The assumption was that if we could only help the body regain its homeostasis, we would promote mental health. I am not at all sure that this is the case. In fact, it seems to me that we have to consider a type of behavioral homeostasis of a totally different order. My present thinking about it goes something like this: that the individual grows up in a society and culture which has a great number of sentiments, attitudes, and so forth, in common; that by and large he is going to assimilate more of the normal than the abnormal patterns of this culture; that when he becomes mentally ill, perhaps because of conflicting goals and purposes, he deviates for a time and is asocial or antisocial. But if he can be kept in a reasonable state of balance by maintaining socialization, such as is attempted in our mental hospitals, as time elapses and the problems become less acute, either because new figures of importance arise or simply because of the passage of time, the weight of the more normal socializing forces will again gain the upper hand. This is the type of homeostasis that we must be studying in relationship to psychiatry.

chapter 10

Confronting the Communication
and Concept Barriers

◆ ◆

GERARD: I was surprised that I was accused of objecting to teleology, for I thought that I had already spoken, though briefly, in acceptance of it. The scientist cannot get along without purpose and directional thinking any more than can the psychiatrist. And, another point of agreement, when we can look backward as well as forward in time, we add mechanism and therefore gain power of analysis and control.

I would, however, like to say a word or two about the matter of language. We are now in the scientific mode of discourse—at least it has been said that a scientist is a person who views the activities of his colleagues with quarrelsome interest—but I am happy to say that the quarreling is being done with propriety and good nature. Chairman Whitehorn asserted that molecules do not have motives, so the biologist does not have the problem of using terms that are relevant to motives or goals. I wonder. It seems to me that, although psychologists and psychiatrists deal with essentially the same materials and problems, yet in the matter of language the psychologist and the physiologist find it possible to talk with each other more easily than with the psychiatrist. Perhaps more than materials is involved.

Dr. Cameron quite legitimately assumed that when I said the biologist was speaking English and the psychiatrist, Hungarian, that this was an attempt to imply that the biologist had the universal language and the psychiatrist, only the parochial one. Both Dr. Cameron and Dr. Whitehorn made the point that we really are not talking about the same thing. This is a basic question. If we are not talking about the same thing, then this is all nonsense. If we are talking about the same thing, then it is extremely important to find out to what extent we are on common ground, and where the psychiatrist goes beyond what the biologist is doing. I am proud that people dealing with the mental and social sciences are exploring ahead; all I ask is that we keep our liaison in effect.

I suspect that if we would really examine our words and the concepts to which they refer, we would find much more in common than we now recognize. From this realization we would derive the advantage of becoming aware of the formal identities of our domains and of the possibilities of sociological extension. We would become able to move from one level to another with greater effectiveness and much sooner than we could otherwise do. It is much the same situation as when electricity was first thought of as a fluid. The equations of liquid flow could thus be applied to the electric "current" at once, thereby tremendously accelerating the advance of electrical knowledge, although nobody thought that electricity actually flowed like water.

This same procedure is being applied today in the field that we are now considering. For example, there is the wide applicability of mathematical equations that were worked out to account for the spread of excitation in a network of neurons. It turned out that these identical equations, with all the variables and parameters that were introduced to cover degree of randomness and with suitable change in definitions, also accounted accurately for the spread of epidemics in a population and equally well for the spread of a rumor in a community. In other words, spread of excitation among neurons and spread of bacteria or rumor among individuals are not utterly different things. They have an important common denominator. If only we can get more of these mensurable relationships, we can make great progress.

The power of dimensionality in physics has been in making clear when one knew what one was talking about and when one was not quite so sure. The reason, I think, this approach is important for us is that a vital force does not move molecules and that emotions do not set up nerve impulses. We must not mix the languages. What happens when nerve impulses are discharged from the hypothalamus is that the neurons involved have been activated by other nerve impulses or by adrenalin or some other chemical or physical change produced in the cells' environment via the blood supply or locally. As a shorthand, we have to say at present that an emotion sets off the nerve impulses; but we must be very sure to recognize that we have not really given an answer when we use such mixed language, such Hungarian and English. What we are really saying is that there is a rather complex physiological state in the organism which we do not yet understand, which we may never be interested in working out in its full details, but which we can now describe meaningfully and operate with usefully in terms of its mental or psychological or behavioral concomitant recognized as emotion.

Dr. Cameron says that it is not yet time for the psychiatrist to talk about neurons or the neurophysiologist to talk, say, about complexes. I must admit that he is pretty much right. I like that story of the pink elephant and the green snake that came into the saloon and were told by the barkeeper, "You are too early. He isn't here yet." But after all, there are some bridges, very real bridges. They are tenuous as yet but are going to improve; unless they do, heaven help us. Some of this improvement will come when each of us works quietly in his own back yard and finds what is interesting. When the piles rise above the fence, we will see over and recognize that we are building part of one structure. It would seem better if we got the fence down and communicated with each other from the start. Therefore, I think it extremely important that communication be established as far as possible, that the identities or similarities of our concepts be explored, and that those parts be rooted out that really do not have any valid basis in a physical world. Some of the concepts of phrenology, a fair type of psychiatry in its day, or that of phlogiston, its equivalent in chemistry (and they are not entirely unrelated), are examples of notions that obstructed rather than aided understanding.

Since all psychiatrists have gone through some biology and physiology, they do at least know the rudiments of our language. I cannot say as much for the biologists and the physiologists; most of us do not know even the rudiments of your language. This means that you will have to make at least as much effort as we, maybe a little more, to get together, to help us interact. I am sure most of us want to; certainly there is no antagonism on the part of the people in this room and those whom we represent. It is not a matter of whether phenomena are either chemical or psychological; they are both. And we will all work more effectively toward our common goal of understanding if we do try to make our languages mutually understandable and actually communicate.

As to teleology, purpose, and mechanism, I will only remind you, in closing, of that old saucy question: Does the present exfoliate from the fullness of the past or is it sucked forward by the vacuity of the future?

WHITEHORN: Dr. Cameron quoted me to the effect that molecules do not have motives. I thought that he was misquoting me. It is apparently confirmed by Dr. Gerard that I said something like that. If I did, maybe it was useful. I recall some years ago reading what I thought was a very bright remark of Picasso. The function of the artist, he said, is not to tell the truth. The function of the artist is to tell a lie in such a way that the observer will become aware of a truth. I did not really mean to tell that lie. What I meant to say was that the persons who professionally deal with the interactions of molecules do not in their professional activities ordinarily invoke conceptions of motivation. This involves us in the whole nominalist philosophy; hence I will not carry it further.

ALEXANDER: I should like to speak briefly on three points: First, interpretation in psychology versus observation and explanation in natural science; second, teleology versus cause; and third, statistics.

Today in the scientific world there prevails an order of rank regarding observations. Because of the supposedly greater objectivity in observation and correlation in natural science, the subjective nature of interpretation puts psychology in the second rank. But there is a point which is constantly overlooked and which I do not think is fully recognized in the psychological study of behavior. Operationally the psychologist in comparison with the physicist has many disadvantages. But the psychologist has one tremendous advantage over the physicist; namely, the observer and the observed are of the same kind. What is the advantage of this? If you throw an object into a fluid, you know not whether it will sink or float. Only if you use very precise technics and make very careful measurements of its specific weight will you know the answer. In predicting whether the object will sink or float, the physicist cannot rely upon common sense; he must measure. In psychology, on the other hand, we start on a much higher common sense level. We know a great deal without any measurements, even without studying the individual particularly carefully. We can fairly well predict what another person will do. All average human beings can make predictions about the behavior of another human

being. School boys, for example, can predict with fair certainty whether a certain one of their schoolmates, if challenged, will run away or fight. If they were polled, the majority would make the correct prediction. They knew it. How do they know it? How can they predict with such certainty? They can do so because they know this particular one of their schoolmates from everyday contact. Because they know their own motivations, they can understand the other fellow's motivations. They know when they run away, when they fight; why they run away, why they fight. They can apply the knowledge about their own motivations to the other fellow; therefore they can predict his behavior. Thus in everyday life the use of motivational psychology, interpretive psychology, works very well; without it one could not survive in society.

Common sense psychology is so adequate that for practical purposes it needs no improvement. Physics, in contrast, is dependent upon measurement, and must be developed beyond common sense to be used for prediction. For example, we know much more with our common sense about personality than we know about brain function. Almost everyone here has made this point. Indeed, we know today a great deal more about personality than about common sense, but common sense psychology and scientific psychology are not too far apart as yet. I would propose a thesis therefore: In any field of human knowledge, the farther actual scientific knowledge gets away from and is contradictory to common sense information, the more that is indicative of the advancement of a science.

In physics, my hobby is modern cosmology. Now modern cosmology is completely contradictory to common sense. As a matter of fact, those things which are maintained in modern cosmology cannot even be imagined. From the point of view of common sense, curved space is an entirely impossible idea. It is farther removed from common sense than is the idea that the earth is a globe and not a disc which incidentally, is also completely removed from common sense. So in natural science we can say with great pride that we got away from common sense knowledge and that our contentions are contradictory to common sense. Is that also true for psychology? If it is, I would say that it speaks for some advancement in the very new field of motivational psychology.

Freud's contentions created a tremendous furor because they were contradictory to common sense. Consider, for instance, the notion that children have sexuality, want to kill their fathers and cohabit with their mothers. A simpler example is that of a person who is given a more responsible position or a raise in salary, who does a fine job, yet as a result develops a depression and tries to commit suicide. The common sense point of view would say that if he is promoted, he should be happy. This is true. But a person who has inferiority feelings may be upset by promotion because he may fear that he will not be able to live up to what is expected of him. But why should he try to commit suicide? We learn then that just before he was promoted, he had a dream about the death of the man next ahead of him, to whom he was greatly obligated. The dreamer's unconscious guilt motivated his suicidal wishes.

These are the new facts which dynamic psychology uses to explain behavior unintelligible to common sense. Applying only common sense psychology, we merely know that if a person commits a crime, he feels that he deserves punishment. Modern dynamic psychology extends this by saying, "You do not need to do something bad to feel guilty; the wish alone, even an unconscious wish, can provoke an amount of guilt that can make you feel that you can expiate this guilt only by killing yourself." The man who was promoted expressed his evil wish in a dream; he felt guilty about such a wish; he became depressed and turned against himself because he was promoted. An evil wish had become realized. Such behavior is completely contradictory to common sense. It is not until you fill the gap in what happens to this man by assumptions concerning his unconscious processes that you can understand his behavior.

Common sense knowledge in psychology is more highly developed than common sense knowledge in physics. The common sense knowledge of psychology has been improved by methodical observations and systematic reasoning so that we know today even more than is already known by good common sense. I have raised and discussed the point at issue because I sensed a sentiment among this group, including its ardent adherents of psychodynamics, that dynamic psychology really employs highly subjective and therefore inadequate methods. I suggest that systematic utilization of the interpretive method has a certain advantage over the physical methods. As yet interpretation is not quantitative; and it is here that tremendous changes will come. But it can fulfill such requirements of science as prediction and explanation of unexplainable facts. After all, physics too uses only correct reasoning, but it uses it more precisely than we do in everyday life.

I want to mention only one thing about teleology versus cause; namely, that here the difference between physiology and psychology is not very great. Freud's most basic principle is the stability principle, which is exactly the same as the homeostatic principle. A great part of human behavior can be explained by saying that the emotional homeostasis is disturbed by certain physiological disturbances of homeostasis. For example, one gets hungry. Peace of mind is disturbed by hunger, and the organs will react to restore the equilibrium which obtained before one became hungry. Certain suitable physiological processes take place to restore this equilibrium.

We use the same concepts in physiology. We explain the physiological chain of events which starts out with a disturbance in the homeostatic equilibrium, let us say, the need for oxygen or for energy from the outside world; from this all kinds of processes ensue until the equilibrium is restored. This explanation is the same both in physiology and in psychology.

We approach the matter of psychological equilibrium by two different methods because we are dealing with a human animal which is not only functioning but which at the same time subjectively perceives its functioning. In the case of an automobile climbing a hill which is too steep for its power, we note that the motor begins to miss and to overheat, and from these signs we can deduce that the hill is too steep for the power of the automobile. If, on the other hand, a human being is climbing a hill and gets tired and exhausted, he can tell you of his exhaustion; moreover he can tell you why he is climbing the hill. This the automobile cannot do. We deal here with two different kinds of apparatus: The one can talk and register what is going on in it; and the other, the automobile, which is a teleological mechanism in which every part is used for certain purposes, cannot talk, however, and cannot tell you what is going on, indeed, does not perceive what is going on. In psychology we take advantage of the fact that we deal with human beings who can tell us what is going on in them. This parallel approach is interesting. And we need not speak of rank in order. I do not think that one mechanism is more precise than the other.

Molecules, by the way, have vectors. They tend to go in certain directions; this is the same as saying that they have goals and motivations, except that the language is different. One can even say that a molecule tries very hard to go in a certain direction and that if there is an obstacle, it is deviated from its course but only to an extent which is absolutely necessary according to the parallelogram of forces. One can describe and account for the deviation in mathematical terms. We do the same in psychology in nonquantitative motivational terms.

Now about statistics. I do not criticize the statistical method; I think good statistics are fine; but I do criticize when statistics are loosely used, as is sometimes the case in the behavioral sciences and psychology. In the physical sciences the investigator can count well-defined similar entities; he can therefore confidently ascertain that a deviation could not have happened by chance. Counting comparable items, statistical methods provide a useful tool. But this situation does not always prevail in psychology, where we cannot count identical occurrences quite so easily.

Some years ago an investigator counting happy marriages put into one group marriages which he characterized as happy on the word of the persons being investigated.

He considered his group homogeneous because the members were similar on the basis of their professed marital happiness. But from my own practice I knew another statistic: that when a patient claims to have a perfect marriage, there is more likelihood that that marriage will be dissolved than when a patient admits to having marital difficulties. When a patient tells me about his troubles, I may ask: "What about your marriage?" He may reply: "Oh, my marriage is perfect. That is one thing at least that I cannot complain about." In my experience I have found that these perfect marriages have a much higher incidence of dissolution. Another patient replies: "My marriage is tough. My wife and I are troubled with quarreling." Such marriages very often survive. If my statistics were correct, those of the statistical investigator could not be correct; for he counted in the happily married group, marriages which were very different, some latently unhappy.

I would make a similar criticism of Kinsey's statistics. From computations on a marital group he concludes that 50 per cent of the women have had extramarital relations. He draws this conclusion by regarding as homogeneous the group reporting extramarital relations. Actually it is a most heterogeneous group. It contains girls who went with the same man for several years and yielded in one weak moment before marrying him. The group also contains women whose entire adult lives have been a continuous series of extramarital relations. Here are two entirely different phenomena; yet they are counted the same. Each member of this heterogeneous group is counted as similar. To give no consideration to the frequency of extramarital relations by members of these two heterogeneous groups is completely unsound. Obviously such a procedure can lead only to incorrect conclusions.

Statistics raise questions which require explanation, but of themselves they never explain anything. If we find, for example, as Dr. Richter has suggested, that more or fewer people can be dismissed from one hospital than from another, we do not know why. Maybe the hospital is so good that nobody wants to leave it. Or possibly the patients are not treated adequately. There may be scores of reasons and we do not know the answers. The observation itself is valid. It raises, however, all kinds of questions as to why and how, which have to be investigated and explained by other than statistical procedures. When a cast of the dice always produces a seven, it is a statistical fact. But not until the discovery by other means that the dice are loaded does this statistical figure have a meaning.

FELIX: I believe that Dr. Alexander is expecting too much of statistics. In my opinion statistics do only two things! They tell how many and the distribution of how many by whatever desired expression, whether it be mean, mode, or median; and the probability of something's happening by chance. From the latter it may be concluded or inferred that if a phenomenon happens regularly and often, there is some other factor more significant than chance operating.

Unlike Dr. Alexander, I do not object to Kinsey's data. I have had the opportunity to examine the data for both of his books during their preparation. My objections are to his conclusions and to some of the sweeping generalities which he has drawn. I might also object to one or two technical matters. But if Kinsey's data and methodology are correct, the answers derived are correct for the universe studied.

Another point to be emphasized is this: Statistics are no better than the questions which are asked. If the investigator does not know what to ask, he will not get a satisfactory answer. Hence, he has to have formulated clearly, exactly what he is going to count or measure. Then one thing more. He has to know how to ask the question after he knows what to ask. He also has to know how to record the answer because he can only count, measure, or otherwise treat statistically what his record shows. I learned these basic principles the hard way. At the end of two years on a project I found that I did not know enough about statistics to interpret my results. I could only write some general conclusions, some hunches, which I could not support. My data were so recorded that it was impossible for me to treat them statistically.

Statistics do not explain and cannot be expected to explain why something happens; they only state that it does happen. Well known in epidemiology is the historical incident during the cholera epidemic in London, when Snow, following a hunch, took the handle off the town pump and some time thereafter the epidemic began to decrease. If that had been repeated x number of times with the same results and if there had been no further reasoning, it could have been concluded that there was a positive relationship between town pump handles and cholera.

One kind of statistical treatment to which some object but which I think is highly useful is what is called nonsense correlations. These become extremely helpful when the investigator is casting about for something to grasp from which he can extrapolate and possibly create hypotheses. Sometimes these relationships are used to ridicule statistics. But these associations also have their uses. We found a very significant positive correlation between the number of chickens in farm yards and the incidence of schizophrenia in rural areas. This is an isolated piece out of a series, but it is a valid statistic. It does not explain anything by itself.

It seems to me that statistics can either help to answer certain questions, or what is of greater importance in the field of mental disease, they can point the way to asking other questions. Indeed, they frequently raise more questions than they help to solve. This can be a frustrating experience and a source of objection. We have been fortunate recently, at the Institute of Mental Health, in getting data from one hospital where a very careful cohort study of patients has been carried on until it is now in its thirty-ninth year. The investigators were unable to analyze the data for financial reasons, and we have undertaken the analysis for them. Our statistician came in the other day and said, "I have a series of questions to ask you." He said: "In going over the data of this hospital on first admissions at ages between 35 and 45, I find out that the length of stay of female patients admitted with the diagnosis of depression is identical with the length of stay of female patients admitted during the same period of time with a diagnosis of involutional melancholia. Are these the same things? Is that confused diagnosis? Does it offer a lead?" Then he asked, "Why is it that we find but few cases of admissions with the diagnosis of schizophrenia in patients under 15 years of age, but when they are admitted, they have a longer average length of stay than any other group of patients admitted with the diagnosis of schizophrenia? Why is it that the older a patient at first admission, the shorter the length of stay before discharge? Why is it that among patients admitted with the diagnosis of schizophrenia, the length of stay for males is longer than for females of the same age group?" I bring up these questions because, it seems to me, they touch on sociology, psychology, and many of the fundamental biological sciences.

Just to point up this matter further, I was asked: "Why is it that what happens to the schizophrenic patient in a hospital continuously for more than two years seems to have so much less effect on the outcome of his illness than what happens during the first year to two years of his hospitalization?" These are not answers to questions. Rather they are significant questions which lead to other questions which can also be treated statistically. I always feel as though one of my most reliable assistants is being maligned when I hear statistics inappropriately criticized and misunderstood.

ALEXANDER: My objection was not to statistics. What I want are good statistics. My only contention was that statistics today in the behavioral sciences are mostly applied to cases that have nothing to do with each other. This application is wrong statistics. Also I do not believe that Kinsey's facts are correct, and his interpretations are obviously wrong. I think that his statistical data are incorrect because he committed exactly the error of counting categories which contain heterogeneous elements; he counts them as if they were the same and then draws conclusions from them.

FELIX: Kinsey was counting the number of women in his sample who had had premarital intercourse. He was not counting those who got a little emotional the night before their wedding; or those who got a little emotional the night that they graduated from high school and then had relations every week thereafter with a different man. Let me repeat that he was counting only the number of women who had had intercourse before they were married.

I have had data brought to me which has been rated by categories as to its "goodness." When qualitative or value judgments like these are applied to data, I cannot treat them. I can count black, green, white, yellow; I can count quarts, pints, feet and inches, not all together but in their own categories. I think that our problem is to reduce our data to a countable unit and then treat it statistically until we can form hypotheses.

LANDIS: Some years ago a young psychiatrist who had just finished his psychoanalysis discussed with me some ideas which grew out of his analytic experiences. He pointed out that during his analysis there had been possibilities of differences in the interpretation of his dream material. He was often uncertain which possible interpretation was of significance. After some discussion we decided that it might be worth while to do a relevant experiment on this problem. From the psychoanalytic literature we selected reports of dreams which seemed to us to be clear illustrations of apparent motivation or of wish fulfillment and which had been interpreted in this light. As subjects we utilized 10 voluntary patients resident at the Psychiatric Institute who had not been (and were not at the time being) psychoanalyzed. An additional 10 patients who had been psychoanalyzed (probably unsuccessfully) and who were also resident at the Institute were utilized. Each of the selected dreams was read to these 20 patients at various intervals and they were asked: "Now this is a dream which another patient had. If you had had this dream, what would you think it meant?" We were seeking the similarity and differences in interpretations from unanalyzed patients. Over the period of several months we collected quite a few responses. With this collection of responses in hand, the problem of proper classification and evaluation of them then confronted us. It seemed to us that some outstanding psychoanalyst might be willing to assist us at this point, so we discussed the matter with Dr. A. A. Brill. When we told him what we had done and what we desired to accomplish, he was at first practically speechless. Then he pointed out very emphatically that this kind of study could not and should not be done, that it was unfair to the patient and to analytic theory, and that it could only lead to meaningless confusion.

Thinking that perhaps Dr. Brill was a little emotional about our experiment, we next consulted Dr. Smith Ely Jelliffe. He was more calm in his response to our request, but he insisted that this was not a legitimate way to approach the interpretation of dreams. Essentially he said that this was not a valid approach to this kind of a problem, that we had completely misunderstood the meaning of dream interpretation, and that our approach was irrelevant to the essential problem. Hence, we concluded that we could not obtain assistance from the psychoanalysts.

My colleague, still undeterred, next presented a preliminary report of this work to the Department of Psychology at Columbia University for possible acceptance as a thesis topic for a Ph.D. degree. The Department, after due consideration, decided that no thesis could be made from such material since it consisted of interpretations which could not be validated. The data were then filed in a wastebasket. I submit that this is an example of the all too frequent outcome of attempts which have been made to apply an experimental approach to psychodynamic concepts.

WHITEHORN: While Dr. Kubie was pointing up what I thought was an admirable orientation to where the need and the affector mechanisms became linked sometimes by mechanisms of great symbolic importance and sometimes by fairly simple physiological mechanisms, I was reminded of some experimental work relating heart rate to muscular exertion which I did some years ago. I think it points out this linking in a rather neat fashion.

One of the observations was that in many instances the heart begins to accelerate before the physical activity starts. This is most dramatic when observed in a sleeping subject. After some experience in watching the apparatus recording the heart rate, the observer comes to know that it is now time to look because the subject is going to move. Before the subject moves, his heart rate shows acceleration. This is a phenomenon which has been observed by others too. It raises very interesting questions, particularly of this character: Is there some emotional excitation preceding the movement? Is there a state of uneasiness? This kind of a problem appears in a study which Dr. Gantt and I have been making with dogs. We have been seeking to discriminate, if possible, states of eager expectation from apprehensive expectation by descriptive means. The heart rate appears to be one of the items in such a discrimination. Here too it is possible to note quite marked acceleration of heart rate preceding motor activities in the so-called questioning reflex.

This phenomenon imposes a kind of problem not readily disposed of by saying that all approaches are all right. For then the problem is reduced to a specific crucial question: Just exactly how are the components interrelated? The burden of the question is this: It is desirable, first of all, to agree that all approaches are good and that one does not displace the other. But it is then necessary to point out that in concrete situations the question of the manner in which the parts fit in with each other must be confronted. How can ideational processes derived from one type of study fit in practically with ideas of another set of workers so that together they can constructively fill a gap?

KUBIE: I hope that a full understanding of how our symbolizing processes constitute a bridge between body and mind, and between the inner and outer world will clarify the interrelations between levels of organization, and may give the neurophysiologist a tool with which he can coordinate his physiological experiments and our psychological observations.

COBB: Did I understand you rightly to remark that symbolization was the unique possession of man, which separates man from lower animals?

KUBIE: In a moment of enthusiasm I may well have overstated the case. Actually this, of course, is a relative difference. The degree of symbolic function of which man is capable is infinitely greater than that of which even the higher apes are capable. This is a difference in degree which means a difference in kind. I would not, however, state it as an absolute.

COBB: Since Dr. Kubie brings up the relation of stimulus to the central nervous system and to the soma, it seems to me that the topic leads to consideration of steps. In this it would be worth while to bring in the thinking of the neurophysiologists by asking them about the first step on the stimulus end.

LINDSLEY: I have an idea which possibly ties in with the relationship of the availability of information on the outside to the organism; that is, how certain kinds of stimuli actually do have access to the cortex or higher brain centers, and what factors appear neurophysiologically perhaps to limit the intake of information. Here I was thinking particularly of the concept which, I think, originated with Drs. Bishop and Bartley; namely, the possibility that excitability cycles are associated with brain rhythm and that the alternating aspect of the phenomenon limits in a time dimension the intake of information. The time sequence of events and the timing of excitability of central processes are important. The matter of misinterpretation of signals from the outside, particularly in connection with hallucination, but perhaps also in connection with other matters which are not hallucinatory, has already been mentioned. When we attempt to define consciousness or unconsciousness, I wonder to what extent we are talking about matters of perceptual discrimination, at least in the elementary phase. And then I wonder to what extent the inability to make adequate discrimination may determine the kind of response or behavior that subsequently ensues. It seems to me that there are aspects of nervous system function which might, at one time or another, tend to make signals from the outside be misinterpreted because of the time at which they occur. In other words, there may be factors in the nervous system which are not limiting the intake of information as they should, or at other times there may be factors on the response end which, because of feedback, make it impossible for the individual to interpret properly the kinds of stimulus settings in which he finds himself. It is that kind of consideration that might help us to get back even to the effect of psychosocial factors. For as one looks at the picture ontogenetically and developmentally—the progression through elementary discriminations, up to concept formations, symbolic formulations, and the final tie-in of these with the larger social frame of reference in which they occur—one realizes that the stimulus setting and the problem become so complex that they are much more readily misinterpreted.

chapter 11

Next Steps for Further
Interrelation, Convergence,
and Integration

◆ ◆

REDLICH: In a short time we will be thinking about what we got out of this Conference. Often enough this is a somewhat depressive feeling; but I always feel that if there has been one good paper, one good thought, a conference has been worth while. In the present instance I believe that there has been more than one good paper and one good thought for all of us. It might be worth while now to pull together the various thoughts and ideas in terms of further interrelation and convergence and integration. More simply stated, we should perhaps think about what we have acquired from each other in the way of theory, method, and the delineation of problems. For a while during the discussion it looked as though there would be one camp for, and another against, statistics. This threat of division dissolved when we saw that what we want is good statistics, just as we want good interpretation in psychodynamics.

Now we come to consider how we are going to implement some of our approximations in actual work. After all, when we leave here, we hope that some of the thoughts which have been brought out will be put to work, that the Conference will lead to actual collaborative, interdisciplinary work.

So far, most of us, particularly the psychoanalysts amongst us, have been lonely cave dwellers, never working with any other person. That we have come out of our caves and are working with a fellow scientist is a very new experience and enterprise. Maybe the greatest difficulty is not so much in listening to other theories, thinking about them, borrowing something according to our needs, as it is really working with other people. It means more than overcoming intellectual or emotional blocks. Research is a lonely occupation. There is a tremendous amount of narcissism in it; hence, to admit that somebody else has something worth while in research, to work with him and forget about one's own narcissim is quite the most difficult thing of all, particularly if it involves other professions, other disciplines with other working habits. It is a tremendous task. I know this from my own work with social scientists at Yale. They have completely different work habits than I have. They spend full time on the project; I have to snatch an hour here and there. This is my way of working because I have clinical obligations. But the difference annoys them. There are also difficulties of status. They are scientists; we are clinicians. Whether we can overcome these emotional difficulties or not will decide whether we are going to do or not do something, whether we stay by ourselves.

A Neurophysiologist Looks Ahead

GEORGE H. BISHOP

I should like to discuss the question of how one specific branch of neural function can be associated or integrated with other branches. How can we integrate or correlate the results of the science of neurophysiology with those of the sciences of mental behavior? What is the relation on an operational basis between organic neurology and, may I say, mental neurology?

In the first place, to me correlation means a one-to-one comparison. What does the neurophysiologist have in units to compare with the psychiatrist's units? I think that it is obvious that neither has anything. The psychiatrist has nothing that corresponds to a nerve impulse. The neurophysiologist has nothing that corresponds to an idea. To get around that dilemma is a bit complicated. It is necessary to make an assumption that there is such a thing in mental activity as a neuronal unit, an impulse. Do impulses correspond in any way to mental activity? I do not know.

In discussing mentation and nerve impulses we are talking about functions of the same tissue, neural tissue. Let us make an assumption that if we knew enough, every mental activity could be represented in terms of nerve impulses in extremely complex networks of nerve cells; and that impulses really represent one aspect of the nerve cell function while mental activity represents another. In that case all our comparisons, our correlations, would come out neurologically in patterns of nerve impulses. Obviously the neurophysiologist is still working on one neuron or on a small sample of neurons; he has found what happens, for instance, in dendrites as compared to the cell body. He is still at that level, whereas the psychologist and sociologist are talking about a behavioral pattern in complex animal civilization. These are the two extremes in the range of neural activity. Concerning the solution of this puzzle, I can only state an ambition and an ideal which certainly cannot at present be fulfilled. It is that some day, by some manner, a neurophysiologist and a neurologist will be able to study a complex enough group of nerve cells, observe their pattern, and find how they behave; and that then a psychiatrist or psychologist will be able to find a small portion of mental behavior that will correspond to the neurophysiological pattern. Can we break down mental behavior into small enough units so that it will be possible for a neurophysiologist to find a corresponding group of units of the same level of complexity? We certainly cannot do it now. It seems to me that if we are going to make a one-to-one correlation between these two branches of neurological science, i.e., neurophysiology and mental behavior, it will have to be between their simplest components at the lowest level of complexity.

We have to consider and be prepared to meet the contingency, however, that this correlation is not possible in fundamental units. I do not know that mental behavior actually is a matter of one cell acting after another in a network. I am not sure that nerve impulses are anything more than the carriers of something between cells. Perhaps the state of the cell in some other respect altogether is the background of mental behavior. It may be that the nerve axons are simply the carriers of the impulses from the periphery, representing the environmental influence on the center; and of impulses to the periphery, expressing themselves in overt behavior. Maybe what happens in terms of mental behavior is not a mass of impulses at all. In that case we will be foiled. We may be thwarted if we try to make the one-to-one correlation between patterns of neural impulses and patterns of mental behavior. But we will never know until we try.

I suppose that if we ever approach that problem, we will have to go through the experimental psychologists. They are nearer the nerve physiologist than is the psychiatrist because they are dealing with animal experimentation which tries to transpose the behavior of animals into terms of neurological behavior, such as impulses and circuits. That is a natural approach from neurophysiology over into psychiatry and psychology. However, suppose that this correlation is not possible, that our impulses are simply one of the determinants among others, such as steady states, chemical states, mentation; then we have to resign ourselves to talking about, not a one-to-one correlation between neurological behavior and mental behavior, but rather a neurology of mental behavior. By that I mean: No matter how complex the behavior is, how complex the environment is, every bit of information that comes into the brain, into consciousness, must come in a code. Except for some hormonal and physiological chemical effects, the code carrying the messages appears to the neurophysiologist entirely in terms of nerve impulses in axons, not even nerve cells but axons. With all the information carried over telegraph wires

into the center, we do not know what is going on there. In that same way the neurology of mental behavior would be the study of this unknown central activity in terms of the impulses that go into it and come out of it.

We know that the derangement of impulses that go in can affect behavior, can distort it, can make the behavior abnormal. We know also that the impulses that come out will be indicative of the state of the center. So from external causes and effects we may learn indirectly about what lies between in the neurology of behavior, rather than its essential character. Neither of these possibilities has ever been explored to a satisfactory conclusion. I would not say that there are any immediate prospects of ultimate success. But if the correlation upon which this Conference is focused is to be found—the correlation between neuron physiology, organic neurology, and mental behavior—it seems to me that these are considerations that must be taken into account.

A Psychologist's Views on Next Steps

H. E. KING

We have heard statements on the positions of different schools of thought on the etiology of mental disease, comments on interdoctrinal agreement and disagreement, and evidence of the compatible relationship between the data drawn from different schools of thought in certain types of inquiry. All this is basic to the main purpose of the present meeting which we are to consider now: the suggesting of steps we may take in the future to facilitate the correlation of the body of knowledge determined by each school of thought, and the discussion of plans calculated to increase the fund of evidence of the coordination of data produced by different approaches to our common problem.

The recognition which has been given to

the continued need to attack the problem analytically, by restricting our individual observations to a controllable number of variables, indicates that each is a valid approach; and that no one approach has so demonstrated its fruitfulness that we are prepared to abandon other approaches to the problem at the present time. In view of this, our task in the discussion of ways to improve the synthesis of knowledge from different sources appears to be more one of determining a framework for the correlation and integration of data than of making an attempt at convergence in the sense of fusion of objectives or of methods of inquiry.

In many ways this task is not unlike the situation met in attempting to achieve broad synthesis in presenting the results of interdisciplinary research. The value of attacking certain problems central to several scientific disciplines by a combined effort employing the investigative methods of each is by now familiar to us all. The problems of integration which beset such efforts are often those which concern us here, and we may usefully draw upon this model both in formulating questions for discussion and in seeking a solution of our own interdoctrinal problems. We might also profitably follow this model in action, in certain instances, by organizing interdoctrinal research around a central problem by employing the investigative methods of the several schools of thought represented here. There are precedents for this, but they are remarkably few.

Interdisciplinary integration has found that its primary need is for improved communication. Not only do the objectives and methods employed by diverse scientific disciplines differ, but the manner of expression of abstract ideas is so different as to cause great difficulty in understanding between groups. There is, as a rule, relatively less difficulty met in understanding the concrete descriptions of known events than in understanding postulated unknowns in theory and in model construction. How similar is our own problem! Such faulty communication appears to root in lack of knowledge and human frailty. We can do little to remedy the latter so that we may all be expert in all ways, but we may well undertake the discussion of ways and means of improving intercommunication among the groups represented here by increasing the availability of essential knowledge.

Other needs have also been manifest in such work, and lessons have been learned which may well be incorporated into the discussion of our own future course: the matter of necessary "sacrifice," for example, and how it should not be confused with the compromise of objectives. If we are to achieve much in the way of integration of our separate schools of thought, we will be required to make an active effort and necessarily suffer some loss of time, perhaps of prestige; for one has the additional task of achieving the interrelation of his findings

with those of other groups. It would, for example, be simpler for the psychotherapist not to trouble to make his record of therapeutic success and failure available to the psychologist, but doing so may be the only way to test the validity of certain assumptions. As a corollary, the psychologist may invest much time and gain little in seeking answers to questions he himself might raise by applying his measurement technics in investigative work of interest to the psychotherapist; but again, it may be the only way to test the validity of certain assumptions. The need for improved criteria in all of the behavioral sciences becomes especially clear when an attempt is made to match their data with those of the biological sciences. Also, it has been learned that a large number of purely practical problems have been found to be of greater relative importance than have the theoretical differences which exist between disciplines, most of which would find a ready parallel in interdoctrinal research. Examples are: the scheduling of time requirements; problems of human working relationships; the fact that medicolegal restrictions, as well as scientific considerations, enter into the planning and carrying out of combined work. Several of the lessons learned in such work also seem to have obvious implications for the planning of interdoctrinal research as well. For example, there is the need to reach a clear understanding as to the order of problems for investigation: which are proper choices for combined investigation and which might be undertaken best by individual study. Furthermore, there is the absolute necessity of making a small pilot study and evaluating its results before bringing to bear the more cumbersome and expensive machinery of full-scale interdisciplinary investigation. In brief, we face, in attenuated form, most of the problems met when different sciences attempt the intercorrelation of methods and results, and the errors and advantages known to occur in such work furnish a large number of topics we might profitably discuss today.

Perhaps making one broad classification of our subject matter might be productive in designating where further interrelationship is possible and should be actively pursued, and where a more fundamental cleavage exists which appears to be healthy and which, at least at present, may be tolerated. It seems clear that the doctrines represented here, although all begin with disordered behavior as a starting point, fall into two broad groupings: those allied to "biology" and those allied to "sociology," these terms being used in the broadest sense. If this is a valid classification, would it not be logical to seek, as a first step, the closer interrelation of the more similar groups in terms of this division? It has been pointed out that each science tends to find the most satisfying explanations of its own emergent phenomena in terms of the laws and principles of the next most immediate scientific antecedents: thus, the chemist is fond of explanations of chemical phenomena in terms of the laws of physics; the biologist always points with pride to the chemical bases of biologic structure and function; the psychologist is never happier than when he can find the roots of psychologic phenomena in biology. If the schools of thought on etiology of mental disease are basically linked to the two sciences, biology and sociology, we thus inherit the traditional difficulties of cross-assimilation of these disparate scientific groups. Might we not, then, stand to profit by initially making our greatest efforts at integration among the doctrines related to biology on the one hand and sociology on the other, with the hope that each such task would be simpler than an initial total integration? And with the air thus cleared, would we not stand to make a more satisfactory total correlation and integration of all the available data eventually?

Whatever direction our efforts may take for the interrelation of data from the different schools of thought on the etiology of mental disease, two procedures suggest themselves as basic: methods for the improved availability of knowledge of the data of each group, and an increased effort to form the bond of truly scientific kinship of differing opinion by improved adherence to the tenets of scientific method in both descriptive and experimental aspects of all of our observations. The need for greater interchange of knowledge and improvement of its basic quality for communication have been mentioned before. Proper interrelation depends upon adequate knowledge of what there is to be integrated. We may safely state that any practical step taken to further knowledge of one another's point of view is fundamental to grouping our efforts into any broader pattern of integration. We may undertake in the general discussion to identify the most adequate and most practical means of approaching this objective: the launching of interdoctrinal programs of research, the holding of symposia including proponents of different points of view on basic topics (e.g., instinct, drive), programs of exchange lectureship or the broadening of training courses in psychiatry to include faculty members with differing "doctrinal" approaches. There appears less obvious need for discussion of how each group may improve its adherence to the tenets of scientific method, for the necessary standards are well known; and most defections result from difficulties in handling the subject matter. Nevertheless, improved integration and, in fact, the very transmission of knowledge and basic data hinges upon the degree of scientific efficiency achieved; this must necessarily form the backbone of any scheme proposed for interdoctrinal coordination and integration.

A Psychodynamicist Projects

HENRY W. BROSIN

There are many promising interdisciplinary investigations now in progress; hence I am faced with the difficult problem of mentioning only a few at the expense of neglecting others which may well be more important. Fortunately, some of them have already been cited. I will list five or six areas in which investigations will, I believe, prove productive in contributing to the confluence of the various existing views.

The first of the important areas for the future is better study of the epidemiology of mental disease and specifically its incidence. There have been numerous surveys and estimates of the incidence of mental disease in a given population, but the numerous variables furnish ample reason for caution in interpreting the results. I will refer to the studies of Goldhamer and Marshall [4] who made a careful comparison of nineteenth century admissions to a hospital with those of the twentieth century. They found no essential difference when proper allowances were made for age, severity of illness, sex, and so forth. They conclude (p. 92): " . . . there has been no long-term increase during the last century in the incidence of the psychoses of early and middle life." They are careful to point out that this does not take into account the psychoneuroses or exclude changes in some organic diseases, such as general paresis. They comment that (p. 93): "These short-term fluctuations in admission rates may represent a true change in incidence, simply a change in the rate of hospitalization, or a combination of these two." "Nonetheless," they say, "the experience of military psychiatry leaves no doubt that there are environmental changes and life circumstances that can have a very marked effect on the incidence of mental disorders."

From my own experience on two visits to Japan and Korea during the last two years, it has been most impressive to learn that the incidence of psychoses has been remarkably stable; namely, about 2.5 per 1,000 troop strength per annum during the entire Korean campaign to date. When these figures are subjected to closer study, it may be possible to show that, while acute episodes are more numerous during active phases of warfare, the incidence of the more stable chronic psychoses may not vary significantly from comparable civilian populations. This would seem to be a most important area for interdisciplinary investigation. It is not easy to assign a single most important interpretation to this phenomenon. If this surmise should prove to be reasonably accurate, perhaps the results would argue for constant genetic factors. The findings would offer no proof or direct evidence for this view. They might only mean that the sociopsychological factors predisposing to mental disease are more constant and more profound than they appear to be at the present time.

Goldhamer and Marshall, in a summary, sharpen the problem (p. 97):

The reader will scarcely need to be warned that the foregoing discussion [on the relation of our data to the several etiological points of view] has attempted only to indicate, in a very brief and oversimplified manner, the range of implications that the present research provides. A single study, such as the one reported here, can help to sharpen the formulation of alternatives, narrow the range of possible solutions to the theoretical problems at issue, and indicate promising directions for further research. Since the secular trend of admission rates has remained constant over the past 100 years, intensive research on short-term fluctuations is especially indicated. This research will first need to determine whether these fluctuations represent true changes in incidence. If this is found to be so, it should then be possible to relate these rate changes to the specific alterations in life circumstances associated with the periods of changing rates. This would remove analysis from the level of the rather vague ascription of causation to broad social developments associated with the "growth of civilization" and lead to the analysis of the more concrete changes in social life that characterize the short-term periods under study. Only the combined and continuing research of laboratory, clinical and social psychiatry can eventually enable us to discard those views that are inconsistent with observed fact. To this process the present report contributes the finding that, whatever may be the causal agents of the functional psychoses, they will almost certainly have to be sought for among those life conditions that are equally common to American life of a hundred years ago and today.

The current population studies which are being conducted by Alexander Leighton in Stirling County, Canada, and by Erich Lindemann at Wellesley, Massachusetts, are excellent examples of the progress being made at the interdisciplinary level on basic research into the epidemiology of mental illness. In Pittsburgh we are trying to understand the family dynamics of the population around our Arsenal Park Health Center. Our goals are less ambitious than those mentioned above. Other projects have been described by Dr. Felix and his associate, Dr. Kramer [3].

The second of the large frontier areas that I think are worthy of interdisciplinary development in the future concerns the correlation of biochemical and psychological factors in the study of organic disease processes. Dr. Gerard stated that it is entirely possible that the solution to the problems of schizophrenia will be found in cell chemistry. I should like to point out that there are now interdisciplinary studies of potential value for the elucidation of the interaction of man's physical organism and his adaptive mechanisms to his physical and conscious environment. For example, Mirsky and his co-workers [8] have used excretion of pepsinogen in urine, the uropepsin, as an index of the influence of various life situations on gastric secretion. They have found that persons with duodenal ulcer have a greater rate of pepsinogen excretion in the urine than do persons without any gastrointestinal disturbances. Conversely, the pepsinogen excretion by patients with pernicious anemia is negligible. Such studies suggest the possibility of detecting susceptible individuals long before the active disease process appears, and of further identi-

fication of the factors which cause the appearance of the overt disease. It is not unlikely that susceptibility to other diseases may likewise be determined, especially in hypertension and diabetes. I refer to the Grinker [10] studies with hippuric acid. These potentials may be present from birth and may not be obvious until middle life. But the demonstration of their presence is also an advance in our conception of the etiology of mental disease; for some of these disorders may be linked to the gross psychoses. These studies, together with those of Benedek and Rubenstein, Margolin and Kaufman, Wolff and Wolf, provide a highly encouraging demonstration that the Freudian model for the ego and instinct hypothesis continues to be useful for correlating human behavior with physiological experimentation.

The third area which I regard as holding tremendous promise for the future is that of developmental processes and learning in infancy and childhood. The mother-child relation has now come to the forefront as a result of the work of David Levy, René Spitz, Bowlby and Robertson, Ribble, Putnam, Rank, Mahler, Fries, Senn, and others. The optimistic hope seems justified. As an increasing number of skilled workers develop new technics for investigating this exciting field, they will lay the foundation for long-term personality studies that will lift us out of some of the ignorance now surrounding the developmental process in both normal and psychotic persons. The fact that J. P. Scott of the Jackson Laboratories, Bar Harbor, Maine, has been able to reproduce the results of human maternal deprivation in pure-bred strains of dogs illustrates another possible means of verifying clinical hypotheses.

The fourth area which I believe may well contribute importantly to the interdisciplinary approach is that of statistics in clinical psychiatry and the projective technics. One of the most gratifying evidences of increased skill in dealing with complex variables is the realization by statisticians that the kind of statistical analysis employed must be appropriate to the nature of the material. This is most clearly seen in the exposition by Lee Cronbach [1] with respect to the Rorschach variables. There is much reason to hope that appropriately used factor analysis will be helpful in distinguishing the clinical syndromes, although the early attempts by Degan [2] in 1952 and Moore [9] in 1931 were not highly successful. I would say that the excellent use of factor analysis by L. L. Thurstone and Ward C. Halstead in identifying key processes furnishes hope that the method can be employed with equal productivity on similar experimental problems. The large number of patients with lobotomies, lobectomies, or other cerebral damage should make available abundant material for this purpose.

A fifth area which raises expectations of fruitfulness comprises long-term studies of both normal and disturbed persons. We are gradually accumulating an impressive group of patients who over a period of years show the ability to be sick with more than one disease. In some patients this metamorphosis takes a dramatic form in which the patient is relieved of his colitis, his asthma, or his neurodermatitis if he becomes schizophrenic. I now have records on more than twenty of these patients. Again, the patient may regain his earlier somatic disorders when the psychotic process is in abeyance. Close inspection shows that normal people have various patterns for disposing of their energies, and that these patterns are recognizable in terms of defenses against anxiety, guilt, or depression. Karl Menninger in his book, *Man Against Himself,* [7] gives examples in a wide variety of cases. The growing comprehension of the adaptive mechanism in such patients, the apparent equivalence of these widely different processes, and the nature of the equilibrium in the disposition of energies will give us a much better picture of the nature of symptom formation.

The sixth area which I think is going to blossom under an interdisciplinary approach is that of the defense mechanisms, such as the ego defenses under stress. In keeping with what has just been said about the apparent equivalence of widely varying types of behavior and in view of the recent interest in military psychiatry, I believe that prisoners of war will provide clinical material for new patterns at the conscious and preconscious levels of behavior. Simmel [11] described the transformations of the ego in the process of a civilian's becoming a soldier, and more recently attention was given to the reconversion process. In recent accounts of prisoners of war, we have a rich material for the systematic study of how the Communists were able to "brain-wash," or how in the much more subtle problem of "brain-changing," they were able to induce some individuals to the views of the Communists. Of course they gained their ends by a clever and consistent use of isolation, threats, promises, indoctrination, interrogation, "self-criticism," group participation, the writing of biographies, and so forth. I want to call attention to a book by Edward Hunter [5] that was issued in Tokyo just a few weeks ago called, *Brain-Washing in Red China.* Mr. Hunter is a newspaper man, an old China hand; but he has much interesting psychological material in his book. I would say that in some cases it appears that the selection of the victims was highly intuitive, and that the methods of persuasion are much more subtle than appears at first glance. We can hope that our government will encourage a goodly number of our very best social scientists to work on this problem. I think that there are many principles to be learned there. It seems to me that a clinician who has worked with a variety of mentally ill patients, especially in the field of the organic brain disease, can detect many similarities between the defense systems used by our PW's and those found in patients with an organically damaged cortex.

Now I would like to turn to a topic already discussed by several speakers who have indicated that the problems of interdisciplinary research may be predominantly interpersonal rather than truly ideological. I will begin, however, with the bread-and-butter question: how to get more research workers, especially psychiatrists, into the field. So, I will discuss recruitment. There is a recent book out which indicates that investigators are attracted to research and enlisted by teachers who may not themselves be either highly original or unusual producers, but who seem to have the properties of being good teachers, who have conviction and enthusiasm, and who can spend much time with students.

It occurs to me that perhaps many of us in psychiatry do not engage in this kind of activity enough and therefore do not set a good example; or if you please, do not provide a sufficient object for identification. The problems of selection of candidates, as you know, are very intricate. We have no rationale or adequate means other than the pragmatic test, even after many, many extensive efforts during the last ten years. Another question is the nature of the indoctrination and training which makes men interested and helps them stay in the field of research. As you know, we have no real knowledge of teaching formal research methods, and most original workers would pooh-pooh the idea completely. Many highly gifted men whom I know say that this is nonsense. They hold that a good investigator is born and not made; and they admonish, "Stop wasting your time examining the configuration of the dynamics of an investigator."

In addition to this problem of indoctrination and training, I want seriously to raise another question: After scientific investigators are placed in a learning situation or in a university department, how is high productivity maintained? There are men in this room who know a great deal about this problem from personal experience. They have more intimate information than others who do not see patients. I refer to Drs. French, Alexander, and Binger, who have related incidents which have been very helpful. Dr. Kubie has published an article in two parts on this general theme [6].

These might be called problems in human engineering or in group dynamics, but it seems to me that they are also very serious problems in individual dynamics. There are many men who apparently work consistently during a lifetime because of high unconscious interest in a particular field. That field may be the ant or the butterfly, or may be mixing water in various forms, or electricity. There is no question that the motivations are fed from wellsprings which have little to do with the initial introduction into the subject or the social supports that feed it from then on. There are many sociological factors that determine occupational choice. But I am not prepared to supply the answers; rather I hope that my questions will stimulate the production of valuable information about how we can accelerate interdisciplinary learning, not at the ideological, but at the working level. Then we would actually have researchers doing this fine work in which all of us believe. I would venture to say that among the small group here many of us have had training, if not mastery, in at least two disparate fields of endeavor. I should like to ask: As a very essential part of the preparation of a scientist to work fruitfully in interdisciplinary work, does he not have to begin with a thorough acquaintance in at least two fields in order to be able to make himself at home in a project requiring teamwork? Dr. Erich Lindemann stated that he acquired a new skill at fifty; that is, he became a social scientist. I am reminded of Helmholtz, who at fifty learned calculus and at fifty-two was writing highly original equations in electronics with the aid of calculus.

A second thought about preparation for interdisciplinary work is that men might be trained not only with different skills but also with an interest in a common subject organized around concepts which are useful in both areas under consideration.

Concerning the essential conditions for high productivity, a question which I have already raised here can suggest two possible important factors. One is that there is an organizing principle—if you like, a conscience, an ideal, or something of the sort —in men who work persistently in research over a long period of years. They are different from the kind of men who receive a great deal of training in very good places, and then at the age of thirty-five to forty seek to retreat into administrative work and suburbia. Some of our finest psychiatric investigators retreat into doing therapy. Something happens which causes them to fail to fulfill the promise of their youth in research.

Another principle which I think should be emphasized is that of the potential for growth, for becomingness. The finest statement of this general principle that I know of is in the biography of Beethoven by Sullivan [12], an engineer and critic. It contains a concept about the meaning of the continuation of a man's ability to learn with an ever-expanding horizon as he advances through the years. It is a wonderful image. I think that it has some relation to the ability to carry on in this highly charged

field of so-called interdisciplinary work, where it is so easy to find many destructive forces at work, to lose one's identity, and to become threatened. In fact, my key notion after many years of living among interdisciplinary projects is that the people most responsible have the obligation to prevent the participants in interdisciplinary teamwork from destroying each other.

REFERENCES

1. CRONBACH, LEE J. Statistical methods applied to Rorschach scores: A review. Psychol. Bull., 1949, 46: 393–429.
2. DEGAN, JAMES W. *Dimensions of Functional Psychosis.* Richmond, Va.: Wm. Byrd Press, 1952.
3. FELIX, R. H., and KRAMER, M. Research in epidemiology of mental illness. Reprint No. 3155, Pub. Health Rep., Federal Security Agency, Feb. 1952, 67: 152–160.
4. GOLDHAMER, HERBERT, and MARSHALL, ANDREW W. *Psychosis and Civilization: Two Studies in the Frequency of Mental Disease.* Glencoe, Ill.: The Free Press, 1953.
5. HUNTER, EDWARD. *Brain-Washing in Red China.* New York: The Vanguard Press, 1951.
6. KUBIE, LAWRENCE S. Some unsolved problems of the scientific career. American Scientist, Oct. 1953, 41: 596–613; Jan. 1954, 42: 104–112.
7. MENNINGER, K. A. Man Against Himself. New York: Harcourt, Brace, 1938.

8. MIRSKY, I. A., KAPLAN, S., and BROHKAHN, R. H. "Pepsinogen Excretion (Uropepsin) as an Index of the Influence of Various Life Situations on Gastric Secretion," in *Life Stress and Bodily Disease.* Proc. A. Res. Nerv. & Ment. Dis., 1950, 29: 628–646.
9. MOORE, ELIZABETH SKELDING. *The Development of Mental Health in a Group of Young Children; An Analysis of Factors in Purposeful Activity.* Iowa City: University of Iowa, 1931.
10. PERSKY, H., GRINKER, R. R., MIRSKY, I. A., and GAMM, S. R. "Life Situations, Emotions and the Excretion of Hippuric Acid in Anxiety States," in *Life Stress and Bodily Disease.* Proc. A. Res. Nerv. & Ment. Dis. 1950, 29: 297–306.
11. SIMMEL, E. War neuroses. IN: Psychoanalysis Today. (S. Lorand, Ed.) New York: International Universities Press, 1944. Pp. 227–248.
12. SULLIVAN, JOHN W. N. *Beethoven.* London: Jonathan Cape, New Library, 1937.

Opportunities for the
Psychosocial Approach

ROBERT J. WEIL

Like Dr. Erich Lindemann I am a latecomer in the field of social psychiatry. Three years ago I participated as the psychiatric team member on a social research project. A sociologist, a psychologist, and I studied some of the relationships of culture and mental diseases. One of our tasks was the study of the prevalence of mental diseases amongst the Hutterites, a Protes-

tant religious sect which lives in communal villages in the midwestern United States and Canada.

Our study was planned as an interdisciplinary research project. From the beginning we were aware of the inherent communication difficulties among three representatives of different disciplines in which each individual member had very little experience with another's specialty and the total team insufficient precedents to guide them. In an adventurous mood I accepted a role for which I had no training whatsoever. In my innocent ignorance I left the protective walls of an office and hospital and assumed the function of an amateur anthropologist. The ultimate aim of our epidemiological study was to find a possible new avenue to the understanding of etiological factors of mental disease.

The interrelations of our three disciplines, the convergence of our views, and the integration of the products of our individual perceptions became a real problem once contact with the Hutterites was established. Besides the professional bias, the personalities of the team members directly affected the three processes. Additional problems were created by the relationship of the total team to our research subjects within a culture that was strange to us. Completion of field work brought more problems: the utilization and coordination of the data assembled by the three different disciplines.

The three main difficulties which continuously jeopardized the attainment of the goal of the study were: (1) the complexities of the human personality; (2) the differences of the abstractional levels on which each of the three representative professions looked upon the phenomena observed; and (3) communication between the members of the research team. Permit me now to generalize on the basis of this observation.

Man with his innate reaction-pattern potential is born into a very complex field which is determined by his material and personal environment, and the value system of the community which he enters and in which he develops and lives. Both his environment and the cultural value system, that is, the shared goals of his society guide, limit, and restrict his self-realization.

Etiological factors of mental disease can be observed on many levels. Projecting the abstract concept of "total personality" into a center-line of a long spectral band, one can divide the total spectrum into a supra-personal part (family, community, society, culture, civilization, etc.) and a subpersonal part (central nervous system, other organic systems, individual organs, cells, molecules, etc.). Thus, integrative processes, influencing and determining human behavior are stretched out on this spectrum from infinity to infinity. The continuous interplay of all these processes, as well as the differences in the speed of events on the different levels, makes it impossible for the observer to comprehend the totality of all the factors—within the framework of this study—that lead to disordered human functioning. The facets of human behavior which we observe in studying mental illness depend upon our "observational position" which in turn is determined by our professional background, bias, and experiences.

Historically, the study of mental diseases was, up to recently, the concern only of psychiatry. From a purely organically oriented medical specialty, psychiatry expanded its theoretical basis to include dynamic, interpersonal, social, and cultural concepts which give it the present bi-polar position as a biological and social science. Many disciplines have contributed to the widening of psychiatry's scope. The investigation of many psychiatric problems, including the etiology of mental diseases, cannot be undertaken without the help of other specialties.

While we have a great deal of observational data available, and have developed many theoretical concepts, and have learned a few methodological approaches on different abstractional levels, all this knowledge still awaits a more effective process of interdisciplinary interpretation. We have to learn considerably more about the organizational and cybernetic interrelations between the simultaneously occurring events on these different levels and between wholes and parts.

This integrative process depends upon a cooperative convergence of interdisciplinary teams upon a specific focus (etiology of mental diseases). Thus, the development of new insight into the causative factors of "abnormal human behavior," just as the solution of many other problems in our society, ultimately hinges upon a greater effectiveness of interprofessional cooperation and communication. Better interdisciplinary communication in turn demands a "need-free atmosphere," a goal-directed determination, and a greater willingness to permit all "relevant" specialties to enter "our specific field" and to overlap beyond the borderline of our "special" functions.

As we learn to combat narrow specialization, to become less sensitive about the breakdown of bias barriers that separate the specialties not only of medicine but of all science, to value facts more than hypotheses, and by experience to acquire better methods of communication with our colleagues in other fields, we will develop new basic concepts. But more than that we will develop new strategical approaches followed by more effective tactics to gain insight into the yet unknown realms of the etiological factors of mental diseases. In the meantime we "have to tolerate the uncertainty of a confusion of facts with no plan to arrange them" [1].

REFERENCE

1. KENNEDY, A. in *Prospects in Psychiatric Research*, J. T. Tanner (Ed.). Oxford: Blackwell Scientific Publications, 1953. p. 158.

chapter 12

Multidisciplinary Knowledge and Research

◆ ◆

CLEGHORN: Dr. Bishop's remarks reminded me of the findings in the physiological field of neurohumors and of adrenalin in particular. The basic work on adrenalin was done long ago, but it lay fallow for a great many years. It had application, of course, in such things as allergic states; but for our understanding of general metabolic principles it actually had little place, and even less for psychiatry. We knew that it changed blood pressure and blood sugar; but animals could get along perfectly well without the tissues producing adrenalin. There seems to be no law in the rate of development of the integration of knowledge from the fundamental sciences to the human sciences. This is very true in the field of adrenalin studies, and I think that it may be true in the field of neurophysiology.

Within recent years Funkenstein's* use of adrenalin and mecholyl in the categorization of psychiatric cases has led to an extremely interesting development in that field. As the result of these simple physiological tests, he believes that the patients can be categorized as to their future progress under electric shock therapy much better than they could be by ordinary clinical methods. Therefore, perhaps we should not be too depressed when we are endeavoring to make applications of methods, data, and concepts that are in an advanced stage of study but still not readily applicable, from basic fields to psychiatry.

I have one more point; it comes out of Cannon's* study of the autonomic nervous system, that is, the principle of homeostasis. This concept has been of very great benefit to our thinking. Of course, as human beings we love neat ideas. But the transference of the idea of homeostasis to psychiatric phenomena, as Dr. Lidz has already pointed out, has not been as successful as might be hoped. In this area we shall have to look for some type of explanatory concepts other than the physiological one of homeostasis.

MILLER: I would like to suggest one approach to the problem of interrelating the various causal factors. Freud has been instrumental in emphasizing for both psychiatry and psychology the importance of drives (variously referred to as motivations, instincts, or needs) and in highlighting the significance of conflicts motivated by different drives. He has also pointed out that motivations can be modified by life experiences, or in other words, by learning. I believe that we are ready to study more rigorously the details of the mechanisms whereby drives are influenced by various

---

* Funkenstein, D. H. The role of ordinary epinephrine and nor-epinephrine in the elevation of blood pressure during stress. J. Nerv. Ment. Dis., 1951, 113: 177.

* Cannon, W. B. Organization for physiological homeostasis. Physiological Reviews, 1929, 9: 399.

115

factors. How do organic factors, such as heredity, influence these drives and help to determine, for example, the susceptibility of a patient to fear? How may certain drives be learned or modified by the conditions of the culture of the family during early childhood?

Some steps have already been made in this direction. For example, we have considerable experimental evidence showing us how sexual motivation depends in part upon hormonal and neurological factors. We also know that sexual motivation can be modified by learning, but we have not really begun to study experimentally that aspect of the problem. Experimental studies show us something about the way in which fear can be learned and can function as a drive to motivate new learning. We are also learning more about the physiological mechanisms involved in fear. Finally, we know that certain drugs, such as alcohol and Sodium Amytal, seem to reduce fear and have significant effects on the personality. I believe that physiological, psychological, psychodynamic, and sociological research on motivation will in the near future yield results which are highly significant for the problems of mental illness.

FELIX: I sometimes get a little confused in my attempts to understand what is meant by interdisciplinary research. It can be regarded as being on two levels: (1) the interpersonal and (2) the interdisciplinary. At the latter level one can construct programs and design work which looks very good on paper. In actual operation, however, it does not always work out that way. One reason is that interdisciplinary research usually brings together a group of prima donnas, each of whom is an expert in his own field and is himself a principal investigator. When these individuals come together, several things begin to happen. First, there has to be some integration of these individuals so that the work can progress satisfactorily; but the integration must occur without too much of a threat to the status of any one in the group. This in itself is an almost insuperable problem. Many times the next difficulty arises in trying to get these experts to speak a similar language to some degree. This is a second

major difficulty, and it frequently takes a long time to develop common understanding.

Then, after these two obstacles have been overcome, operational difficulties are still to be encountered. The methods and the technics of attacking a problem vary from discipline to discipline. And the psychological set of individuals differs from person to person. When research design is mentioned to a physiologist and to a sociologist, their concepts of those words are not quite the same. Perhaps I am a little too pessimistic, but that has been my experience. In any event, to make it short, interdisciplinary research does not spring full-born from the brow of Jove; rather, it is a long, hard rubbing-off process among personally congenial people. In themselves, these people must be sufficiently secure so that status problems do not defeat the project before it gets well started. They must also have an opportunity to work together during the preliminary stages over a long enough period so that they can understand one another as well as live with one another.

There have been times—and I am in one of those periods right now—when I almost believe that interdisciplinary research, as we usually speak of it, is a present impossibility. To give an example of what I mean, at present I know of one project going forward with three men in three different fields of endeavor, working three different ways, on three parallel problems. One man, a biochemist, is working on the fate of certain substances, such as lysergic acid, in the blood and in the body tissues. Also he is trying to develop an effective kind of bio-assay so that the concentration of minute quantities of lysergic acid in various areas of the body can be accurately determined. Another man, a physiologist, has worked for a number of years on the temporal lobes. He has been working on the higher primates; now he wishes to work with man. He is interested in the work of the first man because he surmises that the temporal lobes may have some role to play in what one observes in individuals who have been given lysergic acid. The third man in the group, a psychiatrist, has been interested for a long time in one phenomenon seen rather frequently in schizophrenia, depersonalization. He is interested in depersonalization per se. He is not interested in schizophrenia except as it supplies good material in which to study this particular phenomenon. These three men are pursuing their different individual bents. They are communicating. Maybe some day they will work jointly, but right now they are working individually on projects which may have interrelationships: the temporal lobe, lysergic acid, depersonalization. They are working on the same floor. Their laboratories are within shouting distance of each other—and I mean shouting distance because shouting between them very frequently occurs—but they are not integrated into a team. If one would try to integrate them into a team right now, there would be a three-way rebellion because each man is an independent investigator in his own right and each has no intention of being other than that. I do not know whether that is interdisciplinary research or not. The development of working relationships on the personal and scientific levels takes a long time. It is not something that can be cut out or stamped out of a piece of raw material.

STEVENSON: Yesterday we clearly accepted the desirability of convergence. Today we have been trying to follow it up. We have been struggling for ways of doing it. If we are convinced that convergence is desirable and yet we do not act on that conviction, then somewhere within us will be found the reason.

From my experience I have come to believe that part of the inertia in an institution is due to what might be called institutional homeostasis. In this case the homeostasis produces a resistance to change. There are similar resistances between departments of institutions.

The institution or department resists establishing a relationship with other institutions or groups because liaisons create administrative complexities. For example, it took four years between the passage of the National Vocational Rehabilitation Act and its acceptance in even a small way by New York State. As a practical point it is important that we realize that we not only have obstructions within us individually, but also we are caught in a framework within which we have to work and which restricts what we think and what we feel. Unless we devise ways of disturbing or circumventing these restrictive forces, action toward convergence is going to be slow.

LIDDELL: I want to make a semihumorous, semiserious remark. I have now had about fifteen years of experience in team research, and my plan costs no money. Over that period I have had imaginary teammates. Dr. Stanley Cobb visits my laboratory more often than he knows; and so do Thomas French and John Whitehorn. I find it very convenient and helpful to imagine what my scientific friends would think if I asked them such-and-such a question.

When we meet on an occasion like this Conference, we have teamwork.

FRENCH: Dr. Bishop spoke about correlations between brain physiology and behavior problems. I should like to ask whether he has any reactions to the work that Dr. Koehler has been doing on just that problem, by making psychological experiments on gestalt perception, and at the same time taking electrophysiological observations of various sorts.

BISHOP: The only comment I have is that it is a good thing to do. I would surmise, however, that taking records from the surface of the head is not a very direct measure of what the brain is doing. It is common knowledge that we do not understand what generates the electroencephalographic record. It is not completely a matter of summation of nerve impulses. When this record is filtered through half an inch of skull, it is possible to obtain a fairly smooth record of what is going on.

But there are certain complications. For instance, when the eyes are opened, presumably increasing the activity of the visual system, the activity represented by the electrocorticogram appears to be decreased. Further, the direct leading from different fractions of even one locus of cortex reveals a complicated picture with many significant details that cannot be observed in leads from the surface of the head. Since we cannot work on human subjects to record this detail, animals are employed; and it is necessary to work at all levels of technics to study the functioning of various parts of the brain, of the brain as a whole, and to correlate the results. Finally, we should hope to be able to correlate patterns of physiological activity with the patterns of conscious activity of the human subject.

CAMARGO: As we are considering different points of view about the etiology of mental diseases, I would like to focus on the point of view of culture. I think that we should really start to take into consideration seriously the possibility of conducting some researches in this field. Judging from an account which Dr. Redlich gives of his observations on psychiatry in the Far East, we find, much to our surprise, that the behavior of the patients in mental hospitals in Korea, Japan, and Okinawa seems to be sharply different from the usual pattern of behavior of the patients in the United States and the other Western countries. Even in the wards allocated to the more acute patients, everything is quite noiseless and peaceful, with the patients sitting around looking at the visitors without showing external reactions.

Dr. E. Stainbrook, formerly on the Yale staff and now Professor of Psychiatry at the New York State University at Syracuse, made a trip to Brazil a couple of years ago and was with me at Bahia Department of Mental Health, where he started a research on the psychopathology of schizophrenia. He also was surprised to find some differences in the content of ideas of the patients whom he studied. I myself have been amazed to observe that the rate of suicidal attempts among depressed patients is much lower there than here. Perhaps the time has come for us to study and ascertain whether there is truly some influence of the cultural pattern in the etiology of mental disorders. Emphasis has already been laid on the biological and social aspects of human behavior. Maybe it is appropriate to call attention to the cultural aspects too.

MILLER: I think that without doubt the best way to achieve integration is to have two skills in one skull. It is possible to achieve some useful integration at the level of technics, i.e., having workers from different fields apply their special technics to the same problem. I believe, however, that the most important integration has to be at the level of ideas and concepts. Once such integration is achieved, the application of relevant technics by workers in different fields is a logical outcome. But such integration takes a great deal of time and effort; there is no easy route to it. First the investigators from different disciplines must spend considerable time learning about each other's specialities so that they can understand each other's languages; then they must work hard together to discover the unifying concepts and problems.

The proper system of training can make a great contribution to this kind of integration. Relevant aspects of other disciplines can be introduced briefly, but sympathetically, as a regular part of the training. For example, in about the length of time which we have spent at this Conference, medical students could be introduced to some of the most important ideas of statistics. They could be given enough training so that they would appreciate the value of statistics and could ask the right questions. After this brief introduction, some of them might be motivated to go on and learn more on their own. Similarly, students of psychiatry could be introduced to the basic ideas of culture and social structure and given some understanding of experimental design. The goal might be to train them in the other disciplines up to the point where they could read with understanding or write an intelligent book review. The other disciplines could be introduced in an atmosphere which encouraged learning about them. I am afraid that, in the past, specialists have too frequently sneered at disciplines other than their own and built up barriers which tended permanently to block their students from other avenues of knowledge. Carrying the good will of this Conference into the classroom and making relatively minor changes in our program of training will help our students to produce a superior integration within our lifetime.

But if we encourage our students to cross traditional disciplinary lines, we face another problem. In general, the system of rewards is tied to the traditional academic departments. We must try to find new ways of rewarding and providing professional security for the person who works on both sides of one of these institutionalized boundaries.

REDLICH: It might be worth while to reflect more about the idea of training toward joint research, which is one of the aims of this Conference. It seems somewhat doubtful that many of us of this professional generation will carry it through; some of us will, but it is the hope for the next generation of scientists. I have observed at first hand something of the behavior of "prima donnas" in a group in which everyone was a captain of his own ship and absolutely unwilling to be of lesser rank in the group. When a younger group of scientists came in, and each was willing to be both cook and bottle-washer, we were able to do a little better. A similar relationship exists in research training, particularly upon introduction of the behavioral scientists, in whom medical research is deficient. Young psychiatrists have a certain amount of scientific biological training, which they get in medical school; but they do not receive much training in the behavioral sciences, which for psychiatric research is quite important.

CLEGHORN: There are two points which have a bearing on the development of young men in research in psychiatry. First, the practice of clinical psychiatry at the present time seems to be more glamorous; second, it pays a lot better. In the face of these realistic circumstances it is even more important, and always amazing, to observe the spontaneous appearance of people who are interested in the research. I think that actually there are more of them than the results of our recruitment would show. What is necessary is that somehow or other we increase the glamour and salary of research work, or diminish these attributes of clinical practice. It seems to me that the recruiting of research workers should be able to focus to advantage on such features. There is potential material available, but at the present time, or until recently, we have not been attracting it.

WHITEHORN: I should like to address some remarks to this proposition. There are provisions now being made, some within the United States Public Health Service, to provide decent stipends for people preparing themselves for investigative careers. The next and logically complementary step is that these researchers have some place to carry through their ultimate investigative careers. That means the establishment of possibilities and opportunities with some assurance of long-term continuity. It is, I suppose, basically a political or social responsibility that the state hospital systems or other responsible units should concern themselves with the development of means whereby prestige and income opportunities should accrue to the person who makes this definitely valuable contribution by doing this research, just as these perquisites accrue to the person who does responsible administrative work. This is a matter about which we may not be able to do much today.

What have we done in this meeting which points more practically toward the aims which we all have in mind? I think that we have all done several things. One of them is to increase, I hope, the degree of respect which each one of us and each group here feels toward the operations of some other group. I am quite sure that in the training of research workers, in the development of young men in various fields, an attitude of scorn and derision addressed to other fields has had a very deleterious effect on basic thinking. To some extent we have undermined that deleterious influence here. By that much we have contributed to the development of people who, if they are not trained in various fields, at least will be sympathetically disposed to cooperate with others who are.

LIDZ: This meeting started with scarcely any attention paid to historical perspective. One of the reasons we are meeting here is that psychiatry, perhaps more than any other field, stands between the behavioral sciences and the more purely biological and physical sciences. Therefore, the psychiatrist stands between the two and requires something of a dual orientation. We might assume that it will be the psychiatrist or persons in a closely affiliated field who will have to bridge the gap between the social and biological sciences. I think that it will help clarify our dilemma if we look back a bit to see what has happened to the psychiatrist in recent years.

Only fifteen or twenty years ago it was very difficult for the psychiatrist to find a place where he could train and gain a broad perspective of the field. Outside those university centers in the United States and England where Meyerian influences produced a genetic, dynamic approach to the patient, residency training in psychiatry took place in centers that were primarily organically oriented. Outside of the university settings, there were only a small number of psychoanalytic institutes where one could gain graduate training in dynamic psychiatry.

During and since World War II, there have been two great movements in psychiatry. There has been increasing integration between physiologic medicine and dynamic psychiatry, in which physiologic change has been related to dynamic conflict even more than emotional problems have been related to physiologic dysfunction. The internist and psychiatrist have worked together, having found a common interest in the interrelationships between emotions and bodily change. It has been recognized that interpersonal disturbances can affect physiological equilibrium, and the cooperative effort has not been directed simply at finding the sources of mental illness in bodily dysfunction.

The second important trend has been the clear-cut shift of American psychiatry to a dominant interest in dynamic psychiatry. The analytic institutes have grown and have become the places considered optimal for learning dynamic psychiatry. In view of the great importance of the psychoanalytic institutes in the education of psychiatrists today, it is rather striking that I see teachers from only two or three psychoanalytic institutes represented here. We must face the fact that we are going through a period in which young psychiatrists are primarily interested in gaining psychoanalytic training. In a sense, we must also recognize that the teachers of psychiatry are caught up in a period of expansion of the number of psychiatrists, which limits the time available for research and creative thinking. The period is a difficult one and contains many

frustrations, but research in psychiatry in the future depends to a very great extent on expansion of the number of persons trained in the field today. I believe that one aspect of the present system of training will pass. University centers will teach sufficient dynamic psychiatry so that it will no longer be necessary for so large a proportion of students of psychiatry to concentrate upon gaining training in psychoanalytic institutes. However, we must remember that the student in psychiatry has been given the impression, to some extent by the university teachers and certainly by many of his teachers in analytic institutes, that there is a known, correct body of information which he must acquire before he has a right to think on his own. In the period of transition, it is natural that there are groups of disciples who defend rigidly what they accept to have been the teachings and practices of Freud. We know that disciples can often be more unflexible and unyielding than the master, and can insist upon and defend, where he would modify. At any rate, this attitude has led to a situation where the student, after considerable residency and analytic training, reaches the age of 30 or 40 (most frequently closer to 40) before he feels he has the right to think independently. For scientific purposes this is much too late. By and large, if people are going to develop unique insights, they are going to develop them before the age of 35, and more probably before the age of 30.

What I am complaining about as a teacher, but perhaps as a student too, is that we have held students in a type of intellectual bondage at a time when they should be free to think on their own. We must not only expose students to multidisciplinary knowledge, but also hold up to them how little definitive and final is known in our field rather than give the impression that there is a well-established body of proven knowledge. At the same time, the wealth of our knowledge gained from clinical experience must not be undervalued because it has not been checked in a laboratory or does not now seem capable of being rigidly proven by an experimental approach. This is a difficult gap to bridge, and I am sure that I cannot see how it should be done. Still, it is a fundamental problem which must be solved if the psychiatrist is to be a major contributor to the science of human behavior.

The advantage of being trained in two disciplines has already been mentioned. I think it was Jurgen Ruesch* who pointed out that an unusual number of psychiatrists who have made real contributions had experienced a shift in cultural setting during their developmental years. This phenomenon is probably not limited to psychiatrists. We see it in convergence of cultures which gives rise to new orientations of mankind. I am not going to suggest that we import our behavioral scientists from other cultures. Perhaps it will prove very fruitful if we can see to it that persons have a familiarity with another field before entering psychiatry, or we might see to it that during their period of training they take time out to get to know another field rather than learn only that psychiatric knowledge which they are supposed to have today. This will by itself stimulate curiosity, and surely it is the stimulation of curiosity rather than what we teach our students that will lead our science forward.

BINGER: I do not believe that a meeting of this sort could have occurred five years ago, certainly not ten years ago. I have been impressed with the area of agreement and convergence rather than the opposite. There may be differences about the use of statistics or the concept of teleology, but by and large members of this group can talk to each other in a reasonable way. My own interdisciplinary efforts have been largely from psychiatry toward medicine, and there a great many difficulties do exist. It is true that, in some of the more enlightened centers, physiology and medicine and psychiatry try to lie down together; but this attempt is in a very limited area only, in a very few teaching centers, and there at best medicine does not really incorporate psychiatric knowledge. Those in internal medicine are suspicious, and very often the inwardness of a problem is disregarded by the internist so that the kind of agreement and willingness

---

* Ruesch, J. and Bateson, G. *Communication: The Social Matrix of Psychiatry.* New York: W. W. Norton, 1951. p. 20.

to understand which has been exhibited here for two days is certainly rare in the field of medicine vis-à-vis psychiatry.

WHITEHORN: I would like to comment on the concept of instinct and its utilization. Many years ago I made some efforts to organize my own thinking around this concept; but at that time it seemed not so very useful for reportorial purposes, since the items were all inferences and not strictly observable patterns. There were, however, many features of patients' behavior that were more directly observable, which I thought had a great deal of bearing on what was talked about in terms of instinct. These were matters which I found it convenient to speak of as attitudes.

Attitudes, I found on exploring what literature was available, had become a technical term in sociology. I thought at the time that it was somewhat unfortunate that this was true. The term was introduced for highly verbalized studies of people's reactions to questions, matters of radical or conservative attitudes in politics; whereas the kind of attitudes which, it seemed to me, were significant to the clinician were those that could be immediately sensed in the relation of the patients to the doctor, to the head nurse, to the other patients when they were on the ward—in relations of that kind. Also this kind would bear upon what values the patient had sought in life when he turned from high school to go to college or to take a job, what attitudes he had had with regard to the matters of more vital importance than whether he was going to register with the Republicans or the Democrats. Dr. H. J. Eysenck of London, who has been very much concerned with the problem of attitudes, both in the more orthodox use among the sociologists and also in other relations, has done highly significant work in finding correlations in this complex field.

The question has been put to me: How did you happen to shift from biochemistry to clinical psychiatry? The shift had some relation to attitudes. The psychiatric staff and I from the standpoint of the attitude, would discuss the patients whom they were encountering. The patients were showing changes in attitudes which they might be undergoing in relation to the emotional experiences they were having in the hospitals. I developed a notion then that one of the significant things about therapy (psychotherapy) was that it was important to free the patient for some possible consideration of other attitudes than those which he had on a given matter. But this was not enough. If one wished a *change* to occur in the patient's attitudes, it appeared necessary that he have an acute emotional experience which might be resolvable in a different way than he had been accustomed to. Such important considerations got me so busy talking about the patients and their clinical problems that I was persuaded to wade in and deal with the recalcitrant patients. Being stuck with some of the toughest patients in the hospital, I found that they had potentialities for changing. Some changed for the better. When this occurred, my part in the transaction got called psychotherapy, and I got called a psychotherapist. I do not mean that this was the basis of all my interest in clinical psychiatry.

I geared these remarks to a consideration of the purely verbal use of a particular word, "attitude," as a clearer term for actual reporting and operation than the term "instinct." I think that it is possible, by a careful choice of terms and by the delimitation in one's mind of the experimental referents for which these terms are going to be used, to establish a basis of communication which can be very fruitful.

WEIL: In considering the convergence of viewpoints on etiology of mental disease, we have not clearly defined what part of the broad spectrum of health and disease we mean when we speak about "mental illness." Newer investigations and insights seem to broaden our observed areas on this spectral field. Dr. Lindemann spoke about the shift of adjustment under social stress in which behavior, autonomic innervation, and symbolic language become interchangeable in a pathogenic manner. Dr. Brosin focused upon the reciprocity of "psychosomatic conditions" (e.g., colitis) and psychotic states. Thus the concept "mental disease" has become a vaguer and wider one as we see abnormal human functioning in a different temporal and abstractional con-

text. Together with our other medical colleagues and other professional friends we will have to survey again and again the total field of mental health and disease, develop new hypotheses and ultimately a basic science of human behavior which will serve as a new framework within which we will be able to organize our different viewpoints.

LANDIS: On the basis of some years of experience in research on various problems relevant to nervous and mental disease, I have arrived at three general conclusions relevant to research in this field.

1. Every mental patient must serve as his own control. By this I mean that the investigator usually gains little or nothing by the method of group comparisons. Each patient must be measured and evaluated as an individual at repeated intervals, and any change in measures or evaluation must be related to pertinent events in the life of that individual. At present we can only report that this or that assumed-to-be-effective agent acted in such-and-such a fashion in a certain per cent of cases. Statistical procedures relevant to this approach still have to be invented.

2. As an empirical fact the majority of measures which have been found to be indicative of "changes" in mental patients are measures of very simple and uncomplicated responses. As a general rule, the more complicated the indicator, test, or evaluation, the less reliably it reflects changes. This is not to say that complicated tests are not clinically useful. Rather I believe that the complicated test as a usual thing reveals only that which is known or suspected, and gives no pertinent suggestion as to basic processes involved. My theory is that simple tests are to be preferred because as soon as a test becomes complicated, any human being has too many ways of responding so that the measure becomes unreliable because of variations in the manner of the response.

3. This last assumption, which is the most tentative of the three, is that each individual should be tested with simple, repeated tests. The first application of the test at any test period should be without "load," and the second or repeated test should be

under "load." By "load" is meant that the test is repeated with the addition of some handicap such as ingestion of a drug, a distracting noise, a possible shock, or the like. The idea is that the performance under "load" may give further information as to the reserve integrative ability of the patient.

MILLER: From the experience of the Air Corps' program in World War II, I would not say that the complex tests are always invalid and useless. Simple reaction time was no good for predicting success in pilot training; it was the complex tests that were most predictive.

LANDIS: You are perfectly correct, so far as the Air Corps is concerned. I should have emphasized the point that my conclusions are relevant only to work with psychiatric patients. I am trying to measure or evaluate the efficiency of a single mental patient and how his efficiency has been altered by therapy, drugs, brain tumors, or vitamins. I should repeat that I have no quarrel with the complex tests as clinical guides. They came from the clinic; they are useful in the clinic. They will be helpful in practical situations as long as scientific validation is not demanded. But when the investigator attempts to use them and to validate their results by ordinary scientific criteria, the tests usually prove to be unreliable.

BROSIN: Although content and method are of primary importance, I believe that emphasis upon the individuals who are doing the work might be the most effective way to accelerate the rates of learning and the progress that we make. All of us have incumbent upon us the necessity to improve the ways in which we recruit and select our colleagues, to try to get more people interested in this field, and to get them to work longer and better at it, rather than merely to occupy ourselves with conceptual schemes which might theoretically yield better results. The emphasis should be upon the persons who are doing the work rather than upon the ideas with which they might be working.

HUNT: Some years ago the clinical psychologists had a conference on how to organize a training program in clinical psychology. We came right up against the problem of teaching ethics. We came to the conclusion that ethics could not be taught by precept alone, but must also be taught by example. The teacher must furnish the student an example by the teacher's own behavior. It was a wise conclusion. That was as far as we went with the problem. Recently some of us have been discussing this problem in other fields: interdisciplinary tolerance, combating of the undue influence of financial rewards, encouraging of people to go into research, standards of experimental design, etc. We have come to the conclusion that the views on these problems must be taught by example as well as precept. But what about the problems that arise in the attempt to teach by example? This introduces the whole problem of identification—identification with the teacher by the pupil. Would this be accepted as a principle for teaching? I think that there are certain traditions in science that make such acceptance difficult. I mean the tradition of the impersonality of science. Some people do not like to accept this principle of identification in teaching, even if you dignify and depersonalize it by calling it "imprint learning." It leads to many complex problems involving the dynamics of the people involved.

second CONFERENCE

chapter 13

The Organic Viewpoint on Mental Disease

HERBERT H. JASPER

• •

Scientifically minded workers and thinkers concerned with the problem of the biological foundations of mind and behavior must begin by accepting the principle of biological determinism. We must accept the fact that the verbal symbols employed by psychiatrists, such as "unconscious mental life," "the ego or superego," "the self- or body-image," "suppression or sublimation of drives," describe events taking place in a physical world. They must represent biological events occurring within organisms in reaction to their environment. As scientists we must ignore the possibility of a separate world of spiritual reality. Regardless of our individual religious faith or philosophical preferences, there is no place for disembodied mind in present-day biological conceptions of mental health or disease.

Psychological "forces," or even sociological "forces," do not differ generically from biological "forces" such as, for example, those mediated by the endocrine glands or by innate or learned patterns of behavior, which must have their basis in structural and functional patterns within the nervous system. These differences lie in modes of discourse or in frames of reference rather than in difference in basic mechanisms of the determinants of behavior. For the biologist the stimulus patterns to which an organism reacts are of as much interest and importance as the patterns of nerve impulses they elicit. The one cannot be understood without the other, even though the stimulus patterns may be called social mores or analyzed into specific wave lengths of light or sound and their interrelationships. (The biologist is also aware, however, that the patterns are more than a sum of the parts into which they may be analyzed.)

I have been requested to try to state the case of the organic point of view in terms of "certainties," "probabilities," and "possibilities." I must admit that I have had difficulty in forcing my thinking into these prescribed channels. It is only out of respect for my friend, Dr. Kruse, that I have attempted to do so somewhat against my better judgment.

The "certainties" are so well known that I shall attempt to list only the most important of them as follows:

AREAS OF CERTAIN AGREEMENT

1. *Organic psychoses*—These include:
   Degenerative diseases (e.g., senile and presenile dementia)
   Toxic (e.g., alcohol, bromide, lysergic acid, etc.)
   Infectious (e.g., G.P.I., encephalitis)
   Cerebral neoplasm or trauma

Epileptic (particularly temporal lobe epilepsy, frontal and diencephalic epilepsy)

Endocrine disorders (e.g., anorexia nervosa)

Metabolic disorders (e.g., pellagra)

2. *Genetic determinants*—These include:
Heredo-degenerative diseases
Constitutionally determined modes of reaction to stress

3. *Psychosomatic disorders*—There is general agreement concerning the most obvious disorders, e.g., gastric ulcers, ulcerative colitis, though disagreement as to the extent to which physical manifestations of disease may be determined entirely by psychological causes.

4. *Psychoneuroses*—Immediate and repeated environmental stresses of sufficient severity, depending upon the constitutional stability and past history of the organism, may be sufficient causes for what is termed neurotic behavior, though definitions of what is to be called neurotic behavior may vary and may be conditioned by social standards. Experimental neuroses in animals under controlled conditions make it possible to investigate such phenomena by objective "biological" methods.

WORK OF PROBABLE VALUE

The two lines of biological research which seem to hold greatest promise for the advance of knowledge regarding mental health and disease are: (1) neurochemical and (2) neurophysiological.

1. *Neurochemical prospects*—It is the belief of the so-called "organic" psychiatrist that some of the most severe mental disorders eventually may be related to specific metabolic defects or alterations in the function of nerve cells and synapses. With improved methods of study and progress in the understanding of cerebral metabolic process, such studies may well yield results of far-reaching significance in the near future. This view will have to include neuroendocrine functions, concerning which we have already obtained some interesting leads in certain forms of schizophrenia. I must repeat, in this connection, that even though endocrine defects may be observed, the biologist is quite aware of the possibility

that they may not be the primary cause, but rather they may represent a reaction to persistent stress situations. Stimulus patterns, past and present, are part of the "biological" situation or point of view.

2. *Neurophysiological prospects*—In recent years studies of functional localization in the brain have been yielding much new data, which should be of great value for the understanding of mental process and mental disorders. The production of hallucinations and dream states or obsessive thinking and mental confusion by electrical stimulation of different parts of the cerebral cortex in conscious man has yielded much valuable data, the significance of which for psychiatry has yet to be worked out. Experimental studies of the functions of the rhinencephalon and the new role being found for subcortical structures in diencephalon and midbrain in the regulation of conscious mental process of the brain as a whole give us new neurophysiological conceptions with which to reconsider the neurophysiological basis of the mind.

POSSIBLE, THOUGH DOUBTFUL, "ORGANIC" APPROACHES

One of the principal preoccupations of neurophysiologists during recent years has been the study of the functional properties of single nerve cells and the mechanisms of the transmission of nerve impulses in simple synaptic circuits or in neural nets in the brain. The grosser sampling of the electrical activity of the brain by electroencephalogram is a less precise phase of the same type of investigation. This type of work, couched in the esoteric terminology of the electrophysiologist, even when given the expansive treatment of a cyberneticist, has offered little as yet of real value to our understanding of mental processes.

Perhaps we shall never be able to bridge the gap between these unitary or elemental approaches to functions of the nervous system and mental processes of such global complexity as to be of psychiatric interest. Nevertheless, we should keep on trying, especially when it becomes possible to carry out such unitary analysis of nerve function in patients with mental disorders.

Few neurophysiologists are sufficiently

naïve to think that mental functions or disorders will ever be explained by investigations of the molecular or ionic changes occurring on the nerve membrane associated with the nerve impulse. Ultimately we must understand these elementary phenomena, but the principles of organization of neuronal aggregates are more important. Even in such studies it will be a very long time before we are able to render a satisfactory account of even the simplest of mental operations.

SUMMARY

In the organic approach to mental health and disease, one must assume that all mental processes and behavior characteristics may be expressed in terms of the physical properties of the organism—structural, functional, molecular, and cellular—and in terms of the interrelationships underlying the function of the organism as a whole. The physical properties of stimulus situations, both in the external and internal environment of the organism, are of as much importance to the "organic" point of view as they are to the "dynamic psychologist." The phylogenetic and ontogenetic history of the organism, insofar as it is limited to objective, verifiable data, is also of interest and importance. But, unfortunately, the available knowledge concerning the organic bases for mental processes and behavior is so limited that it is of little use, at present, to those dealing with many of the immediate practical problems of mental health and disease.

The result is that the "dynamic psychiatrist" has been forced to formulate practical working hypotheses based upon conceptions and descriptive terms which are difficult or impossible to submit to scientific validation in and for themselves, let alone be translated into psychophysiological processes familiar to those concerned with a more objective approach to the study of behavior.

We need more *rapprochement* between those concerned with the biological basis of behavior and those attempting to deal with mental and behavior disorders. Less "mumbo jumbo" of esoteric terminology and more attempt at translation into terms which might be of more general significance for the biologist and the dynamic psychologist alike are of the greatest importance to real progress.

chapter 14

The Psychological Point of View

B. F. SKINNER

• •

Any survey of the contributions which psychology can make to our understanding of mental disease will depend upon how psychology is defined. In practice, the methods and concepts of all four of the disciplines represented at this Conference overlap extensively. Narrowly considered, however, the special province of psychology may be taken to be the description of the behavior of the individual as a whole and the explanation of that behavior in terms of environmental factors and conditions. More specifically, psychology is concerned with recording and measuring human behavior and its various aspects, and with relating the quantities so measured to variables in the past and current environment. Many psychologists, of course, have broader interests. In addition to forces which are currently acting upon the organism, or have acted upon it in the past, they may be concerned with variables in its genetic history, the physiology of its parts, or, at the other extreme, its social environment or cultural history. A narrower delineation of the field is, though arbitrary, desirable for our present purposes.

Mental disease appears to refer to modes of behavior which are troublesome or dangerous either to the individual himself or to others. Behavior may be troublesome or dangerous by its very nature or because of the circumstances under which it occurs.

It is not strictly correct to describe such behavior as "atypical," since extreme or unrepresentative values of many properties of behavior do not always present problems appropriately described as the result of disease. Genius is atypical but, presumably, healthy. It is probably also not of any great value to characterize troublesome or dangerous behavior as "nonadaptive," or as violating some principle of "homeostasis" or "equilibrium." The problems of mental disease arise when an individual shows behavior which, because of its character or the circumstances under which it appears, causes trouble. One problem is to explain this behavior, and another is to change it.

One contribution which experimental psychology has to offer, by virtue of its methods and concepts, is a precise description of the behavior under examination. Psychological technics are peculiarly designed to provide the clearest possible record of behavioral manifestations, together with a rigorous demonstration of relations to causal factors. The behavior of the mentally diseased is often so obviously troublesome or dangerous that precise measurement is felt to be unnecessary. But it is possible that such behavior differs from what might be called normal merely by occupying an extreme position on a continuum. Lesser conditions, not so easily detected, may offer a clue to the causal factors involved. Further advances in the study of the mentally diseased may create a demand for the type of description which can be established only by more careful measurement.

In other words, the first question to which psychology may address itself is, What *is* neurotic, psychotic, or defective behavior? We cannot answer this with a logical definition of terms. The question is more specific. Given an agreed-upon example of neurotic, psychotic, or defective behavior, what are its significant properties? The commoner manifestations of mental disease may not at the present time require detailed description, but an eventual account of these phenomena will almost certainly need to lean upon the methods and terms of a science primarily concerned with the behavior of the whole organism.

Among the special topics to which psychology has addressed itself, for example, is the *sensory control* of behavior. Gross instances of hallucinations, anesthesias, confusions, or defective categorizations can often be accepted as symptoms of mental disease without further inquiry, but a comprehensive account of such phenomena, which would relate them to "normal" manifestations, requires the technics of sensory psychology.

Psychology has also been especially concerned with *motor behavior*. The study of gross instances of paralysis, ataxia, loss of skill, or confusion may not require the precise technics of the laboratory, but here again a full description of these "symptoms" may.

Emotional behavior is also a subject to which psychology has given considerable attention. The emotional behavior of the mentally diseased is, again, often so gross that no appeal is made to the methods of the laboratory. But as further precision in characterizing abnormal behavior is required, and as the experimental study of emotion progresses, the psychological characterization of the emotional pattern of the psychotic should become more important.

Motivation has only recently been studied on a substantial scale in the case of human subjects, but much has been learned from the study of animals with respect to the effects of deprivation, satiation, and aversive stimulation. Here again the extreme conditions manifested by the mentally diseased—behaviors which suggest excessive deprivation, or complete satiation, or a failure to avoid or escape from powerfully aversive conditions—may seem to make the precise methods of experimental psychology irrelevant, but an improved account of the psychotic condition must eventually be based upon the relationships demonstrated in such a science.

Lastly, in the field of *learning,* quantitative properties of processes have been demonstrated against which the unusual conditions of the mentally diseased must eventually be evaluated. Many deficiencies in the field of learning are at the present time measured indirectly through intelligence tests, but methods which are more appropriate to a laboratory science are available. The speed with which behavior is acquired in conditioning, the complexity of the behavior which may be so acquired, the rate at which such behavior will be extinguished, and the precision with which behavior may be brought under stimulus control, all enter into many of the characteristics of mental disease. Although a gross effect, such as a conspicuous loss of memory, may not at the moment require precise measurement, an eventual detailed account of the nature of such a difficulty may need to appeal to the methods and results of the experimental laboratory.

Of special importance in the field of mental disease are many forms of behavior resulting from the use of punishment as a measure of control. It is now clear that in punishing a response, we do not simply lower the probability that it will be emitted. Punishment acts by setting up certain aversive conditions from which the organism may escape, or which it may avoid, through many different types of behavior. Among such avoidance or escape responses are frequently found the troublesome or dangerous responses characteristic of mental disease.

The methods and concepts of experimental psychology which are likely to be useful in the precise description of the behavior characteristics of mental disease cannot be described in detail. The present point is simply that, among the four disciplines here represented, it is primarily experimental psychology which has concerned itself with the problem of describing and explaining the behavior of the intact organism in the above sense. The advantage which psychology has gained from the laboratory control of the variables it has studied should be emphasized, even though it may reasonably be objected that the variables so far manipulated are by no means comprehensive or entirely representative.

These are not, strictly speaking, contributions to the etiology of mental disease but merely to the investigation of this etiology. In exploring the *causes* of the behavior characteristic of mental disease, the technical contributions of psychology are frequently joined with the methods and concepts of other disciplines. For example, to investigate *hereditary factors* in the causation of mental disease, we must combine the methods and concepts of genetics with those of experimental psychology. Similarly, if we are to investigate *organic causes,* we need to combine the methods and terms of physiology and experimental psychology. Much the same relation prevails in the study of endocrinological and pharmacological effects. In each case the psychologist is reaching beyond the variables which are usually taken to be characteristic of his special field. His peculiar contribution is to provide, so to speak, a base-line upon which the effect of genetic, organic, and other variables may be observed.

Causal factors important in understanding mental disease are, however, to be found among the independent variables to which the psychologist characteristically turns. An excessive emotional condition, a dangerous mode of escape from anxiety, a troublesome preoccupation with sex, or an excessive enthusiasm for gambling may be nothing more than extreme cases of the effects of environmental conditions. These aspects of the personal history and the current environment of the individual are commonly taken to be in the realm of psychology and within reach of the psychologist's technics. Modes of behavior charac-

teristic of mental disease may be simply the result of a history of reinforcement, an unusual condition of deprivation or satiation, or an emotionally exciting circumstance. Except for the fact that they are troublesome or dangerous, they may not be distinguishable from the rest of the behavior of the individual. Insofar as this is the case, the etiology of mental disease and the possibility of analysis and therapy lie within the field of psychology proper. (At this point an overlap with psychodynamics is obvious. The distinction between the psychological and psychodynamic view is not basically a distinction in subject matter or in the range of factors studied. The distinction is primarily one of method, and it is possible that these two fields will eventually fuse or at least become very closely associated.)

Recent work in the field of learning has enabled the psychologist to achieve an extensive control over the behavior of an organism, and to bring this behavior under the control of complex environmental conditions. By manipulating the event called a reinforcement, it is possible not only to shape up many novel forms of behavior but also to sustain almost any given level of activity for long periods of time. In the field of Pavlovian conditioning, comparable advances have been made in the understanding of the origins of emotional patterns. It is reasonable to suppose that such an experimental science will eventually produce a technology capable of modifying and sustaining any given pattern of behavior almost at will. Suppose it can be shown that an organism with a given genetic history and a given organic condition can be induced to engage in the kinds of behavior characteristic of mental disease through the manipulation of environmental variables. Then in order to demonstrate one type of cause of mental disease, it will remain only to show that comparable environmental variables *could* have been operative upon a given person showing neurotic, psychotic, or defective characteristics. Another technological extension of such an experimental science would be to change the behavior of the mentally diseased, in the direction usually referred to as therapy, through the arrangement of environmental variables.

If experimental psychology continues in its current direction, it may reasonably be expected to show how some of the behavior characteristics of mental disease can be generated and how they can be corrected. By appealing only to environmental variables (while assuming a given set of genetic and organic variables), psychology may make this contribution entirely within its own traditional field. That there are etiological factors lying beyond this field is doubtless true. Here psychology can make only the kind of cooperative contribution previously described. A certain practical hierarchy of causes may, however, be pointed out. Although genetic and organic factors can be efficiently evaluated only by holding environmental factors constant, and although environmental factors can be correctly evaluated only against a stable genetic and organic condition, it is probably a useful practice to explore environmental factors first to see whether any behavioral manifestations remain to be attributed to genetic and organic causes.

SUMMARY

In a narrow, though traditional, sense, psychology is concerned with describing and measuring the behavior of the individual and with relating that behavior to environmental factors. The technics and concepts which it has developed for this purpose may contribute to the study of the etiology of mental disease by providing a more precise characterization of the forms of behavior at issue. The contributions of psychology in this respect will become more important when the gross disorders which first attract our attention are no longer adequate in characterizing a diseased condition. The methods and concepts of experimental psychology are required in the investigation of genetic, physiological, endocrinological, and pharmacological factors in the causation of neurotic and psychotic behavior, although the methods and technics of other disciplines are here also required. Some etiological factors are to be found within the narrower province of psychology itself. Some of the *emotional* and *motivational* conditions which are taken to be symptoms of mental disease may be nothing more than extreme values of the effects of variables encountered in the analysis and control of the normal organism. Behavior which is so troublesome or dangerous as to be said to characterize mental disease may also simply be *learned* —that is, it may be the product of reinforcing contingencies which affect the organism according to the learning processes encountered in the behavior of the normal individual. It is a reasonable expectation that a developing experimental psychology will find itself increasingly more effective in producing behavior which would be said to reflect mental disease, and in changing the behavior of the actually mentally diseased in the direction known as therapy—and all of this by manipulating environmental variables traditionally assigned to the field of psychology. In this latter approach to the problem of the causation of mental disease, it is clear that psychology and psychodynamics overlap, these two fields being distinguished not in terms of subject matter or the causal factors to which appeal is made, but only in technic—a distinction which may be lost as the two sciences are further developed.

Comment on the Position of the Experimental Psychologist

KENNETH W. SPENCE

What is the raw material with which the scientist starts? We can sum up the many recent discussions of this question by scientists and philosophers of science in the following statement: *All sciences begin with events occurring in the experiences of scientists.* A division of labor takes place among the scientists, and different groups of them agree to concern themselves with different aspects or events in the totality of observable experiences.

So far as modern behavior science is concerned, the statement that subject matter of this science is the same in kind as that of other sciences is accepted without question. However, this was not always the case. The older classical psychologies, whether of the structural or act variety, took the view that psychology, if it was a natural science, was a somewhat unique one. Instead of being concerned, like physics, for example, with events mediated by or derived from the immediate experience of the observing scientist, psychology was said to study immediate experience per se. Much was made of the point that psychology had a unique method of its own—introspection, which was regarded as a kind of inner sense that provided for the observation and analysis of immediate experience.

Fortunately, the relation of immediate experience to science has been considerably clarified in recent years by the writings of several different groups of thinkers. The philosophers of science, particularly the logical positivists, philosophically minded scientists such as Bridgman, and within psychology such writers as Boring, Pratt, and Stevens have succeeded in making the point that the data of all sciences have the same origin; namely, the experience of an observing person, the scientist himself. That is to say, experience, the initial matrix out of which all sciences develop, is no longer considered a matter of concern for the scientist qua scientist. Like all other scientists, the psychologist simply takes immediate experience for granted, and then proceeds to his task of describing the events occurring in it and discovering and formulating the nature of the relationships holding among them.

It is worth while calling attention here to a point of special interest to psychologists; namely, that our observable sensory experiences depend upon or result from two different classes of conditions: intraorganic and extraorganic; the former exciting the interoceptors, and the latter, the exteroceptors. The physical sciences, it should be noted, deal only with events of an extraorganic origin, i.e., those received through the exteroceptors. The data of classical psychology, on the other hand, were regarded as also involving sense events initiated through the interoceptors. These latter were regarded as being stimulated by such internal mental processes as thinking, desiring, emotional reactions, perceiving, and sensing, and hence were thought of as providing primary data concerning them.

It is apparent, however, that these internally initiated experiences differ rather markedly from the externally aroused ones in the extent to which they are publicly controllable and communicable. At least, if we can judge from the interminable disagreements of the introspective psychologists themselves, this class of experiences does not meet too well the requirements of intersubjective testability demanded by the scientist. It was in the face of this difficulty that Watson made his suggestion that the psychologist, like all other scientists, should confine himself to those segments of his experience which have their origin in extraorganic conditions. In other words, the events studied by the psychologist, Watson held, should consist in observations of the overt behavior of other organisms—other, that is, than the observing scientist himself. In the experiments which we shall consider, the observations will not involve any reference to interoceptively aroused experiences of the observer. For the most part, they involve instruments that reduce the observational evidence to visual experiences involving spatial and temporal relations, frequently specific pointer readings.

As everyone knows, however, most behavior scientists, when dealing with humans, still make use at one time or another of this introspective type of material in the form of objectively recordable verbal reports. To some critics of the behavioristic viewpoint, this acceptance of verbal reports as a part of the data has seemed to represent an abandonment of the strict behavioristic position. Such a contention, however, fails to note a very important difference in the two positions. The introspectionist, it should be recalled, assumed a strict one-to-one relationship between the verbal responses of his subjects and the inner mental events. Accordingly, he accepted these introspective reports as *facts* or *data* about the inner mental events which they represented. The behavior scientist takes a very different position. He accepts the verbal response as just one more form of behavior, and he proposes to use this type of data in exactly the same manner as he does other types of behavior variables. Thus he attempts to discover laws relating these verbal responses to environmental events of the past or present, and he seeks to find what relations they have to other types of response variables. He also makes use of them as a basis for making inferences as to certain hypothetical or theoretical constructs which he employs. In contrast, then, to the introspectionist's conception of these verbal reports as mirroring directly inner mental events, the behaviorist uses them either as data in their own right to be related to other data, or as a base from which to infer theoretical constructs which presumably represent hypothetical (internal) processes in their subjects.

Comment on the Experimental Psychological Point of View

H. E. KING

I should like to add some remarks to those given by Dr. Skinner in an effort to amplify the description of the point of view taken by experimental psychology on the etiology of mental disease.

Ours is a varied field, often difficult to summarize and troublesome to define. For this reason one may ask, at the outset, Why does the psychologist concern himself at all with the problem of etiology in mental disease? Are not diagnosis, treatment, and the search for causal factors problems for the physician who, by definition, assumes these tasks for all forms of disease process? In answer we say that an understanding of the *etiology* of mental disease is of direct concern to the psychologist, and far more important to him than are associated problems of diagnosis, care, and treatment. This is so because the subject matter of psychology, in the broadest sense, is the study of the responsive properties of the animate organism, particularly the human, to conditions in its surroundings and within itself. The study of behavior, both "normal" and "abnormal," requires us to search for its origins or controlling influences wherever the roots of the phenomena may lie, whether the behavior in question is academic success, individual differences in color perception, faulty psychomotor performance by persons with brain damage, or the aberrant behavior patterns seen in mental disease. Thus, gaining an understanding, by means of proper investigation, of the factors resulting in disordered behavior is indeed our concern as a scientific discipline. The application of known facts and principles to correct or improve faulty behavior in an individual or group falls outside our sphere of interest as an experimental science.

What is to be our contribution to an understanding of the aberrant behavior called mental disease? Need we limit our investigations to those purely psychological forces active in producing deviations of behavior? Clearly not, for we are concerned with behavior per se, and no limitation, other than human frailty, need restrict the investigation of what its determining influences may be. These may, at times, be found to be immediately psychological in nature, e.g., the effect of experience as a determinant of behavior, such as that seen in the conditioned response. In other contexts we may find physiological causes to be primary, as in the mental retardation associated with myxedema; or physical limitations may exert a controlling influence, as in athletic behavior. Our chosen task of identifying the determinants of the behavior expressed must take us wherever these causes lie. We have need for great depth as well as breadth of study. This annexation of fields of knowledge to account for the observed behavior is a matter of logical necessity, not grandiosity, and serves to make psychology "the most difficult of the sciences." It might be simpler to limit our investigations to psychological forces alone, but to advocate such limitation would be as ill-advised as to say the physiologist need not reckon with the chemical or physical antecedents of his phenomena.

The point of view of the experimental psychologist, then, is that the etiology of mental disease must be studied by every means available, even as we must also make full study of the biological variant, the maturational process, the effect of living in collective groups upon behavior of the individual. All must be explored for what they may tell us of the origins of behavior itself. To the task we bring methods for the investigation of behavior and mental

process which have proved fruitful in other contexts, and a willingness to devise whatever new tools may be required to obtain answers to the questions before us. In contrast to the other positions represented here as implied in their very names—organic, psychodynamic, psychosocial—the position of experimental psychology as here described is not dedicated to any specific hypothesis or order of mechanisms which it holds to be the essential factor in the production of mental disease. The point of view of experimental psychologists is, rather, that the behavior seen in the psychopathological deviant is a product of natural causes which will yield in time to systematic, scientific investigation, even as we have succeeded in bringing some order into the explanation of such psychic phenomena as intelligence, memory, and perception which so puzzled our grandfathers.

Our position, scarcely unique, is summed up by the term experimental. At this point in time we believe that all of the postulated etiological factors which are represented at this Conference are valid, important approaches in need of further study. We place our strongest confidence for the eventual solution of the problem, however, in method and attitudes of approach to the problem, rather than in any of the hypothesized explanatory mechanisms current; for it is unmistakably clear that a variety of factors play a part in the etiology of mental disease, and that to date no single factor has demonstrated convincingly its paramount importance. The approaches represented here and others provide a theoretical framework in which to gather further basic data, so sorely needed to improve the empirical base upon which any theory of mental disease must rest. This is a task for the experimenter.

He may contribute to this objective by trying to clarify the description of the disordered psychological states themselves, by attempting to establish degrees of mental deviation along quantitative continua, and by relating psychopathological reactions to those of normal individuals under unusual circumstances, such as mental or physical stress. He may add to existing knowledge by seeking parallels to human reaction patterns in infrahuman species, testing the effects upon pathological mental states of physical or environmental manipulation, or evaluating the mental structure of persons biologically akin, or living under markedly contrasting social conditions. The experimental psychologist regards what is called mental disease as the reaction of the individual to a myriad of forces acting upon him, about which we have only the most incomplete knowledge at present. His view is necessarily eclectic and seeks to bring the phenomenology of mental disorder into the science of behavior, which he actively studies for all of man's activities, whether the behavior expressed occurs under conditions of sickness or health.

chapter 15

Fundamental Concepts, Basic Principles and Assumptions of the Psychodynamic Position on Mental Disease

FRANZ ALEXANDER

BASIC DYNAMIC PRINCIPLES

The psychodynamic position maintains that independent of their origin, mental diseases consist in dysfunctions of the ego. The ego is that part of the organism which has the task of gratifying subjective needs by coordinating (adjusting) the different needs to each other and to the existing environmental conditions. Whenever the ego is incapable of performing this task, conflict arises—either internal conflict or one between the ego and environment—and some form of mental disturbance results.

This statement requires a definition of the ego and its functions. Although the ego is a psychological concept, it refers to the highest coordinating centers of the nervous system. It is preferable to speak of ego functions instead of the more abstract concept of an ego. What we observe, describe, and utilize conceptually are ego functions. We assume that they are the functions of an organ system. What we actually observe are, however, only the psychological manifestations of this apparatus.

All the observations concerning this central coordinating function can best be stated, although only schematically, as follows. The ego's primary function is to maintain stationary conditions within the organism (the principle of psychological homeostasis). Life consists in a continuous cycle of output and resupply of energy. During the life process energy is consumed and must be regularly replaced from the environment. In the higher animals the primary function of the cerebrospinal and autonomic nervous system is to maintain this dynamic equilibrium which is constantly disturbed both by external stimuli and by the process of living itself.

Disturbances of equilibrium appear psychologically in the form of needs and wishes which seek gratification and serve as the motives of voluntary behavior. The basic tendency of the organism is to keep these psychological tensions at a constant level. Freud borrowed this principle from Fechner and called it the "principle of stability." Its physiological counterpart was first recognized by Claude Bernard and formulated by Cannon in his principle of "homeostasis," the tendency of living organisms to preserve internal conditions, such as temperature and the concentration of body fluids at a constant level. Freud's principle of stability and that of homeostasis are identical, one describing the same principle in psychological, the other in physiological, terms.

The psychoanalytic theory of the ego is that its function is to implement the principle of stability. The ego performs this function by four distinct performances: (1) Internal sensory perceptions by which it registers internal disturbances of the physicochemical equilibrium, perceiving them as impulses, needs, and sensations.* (2) External sensory perceptions by which it appraises the environmental conditions upon which the gratification of its needs depends. (3) Integrative (cognitive) function by which it correlates the data of internal and external perceptions and finds the solution for the gratification of the needs by confronting them with each other and with the existing external conditions. (4) The executive function; the ego is the center of motor control and carries out actions which are conceived conceptually through the integrative function.

To these four functions a fifth must be added—the protection of the organism from excessive external stimuli. This is achieved partially by an inherited threshold of sensitivity and partially by action by which it tries either to eliminate the external sources of excessive stimulation or to escape from the source of stimulation.

The principle of stability does not distinguish the quality of different instincts, drives, or emotions, but it applies to all of them, whether they represent such fundamental needs as hunger and sex or more complex impulses like curiosity and creativity, pity, and revenge, or complex emotional tendencies which find expression in such processes as weeping, laughing, or sighing.

It is evident that the principle of stabil-

ity is identical with the so-called instinct of self-preservation, but is a more precise and useful formulation of the same thing; namely, that the organism strives to preserve those optimal internal conditions under which the process of life is possible.

Every organism is born with automatic functions, the unconditioned reflexes, which are useful for maintaining life, or more precisely, for maintaining those constant conditions within the organism which are necessary for life. All internal vegetative functions such as digestion, the circulation of the blood, breathing, and excretion are examples of useful automatic mechanisms. They do not require conscious effort, and, with the exception of certain alimentary and excretory functions, belong to the hereditary equipment of the organism.

Other functions, most of which regulate the relation of the organism to its environment, must be learned through trial, error, and repetition. Behavior patterns which prove adequate in maintaining biological and psychological homeostasis are repeated until they become automatic and are performed with minimum effort. This whole process is called learning. It consists of two phases: (1) groping experimentation through trial and error, and (2) repetition of the adequate behavior patterns which have been found useful by trial and error. Learning aims ultimately at the gratification of need with the least expenditure of energy. Through repetition useful behavior patterns become automatic and effortless. Next to the principle of stability, the most common and basic tendency of the organism is to replace adjustments requiring effort inherent in experimentation by effortless automatic behavior (the principle of economy). This second phase of learning merely consolidates the newly acquired learning by repetition. The stability principle expresses merely the tendency of the organism to maintain constant optimal conditions for life, and alone it is not sufficient to describe animal behavior. This tendency toward stability is further defined by the principle of economy; namely, that the organism tends to perform the functions necessary for maintenance of constant conditions with minimum expenditure of energy.

---

* The original biologically determined impulses are called "id impulses."

The advantage of the principle of economy to the organism is obvious. It permits the saving of energy which adaptation to the environment requires. The energy saved by automatic behavior can be utilized to meet novel situations which require strenuous groping experimentation.

It is important, however, to realize certain disadvantages in automatic behavior. Conditions change, and owing to growth, the organism itself changes. Changed conditions require fresh adaptation. The adult cannot, like an infant, satisfy his needs by relying upon maternal help. He must learn independence and become active instead of passive. He must walk, eat, and ultimately satisfy many other needs on his own. Growth requires continuous learning. The principle of economy impels the organism to cling to automatic behavior which was satisfactory in the past but which is no longer adequate. This indolence was recognized by Freud, who called it *fixation*. He also discovered that when conditions become difficult and novel or threatening situations present themselves, earlier patterns of behavior tend to reassert themselves. This disposition, which he called *regression,* has proved one of the fundamental factors in psychopathology.

Changing conditions require *flexible behavior* or, in other words, rapid *ad hoc* responses which are suitable at the moment, but might be inappropriate in another situation. The capacity for sudden shifts of conduct belongs to the most highly developed functions of the personality. It rests on the ability to learn from past experiences through memory and to exercise reason in abstraction and differentiation. By memory and reason man is able not only to continue behaving in ways he has found useful but also to change as actual situations require. Life is thus a continuous struggle between the organism's tendency to retain old patterns on the principle of economy, and the challenge of growth and changed circumstances to adopt new ones.

The progression from birth to maturity can be viewed as a series of steps toward the mastery of functions which make the human being independent of its parents. Man first learns to masticate food and focus his eyes, then to coordinate movements which make grabbing possible. He then learns to walk, speak, and take a reasoned view of the world; and finally achieves maturity in his sexual development. The child, however, clearly resists his own progress toward maturity, and clings to acquired adjustments in accordance with the principle of economy. Whenever he is tired of the arduous task of constant readaptation or is confronted with new and difficult situations, he tends to fall back on earlier modes of behavior. Particularly successful previous adjustments serve as fixation points to which he regresses in times of emotional stress.

This resistance to growing up is a most conspicuous trait in all children, but it is only one aspect of the total picture. Growth, of course, is biologically predetermined, and the organism has no alternative than to accept it as an unalterable fact and adjust itself to it.

There are, however, many psychological factors as impressive as economy and regression which point toward growth and independence. Everything which the child learns is acquired originally through spontaneous playful experiment. Activities such as moving of the limbs, focusing of the eyes, and experiments in walking are not at first utilitarian but merely pleasurable. The young colt exuberantly racing in the meadow illustrates spontaneous pleasurable exertion.

It is true that by these playful exercises the organism prepares itself for the serious struggle for life, which begins when parental care is outgrown and the organism is thrown on its own resources. In learning spontaneously and playfully to master the body, however, no such practical foresight governs the behavior. The child plays and exercises its voluntary body functions merely for the sake of the pleasure derived from these activities. The hands grab for the sake of grabbing and not to obtain food; the eyes focus for the sensation of seeing; and the legs are used in walking and running because these activities are enjoyable. One of the fundamental discoveries of Freud was that these playful exercises and the mature manifestation of sexuality belong to the same category, which he called "erotic."

Erotic phenomena do not follow the principle of economy. They are designed, not to save energy, but to expend it spontaneously. They are creative and progressive, and serve as the dynamic motor power behind growth and propagation. They do not represent automatic repetitions or utilitarian adjustments; rather they lead the organism toward new ventures and experiments. The practical utilization of the faculties which the organism has acquired by pleasurable experience is a secondary step. The faculties must first be acquired separately before they can become integrated in a sensible manner for adaptive purposes. The energy spent in this lavish experimental and playful manner is surplus energy, not used for preserving homeostatic stability or survival. Its discharge, however, is one specific manifestation of the homeostatic principle. Excess of unused energy disturbs homeostatic equilibrium and must, therefore, be discharged.

In order to consider the origin of surplus energy, I introduced the vector analysis of the life process. From the point of view of energy, life can be viewed as a relationship between three vectors: (1) the intake of energy in the nutritive substances and oxygen; (2) their partial retention for use in growth; and (3) the expenditure of energy to maintain existence, as well as its loss in waste, in heat, and in erotic playful activities.

In the mature organism the erotic activities assume the form of propagation. This occurs first in puberty as a new kind of eliminating function: the production of germ cells. Propagation may be understood as growth beyond the limits of the individual biological unit. It follows the pattern of propagation in monocellular organisms. The process of growth has a natural limit when the cell reaches maturity. Thereafter reproduction occurs through the division of the cell. When a biological unit reaches a certain size, addition of substance and energy becomes impossible; for the capacity of the unit to organize living matter has reached its limit. Individual growth then stops, and propagation serves as a means of releasing surplus. Otherwise the homeostatic equilibrium would be disturbed.

Energy which is not needed to maintain life is the source of all sexual activity. In the infant, whose needs are satisfied by adults, the incorporating and retentive vectors outweigh the elimination: hence, the rapid growth. In spite of retention in the form of growth, there is still much surplus energy, neither stored nor used to maintain existence. The residuum is released in erotic activities. This explains the preponderance of erotic over utilitarian behavior in the child.

When the child expends energy erotically, he discovers at play new uses for his organs and exercises them until mastery is achieved and their different functions become integrated in a utilitarian fashion for independent existence. Erotic play for the sake of pleasure is the first phase, and the utilization of the functions acquired during erotic play is the second. This may appear paradoxical, but the prolonged dependence of the child upon the parents permits him the luxury of playful erotic activities. Thus the energy-saving principle and the creative use of surplus energy are interwoven and combine to maintain life and permit propagation. Repetition makes useful functions automatic and saves energy, which can be used for growth and procreation.

THE PSYCHODYNAMIC CONCEPT OF MENTAL DISTURBANCES

We may now return to the psychodynamic concept of mental disturbances. Whenever any of the above-described functions of the ego fail, mental disturbance results. This is independent of whether the breakdown of the functions is due to constitutional deficiencies, early or later environmental influences, interpersonal relationships, organic disease processes, toxic influences, or the aging process. The breakdown of the functions, independent of their origin, can be studied by their psychological manifestations.

The psychodynamic approach concerned itself in the past mainly with the large variety of disturbances called neuroses. It is assumed that in the etiology of neuroses, in addition to a basic constitutional component, the main factor consists in early emotional experiences in the family which lead to repression and thus interrupt that learning process by which the ego acquires its coordinating and executive functions.

The most universal factor responsible for neurosis-formation is inherent in the fact that the infant's and child's ego only gradually acquires in full measure its integrative function. Any internal impulses which the ego cannot synthesize in a harmonious way with other impulses or the existing environmental conditions, including the prevailing parental attitudes, are eliminated from consciousness and thus cannot participate in the learning process.

Neurotic symptoms and neurotic behavior patterns are unsuccessful attempts to gratify these ego-alien impulses which were excluded from the learning process and consequently were not brought into harmony with the external and internal standards. They are substitutive symbolic gratifications of ego-alien impulses. Although they are disguised and appear unintelligible and unmotivated, nevertheless they create internal conflict; hence, the ego has failed in its function to reduce internal tension and preserve stability.

Repression impoverishes the dynamic reservoir of the ego in two ways. Both sexual and aggressive impulses which otherwise would be modified and adjusted to the existing internal and external conditions are excluded, and in this way a dynamic impoverishment of the ego results. Moreover, the ego has to spend a great deal of its energy to hold in check the expressive tendency of the repressed impulses by different defense mechanisms; this expenditure of energy further depletes its dynamic reservoir.

Among these different defense mechanisms, in addition to repression, the best studied are: projection, displacement, substitution, overcompensation, rationalization, turning of the impulses against the self, and finally regression [1, 2].

A particular form of substitution has been called sublimation. This consists in substituting for original impulses other related ones which have a socially acceptable content and direction. Freud considered the capacity of sublimation an important factor in healthy development.

In addition to repression, regression is the most common defense mechanism in neurosis-formation. The solution of a conflict is attempted by the regressive return to earlier phases of development during which the person was still well-adjusted. This brings about a secondary conflict because, in the meantime, the ego has accepted certain standards which are contradictory to the regressively revived impulses.

A most common manifestation of this conflict appears as guilt feelings. The original impulses have been repressed or modified under the influence of parental standards, which are dependent upon the cultural milieu of the family. In the course of development these standards become incorporated within the personality by identification with the parental images (superego).

The regressive revival of earlier impulses thus creates a conflict with the incorporated superego standards, and this conflict may manifest itself as guilt feelings. Guilt feelings do not always appear in consciousness as such; sometimes they are only felt as anxiety, the source of which remains unconscious. The most common defense mechanism against guilt feelings is self-imposed suffering (self-punitive reactions). The fact that every neurotic symptom has a connotation of suffering is to a large degree due to the self-punitive component which is present in the neurotic symptom. By this self-imposed suffering, the ego tries to resolve anxiety due to unconscious guilt.

The conflict caused by the regressively revived earlier impulses may manifest itself not only in the form of guilt feelings but also as inferiority feelings. These develop because the regressive tendencies represent infantile strivings which are in contradiction to the standards of adulthood. A most common form of such secondary conflict is regression to the dependent attitude of childhood, which creates inferiority feelings. The ego may now defend itself against such inferiority feelings by overcompensatory attitudes such as excessive aggressiveness, bravado, hostility. These in turn become the sources of tertiary conflicts with the environment.

Every defense reaction may thus become the center of a new conflict against which the patient must employ new defensive measures. (See page 144, "The General Scheme of Neurosis-Formation.") Accordingly, every neurosis has a dynamic structure consisting of a system of primary, secondary, tertiary, etc. defenses.

Another important factor in neurosis-formation consists in the fixation to earlier successful phases of adjustment. Such fixation points determine the "depth of repression."

Another type of fixation (also known as repetition compulsion) consists in fixation on a traumatic situation which remained unresolved. The ego's basic function consists in resolving conflict situations. If it fails in solving a conflict situation, its tendency is to persevere and repeat the unresolved conflict in a futile attempt to solve it subsequently. This mechanism explains the stereotyped repetition of conflict situations in later life. This fixation on the trauma is of primary significance in the "traumatic neuroses."

THE THEORY OF TREATMENT

This theoretical system supplies the rationale of psychoanalytic therapy. It consists in re-exposing the ego to the unresolved conflict situations of the past, and in giving it a new opportunity to grapple with them in the transference situation in which the patient, because of the repetition compulsion, repeats the traumatic interpersonal relationships of his past in his emotional reactions to the physician.

Freud emphasized two quantitative factors which are responsible for the therapeutic effect of this procedure: (1) The repetition of the original conflict in the transference is less intensive than the original conflict was because it has no basis in the real relationship between the physician and the patient. (2) Now in the transference the adult ego is exposed to the same type of conflict which the weaker ego of the child could not resolve. Accordingly, psychoanalytic treatment consists first in the revival of the old conflict (transference

neurosis), and then in the resolution of the conflict by the simultaneous re-experiencing and understanding of it (emotional insight).

Recently, emphasis was laid upon what is called the corrective emotional experience in the transference situation. This consists in the fact that the physician's reactions to the patient's emotional attitudes are different from those of the original persons who were important in the patient's past development. Every neurosis can be considered as an attempted but unsuccessful adaptation to an interpersonal situation. It has a sense in the past; in other words, it was an adaptive reaction to the early family situation. When the same earlier attitudes are revived in the transference situation, they do not fit the therapist's attitude. This induces the patient's ego to find another solution which fits the present situation.

FURTHER ETIOLOGICAL CONSIDERATIONS

The recognition of the pathogenic significance of early experiences in the family is not contradictory to the existence of other pathogenic factors. In general, it is assumed by most authors in this field that a complementary relationship exists between constitutional factors, early experiences, and later experiences. If the constitutional factor is great, family influences, which in a person with a healthier constitution would not be pathogenic, may become harmful. Similarly, later traumatic experiences in a person with a good constitutional background and healthy childhood will produce a neurosis only if they are extreme.

The combination of these three categories of factors (constitution and early and later experiences) allows a great many etiological equations. In certain cases, constitution; in others, early family experiences; and again in others, later traumatic occurrences may have the most important role. In general, however, all three factors must be considered in every neurosis-formation.

There is a divergence of opinion in the evaluation of the psychodynamic factor in psychoses, particularly in the schizophrenias. Some authors maintain with Freud that in these cases the constitutional factor is of overwhelming importance. Others believe that early experiences of the child, particularly the mother-child relationship, might be of decisive importance. In general, as in neuroses, so in the psychoses, all three factors must be considered. Most authors seem to agree, however, that in the majority of psychotics the constitutional element is more important than it is in psychoneurotics.

The General Scheme of Neurosis-Formation

Schematically, the development of neuroses can be described as follows:

1. *Precipitating factors*—The actual situation with which the patient cannot cope.

2. *Failure in the solution of actual problems*—Unsuccessful attempts at adaptation of shorter or longer duration.

3. *Regression*—The replacement of realistic effort to gratify needs by regressive fantasies of behavior.

4. *Primary conflict revived by regression*—The revival of old conflicts by regression to old adaptive patterns which were abandoned in the course of growing up.

5. *Self-punitive measures*—A futile struggle to resolve neurotic conflict by a combination of substitutive gratifications and self-punishment expressed in symptoms. The futility of the attempt to resolve the conflict is due to the fact that the regressive desires, the guilt, and the resulting need for self-punishment are all unconscious. Only their disguised representations are conscious. Defenses against primary conflict may create new conflicts and provoke secondary defenses.

6. *Tertiary conflict and the impoverishment of the ego*—The longer a neurosis continues, the more fully a vicious circle develops. Symptoms absorb a patient's energies and make him less effective in dealing realistically with life. These are the tertiary conflicts which necessitate further regression and symptomatic outlets, which in turn increase conflict and absorb more energy.

COMMENTS

The views outlined here represent an attempt to account for the actual psychological observations in a theoretical system which has internal consistency (the structural-dynamic theory of the ego). The underlying psychodynamic observations, particularly the phenomena of repression, regression, and the other defense mechanisms by which the conscious self tries to deal with conflictful internal tensions, can be considered as having full factual evidence. The structural-dynamic theory of the ego is based on these observations and is a theory which, at the present state of our knowledge, gives the most adequate account of them.

There is no reliable method available at present to appraise quantitatively the observed psychodynamic processes. All reference to quantities in psychodynamic conflict situations, as well as in the appraisal of the relative importance of constitutional factors, and of early and later experiences, is merely approximate and is not based on sufficiently reliable criteria. For example, in a severely neurotic or psychotic person, the absence of severe traumatic experiences in early childhood and later life would indicate a significant constitutional vulnerability. Conversely, if a person develops a neurosis only in later life, in spite of the fact that he had an extremely traumatic childhood, this would indicate that his disease was precipitated by traumatic circumstances of later life.

This type of evaluation of the etiological factors is obviously quite crude because it deals with concepts which cannot be measured directly, such as constitutional vulnerability and severity of a traumatic experience. The lack of precise quantitative methods therefore makes the evaluation of the therapeutic chances and general prognostication highly speculative. Consequently, the treatment of mental diseases is still based on a great deal of empiricism. The same pertains, even more so, to prognostic evaluations. This is best illustrated by the fact that frequently cases which initially appear hopeful turn out as therapeutic failures. On the other hand, not infrequently cases which impress even the highly trained specialist as doubtful therapeutic chances have unexpectedly good therapeutic results.

While understanding of the psychological content and etiology of mental diseases has greatly advanced in the last fifty years, very little progress has been made in introducing quantitative methods. This is due, partially at least, to the fact that psychodynamic knowledge has been obtained primarily in the therapeutic situation and not by an experimental approach which allows control of the different variables. The quantitative appraisal of psychological phenomena will of necessity come from experimental procedures by which the theoretical assumptions and formulations can be further substantiated, refined, and quantitatively explored.

In my outline of the psychodynamic position, I have disregarded all theoretical and speculative assumptions concerning the "ultimate nature" of the psychological impulses and of the instinctual drives (classical libido theory). Such assumptions can be considered as a theoretical superstructure which do not affect the validity of the observational substratum or the psychodynamic theory of the structure, functions, and dysfunctions of the mental apparatus.

REFERENCES

1. ALEXANDER, FRANZ. *The Fundamentals of Psychoanalysis*. New York: W. W. Norton, 1948.
2. FREUD, ANNA. *The Ego and the Mechanisms of Defense*. London: Hogarth Press, 1937.

Comment on the Psychodynamic Position

ROY R. GRINKER

1. I disagree with the broad statement that mental disease consists of dysfunctions of the ego resulting in or from modifications of its capacity to perform its homeostatic tasks. Although Dr. Alexander postulates later a general scheme of multiple factors concerned in the development of mental disease, here he talks of a single cause or at least of a single intermediate cause. Causes of mental illness, I believe, can only be viewed as many variables within a large field of events occurring in time. To pinpoint the ego even as a representative of past events neglects a host of dynamic processes.

2. The principle of stability of homeostasis may be valid as a conceptual scheme for considering self-preservation. But to make this principle consistent, we have to be prepared to jump from one level or organization to another to guarantee that with loss, defect, or death some organization is preserved. This scheme does not take under consideration those goal-changing forces which move the organism out of rest,

stability, into new transactional fields either in growth or evolution.

3. The vector theory is unfortunately couched in terms combining energy constants and psychological satisfactions. Random first movements, beginning of function of part-processes preparatory to their integration in developing larger organizations, should not be considered in erotic terms. Granted these are functional, and granted that adequate use of structure-in-function is pleasurable, the frame of reference must be in terms of either the psyche (pleasure) or the organism in transaction within its environment. From the latter aspect, expenditure of energy can hardly be considered a goal.

4. In the discharge of surplus energy in propagation as a means of maintaining homeostatic equilibrium, Dr. Alexander again transcribes a concept from one system to another. Here again he comes into difficulties because he uses energic parallels, when communication without regard for energy distribution is as far as we are able

to go. The use of "surplus energy" is justified only with poetic license: it is not scientific. The sexual act is not propagation, and as a satisfying process it need not produce anything or give anything except *to* the actor.

5. Dr. Alexander discusses failures of the ego in its capacity for learning and integration, and speaks of ego-alien processes resulting in repressions and regressions and their systematic results. These occurrences and the tendency for repetition constitute a phenomenon observable in all personalities and in the mentally ill. The emphasis here is again on the single focus; however, in a wide number of situations, failures of the ego are not necessarily related to its processes patterns but to the demands made on them.

6. In the next sections Dr. Alexander gives his pluralistic concepts, but in the form of lists. Such statements give to non-dynamic psychiatrists and those of other fields a notion of psychodynamics which has static implications. The task of psychodynamics is to observe and categorize the transactions of these variables; but to list them is to give them no more than lip service. When the chips are down and the psychodynamic formulation emphasizes a structure-function such as the ego as the culprit causing disease, we have failed. We have failed when we do not consider more than the internal or the external environmental part-processes as "entities."

7. The absence of quantitative methods is due to the narrow focus of psychodynamic research. Quantities of change in terms of "yes or no" and sometimes in "how much" can be achieved in a psychodynamic field study but not by measurements of an observer in the system he is studying. In fact, quantification requires that he use a frame of reference viewing at least three systems in transaction. Then I believe quantitative studies may be made.

8. I would agree completely that the libido theory is a super-theory that the psychodynamicist does not need any more than the physicist needs to speculate on life-force when he works with nuclear processes.

chapter *16*

The Psychosocial Position—
A Preparatory Statement

THOMAS A. C. RENNIE

• •

The proponents of the psychosocial position are concerned with the impact of culture and social environment upon the growth of personalities and in the incidence and variations in psychopathological states. We recognize that all human beings have unique hereditary endowment, each with special liabilities and strengths. (Kallman's studies on identical twins and schizophrenia seem incontrovertible.) We accept the fact of organic, metabolic, and hormonal participation in all life reactions, as evidenced, for example, in physiological studies of stress. We are aware of the unique symbolic functions in psychodynamics. However, the primary emphasis of the psychosocial position is on the impact of the particular cultural setting of uniquely different individuals on all three of these determinants.

By culture we mean the gamut of patterned family and social influences, acquired and transmitted by symbols, forged into a way of life, affirmed and reaffirmed in the common currency of custom, and having a significant discernible meaning and value for the individual. Culture is the transmissible body of facts, artifacts, and historically derived ideas, regulating patterns of behavior, ethics, child-rearing practices, taboos, social integration, attitudes

toward health and illness, religious values—in short, those elements which ultimately are incorporated into personal functioning and social controls of behavior as the dynamics of superego formation. [9] Every individual lives his life span in a constant homeostatic relationship with this total environment. Just as every personality possesses unique qualities, so do families vary in subtle and unique composition. Social groups, too, have their special describable characteristics. And finally, just as every life has a beginning, middle, and end, so families have growth spans (a beginning, middle, and end), and so do cultural communities. Often we study man at specific intervals in the life biography but fail to view him at a unique moment of time in the historic evolution of his family and of his society. Psychiatrists work pragmatically with just such kinds of data in the orderly accumulation of their case records, but the attempt to formulate principles of interrelation between persons and culture has lagged in psychiatry behind that of the social sciences. There have been numerous exceptions: Rank, Rado, Kardiner, Ferenczi, Sullivan, Horney, and Roheim, to mention a few hardy pioneers; some of them were influenced by their direct work with

147

anthropologists such as Linton, Sapir, and Benedict.

This uniqueness of culture is easily recognized in the field studies of diverse and rare ethnic groups, the so-called nonliterate cultures. There the contrasts are vivid and dramatic. Less readily understood in our contemporary Western cultures, made up as they are of widely varying socioeconomic and ethnic groups, is the range of differences that exist within the generational level: the religious sects, the geographic migrants, those who have experienced social mobility upwards and downwards. These variances in life-course create for the residents of any modern city a definable difference in value systems, roles, aspirations, and culturally determined stresses. It suffices to mention the special problems in adaptation encountered by members of minority groups or by the relatively anonymous dwellers of large urban centers. Perhaps the most dramatic of these in New York are the problems of Puerto Rican migrants who, coming as they do from a largely agricultural society in which male dominance was once outstanding, suffer severe disruptions in acculturation,—a manifestation of a society in transition—, including a shift in the male role to greater subordination in the social scene, more jobs for females, the female role-conflicts, disrupted families, multiple marriages, changes of common-law partners, and attendant disorientation of children. The resultant toll of a high incidence of antisocial behavior, of language problems, job instability, and even of psychosomatic disorder is the common talk of this town, in lecture, article, and press. Kinsey makes explicit the differences in sexual patterns among males of different educational level and social status. C. Wright Mills, Clarence Senior, and R. Goldsen have just begun the story of what they aptly call the *Puerto Rican Journey*.

THE EVIDENCE FROM ANTHROPOLOGY

Beginning with Kraepelin, there have been general observations that psychopathological categories vary with culture. Bleuler, in Switzerland, discovered even more subtle variations in the schizophrenia symptoms of Germans, Italians, and French. [2] An intensive analysis of psychopathological differences in different clinics would, I am sure, reveal substantial contrasts. On coming to New York from Baltimore, I was personally much struck with the much more frequent paranoid features among Payne Whitney cases, and the greater incidence of overt and latent homosexual dynamics in patients from New York. Differential rates, differential diagnoses, and gross variations in psychopathology have been regularly reported from culture to culture, in the Javanese (according to Kraepelin), the Malayans (the Catah reaction), the Siberians (according to Czaplicka), Africans (see J. Corothers, *The African Mind,* W.H.O. Monograph, Geneva), and Marquesans. The Marshalese and Okinawans, unexposed to Western Christian concepts of original sin and guilt, are reported to be remarkably free of anxiety and neuroses. Findings on the epidemiology of mental illness have been well reported in the Milbank Memorial Fund publication, *Epidemiology of Mental Disorder,* 1950.

As history and culture change, new styles of mental illness arise. The dancing mania of thirteenth century Italy, described by Ferdinandus and Baglivi and redescribed by Sigerist, can be duplicated in anthropological literature. The Vailala Madness in New Guinea (reported by F. E. Williams), the Ghost Dance of Plains Indians (by Cora DuBois), or the Ute Indian Ghost Dance (by M. K. Opler) demonstrates that there is little about mental illness which is immutable in time or hard to duplicate cross-culturally in special times and places.

THE EPIDEMIOLOGICAL EVIDENCE

More important in the sense of larger populations, however, are the attempts to specify the particular psychopathological differences in our *own* cultural groups: the higher incidence of alcoholism in the Irish, [1] the claims of a greater incidence of sociopathic disorders in the Italians (studies of Hyde and colleagues of Selective Service registrants in Boston [8]), give indications that even within our own culture specificities exist. The different rates of suicide in Western countries can clearly be related to the cultural (specifically religious) differences. [15] The Durkheim [4] concept of anomie has been utilized by Merton and Riesman to denote not merely a nondescript anonymity but a personally felt sense of alienation from others. The class-linked matrix of schizophrenia was early noted by Faris and Dunham and later modified to the concept of downward mobility and selective "drift" by Gerard. [7] The studies of Redlich and Hollingshead in New Haven point to a higher frequency of schizophrenia in the lower socioeconomic groups, a higher incidence of neuroses in middle and upper class groups. It has been claimed, too, that psychoneurosis is an inevitable consequence of upward social mobility, moving through more than two levels of socioeconomic strata. Ulcer has been described as a middle class disease. Worthy of note is the shift in sex ratio of certain psychosomatic disorders, most particularly peptic ulcer, which from once being predominantly a female disorder is now predominantly a disease of men. Ebaugh [6] has discussed this disproportion in sex incidence of many psychosomatic disorders. According to him, childhood asthma and duodenal ulcer occur more often in males than in females. Exophthalmic goiter, gallbladder disease, and rheumatoid arthritis seem to afflict females more than males.

Certain of these illnesses, which occurred more often in females (e.g., peptic ulcer, exophthalmic goiter, and perhaps essential hypertension) in the nineteenth century, have been appearing in an increasing proportion among males during the twentieth century. Other psychosomatic illnesses (e.g., diabetes) which were predominantly diseases of males during the last century have occurred increasingly among females in the present century. The phenomenon of "sex shift" probably provides a statistical indication of the changes that have taken place in the "personality type" of the sexes as a result of social changes that have led to "female emancipation."

As Ebaugh [6] says: "Another phenomenon accompanying the rise in incidence of psychosomatic disorders is known as the 'age shift,' which refers to the fact that certain of these illnesses are increasingly making their initial appearance in younger age groups" (i.e., gastritis, peptic ulcer, and the anxiety states).

As further evidence of sociological determinants, there have been studies to indicate that psychoneurotic and psychosomatic diseases tend to occur in clusters in certain families. Such patients give a significantly high history of the same or similar disorders in parents, siblings, or relatives. A recent study among Bell telephone operators in New York City indicates that a high incidence of psychoneurotic absenteeism was regularly accounted for by the same 25 per cent of the workers and that psychoneurosis commonly occurs in the same person in collaboration with a high percentage of organic diseases. We should not ignore the evidence of Buell and associates from their studies in Minneapolis-St. Paul (probably applicable to all large cities) that approximately 25 per cent of the population regularly and constantly utilizes 80 per cent of the health resources of a city.

As Opler [13] has stated:

Prevalence and incidence studies, conducted in national and regional illness censuses, constitute one method of epidemiological survey. Although useless etiologically, they do have great practical importance in providing guidance of a general sort for over-all planning, public education in mental hygiene, and the assessment of mental ills in the total health and economy of the nation. When H. Emerson, at the First International Congress on Mental Hygiene in 1930, gave gross quantitative evidence of the magnitude and extent of mental disorders as a public health problem and in the same decade outlined the first inclusive epidemiological research of this type, the movement was felt as a part of a long overdue attack on the chronic, degenerative, crippling and neoplastic processes, more challenging and by this time more widespread and baffling than the germ-specific, mechanically isolatable, and pharmacologically treatable ailments.

Freeman, first in a number of epidemiological research innovations, stimulated in 1936 the first comprehensive survey in a major population of over 50,000 persons, the Eastern Health District of Baltimore. This field work was carried forward by Lemkau, Tietze, and Cooper. Then, in rapid succession, in 1938, there was the Williamson County, Tennessee survey of Roth and Luton, next the work of Dunham in Chicago, later Hyde in Boston, and Stott; along with these, there were the formal programs of incidence study in New York and Massachusetts. The former were no doubt also influenced by Pollock's work in the 1920's, Nolan's in the decade before, and Malzberg's imposing surveys.

The two world wars, particularly World War II, gave decided impetus to studies of induction and rejection data, Hyde's mental rejection rates being wholly of this type. Subsequent studies of community population samples pushed beyond the frontiers established by Faris and Dunham, and the type of epidemiological team, now used, included the psychiatrist, anthropologist, sociologist, statistician, psychologist and social worker. The German studies of Brugger in Thuringia and Bavaria, in the 1930's, and a host of Scandinavian studies; Stromgren's in Danish rural and fishing communities; Sjögren and Böök's in Swedish villages and island districts, and Odegaard's of the Norwegian hospitalized antedated though mostly in rural circumstances the American urban and state surveys.

These studies are not comparable because of methodological differences in gathering data. Yet Brugger found a constantly higher rate in every diagnostic category per 1,000 in Bavaria. The Tennessee survey with its rate of 69.4 per 1,000 is no more reassuring than Paul Lemkau's with its rate of 60.5 per 1,000; and the Dunham, Stott, and Hyde studies tell a similar story of high rates, in no case pinpointed to the end result of being etiologically useful to dynamic psychiatry or psychotherapy.

Further evidence of cultural impact can be studied in certain mass phenomena of our times: the panic reaction to disaster, the "springtime rites" of certain college groups. Consider, too, the class-linked patterns of juvenile behavior. Antisocial acts in an East Side slum area of New York may well be adaptive behavior of a not-unhealthy survival type, quite different in interpretation from the same act as committed by an upper level boy in a private school setting.

THE EVIDENCE FROM CULTURAL CHANGES

In addition, it is difficult to avoid the conclusion that psychopathologies differ at given periods of time in the same culture. A study of hospitalized psychiatric patients over a period of the past twenty years reveals interesting shifts in prevailing clinical syndromes and manifestations. As Diethelm [3] has noted, the classical hysterical reaction of the eighteenth century, related to religious aspects and witchcraft, gave way to the hysterical convulsions of the nineteenth century—hysterical phenomena which are almost never seen today. In their place we are observing a rise in psychosomatic disorders, anxiety and phobic reactions, and sexual difficulties. The frequent psychopathological features of schizophrenia, as described forty-five years ago—catatonic posturing, autistic withdrawal, smearing, echolalia, echopraxia, nelogisms—are rarely seen in modern psychiatric hospitals. The quite common disorder of involutional melancholia of a decade ago, with its characteristic features of agitation, hypochondriacal delusions, or delusions of excessive sinning are today infrequent. They are occasionally observed in rural populations but rarely in educated and urban populations. Attitudes toward disorders of menstruation and menopause have radically shifted in the past twenty years, no doubt because of a higher level of public sophistication. At any rate, such disorders are less common. In psychoneurotic illnesses, the obsessions, compulsions, and hysterical symptoms appear to have decreased in frequency and depressions of psychoneurotic origin seem more common. Contemporary cultural studies might clarify the meaning of these changes.

SOCIOLOGICAL EVIDENCE

That the disappearance of many of the classic symptoms described in earlier psychiatric literature is in part culturally determined is evidenced in the growing number of studies of the psychiatric hospital itself as a cultural milieu. Stanton and Davies threw considerable light on this in their studies at Chestnut Lodge where specific psychopathology such as soiling seemed to be a reaction to a specific milieu. With the vanishing of authoritarianism in hospital settings and the emergence of permissiveness and social expectations of appropriate behavior, many of the more distressing features of the schizophrenic illness have simply disappeared.

CONTEMPORARY CULTURE STUDIES

Looking more closely at our own American culture, it is abundantly evident that infinite variety exists in the cultural communities comprising our own nation. Eaton's study of the Hutterites describes a remarkably stable and homogeneous population, a population group with a seemingly higher than average incidence of manic-depressive disorders. [5] It is difficult to conceive as culturally similar the small town and the urban world, with the latter predominantly characterized by crowding, density, heterogeneity, anonymity, secularism, social mobility, extremes of socioeconomic difference, and ethnic diversity.

It is hard to avoid the conclusion that the family structure is materially altered by such factors. In our own community studies in Yorkville we find abundant evidence of this. An Italian family of lower socioeconomic status is in no way comparable to a Germany family of similar status. The Italian mother is warm, loving, really permissive. Her sphere is the care of children, and her child is rarely absent from her. She is greatly concerned with the problems of nutrition, rich blood, hearty diets, and specific foods for building vigor and strength. While the male is dominant, the woman's role as housekeeper and mother is of paramount importance, and in it she earns complete status and recognition. Almost the reverse is true in the German family with its strong authoritarian tinge, the absolutism of the father, the subservience of the wife and children. The Czech family is a tightly cohesive one, and one with much maternal authority. It still clings rigorously to its old-world cultural patterns, holding tightly together as a community, preserving its own ethnic folkways and

family organizations, and cultural identification. The Puerto Rican family is characterized by lack of cohesion, loosely maintained bonds, and a bitter struggle between the parents as to dominance role. Within the context of any family there are, in addition, very dissimilar roles allocated to males and females, and to siblings of different numerical order of birth. Studies of individual psychodynamics give ample evidence of the crucial impact of such factors on the growing personality. We need to quantify such determinants in statistical studies of carefully matched family groupings.

An interesting substudy by one of my associates, Lorraine Loustalot [11], of hospital behavior of first- and second-generation Italians gives a vivid picture of the acting-out, emotionally flamboyant, dramatizing Italian mother, with her apparent uncooperativeness by refusing hospital food and medical procedures, and her insistence on needing home-cooked food for its rich blood-building character.

Further, if we look at one specific aspect of our own American culture, the rural-urban continuum, it can be safely hypothesized that the impact of the family on children is conditioned in part by the neighborhood community in which it lives and moves. Obviously the family does not exist in a social vacuum. On the contrary, we postulate that its internal relationships and functioning, particularly during crises, tend to reflect the neighborhood and communal institutions enveloping it. Moreover, in the large areas of a child's movements outside the home, he is directly influenced by the neighborhood and community setting.

We hypothesize further that the neighborhood qualities that are significant for child development are those associated with the urban-rural continuum of community types. The metropolis and the town tend to be identified as the extreme types on this continuum. The major contrasting qualities of these two types include the following:

1. *Population density*
   a. the town: low density and spaciousness

    b. the metropolis: high density and crowding

2. *Cultural differentiation*
    a. the town: relative homogeneity
    b. the metropolis: great cultural heterogeneity in terms of socioeconomic and ethnic differences. It is postulated that these differences make for a bewildering multiplicity of standards (lacking in the town) both for the child in his autonomy strivings and for the parent in his authority-and-disciplining role.

3. *Stability* (in space, i.e., residence, and in the status hierarchy)
    a. the town: relatively stable
    b. the metropolis: highly unstable, i.e., frequent residential movement, making for rootlessness; and rapid status mobility, making for stressful conflicts and frustrations that tend to accompany both successful and unsuccessful efforts to "climb" economically and socially.

4. *Religiosity*
    a. the town: church and religion tending to occupy a central place in community and family life.
    b. the metropolis: pronounced drift toward secularization in the family, with the church tending to be a peripheral institution.

5. *Social integration*
    a. the town: high interpersonal and interfamilial integration (interrelatedness), large "visibility" of individual family, bringing stabilizing group (neighborhood) support to the family's internal equilibrium.
    b. the metropolis: little interpersonal, interfamilial integration on the neighborhood level, and low "visibility" of the individual and the family. Such anonymity and isolation involve attention or absence of neighborhood group support, exposing the family to greater internal instability and dysequilibrium.

In combination, therefore, the qualities associated with the town, it is postulated, make for neighborhood and institutional support (*a*) for the parent in his child-training role, (*b*) for the family as a whole in crises and stressful situations, (*c*) for the individual's sense of security, rootedness, and stability.

On the other hand, it is hypothesized that the qualities associated with the metropolis, in combination, tend to make for attenuation of neighborhood and institutional support (*a*) for the parent in his child-training role, permitting inconsistencies and failures in this role; (*b*) for the family as a whole in crises and stressful situations, tending to induce overreaction and dysfunctional behavior; (*c*) for the individual, exposing him to insecurity, instability, malaise, and self-to-group alienation.

All of these hypotheses may contain variation in actual working out. No one thinks seriously that urban Irish turn secular, or that upper status groups in New York or elsewhere have any great rates of residential mobility. However, it is precisely these variations, entering into people's lives deeply, that need testing. The studies of Lemert [10] have already thrown doubt on the broad claim that rural communities are havens of good mental health, as has the work of Eaton and Weil [5]. Mangus [12], in Butler County, Ohio, found that differences in urban, rural, and farm population rates of children's personality adjustment did not favor any of the groups considered, while Lemert found a poor rural area most problematic. (See also 14.) The Yorkville study, by calibrating its methods with the Stirling County study in rural and semirural Nova Scotia, hopes to answer questions concerning the urban-rural continuum in a definitive fashion. It is at least clear at the present time that rate of incidence variations do exist for psychiatric disorder, that some urban and some rural scenes have higher rates than others, and that the etiological reasons must be made clear if we are to answer the popular questions about the impact of urban tempo on mental health.

Furthermore, we begin to have evidence that the frequency and nature of mental disorders vary among ethnic subcultures, as well as among the socioeconomic subgroups of a given population. It can be safely assumed that childhood experiences, so basic in the formation of character and personality, will be markedly influenced by the general physical health of parents, the anxiety-tension level of parents, interparental compatability, partial or complete absence of one or both parents, family participation of other kin, family economic hardships, father's occupational mobility upward or downward. Within this cultural fluidity there will always remain problems of identification, peer-group relationships, educational and vocational opportunities; and these are uniquely predetermined for certain subgroups in our society in a characteristic way.

Much attention needs to be paid to the unique differences in contemporary ethnic subgroups: the markedly different roles played by mothers in the Irish and Italian families versus those of the German family; differences in roles played by the father, as for example in Puerto Rican and in Czech families; and the classic conflicts generated in the process of acculturation and in the struggle inherent in first- and second-generation adaptation. The immigrant of first generation is usually in the earliest and most intense stage of the acculturation process. With the second generation the acculturation stresses take a different form in that they arise from the disparity between the cultural patterns of the home and those in the outer American world, and the authority-autonomy conflict between the child and his immigrant parents. While many of these cultural determinants of human behavior remain to be put to rigid scientific test, there have been notable beginnings in the prevalence studies of Roth and Luton in Williams County, Tennessee; the Lemkau studies in the Eastern Health District of Baltimore; and the current community research studies in New Haven, Yorkville, and Nova Scotia. The latter three are designed not merely to be epidemiological in nature, but also to attempt to probe the etiological variables inherent in the cultural stresses extant in our own society.

There is much need for further specific and systematic study, but there is gathering evidence to support the belief that the study of man must increasingly view man in the cultural environment which molds him. Adolf Meyer had begun to be aware of this when he formulated his concept of psychobiological man as a reacting organism. Increasingly it will be necessary to speak of the "psycho-bio-social" man if we are to understand more completely the unique integration of man living in a social structure, not man in a cultureless vacuum. This is the chief emphasis of the psychosocial approach. The approach obviously has its implications for therapy, not to mention its more immediate application in terms of planning mental health resources and preventive services. For therapy it means constant awareness of the realities of the personal, family, and social milieu. The painstaking elucidation of personal psychodynamics, helpful as it undeniably is, often leads to a picture of the person which is distorted and unreal. The person's portrait of his background, as symbolically experienced in a highly personalized fashion, may be far from the realities as they actually existed and operated. In viewing the person from the psychosocial point of view, one must see not only the impact of family members on the patient (or as perceived by the patient), but also the total interactions and counter-impact of the patient and his illness on other members of the family, the subtle shifts of relationships necessitated by the changes being brought about in the patient, and the disruption in the family homeostasis that occurs both with illness and recovery, and with restoration of more healthy modes of interpersonal relationships. In one of my cases of ulcerative colitis, the patient's life was in actual jeopardy because of the severe bleeding which occurred every time his unconscious rage was aroused by the interference of a dominating and devouring mother. Psychotherapy for the mother with attention to her needs brought an easing of the mutual tensions, which made it possible for the patient to stop bleeding and eventually recover. The best individual therapy can be defeated by the family which is not prepared to give and take in a change of relationships which the recovering patient with his own new insights and greater freedom demands. Many a schizophrenic patient is doomed to permanent hospitalization because families are too basically rejecting and are unable to adjust to the shifting relationships. Similar factors may well be operating in the shifting social scene. Our society has moved a long way from the rigid Victorian era, with its sexual pruderies and lack of communication, to the present era, in which it may be, as Sullivan [16] held, that the central problem is no longer one of sexual frustration but one of personal loneliness.

REFERENCES

1. BALES, R. F. Cultural differences in rates of alcoholism. Quart J. Stud. Alc. 1946, 6: 480–499.

2. BLEULER, EUGEN. Dementia Praecox or the Group of Schizophrenias. Tr.: J. Zinkin, New York: International Universities Press, 1950, pp. 336, 463.

3. DIETHELM, O. Annual Report. Payne Whitney Clinic. New York, 1953.

4. DURKHEIM, E. Suicide—A Study in Sociology. Tr.: John A. Spaulding and George Simpson, Glencoe, Ill.: 1951, The Free Press.

5. EATON, J. W., and WEIL, R. J. The mental health of the Hutterites. Scien. Am., 1953, 189: 31–37.

6. EBAUGH, F. G. "Psychosomatic Medicine. A Review." International Forum, 1954, 2:75. In Therapeutic Notes (Parke, Davis & Co.), 1954, 61. Ibid.: p. 75.

7. GERARD, D. L., and HOUSTON, L. G. Family setting and the social ecology of schizophrenia. Psychiat. Quart. 1953, 27: 90–101.

8. HYDE, R. L., and KINGSLEY, L. V. Studies in Medical Sociology. I. The relation of mental disorders to the community socioeconomic level. New Eng. J. Med., 1944, 231: 543–548.

9. KROEBER, A. L., and KLUCKHOHN, C. Culture. Papers of the Peabody Museum of Harvard Univ., 1952, 47: 181.

10. LEMERT, E. M. An exploratory study of mental disorders in a rural problem area. Rural Sociol. 1948, 13: 48–64.

11. LOUSTALOT, LORRAINE. Families of Three Ethnic Groups as Seen in a Child Guidance Clinic. New York. Columbia University, N.Y. School of Social Work. M.A. Thesis, 1953.

12. MANGUS, A. R. Mental health of rural children in Ohio. Ohio Agric. Exper. Station, Research Bulletin No. 682, 1949, 34 pp.

13. OPLER, M. K. Culture, Psychiatry and Human Values. Springfield, Ill., C. C Thomas, 1956, pp. 40–42.

14. STOTT, L. H. Some environmental factors in relation to the personality adjustments of rural children. Rural Sociol., 1945, 10: 394–403.

15. STRAUS, J. H., and STRAUS, M. A. Suicide, homicide, and social structure in Ceylon. Am. J. Sociol., 1953, 58: 461–469.

16. The Contributions of Harry Stack Sullivan. P. Mullahy (Ed.). New York: Hermitage House, 1952.

Comment on the Psychosocial Position

J. P. SCOTT

Dr. Rennie has given an adequate and inclusive statement of the approach to mental disease through the influence of the social environment. As he has pointed out, there is no essential conflict between this position and those of the other schools of thought which have been presented here. In this comment I shall attempt to amplify his statement in the light of certain general biological theories and areas of research.

THE CONCEPT OF LEVELS OF ORGANIZATION IN RELATION TO MENTAL DISEASE

A fundamental concept which has arisen from the study of biology is that of levels of organization. These can be defined in various ways but usually are considered to range from the submicroscopic viruses to entire populations of animals. As can be seen from Figure 1, the various positions which are taken on the etiology of mental disease fit very nicely into the different levels of organization. The organic viewpoint covers any level within and up to the organismic or individual level. The psychological viewpoint covers factors which op-

various positions show a common tendency to reorganize factors more central to the various regions. That these factors are related, as well as mutually compatible, is brought out by general biological theory.

Generally speaking, evolution has proceeded from lower to higher levels of organization. As this has occurred, factors working at lower levels have been integrated on higher levels, but the basic fac-

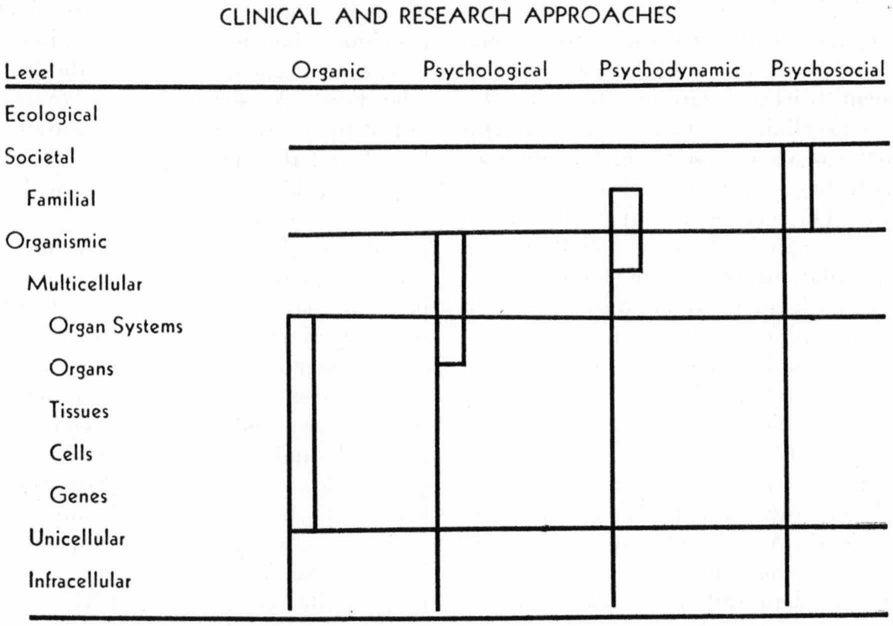

FIG. 1. Factors affecting mental disease in relation to biological levels of organization. Double lines indicate areas of primary emphasis; single lines indicate recognized but less emphasized areas.

erate on the organismic level and is directly concerned with organ systems, such as the nervous system on the level immediately below. The psychodynamic approach includes the lower part of societal organization, particularly that of the family, and overlaps the organismic level of psychology. The psychosocial position emphasizes environmental social factors arising from entire human societies. Each of these points of view tends, if broadly expressed, to include and explain the operation of factors at lower levels of organization. One would expect the greatest degree of disagreement in the areas of overlap; but as expressed by the contributions to the Conference, the

tors are little modified [8]. Factors operating at the higher levels tend to affect the level immediately below most importantly and to have relatively little effect on the very lowest levels. This means that if we take a unit at any one level of organization (as, for example, the human individual), factors at lower levels will be working internally and factors from higher levels will be acting upon it externally. The behavior of the human individual will be affected both by the action of genes working at the very lowest level of organization and by the action of the general ecological environment working at the highest level. The action of factors working at a lower level may be partially integrated by those at higher levels, and conversely the action of the latter is limited by factors at lower levels. A complete picture must include consideration of factors working on all levels.

THE SOCIOBIOLOGICAL OR ECOLOGICAL POINT OF VIEW

It will be seen from Figure 1 that none of the different points of view expressed in the preliminary reports to this Conference refer to factors at the highest level of biological organization, and I should like to comment briefly regarding them. So far there is no clinical school which represents this point of view, and its chief importance probably lies in giving a clear theoretical picture. The ecologist and sociobiologist look at animals in terms of socially organized populations of various kinds of species, which in turn are organized into animal communities. In this context the problem of mental disease becomes one of adaptation and survival, and a mentally diseased individual is one which shows nonadaptive behavior.

Naturalists have found very few instances of truly nonadaptive behavior in wild animals. An animal may be unable to adjust to a situation; but he usually does his best to adapt and, if he fails, he tries to escape from the position. Failure, of course, usually results in death, and there is probably little opportunity for serious nonadaptive behavior to develop.

On the other hand, certain cases of nonadaptive behavior have occurred in wild populations; the behavior of lemmings is an outstanding example. In these and some other rodents, there are occasional reports of mass migrations in which the animals simply keep moving without regard to obstacles and without any attempt at adaptation; a high death rate almost always results. This is a case of a disorganized population; and as the social organization of such populations is understood, it becomes more evident what causes the nonadaptative behavior.

Most small rodents have a rather restricted range and live peacefully with those with whom they grew up but fight with strange individuals. This conflict tends to maintain pressure from all sides on the social groups, but this pressure is not very well regulated with regard to physical boundaries. Calhoun [2] recently reported results of trapping out all rodents in a given area with a heavy population of them. It was expected that all rodents would soon be caught, and for the first few days the rate of catch fell off. Then, contrary to what might be expected, the rate of catch began to increase, and Calhoun concluded that he had produced, in a small way, a phenomenon similar to the lemming migrations. As the rodents were trapped out of the central area, the pressure was released and they tended to migrate inward, reaching a higher concentration as they did so. Such an effect, occurring in a heavy population of wild animals, takes them outside their normal territory and throws them into the company of highly stimulating strange animals so that the migration becomes essentially a mass panic.

In contrast to these rather rare outbreaks of nonadaptive behavior in wild animals, confined and domestic animals show a great deal of nonadaptive behavior. The average farmyard or zoo will show a great variety of abnormal behavior, and much of it can be identified with human symptoms. It is to the credit of David M. Levy, the psychiatrist [6], that he was able to recognize these symptoms in animals and relate certain of them to the factor of confinement. As he points out, while the confinement in animals usually consists of actual fences and cages, a corresponding confinement can be produced in human beings by various sorts of training and social pressure. When the classified experiments by such workers as Pavlov, Liddell, Masserman, and Maier on animal neuroses are considered, it is found that all of them include the element of confinement or lack of opportunity to escape from the situation.

All of these experiments also have in common the circumstance that the individual is hyperstimulated or hypermotivated. In most cases hypermotivation is produced by training, and the experiments of Skinner [11] on reward schedules throw much light on how hypermotivation may be produced in this way. All of the experiments are also set up in such a way that it is impossible for the animal to adjust to the situation which inevitably results in frustration.

In its present state, animal experimentation on the production of nonadaptive behavior seems to indicate that three things are necessary: (1) hyperexcitation of some kind, (2) a situation in which it is impossible to adapt, and (3) no possibility of escape. It is possible that the picture which we have at the present time is too simple and that additional important factors will be discovered. It should be pointed out also that none of these factors by themselves will produce nonadaptive behavior; in fact, hyperexcitement may, under certain circumstances, produce excellent results. It should also be remembered that the factor of genetic differences may play an important part in determining what is an unbearable situation. For example, bears in confinement are motivated to move around and as a result develop stereotyped movements. Members of the cat family, on the other hand, if well fed, will adjust themselves very well in small cages and apparently be undisturbed by such a situation.

THE PROCESS OF SOCIALIZATION

A line of research which has been largely undertaken from a sociobiological point of view and which has important implications for human problems is that on the process of socialization. All highly social animals have some means whereby, during the course of development, an animal forms social attachments to particular individuals and rejects certain others. Ants of different species, when reared together, live peacefully although the adults normally attack each other. In certain birds, as Lorenz [12] has found, the young may be socialized (or "imprinted") in a short period of a few hours or a few days.

The socialization process in mammals has not been sufficiently studied to have resulted in any generalizations, but certain examples may be given. In sheep, the attachment of the mother to the offspring has to be made within approximately four hours after birth or the mother will reject the lamb [3]. The lamb, on the other hand, forms the attachment with the mother much more slowly; but, since it is rejected by all other mothers, it has no alternative except to form a strong relationship with her. If prevented from forming such a relationship with the mother, the lamb has little opportunity for forming such attachments and may be isolated from the flock [7].

Another example is that of wolves in which it is found that the young cubs normally become socialized to the litter mates and other adults in the vicinity, but at the same time develop very strong fear and aggressive reactions toward strangers. If a wolf puppy is taken from the adults before its eyes open and is raised with people, it will become socialized to them very much as a dog will; but, taken a few weeks later, the pups are so wild and fierce as to be very difficult to socialize. In domestic dogs the tendency to develop fear reactions has been greatly decreased by selection, but genetic differences between individuals and breeds do remain [9].

In domestic mice it has been found that males which are brought up together in the same litter rarely fight, even after reaching maturity and being held in the same cage for months [10]. The same individuals, placed with strange males, will fight immediately and often with considerable mortality resulting.

It may be concluded, on the basis of the examples given, that in mammals the process of socialization includes the development of positive reactions through feeding and other contacts; and that socialization toward strange individuals is prevented by the development of fearful and aggressive reactions.

These phenomena have been subjected in mice to painstaking analysis. Fredericson showed that male mice, until approximately 33 days of age, which is a time in development corresponding to the appearance of the male sex hormones, would not ordinarily attack strangers. King [5] found that if male litter-mate mice were isolated from each other prior to this age, they fought much more slowly, if they fought at all, than those who had not been isolated. He varied the time of sibling contact and found that the effective period lay between the 20th and 30th day of age. Williams [13] has shown by observation that this is a time when young mice have a good many playful contacts with each other. Presumably the young male mouse forms a habit of making close contact with his litter mates, which later leads to quick and effective fighting with strangers. If his later contact with mice is limited to males, with whom he may fight, there is no opportunity ever to learn close contact, and the effect under these conditions tends to persist indefinitely.

Another series of experiments by Kahn [4] illustrates another point. He trained male mice to attack others; he also subjected young mice, some at 21, others at 35 days of age, as well as still others in adulthood, to attack. When the latter three groups of mice were later forced into the fighting by dangling helpless males in front of them, the mice which had been attacked at the younger ages fought back less rapidly. However, before long they were fighting just as vigorously as those which had not had experience in early youth. In this case, the animal is forced into close contact, and the results of the early experience do not persist.

The tentative conclusion can be reached that during the process of socialization, certain habits are formed which interfere with making positive social attachments to new individuals. Experimental modification of such habits may take place at certain periods in development, which may be spoken of as critical periods. The results are not necessarily irreversible, but the habits so learned may interfere strongly with future learning.

The implications for human abnormal behavior are obvious, particularly in the field of early family experience. There may exist particular critical times at which socialization can be easily accomplished, and these times may be modified by genetic differences. Bowlby [1] has reviewed a considerable body of work which indicates that similar effects and conditions do exist in human development, and that the process of socialization can be altered by such conditions as separation from the mother during the child's infancy, particularly between six months and three years of age.

The study of animal socialization is far from complete, but the results look hopeful from the therapeutic point of view. While it is easier to produce positive socialization at an early age than later in life, it is not impossible later. The usual factors which tend to interfere with or prevent such positive socialization are habits, particularly of fear and avoidance. On the whole, this result tends to agree with certain clinical therapeutic practices although these have usually been explained in different language.

SUMMARY

Numerous factors appear to be related to the problem of mental disease. These factors do not interact at random but operate on various levels of biological organization. Factors operating at lower levels are partially related to each other by integrating mechanisms operating at higher levels. From this point of view the various clinical and research approaches to the problem of mental disease may overlap but do not necessarily conflict.

Theoretical work on the ecological and sociobiological levels of organization throws some additional light on causal factors of nonadaptive behavior. Disorganized populations may give rise to mass abnormal behavior, as in certain rodent migrations. Other than this, nonadaptive behavior is rarely seen in natural animal populations. A survey of experimental studies shows agreement as to three major factors productive of nonadaptive behavior: hyperexcitement, prevention of adjustment, and prevention of escape. The factors which in turn produce each of these conditions can be extremely numerous and variable.

Recent work on the problem of socialization indicates that highly social animals have developmental behavioral mechanisms whereby positive attachment is produced toward certain individuals and such attachment with other individuals is prevented, particularly in later life. The results stress the importance of positive socialization in certain critical periods of early life, which vary from species to species. It is indicated that the results of negative socialization are not necessarily permanent but can be at least partially overcome. The results of these studies have considerable bearing on the problems of acculturation, as related to the psychosocial positions, and to primary family relationships as related to the psychodynamic position.

REFERENCES

1. BOWLBY, J. Maternal Care and Mental Health. Geneva: W.H.O. Monograph, 1951.
2. CALHOUN, J. B., and WEBB, W. L. Induced migrations in small mammals. Science, 1953, 117: 358–360.
3. COLLIAS, N. E. Some factors in maternal rejection by sheep and goats. Ecol. Bull., 1953, 34: 78.
4. KAHN, M. W. The effect of severe defeat at various age levels on the aggressive behavior of mice. J. Genet. Psych. 1951, 79: 117–130.
5. KING, J. A., and GURNEY, N. L. Effect of early social experience on adult aggressive behavior in C57BL//10 mice. J. Comp. & Physiol. Psychol., 1954, 47: 326–330.
6. LEVY, D. M. On the problem of movement restraint; tics, stereotyped movements, hyperactivity. Am. J. Orthopsychiat., 1944, 14: 644–671.
7. SCOTT, J. P. Social behavior, organization and leadership in a small flock of domestic sheep. Com. Psych. Monog. No. 96, 1945, 18(4): 1–29.
8. —— "Implications of Infra-human Social Behavior for Problems of Human Relations," in Group Relations at the Crossroads, M. Sherif and M. O. Wilson (Eds.). New York: Harper, 1953.
9. —— "The Process of Socialization in Higher Animals," in Interrelations Between the Social Environment and Psychiatric Disorders. New York: Milbank Memorial Fund, 1953.
10. SCOTT, J. P., and FREDERICSON, E. The causes of fighting in mice and rats. Physiol. Zool., 1951, 24: 273–309.
11. SKINNER, B. F. The Behavior of Organisms. New York: Appleton-Century-Crofts, 1938.
12. Symposia of the Society for Experimental Biology, No. IV. London: Cambridge University Press, 1950. See Chapters by: Lorenz, K. Z., "The Comparative Method in Studying Innate Behaviour Patterns," pp. 221–268; Tinbergen, N., "The Hierarchical Organization of Nervous Mechanisms Underlying Instinctive Behaviour," pp. 305–312; and Thorpe, W. H., "The Concepts of Learning and Their Relation to Those of Instinct," pp. 387–408.
13. WILLIAMS, E., and SCOTT, J. P. The development of social behavior patterns in the mouse, in relation to natural periods. Behaviour, 1953, 6: 35–64.

chapter 17

Areas of Acceptance

•••

KRUSE: In preparation for this Conference, a representative of each position was asked to re-examine its thesis and set forth its fundamental principles in three categories: what is demonstrable and certain; what is logical, probable, and presumptive; and what is possible. Members of the same persuasion were invited to amplify, modify, or take exception to the exposition on the tenets of their approach. Today we are to seek areas of mutual acceptance in the principles of the several schools. First to be considered is the organic point of view.

METTLER: Presumably what Jasper means in his presentation of the organic position is that in a series of diseases the cause, not the whole process, is certain. A condition like a senile dementia, for instance, has many aspects to it which are far from certain.

FINESINGER: His exposition, then, is supposed to illustrate situations in which there is precise, certain, known, acceptable information as to the etiology.

METTLER: The organicist would say that in senile dementia, for instance, age, either biological or chronological, plays a role in determining the condition. That would be only a statement of a determinative element in the more complete situation which composes true etiology. Other secondary etiological and conditioning factors would also be operating.

FINESINGER: Jasper is saying, then, that in senile dementia, age is a factor. It is found in elderly people. That is the certainty.

KRUSE: I take it that what he means is that senile dementia has an organic basis. I do not know how far beyond that he would go, whether he regards senile dementia as an exclusively organic disease or whether he accepts the operation of other influences. What he is saying is that there is a group of diseases which have an organic basis.

FINESINGER: Let us consider the possibilities that arise if age is regarded as one of the determinants of the sickness. Take two patients, both of whom are seventy years old and have senile dementia. One runs around the house and believes that people are setting fires. The other is quite calm and placid but cannot remember. Are we going to try to describe merely the overall diagnosis, or are we going to try to explain the details of the symptomatology?

METTLER: I would not accept the latter.

FINESINGER: You believe that organic details will not explain whether the patient will have hallucinations.

METTLER: Absolutely, they will not. Furthermore, I do not see any point in propagating such obsolescent terms as "senile dementia," and "involutional psychosis." The states are now called schizophrenic reactions. The idea that senility is chronologically determined needs clarification. I do not think that senility has necessarily anything to do with age. It could be metabolic.

HOLLINGSHEAD: I should like to inquire, To what does "certainty" apply? Does Jasper mean that the causes are known?

160

Or does he mean that certain necessary conditions are associated with an illness that is diagnosed clinically as senile dementia?

The broadest point of view would be that in order to have organic behavior there must be an organism. I would say this is certain. But when Jasper's exposition goes into specific reactions and their cause, I become skeptical.

KRUSE: I think that we go afield when we attempt to run down a list of diseases, for we are trying to deal with principles. We should bring in only enough specific instances to provide evidence for the concepts. A consideration of the present classification of diseases which might be regarded as organically oriented is not relevant to the agenda for today.

FINESINGER: To me the assertion that there cannot be a disease unless there is an organism is acceptable; but this is a very broad, over-all, almost meaningless statement. Broad statements usually do not mean much. Is that not a difficulty?

KRUSE: What this exposition states is: Here are a group of diseases which have an organic basis.

FINESINGER: I would not say "basis"; rather I would say "which have a pathology."

KRUSE: My next statement would be that in many instances there is demonstrable pathology.

METTLER: Let me reiterate the approach which the author of the exposition on the organic point of view was asked to take. Phenomena were to be categorized in three classes: In the first area, the area of certainty, he was to put forth only those things which he regards as certain. The second area was to contain points which at present are not certainly demonstrable by methods which compel scientific acceptance but which seem probable. The third area was to include matters which have no basis for a strong conviction, but which are possible.

Where valid, demonstrable, scientific evidence is available, there is no question about what one has to do. One has to accept it. But from a practical point of view such necessarily partial data often do not help us to live our daily lives within a framework of rather arbitrary, variable, and often whimsical, social systems and laws. More particularly, the demonstrable evidence which is available in the field of scientific knowledge is often inadequate to deal with the exigencies of medical practice, and even, for that matter, with the classification of disease. So, for practical purposes, the clinician is forced to move outside of the region of scientific certainty into an area of probability, or even farther into an area of possibility, both beyond demonstrable evidence.

When we move into the area of probability, permissive alternatives need to be considered. Hence, we have to allow for differences in points of view. It is not necessary to be obsessive about any of them. And when we move into the area of possibility, we have to allow for *chacun à son goût*. It is more or less a matter of taste.

Dr. Jasper seems to be trying to transfer the procedures and criteria of what might be called scientific certainty to the areas of probability and possibility. It cannot be done.

FINESINGER: I would expect that in the area of possibility we would make use of certain kinds of technics.

METTLER: Exactly. That area leads us into methodology.

FINESINGER: Even in the realm of possibility, an irrelevant statement is not allowable.

METTLER: A statement cannot be put there just because it will not fit in either of the other two areas.

FINESINGER: There is a set of rules which operates even in the area of possibility. Logic and correlation, even a very low level of correlation, are employed.

METTLER: Would you be willing to say that in the area of possibility it is not allowable to hold a point of view which is in disagreement with what we know in the area of certainty?

FINESINGER: It is not permissible to be illogical, even though the point seems to be within the realm of possibility.

HOLLINGSHEAD: Jasper's essay starts with a positive statement about the principle of biological determinism that would exclude the possibility of soul, mind, and spirituality. Many people would not go along with this position. They would admit that it is certain that everybody is going to die, as the term is used scientifically, in a physiological sense. Yet they would be willing to fight, in terms of their religious belief, in an area of possibility, when all empirical evidence is against the reality of the possibility. They will be very certain; but they will have no scientific proof.

METTLER: It is in just such a situation in everyday life that we become entangled and cause one another a lot of grief. We state, for example, that it is certain that all men are going to die. That is a scientifically demonstrable fact. Then we move into the area of logic and probability. We form life insurance companies and, on the basis of experience reduced to tables, we say: "This baby, born now, has a life expectancy of sixty-five years. This is a logical matter; we will put money on it." Then, this baby has to be baptized. In what faith shall it be baptized? This is a matter of possibility; a matter of taste. Why argue about it? One man has one, another has another, point of view. Certainly it would be unsound for someone to say: "I am not going to baptize my baby because he is never going to die."

HOLLINGSHEAD: We mix up these different levels.

FINESINGER: What is certainty? What principles are to be considered? How much evidence is needed for certainty? What are the methods of determining it? There is a selection of methods to cope with the different degrees of certainty found in different fields. For example, in physics certain types of design can be used which are not helpful in psychiatry. Furthermore a physicist, by conducting, let us say, two critical experiments, can obtain enough observations for certainty; for he can control all the variables. The biologist may have to have a hundred experiments because he cannot control the variables.

METTLER: That has nothing to do with certainty.

HOLLINGSHEAD: There are many things done in psychiatry that cannot be done in physics.

FINESINGER: From the autobiography of a patient whom he never saw, Freud* was able to evolve an hypothesis which turns out to be of great interest. Most people say, "Isn't that nonsense? Out of one case, what can he do?" I do not think that it is nonsense; for he really brought forth an hypothesis. On the other hand, to say that he proved the point would be nonsense. There has to be some sort of—

METTLER: —hierarchy of data. There is absolutely no difference between the formulation of an hypothesis in the field of psychiatry and in that of physics. Both hypotheses would have exactly the same value and validity.

FINESINGER: Here we need clarification. Many workers who are at present concerned with hypotheses in psychiatry, psychoanalysis, or psychodynamics become so emotionally entangled that it becomes difficult to recognize and to compare the value of these hypotheses with others found useful in other fields. I wonder whether this Conference could restate such matters.

HOLLINGSHEAD: The scientific method which leads to some certainty of knowledge is no different from one science to another. The methodological procedures, the technics, and the application would perforce have to be adapted to the problem under investigation and would therefore vary.

METTLER: Much is said about how exact physics is. There is a fundamental difference between descriptive science and the kind of science pervading physics. The latter is a symbolic science. The physicist uses the language of mathematics. We hear how precise mathematics is; how it represents the essence of science. Is such a point of view really valid?

The biologist never says, "Let X represent a rabbit." For him, a rabbit can be considered directly. It is an animal to be described. There is no intermediary phenomenon. The substitution of symbolism creeps into all the mathematical sciences and all the creations of science using mathematics; e.g., cybernetics. The descriptive

---

* Freud, S., "Psycho-analytic Notes in an Autobiographical Account of a Case of Paranoia (Dementia Paranoides)" in *Collected Papers.* London: Hogarth Press, 1950. vol. 3, p. 607.

scientist is always tripping over it. The biological scientist cannot use symbols.

LIDDELL: He does use symbols.

METTLER: Yes, I accept the correction, everybody does use symbols: but the biological scientist does not use analogical symbols.

LIDDELL: One highly important type of evidence is the singular observation. It suggests promising leads for investigation. For example, our flocks of sheep and goats intermingle except at feeding time. But we have a middle-aged sheep which feeds with the goats. Apparently this sheep considers itself a goat. We would give anything to know its history.

FINESINGER: That observation takes on meaning only when there are more observations with which it may be related.

LIDDELL: In our field we must never forget such singular observations.

HOLLINGSHEAD: In any field it is necessary to know what is pertinent to the problem at hand. This is part of the investigator's training; it is part of his technic. But this does not mean the process of reasoning is different from one science to another. Rather, it is the same. The technic of observation, however, will vary. To operate in the area of certainty, it is necessary to have certain principles of knowing.

METTLER: Is not the essence of material in that area that it is demonstrable evidence?

HOLLINGSHEAD: Yes. But it is necessary to have accepted principles which will give demonstrable evidence. Perceptions, observations, and tests are needed. These are the principles of science.

METTLER: Consideration of logic leads to the second area, that of probability, in which things are logical but not demonstrable.

HOLLINGSHEAD: In the development of science it is possible to move from one area to another: from possibility to probability to certainty.

METTLER: Not as a scientist.

FINESINGER: That is a rather sharp distinction.

It seems to me that the way in which this Conference is set up, the plan to have a person set forth the principles of a particular point of view, usually makes him feel that he has to defend that position. In consequence, he tends to overemphasize items about which there is already a great measure of agreement.

KRUSE: It is an interesting fact that it is difficult to obtain a precise statement of the principles of the different approaches. By and large, experts do not take time to think of the principles of the disciplines in which they work. The general dissatisfaction which you have expressed over the exposition of principles would seem to indicate that all is not well there. When you say everybody agrees about this, I ask you, what do they agree about? That is what we are trying to put into words. It is extremely easy to say that we agree on almost everything, but it becomes difficult to put down on paper the principles on which we do agree. How are we to make progress in this field of mental disease unless we become concrete?

Secondly, there is much verbal agreement, with a large amount of mental reservation. As human beings, we try to be polite, to conform and agree, when there sometimes is not real agreement. After wearing the mask of politeness for many hours to the point of fatigue, we reach a candid moment when we admit to ourselves and sometimes to others, that we wish we had spoken our minds and taken issue. It is my feeling that we will get ahead farther and faster if we hold a friendly discussion about what we can accept. Let us put down what we can accept among the different points of view; and then we can move on to the area of unacceptance, not, however, with the thought of emphasizing disagreement.

The program is aimed toward interdisciplinary planning. Unless the principles of the various points of view are clearly understood and mental reservations are resolved, how are experts seated around a table ever going to be able to plan? This was the rationale underlying the organization of this Conference.

FINESINGER: I am wondering how the statements of positions could be set forth more constructively. For example, if each author had been asked to present the limitations of his point of view, he might have been less defensive. Furthermore, if the experts were asked to consider the limitations of each other's point of view, it might tend to obviate their immediate opposition.

Concerning your other point—the determination of the precise degree of agreement—there, I think, you have something. It is very important that it be spelled out; for to me it is the major problem. How can participants in a conference be induced to say things which are understandable and which they really mean, instead of their putting up a front and fighting about points of view. My own personal belief is that one of the big gaps is between verbal agreement and operational agreement. The latter shows whether the investigator has really incorporated the points.

KRUSE: You put your finger on the purpose of the Conference: the hope that its deliberations will be translated into the operational area.

LIDDELL: I know that my own emotional reaction as an investigator has reciprocated the "so what" attitude of my medical confreres in the field of human behavior.

HOLLINGSHEAD: Perhaps part of the difficulty is our conception of psychiatric disorders as disease. Most of the psychiatric disorders, such as the psychoneuroses, the psychosomatic difficulties, and functional disorders, are behavioral reactions rather than disease in the traditional medical sense. I am not sure that we can discover and assign a cause to them in the same way as has been done for typhoid fever.

KRUSE: In the biological and medical world, the conception of causation of disease which sprang up in the bacteriological era still prevails. Expressed in its simplest terms it is: causative agent (e.g., microorganism) produces disease. It is now well recognized that this represents oversimplification. The unitary causative does not always produce its effect of disease; whether it does depends on numerous conditions. Yet, even though the operation of multiple factors and conditions is accepted, their influence is rated low. For in their everyday thinking and speech, investigators still revert to the old formula, perhaps revealing their inner desires to keep the whole thing simple.

In research we are now moving on increasingly to such types of disease as cancer and mental disorders, in which multiple factors appear to operate in causation. Sometimes all of the factors are not now known. All too frequently an investigator working with one group of factors tends to neglect the others. The first task is to ascertain and identify all of the qualitative factors that enter into the etiology. The second objective would be to devise methods to measure the proportional effect of each factor in each instance; for it is not unlikely that their relative impacts in the production of a disorder vary from person to person.

FINESINGER: Kruse's point about the multiplicity of factors in causation is basic. In rating the importance of the various factors that bring about the end result, peptic ulcer, for example—the sociological factor, the stomach factor, and the personality factor—the influence of each is impressive. At present we can only list and estimate them. We need to be able to quantify them. Just because organs are functioning and life rolls along, is no reason to doubt that symptoms and causal elements can be quantified. A normal person who projects a little and is a little suspicious can be distinguished from a paranoid schizophrenic patient who projects everything and is highly suspicious. There is a quantitative difference between them; of course, there may be qualitative differences, too.

In my opinion, investigators will begin to study the personality factors of people who get infectious illness. When they do, they will find, I would predict, that the problem of resistance is related to personality factors. Of course, it may well be that in some infectious diseases, the influence of the psychological factors will be minimum.

METTLER: The problem of quantification is very important and presupposes not merely the existence of units of measurement, or some sort of scale, but also agreement upon the frame of reference wherein value is arranged. In clinical projects we are constantly facing the question, Are the patients better or aren't they? The psychologist says that the patient is better; the analytically oriented psychiatrist says that the patient is no better. The psychologist, when asked the reason for his opinion, replies: "Because the patient can now fit so many round pegs in round holes and does not try square pegs in round holes." The analyst explains his contrary opinion. "The patient still has hallucinations." From a practical point of view, for instance in hospitals, what is done in deciding whether a patient is better? A completely different frame of reference is selected. The patient is paroled and his course followed. Some can remain out of an institution. Despite hallucinations, they make a living.

FINESINGER: You are saying that agreement depends on how broad the parameter is.

METTLER: If the psychoanalyst says, "This is the important thing. See, there is this much of it," then I say, "What difference does it make? What is important?"

FINESINGER: The analyst is reasoning a priori; he assumes that what he is doing is most important. To place the matter in its proper perspective and to obtain a more balanced answer, it is necessary to consider the observations and views of authorities from several different approaches, each of whom thinks that his field is important. Then someone has to weigh and evaluate the contribution of each. In judging whether a patient has improved, I would ask the analyst about his observations, not how important they are. I would consult the psychologist similarly. Maybe all that we can hope for in trying to decide whether a patient is "better" is a profile which will include the observations of competent men in various areas.

METTLER: Then you agree that in essence we are dealing with a situation in which we have an uncontrolled number of variables, and that we have to use a multidisciplinary approach.

FINESINGER: Certainly. In this particular problem it turns out that a multidisciplinary approach is indicated. However, I can visualize another kind of a problem in mental disease which is best attacked by an individual investigator and in which a multidisciplinary approach would be a waste of time.

KRUSE: It will be interesting to see what happens when the gap closes between the dynamic and experimental psychological approaches because then in some way the organic and sociological approaches will be drawn in and the pattern will take form.

HOLLINGSHEAD: Each of us around the table here represents a discipline which is a part of a jigsaw puzzle. And we are going on faith that all parts of the puzzle can be put together. The animal experimental psychologist and the psychodynamicists can communicate readily. In the process of trying to get at the conditions that give rise to psychiatric disorders, they are, of necessity, going to pull in the organicist and the sociologist. Only time will tell which will be found to be the more important in the production of psychiatric disorders, the organic base or the sociological stresses associated with living in a society that makes contradictory demands upon an individual at different hours of the day, in different facets of his social behavior, and in different phases of his life cycle.

KRUSE: All the different conducive factors are probably in operation. The degree of significance or importance attached to any one factor depends arbitrarily upon the chosen criterion: whether it be the greatest proportion in quantity, timing, or amenability to control. If timing is the standard, a factor of lesser amount may be deemed highly important in one instance because it tipped the scale toward pathogenesis at a particular point. Judged by any one criterion, what might be most important at one time may be less important at another.

HOLLINGSHEAD: Among the particular types of abnormal behavior which may be diagnosed by the practitioner, the most important responsible factor may differ from one to another.

In one type of disorder such as general paresis, the organic factor is of the prime importance. In it the spirochete and neuropathology loom large, although very clearly there is a sociological component. In another category of disorder, such as the psychoneuroses or schizophrenia, the social stresses, frustrations, appear to be more important.

FINESINGER: But when you say "more important," what you mean from a therapeutic standpoint is "more amenable to modification."

KRUSE: It is also noteworthy how often the precipitating factor is given the highest significance. On a quantitative basis, it may be the least potent; but just because of the timing, it has major importance conferred upon it. It tends to obscure all that has gone before, all of the factors that have produced the final end product.

FINESINGER: A factor may well be especially important because of what can be done about it. In the planning of psychotherapy it becomes item number one. The psychiatrist assumes that organic, psychological, dynamic, and sociological factors are in a patient's background. The one that the psychiatrist can modify becomes the most important.

KRUSE: The assignment for today is to bring out points of acceptance between schools of thought on causation. It should also be borne in mind that the concepts and principles and the evidence underlying them are influenced by the methodology.

HOLLINGSHEAD: In commenting upon the areas of acceptance I would suggest the following order: first, the organic, because it is most firmly entrenched within the institution of medicine; second, the psychological, because it also is well accepted in medicine, though perhaps to a somewhat lesser extent; third, the social, because it has been even less completely adopted; and finally, the dynamic, which I put at the end because I think that it would bring together and integrate the other three.

FINESINGER: All points of view can be considered and expressed descriptively or dynamically. By the dynamic approach I mean emphasis on the causes, mechanics, functions and their interrelationships.

KRUSE: Under the suggested order, Dr. Mettler will state points in the psychological, sociological, and dynamic approaches which are acceptable to him as an organicist.

METTLER: The material which is pecul-iar to these three areas of endeavor is not something with which someone outside can disagree, because it is in itself an authoritative statement. One must accept information which has been arrived at by industry and intelligent application of methods which are peculiar to these fields. No one will gainsay experimental evidence in or out of his field when it is collected in a valid manner. How can a person with one point of view fail to approve the activities of his colleagues with other approaches and competences when they are proceeding in good faith and with good will?

The things with which one is most likely to agree are those which have been best worked out. Where results seem to me to be most easily verifiable by technics and methodologies with which I am familiar, or where they appear to be most consistent with information with which I am familiar, I am of course most likely to accept them immediately, and also to utilize them in my own thinking. This is just another way of saying that utilization of material is in direct proportion to one's ability to evaluate it and find concurrence with one's past experience. Furthermore, where material from other approaches impinges upon or supplements material which the organicist uses, it is most valuable and is most likely to be accepted by him.

KRUSE: Of the three other approaches, which at the moment is most readily acceptable to the organicist on the basis of its relationship and utilization?

METTLER: The one which is closest to the organic field is the psychological because its methods are very close to those of physiology. In fact, in many instances the psychologists are better trained in physical procedures than are the physiologists. The next closest is the field of psychodynamics with its mechanisms of mental disorders. The one which is farthest is the sociological. But, peculiarly enough, or perhaps understandably enough, the organicist is most likely to agree with the sociologist and least likely to agree with the psychologist. For, knowing less about the sociologist's activities, the organicist is much more likely to take his word. On the other hand, because of familiarity with the psychologist's activities, the organicist is less likely to accept his statements unquestioningly. But if the organicist found that the psychologist's material was acceptable, he would be much more likely to utilize it; for he would know what to do with it. It would give the organicist a point of departure and a base on which to build. In contrast, even after he accepted the sociologist's material, the organicist would not know quite what to do with it.

As for "psychodynamics" (incidentally, it is a word which I do not like), I am not too concerned about its principles. What interests me is its particular area, psychological mechanisms; and the fact that there are investigators working in it. Their methods are not peculiar; they are appropriate for this particular field. The psychodynamicist observes and reports what happens there, and assembles this information so that certain sequences may be shown to occur. This information is useful to me for its possible application in conjunction with organic data. In the body of the psychodynamic literature I naturally find most useful that material which I can relate in my own thinking to what might be called neurophysiological principles. I am particularly glad to have it, for it is most unlikely that I would obtain it directly. It comes from an area in which I do not customarily operate. The explanation that the psychodynamicist gives for these phenomena and sequences which he observes is of less interest to me than the raw data. I prefer to make my own interpretation of them.

The topics in psychodynamics that are of particular interest to me are regression and ego disintegration. It has been asserted that perceptual disturbances are evidence of ego disintegration. I am concerned, not with whether these phenomena are evidence of ego disintegration, but with the sequence in which perceptual disorders occur. For instance, in their development there is a stage in which the patient first has intermittent periods of sensory disturbances, which are accompanied by episodes of stress; this then gradually passes over into a stage in which he experiences notable fear and begins to develop a rather systematized personal projection. I see no other way to study these phenomena than by the psychodynamic approach.

FINESINGER: On another level, the experimental level, would you be much concerned over the problem of motivation in conducting physiological experiments with patients? For example, we carried out a study in which we were interested in learning from the patient what was going on inside him when he was breathing air with various mixtures of oxygen. Why the subject was willing to undergo the experiments, his motivations, turned out to be rather important. Would you agree that this is another point which has to be brought to bear in evaluating the results of the physiological experiment? Or take the studies on perception, in which apparently what the doctor sees depends on meanings.

METTLER: Yes, of course. I would say that it is a cardinal problem, not only in physiology, but also in psychodynamics, psychology, and sociology. Usually, motivation is assured to be reasonably well controlled in a physiological experiment. Either the experiment is reported in the particular frame of reference in which it was conducted, or it includes a considerable number of subjects so that the factor of motivation can be expected to cancel itself. But whether motivation is important to a physiological experiment has to be determined in the frame of reference of the circumstances. Much depends on judgment in the experimental design, particularly in sampling. When the sample is adequate, typical of its universe, and suitably controlled; when the means of mensuration or evaluation and criteria are reliable; and when the procedure is uniform, these precautions introduce a considerable safeguard against bias from subjectivity or from interpersonal relations.

FINESINGER: Take the study by Ferris to try to determine the effects of different drugs on the blood pressure of patients. He found that the attitude of the patient toward the doctor was a factor, a variable.

METTLER: Of course, it was a variable; so were numerous, more obviously physiologic circumstances, such as fluid balance, capacity of the heart, and basic condition of the autonomic system. But if the experiment was properly designed, the goodness of the results on the activity of the drugs should not have been vitiated by the activity of any one such variable. If 10,000 patients, let us say, were being tested by 10 doctors, and if the interpersonal relations of one doctor differed markedly from those of the 9 others, the design of the experiment should bring out that difference and provide a counterbalance.

FINESINGER: You believe, then, that such variables are important but that proper design of the experiment ensures equilibration of their effects. With that I disagree. Would I be justified in ignoring the results of any experiment on blood pressure with 20 or fewer subjects, unless there were data on the interaction between the doctor and the patients?

METTLER: That would depend on the nature of the experiment. If 20 patients were given a particular drug, if their reaction to it was very marked and invariable, and if another group given a placebo under the same circumstances exhibited no response, you would not be justified in ignoring the results despite the absence of data on personal interaction. But if, on the other hand, the results are equivocal reactions, then you would certainly have to devise some method of determining whether the patients were reacting to the physician.

FINESINGER: If all the 20 patients respond in exactly the same way to the drug, may not hostility have elevated the blood pressure in some instances?

METTLER: The group receiving a placebo provide an adequate control.

LIDDELL: Suppose that after 2 patients had each received an injection of adrenalin, their word production curves showed that they talked faster and faster. Would you be interested also in their responses to questions?

METTLER: Of course. I would not rule out the importance of content. My criticism of most of the experimental situations, such as studies on the development of personality, is that the author presents, not raw data, but an interpretive phenomenon.

FINESINGER: An inference.

METTLER: Yes. And this I will not accept. I want to find out what the multi-circumstances are, and I want them clearly labeled. I am willing to work with the data of another investigator at the observational level. I am perfectly willing to consider his hypothesis, but I expect him to listen to me too. I do not want to use a telephone that is connected only in one way. I expect the privilege of an exchange of views.

KRUSE: It is important to find points of convergence because these are likely to be the places where we can throw a bridge across and get together on a multilateral approach. It is not a question of right or wrong.

FINESINGER: What is your attitude toward the concept of the unconscious?

METTLER: There is a mass of data interpretable in a frame of reference which to me seems to be extremely complex, notably the Freudian framework. In an area such as motivation, this theoretical formulation has some suggestive value. At least, I do not know how to explain motivation better. However, I feel very uneasy about the formulation. If I have to accept motivation in its Freudian frame of reference, then I feel that I am likely to be lost. The Freudian frame of reference seems so vague, mystic, and obscure. I have ideas about motivation and I would like to be able to apply those ideas. What disturbs me is that I could not if I had to work with them in the Freudian frame of reference. But if I could get the formulation into some frame of reference with which I am familiar, then I would feel that I could work with it. I would feel much better if I could explain these emergences in terms of physiological mechanisms.

KRUSE: Do you find that the concept of "special mechanisms" in dynamics is useful to you? Do you have a physiological interpretation for them?

METTLER: The idea of explaining aggression in a patient in terms of ego destruction or disintegration and then his subsequent recovery on the basis of restitution, reintegration, or even re-establishment of a new ego, I find difficult to accept. I am inclined to interpret the phenomena differently, notably as a matter of conceptual disorganization, followed by recovery or relearning, if perceptual capacity has been preserved.

FINESINGER: If you are studying a patient who does not remember an episode which occurred a month ago, does the reason why he does not remember concern you? Does it make any difference to you operationally, experimentally, or clinically, whether he does not remember the episode because it has been repressed or because it strayed out of his memory? Suppose in studying the effects of a drug, you want the subject to report what is going on in his mind after you give him the drug. Let us say further that sexual material enters into his thoughts but he does not tell you. Would that in any way at all interfere with the results of your experiment? It seems to me that some of these mechanisms may be very crucial in determining the reliability of both the investigator and the subject.

METTLER: Of course they are.

FINESINGER: I do not think that it is accidental that when I asked you a question earlier about the unconscious, the subject was promptly dropped. I now ask myself, "Why did we not proceed on the subject of the unconscious?" It might be because a more interesting topic came up. Or, I might conclude, "Maybe he doesn't want to talk about the unconscious."

METTLER: Of course I don't. I do not have the technics to deal with such a topic. I am perfectly willing to try to study it, but I would be working under a handicap.

FINESINGER: Let us assume that a patient in whom inhibition of the synapse has been induced by an appropriate drug is engaged in conversation with me. Is he aware of the phenomenon? Would you classify this phenomenon as being in the unconscious?

METTLER: With inhibition of the synapse there is bound to be interference with awareness.

FINESINGER: I would say that this inhibition of the synapse is outside of conscious experience.

Let us take another situation. While conversing with a patient, I introduce a topic which he promptly drops. Does he know that he has avoided the topic?

METTLER: Probably not.

FINESINGER: In what category would you place that reaction? You will note that I am trying to get your ideas about the various kinds of behavior that might be considered from the standpoint of "unconscious." The whole concept of the dynamic unconscious, as the Freudians use the term, is clearly defined. The Freudians would not consider inhibition of the synapse in the unconscious. On the other hand, they would locate the factors which make for avoidance of the topic in the unconscious. In both instances, the subject is unaware of the phenomenon. However, in the latter instance he can be made aware of it; the variable which makes him avoid the topic can be identified. It is important to define more clearly the various categories for which the word unconscious is used.

METTLER: There is another possibility. Your hypothetical individual might be a person who is accessible to a great variety of peripheral stimuli. In other words, he might be a person who is not avoiding anything but who is easily distractible. You would have to test that possibility too.

FINESINGER: Without knowing the answer, I have sought to raise what I believe to be an important question: In considering the organic factors, to what extent does one have to bring to bear, especially at the experimental level, the psychological and the sociological factors?

KRUSE: Now, Dr. Liddell, speaking as an experimental psychologist, will describe areas that are acceptable in the other approaches.

LIDDELL: Let me present my credentials to join this group on interdoctrinal acceptance; I am a universal and overenthusiastic accepter by temperament.

As to orientation in my field of experimental animal behavior study, I am at the present time drawn in two directions: on the one hand, toward the new work in ethology, the objective study of behavior, where Lorenz, Tinbergen and others* are studying what we call "instinctive behavior patterns of lower vertebrates"; on the other hand, toward the technical procedures of psychoanalysts. When Thomas French came to my laboratory, he observed what an animal did under a stimulus situation;

* Schaffner, Bertram (Ed.). "Group Processes," in *Transactions of the First Conference.* New York: Josiah Macy, Jr. Foundation, 1955.

and noted that the behavior of the animal reminded him strangely of the dream materials of certain patients. When I went to French's office, he showed me his procedure for receiving a patient upon referral, the couch, the nature of his notes, a sample note page, the amount of notes he puts down in longhand and the amount in shorthand, the proportion of talk by him and the patient—procedural matters. There are no grounds for interdoctrinal unacceptance here.

As another example, when George Daniels came to the farm, I demonstrated the positive and negative conditioned responses of a sheep to him. Toward the end of the hour, the sheep did not want to go on any more; and the differentiations literally broke down. Daniels said, "Well, you know, that reminds me of a situation which I have noticed many times. When production is going at a great rate with a patient, I push my luck too far and I lose ground."

Hence, I think that it is very important that we who work on experimental animal behavior should look in both directions: toward the organic area and toward the psychodynamic area. We cannot afford not to do so.

In this field we have to observe two other musts. First, we must literally fit our daily experiments into the animals' natural life experiences in barn and pasture, as well as in the laboratory. The animal carries away the aftereffects of the experimental hour, as we know, into his relations with other animals, and these aftereffects must be observed.

Secondly, we must re-emphasize and re-employ the principle of homology. In this age of cybernetics and model construction, there is a great deal of thinking by analogy, which, I believe, is not too helpful in exploring interdoctrinal areas. For example, those very enticing electronic models, which behave in such a way as to get their batteries recharged, provide a logical exercise, but have relatively little value in this area of the causation of mental disease. On the other hand, if we seriously accept the principle of homology, as have the group of ethologists; and if we believe that it applies not only to structure but also to behavior,

then the sheep's foreleg is homologous to the human hand and arm, though it has quite different functions. Accordingly, in our animal work we do not feel fended off or self-conscious about freely homologizing these simpler behaviors with human behavior.

In the social field, just recently we have been very much concerned with the sociological phenomenon of loneliness. What can be its origin in the animal? We are on the trail of the answer. One of the sheep or goat twins separated from its mother became immobilized and lonely under monotonous and stressful circumstances; the other twin with the mother did not. The presence of the mother somehow gave the little animal more freedom. The kid or lamb very much needs the mother up to about three weeks, and then it develops other interests. Little rams at three months of age begin herding by themselves. An adult sheep or goat is not lonely in the human sense; indeed, it avoids body contact with others of its species, except during mating and care of the young. Loneliness appears only in the very early ages, when the young is dependent upon the mother.

From a study of kids born at the farm, Dr. Helen Blauvelt, my associate, found what makes a "good" mother and a "bad" mother. Obviously, these are value terms, categorical designations. It is like saying that the mother is protecting the infant. What does this mean actually? For clarity we must resort to procedural thinking and descriptive reporting. It was found that as soon as the kid is dropped, the mother starts to lick it. Then both the kid and the mother start to bleat; they come head-to-head. Moving systematically down the kid's body toward the anal area, the mother keeps licking. Soon she is licking the anal area, and the little tail is wagging and tickling her nose. This activity is reinforced and facilitated by the other new mothers in the room, who are setting up a chorus; for vocalizing is a highly important detail. Things can also go wrong in mother-infant relationship. Instead of using value judgments, "good mother" or "bad mother," we prefer to report this highly intricate sequence in behavior by moving pictures or verbal description. In our interpretation we would adhere to the principle of homology. Human motherhood is not the same as goat motherhood, but the animal experimenter and the child psychologist can make common cause. We want to excite each other to exchange ideas at this procedural level, not the categorical level.

My plea is to break down the terminological areas of research by employing procedural thinking, by stating what has been done and what has been observed.

FINESINGER: Although the experimental situation is viewed as artificial by the experimenter, it is not so regarded by the subject. It is another situation in his life. All the other factors which have operated throughout his life may have some bearing on the way the experiment will eventuate.

KRUSE: Dr. Hollingshead will now give us the sociologist's view of interdoctrinal acceptance.

HOLLINGSHEAD: As a sociologist I am willing to accept an organic base for behavior. Clearly a situational stimulus comes through various organic mechanisms; and it is translated in the organism to some kind of behavioral response. The situational stimulus may be given a dynamic quality in the individual so that it will be perceived in social and cultural terms. The particularly personal meaning of the stimulus to the individual gives a dynamic quality to the stimulus. Then the individual reacts behaviorally to the stimulus situation as it is perceived both personally and socially. In that sense, we need always to keep in mind both the organic bases in which behavior takes place, and the personal and cultural factors which modify organic processes.

As to what may be accepted in the psychological area, it should be realized the psychologist is focusing upon particular mechanisms that take place in the sequence: (1) situational stimulus, (2) reactions within the individual, (3) expression of the synthesis of (1) and (2) through the behavior of the individual. In this process the fields of the organic and the psychological sciences are very closely related. But this is not the whole story. As part of the situational stimulus and the frame of reference of the individual, one must consider the social system, the culture in which the individual lives, and the demands that this system makes upon him. There is a need, therefore, to accept the psychological mechanisms that operate in this area. Indeed, psychologists have made numerous distinct contributions here, particularly in animal experiments. I would add, many things can be done with animals that cannot be done with human beings.

In respect to the dynamic view, I am impressed with its attempts to link together organic, psychological, and social processes and to state them in terms of their effects on the behavior of the individual. More than any of the other fields it brings into focus all three of the facets of viewing behavior, and places upon the behavior of each individual the personal meaning with its dynamic quality. The dynamic view has also tried to build into a conceptual scheme the social symbols of the society, and to show how social symbols influence the personal symbolism of the individual, the actor in the situation. For example, the dynamic view recognizes that the state called anxiety is probably organically based, but it is related also to the social system in which the individual lives. The environment creates stress in the individual, and the individual builds up defense mechanisms to reduce his anxiety or to defend himself against it. I think that the more socially oriented of the psychodynamicists visualize a social origin for these defenses.

LIDDELL: What does the sociologist think about the possibility of solving the problem of stress by corticosteroids?

HOLLINGSHEAD: Most sociologists do not know enough about it to be concerned with the question.

KRUSE: As a representative of the psychodynamic approach, Dr. Finesinger will set forth his views on areas of interdoctrinal acceptance.

FINESINGER: First of all, I should say that many psychodynamicists would consider me to be a highly motivated organicist; on the other hand, the organicists would regard me as a highly motivated psychodynamicist.

It is impossible for me to believe that behavior can occur without an organic, physiological change, whether it be reversible or irreversible. In general, I accept the notion of a unitary man in which the psychological and physiological are integrated. But penetration into the subject raises the question of how the physiological affects the psychological. If we say that they are not really one and the same thing—and we fool ourselves when we say that—then we find that we are back at the starting point, with all the problems of dualism unresolved. On the other hand, in accepting the unitary nature of man, all that we have done is to push one step farther; now we do not have to bother with the problem of mind-body. But once we try to take the next step, to explain the influence of one on the other, we are again in difficulty. I would be inclined to view as a reasonable working hypothesis the statement that the mind and body are the same. I cannot visualize psychological and sociological phenomena occurring without physiological change. Up to now the studies on the physical factors in the schizophrenic have been on the whole unproductive. This record does not mean that such studies should not again be attempted.

In considering the sociological approach, it is obvious that we live in a social group. Therefore, such matters as social experience, patterns of behavior, and the importance of family and other institutions impinge on the individual. Nor can we gainsay the importance of dynamic studies in this area attempting to explain the mechanics of how things come about.

chapter *18*

Areas of Unacceptance

• •

KRUSE: The purpose of this meeting is not to perpetuate any disagreements over approach; not to widen further any dissent or breach over concepts and methods. On the contrary, we are to explore areas of unacceptance because it is a necessary initial step on the road to ultimate harmony and unity. This exploration is to be undertaken with the final objectives in mind: to achieve mutual understanding; to arrive at working agreements; to encourage crossing of disciplinary lines. It is obvious that areas of unacceptance, sensitive and critical spots that they are, stand in the way. It is not enough to say that now they are not common ground. There the unbeliever will not set foot unless to do battle. The issues in these areas must be brought into the open and discussed. The reasons for unacceptance must be fathomed. If it is misunderstanding or unfamiliarity, perhaps a calm and clear explanation will help to reduce, even dissolve, resistance or antagonism. If it is an antithesis arising naturally and warrantedly against a thesis, as in dialectic, a new unity must be synthesized out of both. This adventure is undertaken as an occasion, not for bellicosity, tempestuosity, and destruction, but for mutuality, lucidity, and construction. If successful, it may contribute to clearing the way for enhancement of the multidisciplinary approach and for an advance toward a larger unity.

SPIEGEL: It is easier for me to think in terms of difficulties that get in the way of collaboration between the different approaches than to think of areas or points of unacceptance. If one approach cannot accept a point in a mutually reciprocal problem, neither may the other approach. The difficulties are not all on one side. Investigators with different ways of studying behavior fall afoul of each other when they try to collaborate. There is not much of a problem between those with the organic and those with the psychosocial points of view because they do not attempt to collaborate.

GRINKER: It is a matter of how far apart on the whole spectrum specialists happen to be working. Your point has to do, not so much with what doctrine they believe or what their notions might be about where valuable information can be obtained, but rather with the experimental design for a particular project that might be undertaken. I can visualize that it would be quite easy to set up experimental designs that would be mutually satisfactory to the organicist and the experimental psychologist or behaviorist. But in the present state of knowledge, it would be just out of the question to try it in the other areas.

SOLOMON: It is at the level of collaboration that individuals seem to get into squabbles. Usually it is because the one does not seem to understand the other's language. When each tries to make a lexicon of his discipline, he meets difficulty in obtaining agreement on definition of terms; e.g., emotions.

SPIEGEL: Back of the difficulty about the language is the abstruse problem of conception. It is not just a semantic difficulty;

173

that is usually soluble. But after the meaning of the terms is ascertained, the problem of conceptual clarity remains.

I have often thought that one of the difficulties which members of different disciplines have in attempting collaboration has to do with the degree of clarity which they demand in their habitual approach to problems of reality; or, to put it differently, it has to do with their tolerance for ambiguity. Many people are satisfied with the degree of ambiguity that the word "emotion" denotes or connotes. Others are simply not satisfied with it and want more precision, more clarification, and more specification. They are two different kinds of people. Perhaps their respective characteristics are attributable to their types of training, engrafted upon their inherent natures. The feeling of satisfaction in working with concepts which have certain degrees of clarity and precision presents one of the great difficulties in collaboration.

SOLOMON: What makes it even more difficult is that the investigator who regards another's ambiguity as unsatisfactory often is working in an area where the same concept is prominent. He has many empirical referents; accordingly, he designates the properties of the concept more precisely than does his less exacting confrere. He is therefore intolerant of the latter's tolerance for ambiguity. He becomes annoyed with the latter for not taking into account the obvious empirical information that is available. It seems to me that intolerance for ambiguity happens just as often as personality problems.

For example, a psychologist working in the area of anxiety, let us say, has conducted many experiments and covered much literature on the subject. He then encounters a sociologist who is writing theoretical works with anxiety as one of the concepts, completely unlinked to any of the empirical references, either the physiological or behavioral characteristics, which the psychologist has been studying. The psychologist confronting the sociologist with a passage asks, "What do you mean by this?" The sociologist gives a definition that is useful enough for himself, but the psychologist who is working in the area thinks it is absolutely pointless.

The one specialist knows many important properties of a concept; the other using the concept has never even thought of them and has no conception of them because of his own area of concentration. Actually it is something more than just tolerance for ambiguity. It is also a matter of relative ignorance. Each of us is ignorant in certain areas and not in others. This state seems to be indigenous to every specialization.

SPIEGEL: That should be a temporary problem.

SOLOMON: Very temporary, but it is a bar to collaboration.

GRINKER: We are starting out with the topic: How do we differ in our concepts in relation to the causation of mental disease? I believe that we have to establish what these concepts are before we can talk about any disagreement. Do the psychologists have a point of view about the causation of mental disease?

SOLOMON: It is not a special problem. Psychologists who take an extreme position would assert that the problem is to predict, control, and understand behavior. How the psychologist happens to classify the behavior is just a convenience on his part, but it still is describable in nature. If he can locate the antecedent conditions and a current condition which predict and control that behavior, why does he have to call it abnormal? Why does he have to discuss the problem of mental disorder at all?

The psychologist can produce many seemingly abnormal phenomena in the laboratory; but as soon as he understands how to predict and control them, they do not look abnormal to him. He uses such concepts as neuroses less and less often these days. The old terms drop out in the experimental literature. For example, if an aversion for different kinds of foods is established in animals, it is very rarely ever referred to as a neurotic manifestation. If a psychologist measures how long an animal will starve himself before he will touch an item of food that has been associated with something unpleasant, he will characterize the results in terms of hours and minutes, and also in terms of other behavioral manifestations. But he will rarely ever call the behavior abnormal, even if the animal is shaking all over and obviously showing signs of emotion. He will note the presence of the emotion. But he would not use the term "neurosis."

I do not know whether this is a trend which will reverse itself shortly. It may. Massermann is quite atypical of the general trend because his roots are not in psychology, but he uses psychological technics.

GRINKER: The psychologist, though, will try to specify some basic element in the behavior and quantify it?

SOLOMON: Yes, and also try to determine its antecedent conditions.

GRINKER: The psychodynamic point of view has tried to deal with large segments of behavior without breaking them down into individual, measurable elements. Hence it has become involved with words that indicate categories which do not communicate what is really meant from one person to another in the same field, much less to others in outside fields. For example, what is "anxiety?" Some experts will talk about anxiety as a behavior that has certain ground rules and can be quantified. Others will speak of it in terms of what would happen if something were done to an individual to put him in a different situation, or if certain kinds of defensive rituals were released. Workers in different disciplines have much difficulty talking with each other because they have different meanings for the same word. But if it is specified that "anxiety" is the composite of characteristics and properties as viewed by the various disciplines and that it has measurable referents, then this concept can be taken from the field of human behavior and applied in animal behavior without the word "anxiety" being used.

SOLOMON: Some psychologists would assert that the conception of phylogenetic continuity is not tenable at the moment for psychological concepts; that an animal's behavior is not transferable to man's behavior. Others do not subscribe to this view. When an animal trembles and whines, psychologists of the latter point of view label the whole phenomenon as the anxiety complex, and then unabashedly look for the same phenomenon in human beings.

GRINKER: Let us discuss anxiety, an extremely important behavioral element that is concerned with mental disease, to see how we come to disagreement about it. If we use such a large concept as the causation of mental disease to see how we disagree, I think that we will become mired down.

SOLOMON: I would like to narrow the topic even more than that. Anxiety is still a rather broad concept. Let us reduce it to a more specific component or symptom like tachycardia. The reason for my suggestion is that some of the properties attributed to anxiety will differ according to the observer. When a patient says, "I feel anxious," some regard this statement as evidence of anxiety. But a psychologist would be very likely to say, "This statement may have something to do with the patient's emotional state or it may not." What it really exemplifies is language behavior; hence the observer who writes down, "Patient feels anxious," in his notes is deluding himself. He should write down, "Patient says, 'I feel anxious.'" It may well be that in this patient the word "anxiety" is very high in probability of occurrence in his language behavior and has little or nothing to do with his "actual" emotional status.

I think that it would be better to narrow the topic to a presumed symptom than to attempt to discuss the concept of anxiety. Then we might consider its validity as a symptom and its possible determinants.

SPIEGEL: Some investigators would define psychology as the study of communicative behavior. If we rule out the subjective reporting of an individual, if we reject the validity of the patient's statement, "I feel anxious," we have focused on an area of nonacceptance.

SOLOMON: You think that I have ruled out the validity of subjective reporting when actually I have not. This misconception is constantly arising. What I said is that the patient's statement is a manifestation of linguistic behavior, which describes what his mouth, throat, and lungs were doing at a particular time. This is as highly significant an act as any other act of an individual. But its correlation with other acts is not specified. To say that the patient's statement is an index of anxiety is to profess a faith that it correlates with a certain vague pattern of events. That presumed correlation is still undemonstrated. When the patient says, "I feel anxious, doctor," this statement is an important behavioral item which should be studied; but its validity depends upon what criteria are set. If the statement reliably predicts, say, tachycardia, in many patients, then here is an important functional correlation which ought to interest the psychologists. If it does not predict, it lacks validity and is therefore not as important.

SPIEGEL: You have isolated two areas of nonacceptance. In considering them it should be borne in mind that we are not trying to settle the problems but only to define them. One is the definition of the object and method of study. If linguistic behavior is only a matter of how the lips move and how the voice sounds and does not include the potential scientific properties of communication of meaning, it overlooks a multitude of problems buried in the latter. The other area of nonacceptance has to do with the reasonable degree of precision that can be asked for in scientific work. In raising the question of verification and validity, you said that some psychologists would not be satisfied with a patient's complaint of anxiety because subjective reporting does not have enough elements of verification and validity. That is certainly true. But those psychologists are asking for degrees of precision, verification, and validation which are probably beyond the capacities of the methodology of subjective reporting. Here is a typical example of a difficulty.

SOLOMON: That is, I think, partly true. Yet investigators are at work in this area; e.g., Newman, with his studies of intonation changes. Pure linguistic analysis reveals changes in patients during the course of therapy; e.g., the so-called neurotic whine, which can be identified. When a person says something, what it means is a problem that is certainly in an area of unacceptance.

SPIEGEL: This question is of utmost significance for the sociological approach. Specification of meanings, shared values, and shared assumptions are an integral part of the social point of view. If investigators do not treat with them scientifically, then there is practically no way of setting up collaborations between those interested in the social processes and those interested in biopsychological processes.

GRINKER: This issue lies at the heart of the fields of psychology and psychodynamics, as they enter upon multidisciplinary discussion of any problem or cooperation in its study. I thought that it would be advisable to restrict the concept for discussion to a much smaller segment which could be more easily qualified and measured. As for the subject of anxiety, a patient does not report to an observer in terms of anxiety; he reports in terms of how he feels. An untrained subject is not going to say, "I'm anxious." He states how he feels in terms of certain definite referents; in describing his feelings he speaks about his concern over the future. He may say, "I have a dread that something is going to happen to me"; and he will communicate this in terms of the past, although he may use the present tense. He may talk further as follows: "At a certain time when such-and-such was happening, I had this feeling also." From the point of view of the psychodynamicist, this is the usual and accepted anecdotal way of finding common patterns of behavior of the idiosyncratic person, on the basis of which the psychiatrist can venture a prediction as to what will happen in the future. Even if the patient were isolated while reporting his complaints, so that his pupils, perspiration, or any tremor of his hand could not be observed, and if any tremulousness, hesitancies, and changes of pitch in his voice were removed by proper recording devices, I am sure that his words would communicate his anxiety. Such manifestations seem to be the essence of the working material of psychodynamics and human psychology.

The aspect of communication just considered can be linked with a number of other phases. For example, a developmental history might be elicited to show that under certain circumstances the subject was pushed to a degree beyond his capacity and made to feel ashamed in relation to other people; therefore he has this dread that something will happen to him when he is in a competitive situation, or when circumstances dictate standards of behavior that he feels he cannot live up to. On the other hand, the communication might be linked with such phenomena as changes in his adrenocortical secretions by conducting biochemical tests. This multiple approach should reveal something about his past environment, his present social situation, and the functioning of his body, all in a sequential relationship. But to focus on verbal communication without accepting, as a fundamental principle, that a human being can communicate such states as feeling, which can be recognized and measured, leaves very little science of psychodynamics or psychology.

SOLOMON: When you say that a person has been pushed too hard in the past and is suffering from symptoms now, I think that you have opened another area where we might have disagreement. The psychologist would say that many people have been pushed hard in the past. As a matter of fact, if you go into the specification of what has happened in the past, you will find that everybody has been pushed hard. Therefore, if your specification of being pushed hard has any scientific value, you ought to be able to predict some one part of behavior in contrast with another. This has to do with specification of antecedent conditions related to the development of current behavior. Generally the psychologist goes about the problem differently than the psychiatrist does.

GRINKER: I merely mentioned that being "pushed beyond his capacity" might be one of the conclusions drawn from the patient's developmental history; I did not mean that he would usually make such a statement or that if he did, it would be unquestioningly accepted and used. If it were used, it would be necessary to consider both cultural and constitutional factors. These would constitute another whole area of analysis, which should yield a quantitative statement on the result of the interaction of many factors. All these considerations bear upon anxiety.

POPE: How are you using the word "quantitative?"

GRINKER: It can be used in many ways. One is: A change of any degree that an observer is capable of discriminating in a particular situation.

POPE: Such a determination of quantity is in the nature of a subjective judgment, an evaluation on the part of the observer, rather than a process of mensuration.

SPIEGEL: You are raising the problem of subjectivity in measurement. There are several ways of studying it. By one procedure several observers check on each other's judgment in evaluating the same item or object. The extent of agreement among them indicates the degree of accuracy of the subjective method for that appraisal. By another approach to the problem the question is asked, "What elements go into the subjectivity?" In an attempt to ascertain an observer's cultural point of view and how it may color his judgments, there is inquiry into his values and the culture in which he was reared or socialized. If the influence of culture on the judgments of multiple observers of a behavioral phenomenon is determined, then proper allowance can be made for the subjectivity.

GRINKER: Let me continue my line of thought. Through the use of controls of communication from one person to another, a particular variable can be isolated and quantified. The reliability of the procedure, however, is dependent upon what other measurable changes are associated with variations in degree of the phenomenon under study, whether it be anxiety, anxiety neurosis, withdrawal, or schizophrenia. The topic under discussion does not have to be specified since the reliability of qualitative and quantitative concepts of the human communicative functions depends upon their relationship to other systems of action. In the present state of knowledge and with the present operational procedures, concurrence or disagreement really depends upon the extent to which a transactional operation among many systems can be established. Where this communication is not obtained and where relating proves difficult or impossible, that is an area of disagreement. When it is recognized that what is ordinarily called relationships, covariance, or variances is now being designated by the term "transaction" because communication that is not over fixed processes and known pathways must also be included; then there is usually some degree of satisfaction and concurrence. The outcome hangs upon the present state of knowledge and methods of operation.

SPIEGEL: Dr. Solomon spoke of the psychologist's methods and observations, in which there is emphasis on antecedent and consequent behavior, and the desire to make scientific statements. From the standpoint of concepts and methodology the problem narrows down, in scientific problems, to a series of covariables, both dependent and independent; and avoids a configurational analysis or an operation which Dr. Grinker was subsuming under the heading of transaction. But if the study embraces a much wider network of reciprocal processes, all impinging upon each other, it is practically impossible to isolate them in time so as to obtain a linear function.

SOLOMON: The largest number of variables that a psychologist has been able to "handle" in a configuration has been three.

SPIEGEL: A mathematician cannot handle less than three in a transaction.

SOLOMON: However, that fact does not rule out the possibility of trying to hold constant, under experimental conditions, an array of variables which are varying one, two, or three at a time, so that configurations are taken into account. Any experimenter following the traditional notion of control is varying configuration.

SPIEGEL: This raises two questions: (1) Is it possible in a study of human behavior to hold the variables constant? The experience of investigators studying communicative behavior in disturbed people is that variables cannot be held constant. As soon as one variable is changed, all the other variables undergo change because a network is in operation. (2) Does not this action limit the investigator to the study of only a certain type of behavior?

SOLOMON: It may very well. Probably this point is implicit in some of the areas of unacceptance. The psychologist is narrowing his observations to just a particular realm which he thinks is important. It may very well be that others do not regard that realm as important.

GRINKER: Isn't it also a matter of the time element? The organicists in their work take a special time-bound fragment, slice it out of the whole, and use it as an independent structure for the most part.

POPE: What they are studying would determine whether they would adopt that procedure. Sometimes they are forced to. Do you believe that your comment would apply to what the physical scientist can do in correlating his observations with those of the psychologist?

GRINKER: I give you the story from the past of neuropathology. A person with the diagnosis of schizophrenia dies after being in a state hospital for twenty years. Upon autopsy, cells of the hypothalamus are found to look different from those which the neuropathologist is accustomed to see in persons who die early in life from some infectious disease or accident. He says, "This is the cause of schizophrenia."

POPE: That is simply a reflection of extreme naïveté. Obviously it is a completely uncontrolled experiment. I realize that this illustration has happened in the past, but it is not fair to attribute such uncriticalness to those who are now working in this area.

GRINKER: But suppose that when a patient under an anesthetic has his hippocampal gyrus stimulated, he develops an epileptic fit which is associated with words that refer to body function. Would you say that *the* cause of epilepsy is some abnormality of the hippocampal gyrus and that the location of the body symbols is in the inner portion of the frontal lobe?

POPE: Absolutely not. Perhaps I should preface my remarks by saying that while I am glad, in a sense, to uphold the organic point of view, I really have a very dim view of its possible relevance for most of the problems which I am sure will be discussed. As for your example, it is at least an interesting observation that the surgeon, by applying his electrodes to a certain part of the brain, can produce psychological phenomena which have a direct relationship with the individual's past experience or present behavior, and that he can demonstrate such effects in certain regions and not in others. But it is an extreme extrapolation to assume from these observations that the same sequence of events occurs in the intact organism; that memories are stored in this or that particular region; or even that when a person normally is having memories, this particular region has any priority in initiating them. Maybe it does. I do not see, however, that the evidence is sufficient yet to establish that it does.

GRINKER: I was trying to raise the point that most investigators of mental disease study processes that move in time and that the time unit is very significant.

POPE: The experimental scientist necessarily has to make his own diversion in space and time, but he is beginning to be aware of the significance of what he is thereby doing.

SOLOMON: The element of time appears in any structural function. Those phenomena that are regarded as relatively permanent and can be located at any time are apt to be relegated conceptually to the structural category. The organicist is in no worse position on this than the psychologist who talks about personality structure or the sociologist who talks about social structure. This same problem appears in all approaches. The span of time taken into account in any problem is a matter of scientific convenience for the most part.

POPE: The span of time has more to do with the nature of the experimental procedure than with the nature of the questions.

SPIEGEL: The length of time is a matter of scientific necessity. By convenience you doubtless mean that the method has to be studied to the occasion or to the subject of the study. Actually those who study short-time processes very often have means of reproducibility and verification that are not attainable by those who study processes and behavior which take place over a longer time-period. For example, all of the situations that go into the socialization of a child can never be reproduced because of the long time span. To attempt it for a society would be even more difficult. This built-in difference in temporal span lies behind the conceptual thinking of the various disciplines and impedes collaboration.

KRUSE: However, the time-bound element is not prevalent throughout or exclusively indigenous to the organic school. Mental health and nutrition are two biological processes that operate over the whole life-span. Although they have many dissimilarities, they also have some points in common. If nutrition is studied chemically by determinations on blood samples, it reveals the status for a point of time. On the other hand, morphological changes manifest the cumulative effects of man's entire life. Here, in the organic field, is one instance that is not time-bound, that covers the whole life-span. It is not accurate, therefore, to say that one particular perspective of time is characteristic of the organic school.

SOLOMON: I think that most psychologists would accept your viewpoint on the relationship between the organic and behavioral. A study might be either long-term or short-term depending on the technic. In Dr. Grinker's example on neuropathology the shortcoming was in the experimental design and interpretation, not in the element of time. To say that causality has been demonstrated, when actually there have been no appropriate control observations would be jumping to unwarranted conclusions.

Dr. Skinner's statement on the psychological position contains no relationship to the organic or the physiological. He prefers not to think in those terms; I happen to like to. In subsequent discussion I should perhaps speak from both standpoints. I would say that Dr. Skinner would express a dispassionate satisfaction that investigators are at work in the organic area; but he would point out that there is a whole level of description and correlations in psychology which is independent of the organic approach. I would say "no" to that. My own philosophical position is that a good psychological concept is one which has lots of independent means of verification, some of which are organic and physiological.

POPE: Would Dr. Skinner agree that it is at least theoretically possible, that it would be sound, and that it might lead to important insight to make parallel observations at the levels of the psychological and the physical sciences? I dislike the word "organic" because it seems to carry so many unfortunate connotations.

SOLOMON: Dr. Skinner's main point is that for a good psychophysiology, that is, a relationship between the behavioral and physiological or chemical fields, reproducible laws allowing prediction and control must first be established at the behavioral level so that the organicist has a hitching-post. Dr. Skinner's historical sense tells him this is not the time; for workers who make such correlations now are making them with too imprecise a characterization at the behavioral level, and are therefore victims of the opportunist in the history of psychology. I do not agree with this. I think that correlations all along the way are going to be helpful to both psychology and physiology, especially in the area of psychosomatic medicine.

POPE: Perhaps these are the reasons why the psychologist and the laboratory worker can talk to each other relatively easily: the logic of their statements; their relatively simple operational definitions; their protocol statements that are similar and readily translatable or, if not translatable, at least easily considered in a parallel. But when the laboratory worker moves toward the provinces of psychodynamics, sociology, and anthropology, attempts at correlative statements may violate even the rules of syntax with consequent misunderstanding.

SOLOMON: That point has an important bearing on disciplinary collaborations. For example, if I, an experimental psychologist, should get an idea that has physiological implications, I would rarely ever seek out anyone in psychodynamics, psychosomatic medicine, or psychiatry, with whom to discuss the problem. I would go to an experimentalist in neurophysiology, physiology, or endocrinology, outside of the clinical setting; for I can immediately make a *rapprochement* with no difficulty in understanding at all because we seem to be operating by the same type of logic.

SPIEGEL: Are you saying that when you get an idea that has a physiological component, you seek a physiologist because he knows physiology? Or are you saying that you do not approach a psychodynamicist because you do not communicate with each other? Is knowledge or communication the crux? If it is the latter, then I think that you ought to specify in what way you and the psychodynamicist do not communicate with each other because this is an area of nonacceptance.

POPE: This is exactly the point that I was trying to make. Perhaps this is the fundamental region of nonacceptance.

SPIEGEL: The same type of parallel observations and correlations that can be made between physical or biochemical principles and psychodynamics can be made between cultures and psychodynamics. I do not see that it is logically impossible for the organicist and the psychodynamicist to collaborate. I think that the burden is upon you to prove that it is a logical difficulty.

GRINKER: There is much glib talk about the ability to predict future performance on the basis of the past and present. Many psychodiagnostic procedures are based on a current situation from which the past is reconstructed, and a prediction is made about the existing process, even about its amenability to treatment or its probable seriousness in the future. It seems to me that in view of the extreme number of variables and their importance in determining the course of events, none of us really has enough available information in making predictions. The physiologists and the pathologists have provided observations and data from very short time-spans and the psychologist has studied part-function; in contrast, the psychiatrist has at least the opportunity to observe the larger area of functional behavior. But he encounters the problem of the time of the patient's life at which observations are made. It may bring the psychiatrist to a consideration of quite different aspects of functions than would occur tomorrow, next month, or next year. Then too, in man there are so many nuances of situations and motivations. Actually the psychiatrist knows very little about motivation unless it is evoked by particular situations of various configurations. The psychologist, however, has the advantage that situations are standardized in his laboratory: he can use a rat whose system he knows thoroughly; he knows every person who has handled the rat; he knows what its particular drives are; and he can make it hungry or increase its appetite.

Here is an example of the importance of another aspect of the time element. If a large part of one hemisphere is removed from a patient with a brain tumor, the result will be a considerable physiological deficit. If a whole hemisphere is removed from a child who has been having serious epileptic attacks, the resulting deficit is extremely small compared with that of an adult. Indeed, removal of the left hemisphere improves, rather than worsens, speech. Thus, at different ages, removal of the same anatomical structure produces a different degree of defect.

SOLOMON: If a large amount of the cortex or frontal lobe is excised from an adult monkey who has received tremendous overtraining in solving difficult abstract problems or performing tasks, function is virtually unimpaired. In a sense it can be said that tremendous overtraining to environmental conditions is good insurance against untoward effects from loss of part of the brain. Accordingly, I do not think that you have formulated the correct generalization. I would say that an adult with extensive experience in many instances can resist the effects of surgery much better than does a less-experienced cohort. It has been said that the best insurance against the psychological effects of arteriosclerosis is excessive intellectual pursuits.

GRINKER: I would disagree with your statement.

POPE: How are you going to follow up this observation? Are you postulating that as the nervous system becomes more and more completely integrated, there is greater rigidity and specificity in neuronal pathways that are necessary to control any particular group of functions?

GRINKER: Apparently there is a larger area of possible utilization in the brain of a child. Hence, predictability, which is a problem in the care of patients with mental disturbances, is not too good even in the organic field unless the factor of time is taken into consideration. In the behavioral sciences there are so many variables to be taken into account that predictability of a supposedly healthy male's performance in a given stress situation becomes extremely difficult. In psychodynamics, predictions are not sufficiently accurate. Any two psychiatrists utilizing the same material, the same protocol, the same sound record and pictures cannot make similar predictions. On the other hand, I think that the physiologist would say, "When I apply an electrode in a particular place, I always get the same reaction. I can reproduce it over and over again." Or the pathologist says, "I can stick this slide under the microscope and I can have a thousand people look at it." Likewise, the experimentalist will say, "I know everything about my animals; I can predict their behavior." But, despite the confidence of the organicist in his predictions and the bases for them, it is my opinion that the attempt to predict from observations over short segments of time is fraught with as many variables and difficulties as those that confront the psychodynamicist covering a long span. For, I do not think that observations on behavior over a segment or isolated period of time enable even the physiologist to predict what an organism is going to do physiologically under other circumstances at different times. My contention is that the discrimination among the several fields on the point of predictability is neither valid nor deserved.

POPE: It is a reflection of the relative complexity of the experimental situation in each field.

SPIEGEL: The complexity is built into the subject being studied. The nonacceptance comes from what is labeled as science. There are investigators who designate as science only situations in which accurate predictions can be made, compared, and validated. They will declare that others who are conducting studies containing a larger, indeed an extremely large number of variables, are not dealing with them in a scientific way.

POPE: The former do not stop to think that it is impossible to reckon with all variables. The latter investigator does the best that he can. What he does is still scientific although controlled observations may be difficult for him.

SPIEGEL: When you said "the best that he can," your language revealed a value. It sounded as if he had to make the best of a bad situation and that it would be a good situation if he could apply the methods of the physical scientist. I think that statement is value judgment. Coping with many variables by the configurational type of analysis with simultaneous operations is simply part of the scientific problem. The methods that are used in the study of physical science cannot be used in the study of psychodynamics. New methods have to be discovered or devised; that is not easy. The organicist's nonacceptance of the psychodynamic approach arises from his disinclination to deal with such a large number of variables and to elaborate scientific methods to deal with them. It is much easier to stick with old known and tried procedures.

SOLOMON: I do not go along with the distinction between approaches on the basis of their relative complexity. I have a distinct impression that the psychologist or the physiologist in the laboratory is dealing with every bit as complex a set of phenomena as the psychodynamicist in the clinical situation. But the experimental psychologist or physiologist has a set of methods which enables him to do something very quickly and readily about certain of the variables and not about others. For the most part, the variables that he cannot do anything about are in the same realm, as far as unpredictability is concerned, as those which confront the psychodynamicist. But there is one fortunate exception. The experimental psychologist or physiologist has control of some variables that have very great effects; consequently, against the background of a mass of uncontrolled variables, he is able to produce the illusion of having great control. When this happens, he is apt to say, "I know some of the more important variables." But that statement is not necessarily true. For, if out of the mass of uncontrolled variables, one or more were to achieve for the first time an extreme set of values, they would completely overwhelm the effectiveness of the few variables which

the psychologist or the physiologist is now able to control. Then he would throw up his hands and say, "There must be some new, important variables that I haven't found." He would then look for the reason that his old variables no longer work. In contrast, the psychodynamicist is really at a loss in this situation because he does not know the most potent variables.

GRINKER: Nobody knows now. Some of the most potent probably never will be known.

The point that I am trying to make is this: To the variables on which he focuses the physiologist or biochemist tries to attribute significance in the total behavior of the organism; but actually they are attributes of only a part. He has the same problem as the psychodynamicist in the total behavior of the organism; namely, the inherent covariables express themselves in different qualities and in different times. And he has not yet mastered the problem. Since he rarely controls the variables, he may have, in a given situation, what he calls a relationship between them; but it is only a transitory side-action or side-effect of the elastic biological cycle. With its upswing, down-swing, and movement back toward the previous state, the glucose tolerance test is a prototype. The biologist should know the whole cycle, its qualitative range, its total span, and what other cycles are starting in various quantities and at various times in the relationship. Instead of seeking this information, he takes a single span of time and points to the variables which are in relation to each other in that segment. If he were to look into the past of each of the systems that he has studied to find out what has gone on since the system became active, and to follow that up in relation to other systems, he might find an important pattern of functions which is as complicated as that in behavioral studies. These functions are rarely taken into consideration.

SOLOMON: Experimental psychology employs exactly the same procedure, in which the variables are narrowed down to a few observed over a very short period of time. Very often the individual who believes that he is studying the antecedent conditions of behavior will not go far enough back to reach them. He will bring up a rat for ninety days, run him in an experiment for five days, and then describe only the observations during the five days. But I do not see that this experimental procedure is a big area of unacceptance because some problems can be readily studied in five days.

GRINKER: It is a big area of unacceptance on the part of the physiologist or chemist. He says to the psychodynamicist, "I have studied a function; I have measured its quantity; and I know its time relationship. You ask me to work with you; but you cannot tell me what you mean by something, you cannot tell me its quantity, and you cannot tell me how long it has existed." In my opinion, the physiologist or chemist possesses, in reality, no more complete information in his own domain.

POPE: True. But he can make definite assertions that are relevant for the particular time period that he has been studying. It is true that his results may not be capable of extrapolation in time. But how do such assertions differ from what you might tell me about what is going on in a patient's mind at a given time?

GRINKER: I agree. I would like to tell you but I can't.

POPE: Insofar as both fields are guilty of the same errors or both are aware of the same difficulties, I do not understand how that situation constitutes unacceptance between them. I am fully aware that it is a frequent source of difficulty and that it exists as an interpersonal problem between workers in the several fields. But that is an entirely different question.

GRINKER: It is a common statement of objection.

POPE: Yes. However, is it not just a practical difficulty between individual workers who may find it hard to understand each other? If so, it should be resolvable. Or, does it present a fundamental difference in the nature of the concept or the procedural approach in the several different fields? I would take the latter to be subject to unacceptance.

KRUSE: Over the years the usual procedures in the study of diseases and their causation have been: (1) clinical, (2) epidemiological. They differ in one or more of the following ways: the species; the number of subjects, i.e., the size of the sample; study under natural, altered, or contrived conditions; span of time and space; technics for collecting observations; analysis of data; and the interpretation of results.

For example, in tracing the history of pellagra from its very beginning it becomes evident that these types of methodology have contributed to its solution. It is interesting to note how knowledge about this disease was gained from these approaches, now from this, now from that method, in succession; how further advance would be held up at some point until a missing piece of evidence came from a particular approach; how progress then resumed with the next piece of evidence falling into place. It was a long campaign, not an overnight conquest; and each of the different branches of the scientific service played its part. Then too, there was a particular sequence and pattern, an essential timing in the kind of approach. I would not say that the sequence of its elucidation was the only possible one. But the nature of the first approach must have influenced the subsequent pattern. Perhaps this history of pellagra exemplifies a principle that holds for other diseases.

In a sense these different procedural approaches have their counterparts in the study of mental disease. For example, there are many procedural similarities between the sociological and the epidemiological approaches. Furthermore, although actual collaboration between clinician, epidemiologist, and experimentalist has not been frequent, one has often used the results, in some instances even the methods, of the other in studies.

SPIEGEL: In reference to time there is no real difference between the types of correlations in the psychosocial approach and those of other approaches in the study of any part of human behavior. But the methods of collecting evidence and conceptualizing the process under observation are much different. To take an example of the kind of correlation that might be made, let us consider the statement made by Dr. Solomon that everybody gets pushed. I think that an expert with the psychosocial point of view would question that statement and would say that it should be studied. Is it true that everybody gets pushed? It may turn out that in certain cultures or subcultures a large proportion of people will be pushed in a certain direction. Let us say that in a certain predominant segment of American culture, parents will push their children to intellectual achievement in school; that is, they will bear down very heavily on demands for performance. Let us say further that in other cultures, the parents who are the agents of acculturation of their children do not make this demand. Their attitude toward the children is more permissive, more understanding, more accepting of inherent characteristics. Because these parents do not value external performance, they do not attach high importance to their children's intellectual achievements.

The psychosocial expert would want to know what effect this parental attitude has on human behavior, especially on correlatable components. Given a culture in which parents make this intellectual demand on their children, he would want to find out what it does to the child's personality and to his capacity to integrate his physiological endowment. Or, if the parents, respecting the quality or personality of the child, does not make this demand on him, the psychosocial expert would want to know the effect of the parental attitude on the capacity of the child to integrate. The parental attitude may be found to make the difference in the child's personality. It may turn out that one set of parents, socializing their children in one way, produces conflict for them, whereas the others do not.

Dr. Kruse referred to a classification of approach in terms of a conceptual model and distinguished between naturalism and experimentalism. If the psychosocial expert poses the problem, collects the evidence, studies it, and then makes correlations with psychodynamic and with physiological properties, he is employing the same *kind* of procedure as those taking other approaches. There is nothing *logically* different about it.

SOLOMON: I suppose that the question is, Where does naturalism—the astute and intuitive observation of the world around—end, and experimentation begin. This has been a problem in every science. Biologists and psychologists got along for years by observing the world and got quite a bit of understanding about it. But somehow or other in the history of most sciences, naturalism was forsaken for concerted experimental effort in the laboratory, although return to naturalism took place spasmodically. It seems to me that some sciences revert to naturalism when they meet certain kinds of situations, even after a long history of experimental work. They go back to looking at the phenomena in their natural form. Probably some of the arguments about the differences between these methods are based on man's conception of where the sciences are historically. The experimentalist may say that it is unproductive to look at patients or natural phenomena, that the thing to do is to go into the laboratory for experimentation. The naturalist will reply, "Come out of the laboratory and look at the world as it is because the laboratory does not represent the world." I think that this exchange of words has occurred in the history of every science.

POPE: Perhaps the easy interchange of information and ideas between an experimental psychologist and the physical or biological scientist is due to the readiness with which statements in physical language can be translated into behavioristic psychological terms. To ask a physiologist to specify in exact terms what is going on in the brain of an animal that is exhibiting rather simple behavior, excluding entirely what may be its feelings, is one thing. But to ask a similar question as to what is going on in the brain of the person who is experiencing "faith," that is something quite different. The question may not even be applicable.

SPIEGEL: There are too many intervening variables or concepts. Consider the cerebral activities related to experiencing "faith"; certainly there are psychophysical correlates, but it is impossible to get directly from one to the other. The intervening steps that tie in with "faith" have to be found.

POPE: The predictability of a psychophysical correlate might be relatively simple in animal experiments; but it might be extraordinarily complex and difficult with the human, in whom the correlation might be different at different times. The same phenomena in the brain might not always be associated with the same set experiences; they might differ from one time to another.

SPIEGEL: We have been asked to focus on areas of disagreement, but I sense that we are unable to disagree.

SOLOMON: We are looking very hard for them.

GRINKER: Can't we get somebody here to take a firm stand in a disagreeable manner?

SPIEGEL: This development intrigues me; for it seems to me that we have set up disagreement as our goal for today. We put a positive value on disagreement. From the point of view of our group, if we disagree, we are doing well. We probably are conditioned culturally to value performance and achievement, and we try to satisfy whatever performance aspirations we are given. So, when we disagree, we all feel like good fellows. But if we feel like good fellows and are communicating well with one another, then from a psychological point of view we cannot get mad. And if we cannot get mad and fall out with each other, then we are not likely to air our disagreements. If I start making positive suppositions that I ask you to agree with, then suddenly you are going to start to bristle.

SOLOMON: Yes, I will disagree with you on points.

SPIEGEL: One bristle will lead to another.

SOLOMON: I do not think that this is the way we will get at our disagreements.

SPIEGEL: You are now disagreeing with me because I made a positive statement.

SOLOMON: But I do not feel very strongly about it.

GRINKER: In view of the psychological nature of the other three fields, I should expect some positive statements from the organic approach. Yet I found myself having to make them myself, not because I believed in them but because I wanted somebody to attack them. I think that the or-

ganicist has to stir us up by setting forth definite statements.

POPE: I plead guilty to silence on that score. I can find more to quarrel about with organicists than I can with this group.

SOLOMON: I feel the same way.

POPE: I would, of course, uphold the general proposition that the study of the brain as a physicochemical system and the description of its structure, in the sense of knowledge concerning the orderliness of its spatiotemporal operations, can be expected to contribute to the understanding of mental phenomena. While the brain is the organ which subserves what is called "mind," it is important to remember that, in a very real sense, the opposite is also true and that the object which we can observe anatomically or physiologically or analyze chemically is like all other objects in the outside world, a remote inference from the immediacy of experience and dependent on the operation of "mind." In relation to the causation of mental phenomena, it seems to me a fallacy to regard the nature and action of the brain as necessarily more "basic" or "fundamental" than the corresponding events that must be described in psychological language.

SPIEGEL: I know full well that Dr. Solomon has serious reservations about psychodynamics in the clinical setting and very great doubts as to the validity of some of its concepts. Maybe we have not talked in such a way as to drag those doubts from his preconscious. But I am sure that if I presented an analysis of a clinical case and made statements about it, he would very soon question, "How do you know that?"

SOLOMON: Yes. But I would ask that of almost anyone describing anything. As far as I am concerned, I would never think of gathering information about behavior in a clinical setting; it would be the last place that I would go. It is not a place in which I know how to operate well. If the psychodynamicist wants to operate in that setting and gather information, it could very well help him to further what he considers to be the science of behavior, or mental life, or sociocultural science. But that does not mean it is going to help me to further what

I consider to be science of behavior. Our conceptions are going to be different.

SPIEGEL: Is the difference on the conceptual or on the operational level?

SOLOMON: It is on both.

SPIEGEL: We have plenty of room for operational differences because no two psychiatrists or no two psychologists operate in the same way. But that is not disagreement between disciplines.

GRINKER: What are the conceptual differences? I can set up a protocol of a patient studied psychodynamically that would be similar to that for rabbits studied by an experimental psychologist.

SOLOMON: I have an idea of what it would mean to use my intuition in order to make a sensible pattern out of a wide range of variables operating in all directions at once. But I do not like to try it! It is not neat; therefore I do not find it pleasant.

The clinician has a tendency to report interpretations instead of primary observations. I think that an intuitively sharp clinician jumps to interpretation immediately and hands it on as fact. He records the interpretation in his protocol in such a way that the original event can never be recaptured. Admittedly in many cases genius-like interpretation may be much better than a description of what happened. But at the same time, much is lost. When I ask the clinician what he means by some statement, it is because I cannot visualize exactly what he saw. This is less likely to occur in the protocols of the experimental psychologist, but only less likely. The tradition in experimental psychology is against it. There the tradition is to try to describe accurately, in objective language, what actually happened, what was seen; then the interpretation is set down separately. This separation of the interpretation from the original observations allows others to look at the relationship between them.

GRINKER: What you say may be true of clinical practice. The clinical psychiatrist, like the internist, is not experimenting all day long in his office for the purpose of posterity; he is giving some treatment. But if you are talking about experiments in psychodynamics, there is an increasing trend toward complete recordings, both sound and visual, and toward observations on the therapeutic situation by several observers. It is a matter of setting up a design for an experiment in psychodynamic interpretation.

You brought up also the nature of the consideration of the psychodynamicist's interpretations. I take a communication from the patient which stimulates my thinking; I communicate my thoughts back to him. The response of a patient to an interpretation in the beginning of this relationship is usually, "Yes, I see what you mean. I think you're right," or "I can't see it at all," or "It doesn't make sense to me." Then the therapist who is also interested in scientific investigation very frequently verbalizes to the patient the following statement: "I don't care what you say. If you say you agree, fine. If you say you disagree, fine. Your immediate acceptance or rejection means nothing. But I don't think either of us can rest our case on present evidence. What I say to you is a suggestion, a hypothesis, which needs to be put to the test of time and mental activity, conscious or unconscious. It is verified or disproved by later events. Sometime in the future, in some way or other, you are going to bring out some evidence that this interpretation was correct or incorrect."

The validity of the hypothesis is revealed by the patient's doubts, feelings, and behavior as the result of this interference. I think that operationally you function in the same way.

SPIEGEL: What Dr. Solomon means when he says "interpretation" is not necessarily what you mean. He is really talking about level of abstraction.

KRUSE: There are two observations in the organic field on which it would be interesting to have comment from the psychodynamicist. One is the evidence on the role of genes as a conveyor of potentiality for mental disease. The second is the induction of what appear to be abnormal mental states by means of drugs. What is the view of the psychodynamicist about them?

GRINKER: As for the second question, it has been postulated that the stimulating or inhibiting action of the drug on certain functions of the brain is related to the chemical constitution of the particular cells which have perhaps an affinity for the drug. At one time it was thought that the barbiturates were particularly disposed to associate themselves with certain cells in the hypothalamus. As for the psychological action, I cannot conceive that any drug, through its chemical structure, would have a specific effect in bringing out a certain configuration of ideas or sensory projection. The content of the verbal or behavioral performance which results from the drug's action on the central nervous system is an expression of pattern functions which are part of the past of the organism. Alcohol, for example, may bring out already existing negative feelings in people. Likewise, the production of hallucinations by a drug like mescaline cannot be understood without knowing something about the subject's personality, its whole pattern structure, and its functions.

SOLOMON: The question is how important the effects are. It may very well be that there are effects of mescaline which can be seen above all of the variation which comes from personality differences. In that case I would say that there was a reliable correlation between a physiological or chemical event and a psychological manifestation.

SPIEGEL: Not only the individual differences of human beings but also points in common have to be recognized. In my opinion the effects of the drugs cannot be studied as separate entities without taking into consideration the type and functions of the individual.

SOLOMON: The importance of finding the individual differences needs to be emphasized, but that is not what the investigator looks for first.

KRUSE: According to the view expressed here, a drug capable of inducing abnormal mental states produces specific effects which might transcend the personality differences.

GRINKER: It might have a selective affinity for certain areas.

POPE: There are, of course, some rather remarkable biochemical and pharmacological differences in neurons of different kinds and in different areas. Do you, Dr. Grinker, believe that the abnormal behavioral manifestations induced by, or associated with, certain drugs or deficiency states mimic the behavioral phenomena that are seen in clinical psychiatric syndromes? Or do they simply happen to produce some of the same epiphenomena which are observed in schizophrenic or manic-depressive psychoses? The resemblance is very striking.

GRINKER: I do not quite understand what you mean by epiphenomena.

POPE: Symptoms that are secondary or not invariable. A hallucinatory experience would represent an epiphenomenon. It is a secondary manifestation rather than one of the basic features of the personality structure that you would probably insist upon in order to make the diagnosis of schizophrenia.

GRINKER: Because of the difficulty in differentiating them, toxic psychoses are clinically often misdiagnosed as schizophrenia. The differentiation is based on finding evidence of a drug injection. Then too, the effect is usually temporary. But under certain circumstances the effect may outlast the actual presence of the drug in the body. Once the abnormal process gets started, it seems to go on. High levels of cortisone may bring about psychotic behavior that looks like some of the classical psychoses. Furthermore, it is assumed that the behavior pattern of psychotic individuals shows quantitative differences from the functions and processes which occur in all people. We have not yet been able to determine the qualitative differences.

Schizophrenia is a vague entity which presents itself with tremendous variation. The nature of its etiology, pathogenesis, and even its natural history, is not well known. All the work that has been done has not brought out, either on the somatic or psychiatric side, what the qualitative differences are between a normal and a schizophrenic person. There are differences, we believe. Nevertheless, qualitatively a normal person can recognize in himself manifestations, if protracted, like those seen in schizophrenia.

POPE: And yet at some very basic level there must be an important qualitative difference which indicates that the potential schizophrenic does not think right. For the organicist it has always been a great comfort that certain abnormal behavioral phenomena can be produced by drugs and deficiencies. He then reasons that similar organic disturbances must occur in the person who is primarily schizophrenic. There is, however, no direct and demonstrable evidence to support any such assumption.

SOLOMON: The same items of behavior that are observed in schizophrenia are also perceived in a wide variety of situations and in behavior that we call "normal." This phenomenon is partly situational. People waiting in a subway station late at night, with ten minutes to "kill" before the next subway train is due, and with nothing to read because the newsstand is closed, very often just stand still, looking at nothing. If the circumstances were not known, these persons might be regarded as being in a very depressed state. Hence, the specification of manifestations to be included in the category of abnormal becomes difficult. In psychology it is easy to be led astray by morphological similarity. An individual runs from point A to point B: one observer says, "He is running away from point A"; another says, "He is attracted to point B."

chapter 19

Further Areas of Unacceptance

• •

KRUSE: To move to another area, it has been pointed out that in this country, at least, most of the physicians who have entered into psychosomatic medicine have gone into it from a psychodynamic background. It is also said that, sociologists apart, most of the physicians who have become interested in the social side of mental disease have had a psychodynamic background. The conclusion has been that there are no areas of unacceptance between the psychodynamic and the psychosocial viewpoints. On the other hand, some authorities have stated that Freud was not equipped to work on the social aspects of mental disorders; and that the strictly psychoanalytic school, following the tenets of Freud, would not, therefore, be psychosocially oriented. Are there areas of unacceptance between the psychosocial and the psychodynamic or psychoanalytic schools? If so, what are they?

SPIEGEL: The social scientists assert that the psychoanalyst is naïve where social process is concerned. They hold that although Freud dealt with the subject of sociology at some length, his knowledge of it was limited; but even more than that, he made a number of unconscious cultural assumptions and tinged them with a universal biological component. Many of Freud's contributions to psychoanalytical thinking are concerned with activity and affect in relation to masculine and feminine qualities of an individual. These represent statements that a person living in the same culture as Freud would *think* were evidence of masculine properties or feminine properties.

But actually if Freud had had more familiarity with various societies, he would have known that there is a great deal of variety in these matters and that some of his postulations would not stand up. This is an area of difficulty between the social scientist and the psychoanalyst which leads to the accusation that the psychoanalyst is naïve and unfamiliar with the social process.

On the other hand, in handling an individual the analyst deals primarily with fundamental biopsychological forces such as instinctual drives. He is interested in these forces because they are the motives, the particular assortment of latent considerations, that appear on the surface in relation to cultural attitudes. Values, mores, and customs represent ways the individual has of defending himself against these forces or of integrating them within his personality. But the analyst does not believe that the cultural factors have much significance for understanding information from the patient. Thus, the social scientist and the analyst by-pass each other.

The by-passing, however, is not complete. More and more, the social scientists today accept psychodynamics at a superficial level. Even the sociologists, who are the least dynamically minded of all the social scientists, do not have serious objections to the fundamental point of view of psychodynamics. They might dispute some of its details but not its fundamentals. They would probably consider that psychodynamics provides an explanation of individual behavior. On the other hand, the psychodynamicists would

189

be respectful of society's and culture's bearing on an individual's mental disturbance. Thus, there is an interest on the part of the social scientist and the psychodynamicist in each other's domain. But there has not been much collaboration. When they reach that point, the sociologist raises the same questions of the dynamicist as the psychologist does.

SOLOMON: Such questions as: What type of evidence is this based on? The evidence is coming from the study of very few people and therefore is not really valid.

SPIEGEL: Similarly, when the psychodynamicist comes to work with the social scientist, the task becomes difficult. Among the social scientists, the anthropologist, because he has so many psychodynamic-sounding things to say about culture, is most interested in working with the dynamicist. But then the latter is likely to feel that the anthropologist is speaking only about one culture that he has studied, and to doubt that his observations can permit generalization about other cultures. How can observations on the Bongonese be applied to Americans? This attitude creates a problem when the social scientist and the psychodynamicist try to work together.

SOLOMON: The same relationship prevails between the psychoanalyst and the organicist. Both logically and historically it would seem that psychosomatic medicine and psychoanalytic theory are closely associated; but the psychosomatic area is a very narrowly conceived type of organicism.

GRINKER: Psychoanalysis has been traditionally associated with the field of psychosomatic medicine. Freud was the first to talk about the influence of bodily disturbance on emotionality. He tried to explain anxiety as a direct conversion from repressed libido; this is psychosomatic, too. He very often expressed the view that endocrinology would give many answers about personalities. His psychoanalytic theories reflect his neurological background.

What we call psychosomatic medicine today is really all of physiology and all of medicine; therefore, the neurologist, the internist, the physiologist, the psychiatrist, the psychoanalyst, are all working in the field of psychosomatic medicine. A number of

persons with such complaints as diarrhea or constipation have been analyzed, and correlations have been made. Upon studying the personality of a patient with the diagnosis of ulcer, the analyst found patterns. Passive recessiveness became the number one formulation in the psychosomatic field. Correlations were found at various levels. Some of the analysts talked about the "symbolic meaning" of a symptom and others talked about the disturbance of a particular organ as an expression of the death instinct.

All these interpretations were convergences from particular points of view, mostly with insufficient data about the physiological disturbance. The patient's report that his complaint of a pain in the stomach had been diagnosed, after x-ray, as an ulcer is accepted by the analyst. That is the status quo of the ulcer, and from that time on during the analytic investigation, all the evidence of change in that ulcer is that the patient says, "Today I have pain, yesterday I had pain, the day before I had shooting pain." The interpretation, of course, is responsible for this *modus operandi.*

I do not believe that this operational procedure can be used as evidence of a concept and a stimulus. And in my opinion the psychosomatic field cannot continue much longer without a strong developmental concept of the total process: how the soma and psyche are closely related in function and experience in early life; and how in later life they carry with them the same instinct but each has a different set of experiences. Accordingly, each system has individual affects but both have common affects based on a primary derivation. The retreat from difficult social problems and situations in life is therefore back more to the common features, so-called regression. This approach has nothing to do with specificity. I think that specificity has held back the psychosomatic field. But the psychosomatic is in a different position than the psychosocial field because the latter contains more overt divergence: e.g., sociologists in contradistinction to psychoanalysts. Infrequently a few workers like us get together to try to bridge the gap. But in the psychosomatic area every worker, whatever his special training, is a psychosomaticist; everyone is a part of the whole area and everyone knows it. It would be helpful if in all the procedures everyone would adhere to one concept and one constitution.

SOLOMON: The professor of psychosomatic medicine is offering hypotheses in which he is saying that something in the area of organic symptomatology is related to something having to do with an inner life. An organicist might regard that statement as a challenge; for he, as much as the worker in psychodynamics, has means to substantiate that relationship.

SPIEGEL: Not unless he knows something about psychodynamics.

SOLOMON: I would not say that it is necessary.

GRINKER: Let us assume that an organicist studies anxiety or tension associated with contraction of the gastric musculature. What is anxiety? What is tension? Has conduct been included in the study? Maybe his protocols will be subject to criticism because he does not know what the psychological state is that he is correlating with the physiological phenomenon. He should have a psychodynamicist working with him.

SOLOMON: The organicist could reply that there are many other ways of producing the same symptomatology, and that he would like to investigate some of them because they might give him valuable information on the dynamics of the phenomenon without having psychological factors playing a prominent part. He might find that certain types of chemicals produced it by themselves. He might study enzyme action in relation to cytoarchitectonics.

GRINKER: Investigators are trying to work out the locations in the central nervous system that are concerned with emotional control and pathways from there to the peripheral sympathetic nervous system, then directly or indirectly to the glands of internal secretion; a hypothalamic, hypophyseal, adrenocortical, sympathetic system cycle of events.

KRUSE: Speaking on the relationship between the psychosocial and the psychodynamic viewpoints, Dr. Spiegel said that there are specific points at issue not unlike those between the psychological and the psychodynamic. In Dr. Spiegel we see an attempt in one individual to bridge and to merge two different points of view. In that merger undoubtedly he has had to decide what he was going to give up in one point of view or the other; and how he was going to circumvent, or bring together, or otherwise resolve seemingly unharmonious points. Dr. Spiegel, will you pinpoint the problems?

SPIEGEL: Organicists are not sufficiently familiar with psychodynamics. They have not reached, by and large, a level of sophistication in psychodynamics that they should have if they are going to conduct research on some of the topics in which they are interested. Psychoanalysts have not been interested in social theories. They have been content with the forms of social theory that have been handed down by Freud and have accepted them as the absolute and only word. This is odd, because workers who are trained in social theory are relatively well sophisticated in psychodynamics. The parallel is that the psychodynamicists are relatively sophisticated in organic properties. If they are M.D.'s, they have been trained in the basic biological and medical sciences which are organically grounded. To be autobiographical, I decided that I should learn about social theory and the social scientists' methods, not because I would apply them, but because if I wanted to work with the social scientist, I would have to understand what he says and does. Also, I thought that I might be able to transmit some of the content of social science to psychoanalysts and give demonstrations of its significance.

But, when a psychoanalyst enters upon study in the field of social science, he encounters the problem of identification. So few make this excursion that when someone does undertake it, no one now knows what he is. Certainly he is not a sociologist. But is he really a psychoanalyst, if he is so interested in the social process? He is in danger of falling between the two schools and losing his identity.

This hybridization also creates difficulties in direct transaction with the two schools. When, in talking to a psychoanalytical audience, I attempt to use theoretical concepts of multiple observation that come from the social sciences, such as the social role, a considerable resistance to them develops. The reaction seems to be: These concepts are interesting and probably true, but what is their importance? The psychoanalyst can do what he has to do with the tools that he has; he does not need others.

On the other hand, when, in speaking to a group of graduate students in sociology, I make statements pertaining to psychodynamics, a different series of questions and comment ensues: "How do you really know? Do you know this from the observations of just a very few people? It is interesting but it is not validated; therefore we cannot put too much credence in it."

The topic, the psychology of the interviewer, arouses even greater resistance. There is no question in my mind that both the psychodynamics of the interviewer and his cultural assumptions create problems for him in interviewing. In a project at Harvard, sociology majors have to interview high school students who, because of their adolescence, present interviewing problems. I participated in the training of the interviewers at conferences in which the discussion was given over to how the interview went; where the blocks, resistances, and anxieties were. The discussion in these sessions aroused in the students a great deal of resentment toward me. They felt that I was taking an unfair advantage of them, that I was interpreting their unconscious. Actually I was interpreting their preconscious, not their unconscious. But they were deeply concerned about it.

The psychoanalyst communicates best with the anthropologist among the social scientists. But the degree of rapport depends upon the interest and experience of the anthropologist. If he has worked exclusively in an exotic culture, there will be little interaction between a psychoanalyst and him. The analyst knows American culture, but not the exotic culture. The anthropologist knows the exotic culture very well, but is naïve about American culture. Hence, the analyst who is interested in the impact of American culture on the individual must select for collaboration an anthropologist who is informed about this culture. More and more, our anthropologists are turning from the study of exotic culture to the study of that at home.

Small group dynamics is becoming increasingly important to psychodynamics, especially as therapeutic technics are evolved for group situations in mental hospitals. Perhaps this discipline is easiest for the analyst to understand. On the other side, those who are interested in small group dynamics have to know the psychodynamics of the individual, and the social process of the group; e.g., the ethnic and class components of the people who are in the group. Otherwise they cannot understand the group.

SOLOMON: Having to know something is always in regard to some purpose. There is no such thing as scientific necessity without regard to some specific purpose. And the truth of the matter is that for many purposes the small group dynamicist does not have to know anything about the psychodynamics of the persons in the group. He can arrive at generalizations about characteristics and courses of events in groups of different sizes that hold with respect to a wide variety of psychodynamic compositions.

SPIEGEL: Because of the conceptual models and traditional manipulative skills that have been implicit in the morphological, physical, and physiological sciences comprising the organic field, it is difficult to integrate these sciences with either the psychodynamic or the sociocultural point of view. Differences in temporal spans are encountered when going from the organic to the psychodynamic or the psychosocial sphere. Furthermore, there is the difference in tools. The procedure of decision, duplication, verification, and validation, which the investigator in the physical and psychological sciences finds so congenial to his outlook, comes from a cultural tradition which emphasizes manipulative skills. Things are not clearly understood unless they are brought out into the realm of space and time; and can be manipulated either with the hands or with instruments, better with instruments than with the hand. This traditional manipulation has unquestionably produced many benefits for civilization; and because it has rewarded mankind so richly, it is held in high esteem and prestige.

But since the practices in a culture and its fundamental values assumptions are always in a reciprocal relationship, it is a question not only of the rewards, but also of the high value actually placed on manipulative rather than on psychodynamic skills. The premium is placed on the objective rather than the subjective grasp of relationships; on the external, across-a-distance, rather than internal, apprehension of reality. This external apprehension is necessary in a manipulative situation; that is, whatever is inside must in some way be gotten outside, whether by framing an objective test or inventing an instrument. Since there is a distance between the self and the thing observed, it has to be crossed through space, and technics have to be devised for the purpose. To the organicist it is neater and more assuring if the objects can be laid out as on a dissecting board, examined, picked up, turned around, disassembled, reassembled, and in general treated as the engineer treats his objects.

In contrast, those who are interested in psychodynamics or psychocultural processes are not and never will be able to engage in dissection and disassembly in the same way as does the organicist. The psychodynamicist cannot dissect out, separate, and reassemble the parts of a personality into various patterns to find out what happens. The sociologist or anthropologist will never be able really to take a culture apart and reassemble it in one or another way so as to answer the question, "What is it like when it is assembled like this rather than like that?"

To summarize, part of the difficulty impeding the integration of the organic, psychodynamic, and social approaches derives from a cultural tradition in which manipulative, external performance skills are positively rewarded and the internal apprehension of phenomena is negatively rewarded, indeed is dismissed as too subjective.

GRINKER: Their culture is responsible for the inability of people to integrate cultural factors in their concepts.

SPIEGEL: A vicious circle.

SOLOMON: According to your line of argument, the physical science, astronomy, because it is nonmanipulative and based on the same type of subjective apprehension, would be a stepsister to psychodynamics.

GRINKER: There is manipulation in astronomy. The screws on the telescope are turned.

SOLOMON: For that matter, the analyst puts on his glasses to see the patient. What I mean is that heavenly bodies are moving around out there in space and there is nothing that can be done to stop them. All one can do is to try to understand them. The culture of the heavens cannot be changed.

SPIEGEL: Astronomy has been rescued from this situation because cosmological considerations have turned out to be so important to a basic understanding of the physical universe; the microcosm has to be understood in the same terms that the macrocosm is. The saving feature in this situation is the ability to make an integration with physics. The macroscopic universe is reconstructed on the basis of a physical concept.

SOLOMON: I am interested in your statement that, since astronomy was able to tie up with physics, it was able to survive. By analogy, it would mean that psychodynamics could survive only if tied up with an experimental science.

SPIEGEL: In my opinion ultimately that will be true. But there is a matter of timing. I think that psychodynamics will ultimately become an experimental science of a certain kind; not in the classical tradition of the rat and the maze, but in the sense of subjecting some of its propositions to more rigorous definitions of proof. But that will occur only when an intervening variable, now missing, has been located. For such a problem as the nature of the defenses cannot be taken into the laboratory. It is impossible to produce a laboratory situation which would allow the investigator in isolation or projection to assert that the mechanisms of defense are valid.

Nor do I think that other concepts, such as frustration or aggression, can be subject to immediate experimental proof. The intervening variable has to be inserted; and I think that the intervening variable is the study of the socialization of the child in the family. Whatever the training procedure or whatever the mechanism, whether it is frustration or satisfaction and its relation to a particular defense, it is put into the framework of its interaction in small groups, such as in the culture of the family, because the mechanisms of defense are learned in small groups. Unless it is understood how the small group has created the situation that calls for the defense, all the facts will not enter into the interpretation. It may be meaningless. A dog in a laboratory setting is too different from a child with his father, mother, sisters, brothers, and the whole environment in which the defense is learned. From the experimental laboratory to the actual social setting is too big a jump.

The psychosocial expert believes that the psychodynamicist, in making statements about psychodynamics, does not take sufficient account of the culture and its effect upon the dynamics of the individual. The dynamicist makes propositions as if they were universal, when actually they are based on the study of a few people, without taking note of the way that a particular culture is influenced by its structure.

GRINKER: We have been using the term "psychodynamics" as something derived from, perhaps dependent on or closely related to, psychoanalysis, but nevertheless not identical. Psychodynamics can be considered in a Meyerian sense, or in that of the French school of Janet, or as a development in the Freudian school. The differences are, I think, somewhat important, even though today in this country what we call "psychodynamics" is usually derived from the Freudian concepts. There is, accordingly, a set of assumptions which, although liberalized in many ways in discussion, nevertheless forms the crux of this kind of psychodynamics.

For one thing, there is a model, which is based upon a system of energetics, energy which arises from activities of organs that are concerned with taking in substance from the outside world, elaborating it, and transforming it. The resultant energy, in some mysterious way, becomes what is called "psychic energy." Hence, Freudian psychodynamics is definitely on an organic substratum.

More than that, psychodynamics has a profound hereditary concept in terms of species, in the sense that there are so-called "instincts" which are characteristic of the species; which are the carriers of the energy systems; and which thrust forth and push up into all kinds of hierarchical states of organization in relation to the experiences of the total organism. But, in addition, the personal hereditary factors are concerned with the strengths of the instincts in the individual at birth.

It is a tacit assumption that in some way or other these energy systems, which are the psychological derivatives of the instincts, become modified and distorted, in terms of their goals and their aims, by external events. In the psychodynamic concepts of today, however, they are thought of as functions that have an economy and a topology that are fairly fixed.

When a psychosocial expert tries to communicate to a psychoanalytic group the possibility of a bridge extending from psychodynamic to psychocultural thinking, they misinterpret his views as an attempt to disturb their concept of the internal, instinctual organization. Despite the best efforts of the psychosocial representative, his message does not register clearly in the minds of the psychodynamicists because they become threatened at his ideas. They are not able to grasp that what he is talking about is, not the internal processes, but the sum total, the end result, in which transactions between personality, or what the psychoanalyst call "ego functions," and culture can be observed at a particular stage. Here, then, is a group which is bound in its concepts, with instincts and with energy systems that enter into a conflict with each other and in some way with certain forces in their external environment. And this group is reluctant to leave the internal life and deal in the language of communications. Never has more resistance been manifested in a group that unifies itself than when communication words have been used in dealing with the position of personality in a larger setting. It is a situation that is fraught with difficulties for interdisciplinary understanding.

The dynamicists do agree, however, that

the influence of the environment, particularly of the mother, affects the early child pattern insofar as it acts on zones which are paced in their development through hereditary patterns; which are variable in terms of the strengths of the instincts; and which are the models of subsequent behavior, "modal ways of behavior," as Erikson* calls them. This is a fixed concept in which the emphasis is not so much on any great variability within the child, but on how the mother plays upon these patterned ways of pace development. Hence, the vast variety of influences that are possible from the culture, they attempt to organize in terms of the instincts and the zones that express the energies related to them.

When the psychodynamicists hear talk about the influence of the psychosocial constellation, they listen only so long as what is said does not modify this model. As soon as it becomes much more expansive with the greater possibilities, then the dynamicists turn resistant. For example, they look upon an early illness of a child, which may or may not affect subsequent behavior patterns, in reference to the trauma to those parts of the psychic apparatus that have the function of permitting a discharge of excitation; rather than in reference to a patterned way of response which is induced by a mother who bears a particular cultural difference in the way in which she has been taught how to raise children, based largely on her ethnic origin, and who has a particular family role in response to illness. But the child's mode of reaction and behavior which is precipitated by the sickness depends a great deal on the whole setting and particularly the mother's attitude. An excess amount of love and attention can be interpreted by the child as a command: "This is what my mother wants; because when I am this way, she loves me more. Therefore she encourages me to behave this way." This view does not conform to the psychodynamic principles.

Nor is the dynamicist's concept of heredity broad enough, because it does not take

into consideration that what is inherited is, not a way of dealing with the environment, but a potentiality for relating to people and to situations which are necessary to bring out the individual, or which satisfy particular needs that are excessive in an individual. Hereditary, then, does not mean fixed somatic characteristics such as constitutional types; rather it means a potentiality, even to the point where it strains the people in the environment, and in straining they react in a particular way which their culture has prepared them to.

In addition, the later situational factors which facilitate, modify, or inhibit the functioning of a personality are not sufficiently interpreted by the psychodynamicist as qualities per se which are effected by the groups constituting the situation; but are primarily interpreted in terms of the internal dynamics of the individual based on the genetic concept. Thus an analysis in any conflict with reality is loaded with weight placed on the internal, instinctual kind of organization and its early experiences, rather than on the present reality, which may be facilitative restraint.

In my opinion the only way in which the psychodynamicist can become less conflictual in his relations with either the psychosocial scientist or the psychosomaticist is by understanding the methods of communication. By "methods of communication" I refer not only to communication theory, in which there are ways by which an organization without direct energy exchange may give or receive influences from others; but also to communication as it relates to internal signs, which are a part of the chemical and the neural communications, which in themselves influence organs and organ systems to respond in patterned ways, and which probably become transposed to symbolic communication on a much higher level. Until the psychoanalysts and psychodynamicists begin to speak less of instinct theories and libido theories, and more of communication which does not necessarily involve the exchange of some fictional energy called "psychic energy," I think that there will be steady divergence of opinion and methods of observation.

KRUSE: Do you foresee a change in ter-

---

* Erikson, E. H. *Childhood and Society,* New York: W. W. Norton, 1950.

minology and concept with abandonment of such words as "libido?"

GRINKER: At the present time I see a tremendous resistance to change, a great struggle to maintain an isolated terminology which sets the analysts apart. This is in marked contrast to the situation in the early days of the psychoanalytic school in this country when it attempted to gain acceptance from the psychologists and psychiatrists. Now the analysts are reacting to their great acceptance by being afraid that they are going to lose their identity. It is a struggle to maintain a field of science apart from the general science.

SPIEGEL: Not to mention guild activities.

KRUSE: Does the concept of anatomy of the psyche grow out of Freud's background, or was it absolutely essential that he visualize it in that manner?

GRINKER: Of course, Freud came from anatomy. Then too, the first visualization of the component parts of the personality was so clearly drawn, in a localized form, with heavy lines, separating the id, the ego, and the superego, that as time went on the picture became increasingly anthropomorphized and localized to the point where analysts spoke about a psychological topology, meaning really a structure.

No one would deny that the physiologist can study all the details of the structure and function of a system to advance the sum total of knowledge. Moreover, some part of it may be applicable now or later. Nor do I think that the psychoanalyst should be looked down on because he deals with a two-person, closed system. Maybe that is why he has difficulty with communication theory. He will learn much of empirical value, some of therapeutic value, and some that has applicability to future experiments with or without people.

There is no criticism of any discipline engaged in working with the internal consistencies, the integration, and the defenses against the disintegration of its system. Contrariwise, any discipline that does not attempt to relate its system conceptually and, if possible, operationally, in some transactional field, to the other systems that comprise the living organism, justifiably earns disapproval.

Up to now we have discussed communication, transactions, time, overemphasis on part-functions, and concepts versus operational procedures. All these topics relate to a point that I would like to emphasize. The physiologist or sociologist each may properly perform in his own system, which he has defined by virtue of the variables he measures and which he hopes has some degree of naturalness or existence in nature. But if he wishes to participate in a science of behavior or in the study of mental disease, then he has to be able to utilize the functions of his system in a field of transactions with other systems; to learn to extricate himself from the inside of his system; to stand on its boundaries and gaze in two directions at the same time; to attempt to speak a common language with others who are occupied in other parts of the larger field; and most of all, to be willing to search for the pertinent variables that comprise the total functioning of his system, as they relate to behavior and mental disease. This is one of the critical points which I tried to bring out in my criticism of psychodynamics. Indeed, in all disciplines the worker, having become proficient in thinking about and in working in his own system, is reluctant to put aside this activity and turn to appreciating or depreciating its function in a total behavior.

There is an inertia against giving up any significance of the part-functions of a system and against accepting that the system itself, which may have been the object of lifelong study by a worker, is only a part-function of the total behavior of an organism and is, after all, implicated in mental disturbances.

For many reasons this problem does not usually appear for discussion in a Conference like this. The participants conceive of themselves as being broad-minded, tolerant of the other fellow, as being able to envisage the whole of science, to recognize the significance of other systems. Besides, all that is easy as long as the discussion is on a conceptual level. The pinch comes when the talk gets down to multidisciplinary operation.

I know of a multidisciplinary group which sits twice a week discussing its work. It is held together by a conceptual scheme and models. But when it comes down into the working situation, it is terrifically strained. The number of times that this group can threaten to break up, and sometimes actually does, is striking. When that happens, it brings a realization that the physiologist is Physiology, the psychologist is Psychology, the psychiatrist is Psychiatry, and each man is regarded as representing another discipline, as the system with which he works. There comes to mind a comparison. Think of the integrating capacities of the living organisms in nature that keep all the systems functioning; then consider the lack of the capacity for operational integration in real life among members of a multidisciplinary group gathered around a table.

POPE: In such a Conference as this, we are touching upon problems that the best minds have pondered over for the last 2,500 years without reaching any definitive solutions. What impresses me about the present group is its sense of mutual understanding and respect, and the lack of mutual exclusiveness in the work that is carried on in each of the fields represented. The members have been brought to the problems through various avenues, and probably each one of us is somewhat conditioned by the nature of the measuring instruments that he is accustomed to use. Even within a single discipline such conditioning can lead to dichotomy of thinking.

I repeat my previous stand to the effect that detailed analysis and description of the physical events in space and time that constitute the nervous system in action can theoretically describe a set of operations having a one-to-one correlation with a similar structure of occurrences describable in psychological language. If the central nervous system is thought of as a bridge of internuncial neurons between input and output, with provisions for elaborate reverberating activity and for fluctuating fields of stimulation and inhibition, it is certainly possible to build up a mechanistic picture of it as a system having exactly the properties requisite for conditioning by past experience and for acting on the basis of associations and through previously channeled patterns. Such a picture has much in common with a behavioristic psychology, but difficulty arises when empirical findings are carried over into areas in which meaning and valuation are encountered and which are essentially outside of physical science. Then, almost insurmountable obstacles are encountered in the attempted transactions, and other disciplines have to bring their concepts and methodology to bear upon the problem.

GRINKER: In the application of chemistry and physics to a study of the human organism, the model of study in terms of the cofunction of the systems becomes exactly the same as the transactional model that takes in the relationship of systems to each other. Let us assume that in studying a system these investigators are concerned, not with a fragmentary brief-time situation, but with function conceived as a process. When the biochemist thinks about hypothalamic, hypophyseal, adrenocortical functions, he visualizes a cycle. He thinks about parts of a system in transaction with each other with all the feed-back mechanisms and the braking devices. In that transaction one system is related to others inasmuch as it is necessary for their functioning. If a man does not have an adrenocortical system and does not receive replacement therapy, he dies. That system is indispensable. If his hypothalamus is damaged, he is in a constant state of lethargy. That system is also needed. The functions of the system studied by the biophysicist and biochemist are necessarily part of the total transaction. But they know that, as a system, it is a single variable of many variables. In its full import their information becomes part of the behavioral sciences.

SOLOMON: Your use of the term "system" bothers me because functionally the experimental psychologist can break up an organism into several systems that operate quite independently of each other. These independent systems happen to be using the same organism. Under given conditions, a chronically frightened organism can be produced. Under different conditions, the same organism could not possibly be characterized as frightened.

I know that psychiatrists in speaking of personality like to talk about it as a system.

They make much use of the term "integration," and state how the whole thing makes a nice pattern, a picture. Here is where studies of "part-function," as you call them, play an important role because they demonstrate that tremendous changes in certain aspects of behavior can sometimes be produced without other aspects seemingly being affected. "Part-function" fits in much more with the role-concept than does the systems-concept.

This approach goes way back to statements of faith and the philosophical ways in which the experimental psychologist operates. He takes stimulating conditions very seriously. Students of the socialization process say that one important point in child training is consistency. But the psychologist does not even know what the word "consistent" means because as he breaks down the situation into part-function, he discovers valuable information. The parent may be totally consistent in regard to a certain behavior that the child performs under given stimulus condition S_1, but he may be inconsistent toward the child's behavior under given stimulus condition S_2. Also, there are different types of inconsistencies. For example, when a child says, "I hate you, Mummy," he may be punished if the mother has had a hard day; for the same remark he may not be punished if the mother has not had a hard day. You would probably call it inconsistency. But if the child has any understanding, he soon learns to discriminate between the reaction of "mother after having had a hard day" and that of "mother after not having had a hard day." The inconsistency is immediately erased; the mother is being perfectly consistent. When she has had a hard day, she punishes; when she has not had a hard day, she does not. In giving serious consideration to stimulating conditions, behavior, and their consequences, the experimental psychologist has a powerful tool in analyzing part-functions. Its fruitfulness could serve as a recommendation to those individuals who do not like to analyze part-functions.

For example, it has been stated that the observation that either a thing happens or it does not happen represents one scale of measurement. To an experimental psychologist, that is not a scale of measurement unless the conditions under which the thing does or does not happen are stated. For it may be an all-or-none affair in which, under condition S_1, it always happens; and under condition S_2, it never happens. In counting the number of times that a phenomenon does or does not happen, all that one is doing is substituting a change in the environment for the counting process, or saying that the organism changes if the environment is changed.

What is consistent depends on current theory. When some observations do not seem to fit, the usual explanation is that something is inconsistent. In reality it means that the theoretical notions are not complete. I dislike to have phenomena about personality explained or accounted for on the basis of consistency, for that simply means that the subject did what the investigator expected.

GRINKER: But if the subject does something that was not expected, it means that the investigator did not have accurate or full knowledge of the process. Then he has to find another hypothesis for it. All science is that way. Let us say that 80 per cent of the observations in a study confirm a hypothesis. The next step is to find out why 20 per cent do not confirm it.

SOLOMON: The concepts of integration, totality, and unity which psychodynamicists are wont to use are meaningless for the phenomena which they are observing. They do not seem to be placing their faith very much in their system of thought; otherwise they could not talk about integration, coherence, and consistency.

GRINKER: Those investigators, such as psychologists, who are working inside the problem have it easy because they can get close to the process and still be far enough away to have a unity. In the terms of behavior, the dynamicist has to get far away to see this unity, consistency, and integration, so far away that he cannot understand what is happening.

SOLOMON: I do not feel that way about it at all. It depends on what one is doing. In my work I look for uniformity of process to produce all kinds of inconsistencies. Certain values can be put into an experimental situation, and by another criterion, certain obvious inconsistencies can be predicted in advance.

POPE: Two questions arising from the deliberations of physical science in the twentieth century may be applicable to problems in psychodynamics and psychoanalysis. One is the lessening role of determinism, at least in physics. Psychoanalytic theory has a strong biological flavor. Freud was naturally influenced by the then current mode of thinking in the sciences, which was exclusively centered around the notion of causal relationships. In what way might the decline of determinism as it has taken place in theoretical physics in the last quarter-century play a part in the theoretical structure of psychoanalysis?

The second question has to do with the role of goal-selection and goal-seeking on the part of the organism. This is a problem which has been emphasized in recent years by the cybernetic school. It is the concept that present behavior is influenced as much by what the animal is projecting into the future as by what has happened to it in the past. Is this view going to bring about a more complete psychodynamic theory?

These are two points which contain seeds of unacceptance to physical science.

GRINKER: The determinism that is ascribed to psychoanalysis has to do with forces and factors which are modified to some extent but lead persons into a fairly common pattern. The analysts make interpretations in terms of hypothetical instincts. They can permit themselves to do this by ignoring a tremendous number of variables and by making the interpretation from within a closed system. They have a ritual in their relationships with patients. Very frequently they refuse to have communication with anyone but the patient. Insofar as possible they shut off their own minds that bring their own realities. Isolated, as it were, in a room that is quiet and conducive to fantasies in both of them, the analyst and patient act in a two-person situation and engage in closed communication in which one affects the other in a circular fashion. The analysts are reluctant to consider the variables of other people's influences and of situations which require

forms of adjustment which have not been previously expressed. In my opinion, determinism is a matter of operation.

POPE: In my question I had in mind the role of determinism in the theoretical structure of psychoanalysis. For example, does the analyst consider his reconstruction of a patient's motivational history as theoretically providing a rigorous proof for the cause of his present behavior?

GRINKER: Implicitly; for, the view is not expressed in any definition, is never concerned with a statement or a segment of behavior from a subject as an isolated phenomenon; for, it is known full well that any system is determined also on the parameters that surround it. That is particularly true of psychoanalysis.

The analyst does not immediately accept any statement of the patient. The latter may say, "My mother was a horrible, rejecting person. She never gave me anything." That communication came from the patient. He ought to remember. The way in which the analyst can validate the correctness or incorrectness of that statement is in a contemporary relationship in which he is the participant-observer. To illustrate, the analyst gives patient A a kind remark on Monday, and one a little kinder on Tuesday. The patient wants more on Wednesday, and yet more on Thursday. Finally on Friday, he simply says to the analyst, "You're a so-and-so because you give me nothing." So, it is not a matter of what the patient or a relative says of past behavior and relationships; rather it is actually the patient in a new setting, revealing his conception of what the environment is like.

Obviously, there are two possibilities. If the environment was bad and the individual has the capacity to learn that environments do not have to be bad, he can come to know that there are environments which are not bad. Or if the patient has misinterpreted the environment, he may, by having the same feeling reproduced in him in a controlled environment which he knows is not rejecting, be able to learn that he had misinterpreted the environment in terms of his own needs.

Constitution, not in the structural, but in the dynamic sense, also enters into the mother-child relationship; for, the needs of the child, which are his hereditary, quantitative variations, will to a great degree determine whether the mother is giving or not giving. Suppose the child asks so much that no mother could give it; she is, nevertheless, a not-giving mother. Of course, her capacity is another factor; for there is a level at which it is strained until she cannot give any more. The mother-child relationship is an interaction system; and the only way in which the psychodynamic therapist-investigator has a right to make any statement is by reproducing under his own eyes, as part of the same system, a system-environmental relationship.

SOLOMON: One subject that is likely to stir up disagreement is specification of stimulating conditions. To the experimental psychologist the stimulating conditions gather their significance through their association with the behavior of the organism. Intrinsic properties do not have to be taken into account. This gives the experimenter considerable freedom to specify the situation. Prediction, which is called an understanding of the behavior of the individual, has acquired a significance through relationship with life-history. The anthropologist may remind the psychologist that a life-history is composed of elements in the culture. The latter would then reply, "Just let me know the ones that affected this individual." That is, the psychologist calls on the sociocultural expert to help to specify the stimulating conditions. As for the processes of learning, emotion, retention, forgetting, conflict, and frustration, they presumably have their own laws.

GRINKER: Those dealing with mental disease want to know the common factors, whether in the area of physiology or in culture, that impose such a strain on the organism that they break it. There are manifold examples that linking factors with the break depends either culturally or socially, on the diagnoses themselves. But understanding the situation takes into account the ranges of the system: how far it can be strained, regardless of what strains it. Further consideration brings in the concept of deviation. How is it that this culture has patterns of relationships which **deviate**

from others and are precursors of mental disease.

POPE: Insults and traumas to the psyche go on in the life history of almost everyone. Why is it that one individual has been more influenced than another by them, other conditions being approximately equal? Perhaps they are not equal.

GRINKER: Of course they are not. Many factors would have to be studied: all those subsumed under bodily systems and personal environment. In any argument about what causes mental disease, it should be remembered that the whole organizational system comprises multifarious parts. One part, deranged to a sufficient extent and exerting an influence on enough other parts, will disturb the whole system. Our present methods of observation are so gross that some of the lesser degrees of disturbance cannot be recognized, certainly not by simple inspection.

POPE: Among individuals who have sustained a roughly equivalent amount of psychic trauma, some of whom have become ill and the others not, it is possible that a positive correlation could be established between the presence of mental disease and some as yet unknown factor, whether hereditary or in the mode of operation of the brain. Or will it be necessary to reconstruct the entire story of each sick individual's behavior in dynamic terms? Is a sufficient cause more likely to be found with such an approach?

GRINKER: Enough disturbances of various parts of the organism have been seen to know that there are all kinds of end results in terms of personality. There are various adjustive devices and other systems functioning in compensation, and there are all gradations of acceptance or rejection of deficit. So no one can say that he can put his finger on *the* most important factor concerning mental disease.

SOLOMON: Here are some basic faiths of experimental psychology. They might be a source of disagreement.

The experimental psychologist is much more what might be called a "right-wing" scientist and he is more or less convinced that the traditional methods of the physical and biological scientists are the ones which are going to pay off. So he boasts individually, day in and day out, of trying to control the phenomena as much as he can by varying aspects of the environment or life-history sequence, one at a time, or maybe two at a time, or at the most three at a time; but no more than that because he would begin to lose conception of all the interactions which take place. From this procedure he derives a set of functional relationships that are empirically reproducible; that is, anybody in any laboratory faithfully repeating the experiment would obtain the same results.

In connection with this *modus operandi,* the crucial question really is, Are the phenomena in the groups really important enough to warrant all this work and experimentation? That is where there has been disagreement, although it has not come out here. The psychologist in the laboratory can produce in a dog a state of afraidness of certain stimulating conditions, such as a flashing light; the animal looks afraid, with accompanying signs of nausea and retching, or salivation, urination, and defecation. By producing this phenomenon the experimental psychologist feels that somehow or other he is getting his fingers in a process. To him it makes no difference whether the stimulating condition of the process is flashing lights, buzzers, the approach of a human being, the approach of another dog, these different stimuli are constants that can be used in establishing a state. In contrast, the dynamically or socioculturally oriented expert is apt to ignore the process that enabled the psychologist to produce afraidness in the animal, and to emphasize that it is whether the stimulating condition is a person or a light that is important. Thus, this is a point of disagreement, too. The psychologist is searching for general laws that relate stimulating conditions to behavior. These laws include a specification of prior or antecedent conditions and consequent behavioral conditions in a contemporary set of stimulating conditions. Past stimulation, present stimulation, and behavior constitute the process which the psychologist views. In the viewing, much more attention is paid to change and stability, ways of changing organisms, rather than to characterizing the consistency of personality changes.

As a matter of fact, experimentation with lower animals brings out and underscores the lack of consistency in behavior because the diverse ways of changing the organism's balance are learned. Also, this balance and alteration of it appear to be more under the control of the environment and the experimenter's manipulations. These conclusions deflate the human ego; for, when translated into social life and psychodynamics, what they mean to the experimenter is that the human being is not a consistent machine with its own integrity and balance. Man is extremely lucky that the environment does not change very much. This is a subtle distinction between the viewpoints of the psychodynamicist and the experimental psychologist.

For a while the concept of homeostasis helped experimental psychology. But, from recent work revealing partial irreversible changes it would appear that if there is such a thing as homeostasis, it is certainly shiftable by a set of operations to become a new level of organization. The experimental psychologist has never been too comfortable with the notion that he was bringing the animal back to a state of equilibrium at the end of every learning experiment. The animal is pushed in some direction by environmental changes and it never quite gets back to where it was. Goal-changing is a good example because in experiments the animals look as though they are changing their goals all the time. Of course, the experimenter has changed them in the real sense of the word. It means that the event which will terminate a given behavior sequence is now a different event than it was before.

GRINKER: Were you bringing out the point of differences between the work with humans and animals, or of observation versus experiment? Because, if you were doing the former, I come into some disagreement with you; if you were doing the latter, I agree with you. Experiments in psychodynamics are being carried out; but I would agree that much remains to be subjected to experiment. Nevertheless, I do not think it need necessarily be with animals.

SOLOMON: Psychologists take the path of least resistance. If they are interested in a certain phenomenon and can study it with human beings in the laboratory, they do so. But, if they cannot—and usually it is for a very good reason having to do with ethics—then they have to turn to animals.

GRINKER: I agree that some problems are more conveniently studied in animals; e.g., the responses indicating that a particular system has been disturbed and the biochemical and physiological components of disturbances. If only the disturbances could be produced in animals, knowledge of detailed sequential changes would be enhanced. There is a limit to the number of blood samples that can be taken within a limited period from a patient.

KRUSE: The experimental approach is not exclusively the province of psychologists; the various disciplines in the organic school employ it. Evidence obtained with the experimental approach may provide the basis for formulation or verification of a concept. Attempts to apply this concept by observations on disease in its natural setting, where such circumstances as the time factor and size of sample may be different, may greatly broaden it. Indeed, it may not resemble the original concept. Usually the experimental method has a narrower frame of reference than does the procedure of observations in nature. The difference between the smaller experimental situation and the larger natural setting is not just a matter of size. It is more the difference between the simpler and the more complex. The difference is reflected in the resultant concepts. This is no criticism of either; each has its place.

SOLOMON: I agree. Of course the experimental method, par excellence, is designed for simplification, for restricting. As a matter of fact, the history of it is the history of the restriction of the phenomena under study.

I imagine that the problem is the same as that of the physical chemist who is put in a situation where he has to make a geological judgment. This is difficult for him. Some of the physiochemical concepts are not of much use to him when he has to make decisions about the mountain from the point of view of the geological processes. I would not disparage the activities of the theoretical scientists, the results of which seemingly have no practical application. Nor do I believe that there are too many of them. Indeed, there are not enough.

POPE: Most investigators are too concerned about doing something useful.

SOLOMON: The economics of the situation are quite clear. Researchers are paid more and rewarded more in other ways for the applicable than for the inapplicable. This is a symptom of what could be considered to be a stultifying influence on scientific results. I would like to see some investigators, back in the recesses of the inaccessible, working away because of their curiosity, not caring whether their concepts are going to be applicable. A complementarity is needed. The history of science shows that at some periods of time applied research, at other periods theoretical research, yields the more information. Who is to say what stage we are in, at any particular point? When I am told that some concept that has been developed in the laboratory does not seem to be easily applicable, I suspect that the judgment on it is premature.

KRUSE: Why do you prefer the laboratory to the clinical setting?

SOLOMON: I know in advance that I will not meet in clinical situations any of the conditions necessary for the analysis such as those that I use in the laboratory. Let us suppose that, although I am not a clinical psychologist, I am asked to counsel a person with problems and difficulties. Under the circumstances, I do not act in accordance with laws which prevail in the laboratory; nor am I concerned with the same variables. I am not sure that the generalizations in the laboratory can be carried over into a clinical setting. That does not mean that some may not be useful. All things considered, I use a new frame of reference.

The psychologist who works in the laboratory is not going to relinquish psychological principles just because he does not know the values which apply out in the open world. For example, I could not have predicted too well at lunch today the la tency and amplitude characteristics of your salivation when the food was brought on the table, that is, before it touched your mouth. For I do not know your past history with regard to food and your conditioning characteristics. I might have an idea that the phenomenon would happen; however, there are conditions under which it might not. But I would not know whether those conditions prevailed. The fact that I do not know this does not invalidate the principles.

GRINKER: You would not be able to say from your experimental work in the laboratory that one of the characteristics first and extremely well correlated among the symptoms of depression is the drying up of salivary processes.

SOLOMON: No, because I think I could make it into profuse salivation instead. Experimental psychologists like to think up situations which violate everybody's expectations. By appropriate conditions they can have an animal back away from a situation while drooling profusely. You say that when a person is frightened, his mouth drys out. My answer is that it occurs only under some circumstances. This is a part of a tradition of skepticism. One man propounds a generalization; given enough time, another restricts or upsets it.

A cat is trained to press a lever which results in his shocking himself. At first glance it appears to be a stupid performance on the part of the cat. But viewed as an aspect of the whole learning sequence, it makes perfectly good sense. I do not know whether it would be transferable or have application.

KRUSE: Do the things that are meaningful to the experimental psychologist have significance for the psychodynamicist?

GRINKER: Motivation, both conscious and unconscious, and perception are responsive to the human organism. As for motivation, take, for example, the statement, "I want to succeed." There is nothing unconscious about that assertion. It shows the genesis of the desire to succeed as it has reached a certain quantity, and how much it is willing to push over. If "unconscious processes" come into consideration, another variable has been added. The study

of perception and its various changes under different conditions as related to an effective response is also very important. A person who for some reason is disturbed with anxiety has his perception changed; the external world is altered in speed, character, and form. And the decisions which he makes are changed.

In terms of psychotherapy, the psychiatrist is confronted with a problem; he is dealing with an actual external situation, with conscious motivation, and with things happening to the individual. I object to the psychodynamicist's fixation on internal problems without the proper value placed on the external situation.

In a study going on now we are trying to relate perception and decision to anxiety levels by creating situations in which perception or decision fails to reach a certain standard in terms of the attitude of the environment. The subject is told that he has failed; he is not seeing the right thing; he is not making the right decisions. How his hope succumbs and how his anxiety mounts can be seen. In the design of the study, as in Hebb's, we have to accept the current situation. The long past of the individual is part of it but, nevertheless, not dissected from it. When Hebb talked about his animal's "hope," he was dealing with what he observed at the time. He tried to say that it was related to some internal process, but he had no history of the animal. If we disregard or discard the history, we are left with a patient who has anxiety. Can we increase it by making him fail or can we reduce it by making him succeed in his perception-decision? We will also follow what happens to other sequences at the same time. Some day we may speculate that the kind of situation which made this man anxiety-prone is important; or that the kind of anxiety that he presents in the study is important and requires delving into his past.

ADDENDA

HOLLINGSHEAD: I do not agree with the statement uttered by a member of the organic school that the problem of schizophrenia will be solved by the chemist. It implies that schizophrenic behavior has an organic base, that it is genetically or chemically caused, and it can be rectified by a chemical agent. There may be a constitutional base for the functional psychiatric disorders; I do not know. But I find it difficult to accept such an assertion without evidence.

Furthermore, I question the implication of the organicists that "We are scientific; you psychologists, dynamic psychiatrists, and sociologists are nonscientific, because you do not see things our way."

METTLER: The organicist is frequently guilty of the tacit assumption that the organic point of view is necessarily identical with the scientific point of view.

HOLLINGSHEAD: I cannot accept the extreme point of view of the experimental psychologist engaged in learning studies that problems solved with rats can be applied to man. Many things can be done with animals that cannot be done with human beings. But I take a dim view of the experimental psychologist's tendency to reason directly from animals to man.

LIDDELL: I sincerely believe that none of us will profit by maximizing the animal's behavior out of a realistic setting. We cannot do that. There can be no profitable animal sociology.

HOLLINGSHEAD: There is no animal culture, as far as we know. In our sense, there is no social structure in animals.

LIDDELL: The animal does not acculture himself. I do not think herd behavior, or flock behavior, is more than homologous with human social behavior.

METTLER: Do you believe that to be true of the anthropoids?

LIDDELL: I do not know. Apparently, an anthropoid can bear a grudge for more than a year. Cannon was seriously attacked by a young chimpanzee which he had irritated when it was a baby.

HOLLINGSHEAD: I think, therefore, it is necessary to be cautious when it comes to reasoning from the findings of experimental psychology in a laboratory to human social behavior, because the cultural element is not there, particularly the culture of learned, shared, and transmitted meaning.

As for the psychodynamic point of view, a number of dynamically oriented psychiatrists reify their terms. They employ hypothetical constructs, which may be categories, as if they are verified scientific existences. In an extreme form, the thinking of many psychodynamicists is a postulation of social behavior that society can be reconstructed if they can delve deeply enough in the individual and get at the instinctive base through retrogressive questioning.

Another point on which I tend to disagree with many of the dynamically oriented psychiatrists is that when they are questioned about something that is unknown, they tend to retreat to organic ground to explain it.

Also, I am impressed negatively by their assumption of a cultish defense when the meaning of their terms is at issue. When they are challenged, they may fall back on the pat line, "If you had been analyzed, you could understand what I mean." The implication is, "You have not been converted yet; if you had, your soul would have been saved."

Finally, they find it difficult to demonstrate experimentally the existence of a number of their postulates.

FINESINGER: What disturbs me about colleagues with the organic point of view besides their assumption of a monopoly on the scientific method, is their lack of sensitivity to the psychological subtleties. Those who work in this area are therefore often unaware of the necessity of controlling the psychological and interpersonal variables before they can be sure that their results and statements are meaningful. If they were aware of this need, they could obtain expert assistance in the psychological field through collaboration or consultation. The least I would expect to find in publication of their results would be a statement of their awareness that variables were operating which the psychiatrist would like to have controlled, but which admittedly had not been controlled. I believe that such a clause would lead the organicist to narrow his broad statements. In contrast, the psychologist and psychodynamicist have more refined methods for discriminating the reactions of subjects. Incidentally, I think that the term "organicist" is so all-inclusive as to be misleading. Every investigator in physiology, anatomy, or biochemistry is an individual organicist, with his own notions about the relation between mental and physical phenomena.

Another source of concern to me is the lack of sensitivity of workers in the organic field to the facts and possibilities which exist in other areas. There is a tremendous gap between what the biochemist and physiologist observe in schizophrenic patients and what the psychiatrist observes. It is a long stretch between reactions to stress and the differentiation of delusions in schizophrenic patients.

I have the impression that too few sociologists accept the notion that the sociological aspect is not the whole story and that social experience gains meaning to an individual through personal factors. As might be expected, the social symbols do not mean the same to one person as to another. I think also that sociologists tend to neglect the organic factors. As a matter of fact, this is a major problem in the various disciplines. It is so easy to neglect the other area, especially if it does not appear too attractive, and to put too much emphasis on

the importance of one's own area. The correction of that shortcoming, however, is not to psychoanalyze all the sociologists, because psychoanalysis does not necessarily make a person more scientifically oriented or better equipped to conduct scientific studies.

LIDDELL: I once asked four resident psychiatrists to explain to me the difference between a training analysis and a therapeutic analysis. They all agreed that a training analysis turns into a therapeutic analysis.

FINESINGER: It is true that there is no difference. My impression is that people undertaking a training analysis usually do not tend to overreact as much as a patient does, that their conflicts are not so intense, and that their reactions to conflicts are more modified by outside factors. Basically, what we are saying is that people are human beings and that everyone has exigencies and conflicts. Sickness does not arise because of a conflict. It arises from the intensity of the conflict or the way the conflict is handled.

chapter *20*

Clinical Principles in the Practice of Psychiatry—Their Clarification, Refutation, or Validation

KRUSE: The two Conferences have been based on an assumption that there is a need for better communication among representatives of the four different conceptual approaches to the problem of mental disease. There is no existing permanent organization or arrangement which affords the opportunity for exchange of ideas regularly and systematically. Indeed, such occasions are infrequent. It was thought that if the representatives could be brought together and allowed to ponder over one another's approach to this problem, such a meeting might be conducive to a broader attack on disease by the multidisciplinary approach.

I am indebted to Dr. Whitehorn for suggesting the team meetings preliminary to the second conference, an arrangement which has already proved to be most productive.

The topic for today is, "Clinical Principles in the Practice of Psychiatry—Their Clarification, Refutation, or Validation." Here the division and separation is not among four disciplinary approaches, but between the experimentalist or investigator and the clinical psychiatrist. Just as among the former, so between the latter there is not complete understanding or even sufficient communication. As a step toward enhancing this relationship, it is planned to seek the reactions of the nonclinical experi-

mentalists here to the principles on which clinical psychiatry is now practiced.

It would be helpful, first of all, to have these principles enunciated. Many of them are empirical; hence, they are to be scrutinized by the three experimentalists from a scientific viewpoint. Especially to be considered are those principles, those empirical procedures, which the experimentalists view with reservations, doubt, or disbelief. Emphasis will be placed on the basis and justification for these reactions, and on how disputed principles may be validated or disproved. As the only practitioner of these principles in the group, Dr. Whitehorn sits vis-à-vis three experimentalists. Our first objective is to try to figure out what are the assumptions on which the group operates.

WHITEHORN: My understanding of our task is that we are here in a group to consider, discuss, and formulate a statement about the clinical approach. Our first objective is to try to figure out what are the assumptions on which the group operates. It would be, I presume, simpler and easier if we could have a commission which would be able to enunciate the principles and assumptions for the scrutiny of others.

METTLER: I thought that you would do that, Dr. Whitehorn.

WHITEHORN: Yes, that would be a logical assignment. If I had sufficient time, I might try to do it. But personal inconvenience favors my taking another tack, which may have great advantages. The three others in the group have been closely associated with, and looking over the shoulders of, clinicians at work. By reason of your way of thought, which is different from the clinician's, you may be able more aptly than he to put into words what seem to be the assumptions on which the clinical psychiatrist operates.

This is not just a trick dodge to get out of my own responsibility. To some degree I am here under new colors; for, during at least the first ten years of my familiarity with psychiatric operations, I was a laboratory experimentalist observing the clinician. It is a favorable spot from which to observe and understand how the clinician proceeds in his practice.

METTLER: In speaking of the practice of psychiatry, it is necessary to take into consideration the particular persuasion or orientation of the psychiatrist. The practice of psychiatry varies in type according to circumstances. There are, for example, what may be called the necessary attitudes which must be adopted by the psychiatrist who is practicing in an institution as contrasted with the attitudes of the psychiatrist who is practicing with private patients.

WHITEHORN: Perhaps we are at the point where an elementary assumption might be identified. It is implicit in Dr. Mettler's remarks. This assumption is that the psychiatrist, being a physician and functioning in a role which society assigns to a physician, has a responsibility for the care and treatment of patients. Wherever the clinician might be visualized at work, the assumption would still hold true that he labors under a sense of obligation to care for and to treat a patient. From that point we might begin to split off further assumptions. At the very beginning that process raises a question: Does the psychiatrist treat the patient or does he treat the patient's disease?

METTLER: Or does he treat the environment in which the patient is found? Under some circumstances the psychiatrist's activities are limited entirely to the manipula-

tion of an individual's environment. Those circumstances are the time and facilities at his disposal. He might, for example, theoretically be committed to the proposition of analysis; but practically, by the necessities of case loads and by demands made upon his time, he might be forced into a situation in which he engages only in manipulation of the environment.

WHITEHORN: To take that situation as an example, let us try to disentangle and clarify the underlying assumptions. We might make a logical distinction between care and treatment. Thus, the first dichotomy would be taking care of the patient in contradistinction to treating the patient. The second would be, does the psychiatrist treat the patient or the disease?

Much of the necessary preoccupation of the psychiatrist with the environment is around the care of the patient. There are two aspects to it: one has to do with the immediate household; the other, with the larger social setting. Here is a sick person in need of care. The hospital psychiatrist provides that care first in the form of immediate environment, food, shelter, and clothing. These are not specifically oriented to the nature of the patient's illness. It is simply provision of necessities for a patient who is not otherwise going to get them. The other is to provide social care for the patient because of underlying assumptions that there are factors causative of the illness. Mixed with these notions would be derived ideas and assumptions that if this feature of the environment were to be adequately taken care of, the patient might not then be ill or his illness might be cured.

SCOTT: I should say that on the whole we would not be particularly concerned here with the matter of "care."

WHITEHORN: This reaction illustrates exactly that the different interests and responsibilities need further emphasis. Thirty years ago, psychiatrists in their daily work occupied almost all of their time in the care of the patients. From eight to six o'clock each day they were overwhelmingly concerned with the care of patients. Even today institutional psychiatrists by occupation are innkeepers, with some additional responsibilities because of the nature of their guests. Perhaps this is of very little interest to a scientific group.

KRUSE: Care may be instituted in another sense. In the history of any disease there was usually a stage in which its causation was unknown and effective empirical therapeutic measures were lacking. The clinician preoccupied himself with the care of the patient.

WHITEHORN: As for treatment, I would assume that it would be thought of principally as either treating the sick patient to make him well, or treating the disease so that the sick patient gets well. In contrast, care does not connote so clear an aim. In a sense it regards the patient as sick, and in need of care.

METTLER: In connection with the care of the patient, I get the impression that what you mean is custodial care.

WHITEHORN: I had not meant to limit it to that.

METTLER: If you had, I would say that the care of the patient includes great attention to environmental circumstances.

WHITEHORN: I would include that.

METTLER: Such activities comprehend the fields of social anthropology, genetics, and sociology.

WHITEHORN: There are matters which receive attention under this rubric of "care." It might be personal, household, or social. The latter includes a tremendous range of things, environmental in the broadest way.

METTLER: That is an area of scientific interest.

WHITEHORN: No question about it.

KRUSE: Placing the environment under care does not entirely exclude it from treatment.

KING: I am far from satisfied with the concept of care which has been elaborated. According to this view, care would consist of providing the patient, while under supervision, with things that he would have received on the outside anyway, such as glasses of water, and a place to sleep. Except historically I cannot view this low level of care, simply attending the patient, as anything more than a simple administrative matter if he is being given only what he is used to having. But the patient may not have been receiving proper discipline, sufficient sleep, or adequate food prior to coming under the psychiatrist's supervision. When the psychiatrist provides the patient properly with these necessities, he is bestowing a different kind of care than the patient previously had. In that respect he is beginning a program of treatment. But this distinction is fine-lined and arbitrary. Why should care be split off from treatment? For, it is apparent that care includes most of the measures subsumed under treatment. Perhaps Dr. Whitehorn has something further on "care" that he wants to develop.

WHITEHORN: No, the basic thought that I had in mind was that here among members of different professional groups trying to relate their activities, it might be profitable to consider the activities of those who assume the responsibility for the care of patients. Members of other groups engaged in communication with the psychiatrist might well understand that in talk and action he is of necessity a different kind of person, that he has to do things that they do not. No member of the other groups interested in research on the causation of mental disease, whether he be an anatomist, biochemist, physiologist, psychologist, or sociologist, has the responsibility for care of the patient. This makes a difference in the operating assumption with which he works.

I would not want to quarrel over the notion that there is no feature of care other than perhaps the basic one of a glass of water and so forth, which is not treatment. I would say, however, that the patient could be given a glass of water and the manner in which it is given may be a part of the treatment.

METTLER: May I mention a very old-fashioned word? It is asylum. It has both noble meaning and unpleasant connotation. The care of patients is conditioned by the legal circumstances surrounding the person. This relationship stems from a provision in which a *non compos mentis* individual in Great Britain was the charge of the Crown, and similarly later in the United States was the charge of the State rather than of the community. This is a peculiar relation which the State of New York is only now beginning to expand by the development of Boards of Mental Health in the community. This arrangement arose historically as a necessity of the social structure. I should like to emphasize that whatever may be the theoretical considerations of physicians, when they are brought into the actual practice of medicine with patients in hospitals and homes, very practical circumstances such as the amount of time at their disposal and the social structure in which they work actually govern the extent and nature of their care and treatment of the patient. In speaking of giving water and administering therapeutic procedures to patients, I do not think that we should lose sight of the fact that the state has provided the individual with something that was long needed and completely different, that is, asylum.

WHITEHORN: Dr. King may have had in mind to raise the question, Is this consideration of care pertinent to the statements, propositions, and discussion by which we might seek to find the truth about the kind of behavior with which we are concerned? If it does not have pertinence to that, perhaps it should not have been brought into the discussion. Was that the substance of your thoughts?

KING: If care is at the low level that I conceived it to be, it seemed to me that we could quickly dispose of it. Much of what under another definition might be called care, I think ought to be placed under treatment, and ought not to be confused by being regarded as something separate. For what is done under such a program of care certainly has some influence on the course of the patient. Maybe one way to put it is that care is that which is done to keep the patient alive, and which is in no way intended to alter a specific set of symptoms that brought him into the psychiatrist's ken. Anything done to modify the symptoms is treatment. Sometimes it would look like care; sometimes it would not. Simply removing the affected person from society, we know, is already the process of treatment as well as care. That is why it seemed to me that care is a historical and legal distinction. Unless a measure has to do with treatment, I do not see why we should concern ourselves with it. If it does have to do

with treatment, why not call it treatment? Let us not call it care.

WHITEHORN: I think that your illustration of segregating a person from society is a very good one. It is, in one sense, care; in another sense, it is treatment. Insofar as we view it as treatment, we have etiological concepts in mind about that particular instance. We consider that in some measure society is contributing to the psychopathological phenomenon; hence, removal from society would theoretically be expected to have therapeutic effect.

The point I have been seeking to make is that there is no sharp line between care and treatment. But insofar as the emphasis is put on treatment, it carries the implication of etiological hypotheses; whereas care does not of necessity imply them. I think perhaps now I have succeeded in pointing out the principal practical reason for making such a distinction.

KRUSE: In therapeutics there is a general treatment, which is helpful in many diseases, in contradistinction to specific treatment, which is effective only in one disease or one group of diseases. In our discussion on the differentiation of care from treatment, we used general treatment as the prototype. Certainly, most of the examples would fall into that category. Ultimately, if we pursued the discussion on therapy, we would have to differentiate between the general and the specific, which is even more firmly grounded on etiology.

WHITEHORN: Sometimes "supportive" or "expectant," or various adjectives are used for this more general nursing care.

KRUSE: There is an additional intermediate step. In the provision of care, the clinician sometimes stumbles upon a result which is far beyond what was anticipated. The regimen is continued empirically until it is explained on an etiological basis; then it becomes scientific treatment. Historically, examples could be cited of the sequence: what started out to be care went through an empiricism, and finally received a scientific explanation.

WHITEHORN: That would certainly be true; for instance, food and its relation to vitamin deficiency states. Food might be thought of as just part of the regular care, but with pellagra patients it could have marvelous therapeutic effects.

The scientific investigator may, if he wishes, focus his attention upon etiological hypotheses, or upon studies providing the basis for them. Theoretically the clinician may do so too; but he is saddled with the traditional responsibility of the care of the patient.

SCOTT: From these considerations the assumption is now being made that we are concerned with disease.

WHITEHORN: That assumption is not inherently necessary. We might well analyze whether the condition of the person who has difficulties of behavior is possibly comprehended in whatever it is the doctors mean by a disease; or is troublesome behavior, unprofitable performance, which has a different quality than that of a disease but still needs to be modified.

SCOTT: Probably both of these interpretations are correct; the one applies to a different situation than the other. In experimental work with animals, what is known as abnormal behavior can be produced regularly and predictably under a certain set of circumstances. This behavior does not look like what is ordinarily called a "disease" in the sense that there is nothing essentially the matter with the organism itself. It is just the way the organism reacts under a certain set of conditions. If these observations and conclusions from experiments with animals are translated to humans, the assumption that a person with abnormal behavior is sick would not necessarily be correct. This distinction might lead to different treatment for one condition than for the other.

WHITEHORN: Besides the psychiatrist, the remainder of the medical fraternity have in recent years also become rather sophisticated about this subject, as is evidenced by their statement that the phenomena of organic and infectious diseases conform to the operations of biological laws and are therefore normal in the sense that every step is the expectation of the preceding. This would hold true for tuberculosis, one of the most obvious and grossly abnormal situations, which would not be called a

disease but the logical outcome of biological processes which are perfectly lawful and normal.

SCOTT: That is not quite what I meant. As an example of what I had in mind, several mature male animals, when locked up together, will ordinarily develop homosexual behavior. This is not analogous to the development of tuberculosis, in which an organism attacks and produces physiological changes within the body. Rather the production of homosexuality is just an outcome of a particular situation in which the animal finds himself. There is nothing really organically wrong with him; it is just nonadaptive behavior.

To an outsider it appears as if the whole history of mental disease has been filled with the idea that the patient is bewitched, sick, or has something the matter with him, and that the psychiatrist has to find out what it is. On the other hand, with behavioral manifestations under circumstances such as I cited in the example, the alternative view that they are a situational outgrowth leads to a much more natural acceptance of the patient's abnormal behavior, and consideration of him as a person. This attitude grows out of the realization that abnormal behavior is a natural result when an individual does certain things or is put into a certain type of situation.

WHITEHORN: My reply to this view was that the clinician, whether psychiatric, medical, or surgical, has during the last two generations practically completed a way of viewing disease as also a part of physiology.

METTLER: We are confusing the operation of biological laws with the concept of etiology. Biological laws operate either in a disease or in what might be called a manipulative phenomenon, such as induced behavior in a psychological experiment.

By some observers, the induced behavior may be regarded as abnormal; by others, not. But no one would consider the presence of a tubercle bacillus in a higher biological organism as a desirable or normal phenomenon.

The crux of the matter is that some investigators would argue that the agents which were operative in the behavioral situation described by Dr. Scott are different from those in a truly psychiatric situation.

Let us assume, for example, that the schizophrenic process is based upon an aberration of perception.

WHITEHORN: As a clinician, I would not necessarily agree with you.

METTLER: The occurrence of perceptual aberration might be explained by the application of laws which are implicit in the theories of the dynamicist; let us say, as a phenomenon which the regression of ego structure might produce. In this case the causative circumstance might be an environmental situation operating on a potentially labile substrate. On the other hand, it might be assumed that an entirely different type of principle might be operative, that such perceptual defect might be caused by the presence of adrenochrome. This is a basically different approach.

WHITEHORN: Basically different, but not necessarily the same base that Dr. Scott was discussing.

METTLER: That is true, but in both cases biological laws are operative.

WHITEHORN: Yes, that is right.

METTLER: According to one view, schizophrenia will never occur in a population in which adrenochrome is not present. It would not happen any more than the ecology of a district would be upset without the introduction of a new element, although the usual laws would be operative.

WHITEHORN: I would have to reread the adrenochrome hypothesis to ascertain whether it is offered as a necessary and sufficient cause, or as one factor. Were you citing it as if it were a proposal for a one-factor cause?

METTLER: No. I am using it only as a hypothesis.

SCOTT: It could be either one factor, or the other, or both.

WHITEHORN: As Dr. Mettler first phrased the proposition, it was in these terms: If a person did not have the adrenochrome, he could not have schizophrenia.

METTLER: That, of course, does not mean that there would not be a one-factor cause according to the dynamic viewpoint.

WHITEHORN: No. Nor does it necessarily mean that there might not be other factors too, whereby it would be only one among a group.

METTLER: That, of course, also does not exclude the possibility that the single or multiple factor in the organic point of view might not in itself precipitate the entire train of events.

WHITEHORN: Or it might even be both organic and psychological factors.

METTLER: Precisely. But, to return to my argument that operation of biological laws should not be confused with etiology. I do not believe that a distinction between tuberculosis and manipulated behavior can be based on whether biological laws are or are not operative. For instance, the implication that biological principles are operative in tuberculosis does not in any sense change the fundamental fact that tuberculosis would never occur without Mycobacterium tuberculosis.

WHITEHORN: I do not believe that is disputed. I would agree with that.

In a certain sense we have argued here about how many devils are on the point of a needle. But I do think that this issue is a prolific source of misunderstanding, much of which leads to attributing to the clinical psychiatrist a folklore attitude which he really does not exemplify but rather which confronts him in his professional activities.

For instance, a girl comes to the hospital because she had been quarreling with her mother, has not been eating, and now weighs only eighty pounds. The father was also party to the situation by threatening his daughter with various dire punishments. By this time, the condition is more than just loss of appetite or amenorrhea. Perhaps the psychiatrist calls it anorexia nervosa. That is a name; it means that she has a disease.

The psychiatrist talks with the father to try to get him to behave in a somewhat more sensible way with his daughter. The father says, "Well, now, tell me doctor, what is the situation? Does she have anorexia nervosa, or doesn't she?" The implication of his question is: If she has anorexia nervosa, she is sick. It is up to the doctor to get her over it. If she does not have anorexia nervosa, the father construes that decision to mean that he is responsible for her condition. In his eyes that makes it just a disciplinary problem. He wants to make a dichotomy of it, according to whether she is considered sick or not sick.

Take an excessiveness of oddity or eccentricity in behavior, which constitutes a social problem. When the psychiatrist has to say that such a patient needs to be committed, he does it in legal language. He and another doctor sign a piece of paper, "This person is insane." The patient is then officially insane. He is ill; he has a disease. But the criterion for whether he has a disease is whether his behavior has passed the rule of what is to be endured, and is now intolerable. Legally, insanity may not be a disease, but it is at least an abnormal state. It is "not sane." So the lawyers think that the doctor is saying that this patient is sick and diseased. And the family too understands that that is what he is saying. But the basic thing that he is saying is that the patient has passed a rather vague and indefinite order of tolerance, and is a danger to himself and to the community. This judgment is not inherently connected with the disease concept. But since the doctor makes this judgment, and practical results flow from it, then society has a means of taking such persons under care as if they had disease, or were sick.

Many concepts about disease and insanity are attributed to the doctor, who has to make the judgment. But he may be making the judgment while adhering to a belief in his own mind that the type of behavior on which he is pronouncing is only what might be called a natural reaction to a very bad home situation. Still, he has to make the judgment; hence, to him is attributed some one of a variety of notions about demons, or sanity, or diseases—whatever the person making the attribution has in mind. This attitude burdens the clinician with a heavy load of assumptions which are thrown on his shoulders whether he carries them in his own mind or not.

METTLER: May I point out that this is and always has been the consequence of taxonomy. In nosology it is inevitable that no distinction will be made between classifications with regard to their essential nature as diseases. I would like to plead for a clear distinction between a nosological classification and a disease.

WHITEHORN: That is a difficult distinction.

METTLER: I do not believe so. I think nosological classifications, which are not diseases, are and have been in the history of medicine primarily because they are less well understood than a disease. We might, for instance, designate a situational reaction as a disease. But a nosological classification does not even need to be a situational reaction. It is simply something which is put on the official documents of medicine. It is what appears in the international list of classified, known diseases.

WHITEHORN: Which is, of course, ambiguous.

SCOTT: Although biological laws are far-reaching and very important, I doubt that they will cover all of the situations that we are considering, particularly those involving the social environment. I wonder whether the concept of levels of organization might not help to clarify matters. On the physiological level of organization, events occur inside the body which may produce undesirable effects on behavior. The next level of organization is the psychological, which is concerned with the behavior of the entire individual and its organization in reaction to outside events. Beyond that is the sociological level, which focuses attention on the organization of groups of individuals. These levels are most directly concerned with abnormal behavior, but other levels may include equally important factors. The most basic level pertains to cellular organization and activities with which genetics is very closely related. What is ordinarily known as mental disease may be affected by factors on all levels of organization, or in special cases it may principally involve only one.

This scheme may also be helpful in understanding the different viewpoints expressed at this Conference. For example, Dr. Skinner was obviously thinking only about the psychological organization of behavior. He focuses his attention at one point and pays little heed to organic or sociological factors. Similarly, other speakers tend to focus attention on other levels, with consequent divergence in ideas and emphasis, but not necessarily contradicting the other.

WHITEHORN: In the official classification of the disease, there is a recognition of the psychobiological unit; and diseases are classified at that level of organization.

KING: It seems to me that we are returning to the point from which we started. There is agreement, I believe, that in a given case, each of the factors which we have been discussing may come to bear perhaps in a state of balance. Inasmuch as everything seems to have been admitted to the class of potential factors, the question is which do we think are the most fruitful and most productive to follow?

SCOTT: Experience from animal experiments suggests that the idea of asylum, which has been introduced earlier in our discussion, may be linked directly with treatment.

It is very difficult to produce abnormal behavior experimentally in animals, and it is significant that all studies in which the production of abnormal behavior is well verified and well supported have certain components in common. One or two studies suffice to illustrate the point. Levy* observed the effects on hens of confining them in very small cages, about two feet square. He found that whenever he excited them, they began to go through a stereotyped movement of head-shaking which they ordinarily use when they are shaking water off their heads. Bears in zoos have also been noted to go through stereotyped movements when stimulated or excited.

In Pavlov's classical experiment, he trained dogs to associate the salivary reflex with a circle, and to inhibit the reflex in response to an ellipse. As the circle was progressively made more like an ellipse and the ellipse more like a circle, a point was finally reached where the dogs could not tell the difference between the two figures. At that point their behavior became what

he called neurotic. Actually they tried to bite their harnesses to get out of the situation, and were no longer trainable. It is only fair to say that not all workers agree that this behavior may properly be called neurotic.

These examples and the six or seven other well-known studies on the production of abnormal behavior in animals all have three elements in common: (1) The situation with which the animals are confronted is one in which no adjustment is possible. The experimenter has rigged the situation so that the animals cannot possibly do anything useful. (2) The animals must be highly excited or motivated. They frequently do not exhibit abnormal behavior at the beginning of the experiment. They have to be subjected to the situation for a long time; they have to undergo a long period of training or conditioning. As shown from Dr. Skinner's work, repeated training or conditioning leads to a greater and greater degree of motivation. (3) There is no possible chance of escaping from the situation. Apparently, all three of these conditions are necessary for the appearance of any manifestation of what might be called abnormal behavior in animals.

If the evidence from these animal experiments can be applied validly to human beings, it would appear that the confining and restraining factor in man in most instances is the social situation rather than physical barriers. It has been stated that institutions provide asylum; the institution provides an escape from an unbearable social situation.

METTLER: Some patients will not leave an institution even when they are ready for discharge.

SCOTT: The institution is providing them with one way of escaping from an unbearable situation; therefore, mere admission to the institution might be regarded as treatment.

KING: I will not contest your statement that all three elements have to be in the situation in order for the animals to develop abnormal behavior. But I should like to point out that when the situation is studied scientifically, it is necessary to take care in identifying the elements; otherwise, the in-

---

* Levy, D. M. On the problem of movement restraint: tics, stereotyped movements, hyperactivity. Am. J. Orthopsychiat., 1944, 14: 644–71.

terpretation is misleading. For example, studies were conducted in which air was blasted under rats to make them jump at two doors with different symbols. As the distinction in design was diminished, the animals seemingly were driven into a cataleptic state. On these observations the investigators built a paramount theory, only to learn that it did not really matter what was on the doors. Simply blasting air repeatedly under the tail of the rat produced the same reaction. It placed it in an inescapable situation; hence the jump, a thing that the animal does not like to do. The observers were deluding themselves about the supposed influence of the symbols on the doors. This experience indicates that the elements operating in inescapability have to be identified with more than face validity.

SCOTT: What you have said is very important, and there is another point to be considered. It is possible to induce audiogenic seizures in mice and rats by exposing them to a ringing bell. Loud high-pitched noises are very exciting to these animals. Ordinarily, when they are subjected to a ringing bell, they will try to escape rapidly from the situation. If they can escape, nothing happens. But if they are placed in a situation where they cannot escape and the bell goes on ringing, some, but not all, of the animals may undergo seizures. The number which react depends on the strain. In one strain of mice, over 90 per cent will react with seizures. In another strain, none of them will react. It is clear that a genetic variable exerts an influence. What is a bad and unbearable situation for one strain is not necessarily so for another.

METTLER: It is also a conditionable variable. As Dr. Kruse showed, in magnesium deficiency the susceptibility to audiogenic seizures becomes very much more pronounced. There are many such circumstances: behavioral elements, the susceptibility of the individual, genetics, and chemical changes.

WHITEHORN: Our discussion here provides reiterated evidence that we are oriented largely to think in terms of etiology. We have been talking about what causes abnormal behavior. Also, Dr. Scott's remarks point up the fact that even though we consider the subject of care, it may include specific therapeutic measures which have pertinence for specific etiological factors. The efficacy of the asylum, where the patient is removed from the home situation, is shown to be related possibly to an etiological factor or at least to be explainable on an etiological basis, such as restriction in an unbearable situation. All this emphasizes again the bridge between care and treatment in the involvement of possible etiological factors. Whatever is done, even though it is done out of a humanitarian desire to provide asylum, still might operate on a level which we could conceive of as curative by an etiological rationale.

KRUSE: Closely related to the mistaken identification of factors operating in the induction of an abnormal process, whether it be in behavior or in tissue, is the failure to recognize that multiple factors are in action. Perhaps the most advantageous quality of the experimental method, its potentiality for simplification of design, is at once a source of fallacy. Not that the method itself is to blame; it is man's misuse of it. Implicit in so much of the experimentation is the unifactorial view of causation. The method lends itself so readily to this view; indeed, seems to re-enforce it. Adhering to this belief and finding the method so amenable to it, the experimenter consciously or unconsciously carries it into the interpretation of results.

Of the experimental method it is said that nonessential variables are excluded. That is a partial truth. Actually some variables are excluded; but even more are equalized or balanced by the plan of experimental and control groups. Yet these variables, despite their balance, are in operation. Some of them are essential for pathogenesis. With one factor under study present or absent in the experimental group and the opposite in the control, the experiment is designed to bring out the effects of just that one factor. In the interpretation, the tendency is to ignore other factors that are in action and not only to conclude that the factor under study is active but also to intimate or make implicit that it is the one and only factor operating in the process and solely responsible for the effects. Thus the unifactorial view of causation is circularly refortified.

For example, deficiency of vitamin A in the diet is said to induce pathological manifestations of avitaminosis A. Actually they are not induced in the young animal without growth. Although this desideratum is fulfilled in the experimental plan, ordinarily it is not mentioned in the interpretation. The truth is that many factors besides deficiency of vitamin A in the diet operate in the production of pathology in avitaminosis A. Causation is a much more complex process than is represented.

This practice of misuse has important consequences in the transfer of knowledge gained from animals to man, or as it should more accurately be phrased, from the experimental to the natural setting. When the results from an experiment, with its elementary and restricted environment and the oversimplified interpretation of them, are applied to a natural situation, with its complex and broad social fabric, the limitations and misconceptions are compounded.

In order that I may not be misunderstood, I should like to emphasize that I am not attempting to cast a shadow on the experimental method, on the use of animals in it, or on the transfer of knowledge from the experimental to the natural realm. On the contrary, all three procedures properly utilized are so valuable as to be indispensable. But misuse of them may consist in disregarding or overlooking two cardinal points: that frequently causation inclusively conceived has multiple factors, and that many factors appear in a natural setting that were never encountered or taken into account in the experimental situation.

SCOTT: I agree that there are definite limitations to the information from animal experimentation that is applicable to man. Particularly is it difficult to link with principles of clinical practice, much less to apply, any observations thus far gained from animals. What has been brought out in animals does not directly correspond to what is seen in clinical practice.

In using animal experiments it should be recognized at the outset that animals differ from human beings in several respects:

physiologically and sociologically, to mention only two. With this in mind, two courses are open toward the goal of applying results from animal experiments. One is to study animals, species by species, for their own sakes; to discover everything possible about each species. In essence, the aim is to obtain a broad biological foundation of information by comparative studies between species. If this program is followed with a large number of species, it may be possible to formulate general laws that would be applicable to human beings. This vein has not really been worked to any extent so far; but in the long run, I think, it should be the most fruitful system of studying animal behavior.

The other course is to test clinical principles on animals. Foremost is the careful selection of the species. In this procedure it is necessary to have full knowledge about the species that is contemplated for use: how it is similar to and different from man. Certainly the species should lend itself to the object of the study. Rats, for example, could be useful for some studies; but they are obviously not suitable for psychodynamic or sociological investigations because they do not have a family life which is at all comparable to that of the human. The species must be appropriate to the purpose. Then it may be possible to test one of the factors that is supposed to have importance in human beings. This latter course has a more limited usefulness than the first, yet it has some.

Suppose that the experimentalist finally does get a bright idea that seems to have possibilities of value for man. As we have agreed, findings on animals do not necessarily apply to humans. In order for the idea to have any validity, the clinician has to try it on man. Thus, he is in the key position in any experimental program.

WHITEHORN: We have commented upon two aspects of animal work and its pertinence for the clinical psychiatrists' preoccupations. There has been a round of discussion on the difficulties of transferring knowledge from one field to the other and the need for taking into account the different kinds of animals: human and others.

Dr. Kruse's comment was, I think, pertinent in an additional and special way. The clinician is not uncommonly put into a feeling of inferiority when findings are thrown at him from another area, where controls are more easily included. He is sometimes victimized by this circumstance. But if he knew more about it, he could point back and say, "These controls may have been possible, but they were not used."

This point is pertinent for many interdisciplinary discussions. The clinician comes off badly oftentimes because the experimenter can confront him with evidence from the test tube, animal experiment, or microscope. The clinician is handicapped in answering. Whose conscience should it be on to get these controls? I suppose on the experimenter's, for the clinician does not know how to point out the deficiencies of control.

I am not arguing for a particular point. I am just taking advantage of this opportunity to point out that in discussion across the board between the clinicians and experimenters, the possibilities of control by the latter are so much better that they have a prestige on a scientific basis which overwhelms the clinician. It should be on somebody's conscience to see to it that these possibilities of control are more adequately considered.

KRUSE: May I brighten the outlook of the clinician? To reiterate briefly remarks of mine in a previous session, the elucidation of the cause of a disease has been achieved, as the history of medicine shows, through several approaches: clinical, epidemiological, and experimental in clinic, field, and laboratory. From these approaches with animal and man came the evidence. The clinician, epidemiologist, and experimentalist, each had his essential pieces to contribute to the accumulation of knowledge, and he had to add them at particular times. Sequence and timing were important; for the pieces fell into place in the puzzle in a definite order. Advance can be blocked for many years, awaiting a particular piece; no other will do. Once it is found, other pieces can be assembled. In this progression the clinical is just as essential as the other two approaches. Indeed, the clinician frequently makes the original observations. Thus, he has no need to be self-abasing

about his methods, his record of achievement, or his prestige.

WHITEHORN: There must be a circularity in this too, so that the clinician might have another look after some other pieces are in place.

METTLER: Unfortunately the psychiatrist in many instances is in a situation in which he is called upon to do more than he can do. He is unable to do what he sets out to do in terms of theory. He does not know what the laboratory has to offer. And he does not know general medicine. This is, of course, the basic difficulty. Now, what can he do about it? Because of limitations of time, he cannot do anything about it. He cannot possibly keep up with the developments in other branches sufficiently to be critical or judicious about them; any more than can the specialists in those fields, about psychiatry.

The answer to this dilemma of methodology is the development of an atmosphere of tolerance among individuals, a permissive area, in which one is ready to accept the work of others rather than adopt a skeptical or defensive attitude. For instance, within the field of the physical sciences, an attitude has developed in which the worker in one branch is perfectly willing to accept what a worker in another branch observes. Most of the arguments are between colleagues. But in the field of psychiatry, we find the psychiatrist arguing all over the lot—a curious phenomenon.

What is wrong about the psychiatrist's accepting what an experimental physiologist advances? The physiologist, not the psychiatrist, is the one who knows experimental physiology. Why fight with him? Why worry about a microscopic demonstration? I do not believe that the clinician is being overwhelmed by having the authority of a microscope thrown at him; rather I think that he is fleeing from the vision of a microscope.

WHITEHORN: As Dr. Mettler has pointed out, the psychiatrist is handicapped in this task by the very human reactions of overdone defensiveness. It is not universally true. Some clinicians, here and there, will give at least a tentative acceptance to the findings of the experimental biologist, and test them out to see what implication they might have. You do, however, call attention to a phenomenon in the clinical psychiatrist, that of his being exaggeratedly committed to a particular belief in a manner that makes it hard for him to take a really accepting view of the contributions that are potentially available to him.

KING: To defensiveness I would like to add suspiciousness, which is often well-founded. The very nature of psychiatric research fosters this attitude. Experiments in this field are so difficult that they are seldom done more than once. The procedure of verification in other hands is missing. For example, an investigator reports that a particular family pattern in the South Sea Islands has an impact. Who is going to put that thesis to test? Thus, instances of results practically not subjectable to verification, together with those that fail confirmation, create suspiciousness.

Psychiatry does not have the regularity of demonstration of phenomena that is enjoyed in the laboratories. This fact, coupled with the predilection of its practitioners for assorted points of view, often leads to a preponderance of deductive, armchair reasoning. The defensiveness, the suspiciousness, and the dependence on deduction, frequently for lack of a better method, all instill in them an attitude of trusting nothing. In consequence, the clinician is more likely to accept results from the biological laboratory than he is from other psychiatric laboratories.

METTLER: This phenomenon is not peculiar to psychiatry. It represents a situation in which an individual is trying to operate in various frames of reference at once. In contrast, in the field of science, the individual has to operate within only one frame of reference; he is an anatomist, or a biochemist, or a particular kind of engineer. Others consult him in his own frame of reference, where he remains; and he gives an answer independently and imperviously. Most of his inquisitors are willing to accept his answers. But when the specialist has to make judgments outside of his sphere, for example, an engineer to give an opinion in the realm of sociology, he finds himself in the same position essentially as the psychiatrist, and with just about as disastrous results.

I raise this as a very real question: What should be done in psychiatry? Should psychiatry be subdivided into specialties? There is a tendency in that direction; certain psychiatrists will speak only as organicists, others only as dynamicists. Should the field try to cultivate psychiatrists in the form of whole men, in much the same sense as the term "the whole patient"? Or is the psychiatrist of necessity going to have to function as a member of the group?

WHITEHORN: I think the latter is the tendency.

METTLER: If that is so, is it not inevitable that a permissive attitude must be adopted?

WHITEHORN: The professors of psychiatry in a university or medical school do, in fact, build a department in which there is representation from the different fields of scientific pursuit which might make contributions to the advancement of knowledge. Thus they have an associate competent in a special field, with whom they can discuss reported findings in that area; and another associate in a different province who can advise them concerning the potential profitability of a venture there. This puts professors of a department in an integrative role, which sounds as if it would be an admirable situation for rapid integration of all the different fields. But, of course, human limitations and the pressure of other responsibilities prevent full utilization of the opportunity. I suppose that it is appropriate to be charitable about these human limitations and encumbrances.

METTLER: The basic premise is not an actuality. There is not in the United States, or anywhere else as far as I know, a department of psychiatry which actually has representation in it of competent persons in germane fields. For example, what departmen of psychiatry lists within its group an adequate representation in the field of psychology, which in itself is represented by a number of very important disciplines? What department of psychiatry in the country pays adequate attention to the problems of the private patient as an individual; of the individual in the community;

of the tremendous number of individuals confined in institutions? I would submit that there are whole areas which do not have representation in the department of psychiatry in universities.

WHITEHORN: This, of course, indicates the difficulty of the psychiatrist in having working access to all the current knowledge and theory which presumably is required.

KRUSE: I would share Dr. Mettler's wish that departments of psychiatry have adequate representation from constituent and cognate fields. But it cannot be safely assumed that the organization of the most comprehensive department imaginable with full complement for a multidisciplinary approach would guarantee that it would be the center in which the solution to mental disease would be found. Certainly it would raise the odds; and at the least, valuable contributions might be expected. However, in the history of medicine, the moments of triumph have come in curious ways in unexpected places. A lone investigator with no such pretentious outfit may be the one to put together part of the pieces. This is not an argument against the fully developed department. But I would dislike to have excluded the more modest attempts, which may be highly productive in the long run.

METTLER: I have already pointed out that the psychiatrist is trying to cover an area of human knowledge, both in activity and in theory, which it is humanly impossible for an individual to cover. Then he suffers from feelings of frustration because he is unsuccessful in accomplishing what no one else could possibly do. In remarking that departments of psychiatry are woefully deficient, I was simply trying to indicate the areas in which they are conspicuously lacking. For example, there are departments of psychiatry that do not give any consideration to a question of legal significance. Yet this is a matter of grave concern in the public health. Where, after all, can people turn for advice on this subject except to an educated opinion? Actually, when I asserted that an ideal department of psychiatry would cover all these areas, I was pleading more for a point of view than for facilities.

However, I did not state that the introduction of these facilities would produce a cure for schizophrenia. I simply expressed the opinion that comprehensive coverage of all significant germane areas was a desideratum. I said nothing at all about the yield from such an organization with regard to any particular point. Of course I agree with you that a fruitful idea may be found by an individual under a tree on a summer afternoon.

KING: Medical students and prospective psychiatrists derive knowledge, training, and experience from classes, lectures, conferences, and rounds, as well as from working with both outpatients and inpatients. We have agreed that the multidisciplinary approach is a coming one. I would like to point out that medical students and psychiatrists in training could be given at least lectures on the multidisciplinary approach so that they might form their own opinions of it. In my experience, they do not currently receive any such instruction.

WHITEHORN: A very important point.

KING: My experience over a long period of time in working with medical students prompts me to remark that it is astonishing how little interest they manifest in anything except the clinical concerns with the patient. We have tried every trick, every personality, every visual aid method in the book, and it is very difficult to stimulate interest in the basic problems. Every now and again someone has a wider interest at the outset. He can be recognized at once. But to generate an interest in the others for anything other than clinical concerns, even at the graduate level—. . .

WHITEHORN: I would say, especially at the graduate level. I think you have a better chance with the medical students. For instance, in our teaching program, Curt Richter and Horsley Gantt have contacts with the first-year students. I would say that they meet with an encouraging amount of interest. The students want to work with them, do work with them.

KING: One possible reason for the lack of interest in the experimental psychological aspects is the passive form of education in psychiatry. A person being instructed on how to run a dictating machine listens at one level. But if he is going to use it right away, he listens at another level. He has to demonstrate what he took in. There is little of this demonstration level in psychiatry other than on the clinical aspects. The psychologist hopes that the students hear what is said about the relationship of pure psychological concepts, but they do not have to demonstrate the concepts.

KRUSE: On causation of disease, some minds continue in the pattern of thinking laid down in the bacteriological era. The simplest example is: The tubercle bacillus causes tuberculosis. If this statement is supposed to represent an inclusive view, if it means that the tubercle bacillus and it alone produces tuberculosis, then it is a fallacious oversimplification because it is contrary to fact. Not all persons exposed to the bacillus contract clinical tuberculosis. Other influences enter into the determination. But if implicit in the statement "Bacillus tubercle causes tuberculosis" is the acceptance of all other influences, and if the intent is to convey that a particular microorganism produces its specific pathological and clinical effects, this is no denial of plurality. It is a difference in usage of a term rather than in a view. It hinges on the definition of cause.

However, it is not my purpose to enter into a discourse on causation per se. Rather I would point out that the importance of causation in disease derives from the light that it sheds on prevention and therapy. The view of causation colors the approach to prophylaxis and treatment. Certainly multifactor causation offers single, alternative, or combined approaches. Yet it is not inconsistent to adhere to a plural system of causation and to find comfort in having several strings for the therapeutic bow; but at the same time to hold high expectations or opinion that of all appropriate measures, one will be most efficacious, or most widely applicable, or have some other preferential property.

Most of the outstanding unsolved diseases, the menaces to public health, today give every indication of having multifactor causation. Conspicuous among them is mental disease. To judge the relative place and qualities of each part in the causal complex, it is helpful, indeed necessary, to visualize the whole. For, the various pieces have to be put together. Who is to do it? This is not to say that the entire project will be completed in a single gigantic effort by one man. It may well be evolved over a period of years by many minds. Basically they may be members of any conceptual school; they should have breadth of knowledge, powers of analysis, the gift of shrewd speculation, and competence in synthesis and integration. Such qualifications are apt to be found in medical philosophers. Unfortunately there is a shortage of them in this country. I recently remarked to Professor A. V. Hill that I admired the quantity and quality of medical philosophers in England, who have their creations published regularly as leading articles in medical journals. His reply was, "Yes, but America has the medical engineers." Without yielding our primacy in medical engineering, a stronger wing in medical philosophy would yield a potent balance.

METTLER: There is no question that both the medical engineer and the medical philosopher are important in the history of medicine, but almost all the advances which have been made, not merely in the history of medicine but also in the history of science, have occurred not so much as the result of taking thought—science has not made progress within a discipline by raising itself by its own boot straps—as of the introduction of a new technic, or a new idea, from an outside field.

Usually what happens is that science proceeds in a curious kind of a spiral, which goes round and round with conceptions reinforcing the data which are found, and the data reinforcing the frame of reference in which the investigators are working. This course continues and is self-propagating until suddenly, from the outside, some new piece of evidence is discovered and brought into relationship with the spiraling area. It now becomes impossible for the previous motion to proceed, and the whole activity is sent off on a new vector.

This was the historical effect, for instance, of the discovery of the microscope, in which the entire organization of medicine was altered when structural information became available. The introduction of methods of staining changed things again, and the introduction of the vacuum tube brought further change.

In brief, the sequence is that a line of thought becomes impossible because of the demonstration of a new principle or technic; and that usually comes from outside the area.

KRUSE: I note that while emphasizing instruments and technics, you did not fail to include new principles and ideas in the spiral. On the other hand, in arguing for conceptualization and synthesis, I assumed that it would be understood that data from instruments and technics were a prerequisite. All are needed.

My point is that in comparison with its emphasis on and achievements in technology, this country is numerically low in its corps of integrators and theoreticians. It is perhaps less true of psychiatry than of medicine in general, but nonetheless true. Ultimately, integration has to take place, and technics will not do the necessary thinking. Their function is to provide the data for reasoning. I yield to no one in my appreciation of the ultracentrifuge, electron microscope and tagged atoms. But I am also cognizant of the matchless creations of the great theoreticians and integrators; Willard Gibbs, in physical chemistry; Lawrence J. Henderson, in biochemistry; and Albert Einstein, in theoretical physics. The full fruits of Gibbs's and Einstein's thinking are yet to be derived; moreover, instruments and technics were devised to verify Henderson's predictions.

Creative thinking is ranked as the highest form of mentation, and integration is surely creative. Yet, paradoxically, it has seldom been held at a premium, as judged by the usual rewards. I would not want the search for new instruments and technics, as one arm of investigation, to slacken; rather I would favor its intensification. At the same time I would bespeak an endeavor to strengthen the presently emaciated other arm, integration.

WHITEHORN: Since we have been discussing the psychiatrist's presumed proper role in integrating multifactorial considerations, I should like to present what may be

an unpopular point of view. I think that the narrow approach, from the scientific point of view, has certain advantages. It makes a sucker out of the investigator who adopts it. But if he can push to the limit the possibility of a single approach and see what can come from it, this is a service to science, and it is a useful role that should be filled. Admiration can be combined with pity for him as he works himself out on a limb and has to drop off. But if investigators were not disposed to work themselves out on these narrow lines, we would lose something.

SCOTT: The very narrow point of view seems to work out very well in experimental science, but I am not sure that it is useful in more natural situations. If a multifactorial approach is adopted, and I think it is probably the only sound one, it seems to me that all factors may enter into a given situation involving a patient and that all points of view have something to contribute. Can an individual psychiatrist satisfactorily combine all viewpoints? Or, alternatively, can he satisfactorily take just one point of view and work with that?

KRUSE: If the latter question is recast to, "Can an investigator taking a single track shed any light on etiology?" the answer is, "Yes, he may make a contribution." For an individual pursuing one course, whether he knows it or not, is putting down facts that a contemporary or subsequent worker can use. The second worker will pick up the findings of the first and put them in their proper place in relation to other data.

METTLER: There are obstacles to relating and integrating. In descriptive science, the worker is often content to offer descriptions, and then stop. If he is asked to explain the significance of his description, he is likely to become frustrated or not know quite what to do. One reason that he has such a feeling is that he knows that the minute he brings his material into relationship with another area, he is out of his depth. He hesitates to get out of his depth because, under such circumstances, he is afraid of seeming stupid. Consequently, he will tend to remain purely descriptive.

To the outsider, a curiosity about the

psychiatric literature is that it lacks road signs with regard to what is demonstrable, what is more or less well-accepted theory, what is personal opinion, and what is just put in for the sake of stirring up discussion. It appears to be an amorphous mass. The stranger feels as if he is lost in a moor. But the psychiatrist is at no loss in this because he knows where the tussocks are and where the quagmires lie. He hops and threads his way through this marsh in a sort of dexterous manner, avoiding a submersion, or at least avoiding getting his feet wet.

But this agility requires a rather elaborate and peculiar kind of training which is perhaps unnecessarily complicated, especially if it is only for the purpose of being able to read the psychiatric literature critically. I wonder whether there would be some way of grading psychiatric literature on the basis of what is fancy, what is theory, and what is fact.

WHITEHORN: I think that you exaggerate the competence of the psychiatrists in treading this quagmire. But you do point out a very vital need. Furthermore, I do not know of any group other than the psychiatrists on whom would rest this basic responsibility to delineate for themselves and for others what areas, for that culture and generation, are considered sound. To some extent they do it in annual reviews, textbooks, and monographs. However, I presume that one of the reasons why this need is not more adequately met is the difficulty in surveying the granite on which it would be perfectly sound to step.

Why should that assignment be any more difficult for the psychiatrist? I suppose that it reduces to the fact that he has a task of looking after and taking the best care that he can of an enormously heterogeneous group of people, a task involving social considerations and other matters where the guide lines to solid truth are not very clear. It could be said fairly, I think, that here is a clinician whose case material impinges at almost every turn on social considerations. For example, consider why patients are committed. Is it by reason of delusions, or impairment of judgment and social relations, or dangerous behavior? Consider also how the psychiatrist is to judge when a pa-

tient is well again. Partly by the criterion of social tolerability. Those questions illustrate why it is more difficult in psychiatry than in some other fields to say where is the solid footing. What I am saying is that the psychiatrist works in a field where the solid formulations are not so easily evolved.

A teaching psychiatrist feels the greatest obligation to the students and the house staff. Routinely at case presentations he tries to indicate what knowledge concerning a particular patient is well documented and sound; what evidence is hearsay; where judgments enter in; the source and the nature of these judgments; out of the so-called accumulated knowledge, those principles that are fairly sound and well agreed upon; and finally, speculative notions. This is part of a psychiatrist's daily chores.

METTLER: As an example of such a daily chore, would you say that you could give a statement as to the efficacy of any particular form of psychiatric therapy which was in use today?

WHITEHORN: Surely. I do it all the time.

METTLER: How would you do that?

WHITEHORN: Suppose we consider a patient with what are called hysterical gastric complaints. Do not ask me to explain what that is, because I have had a quarrel with my staff for years over what they mean by hysterical gastric complaints. To me the term is almost nonsense. But patients are presented with this diagnosis; and I take it, in general, to mean neurotic complaints.

But suppose a patient has, in addition to this, some motor paralysis of an arm and also hints of marital maladjustment. In my opinion this kind of a case presents a better prospect of radical improvement through psychoanalytic technic than would another patient presenting obsessive symptomatology, shall we say. Thereby, a judgment is made concerning the pertinence and value of a treatment method.

For another patient, a middle-aged person who showed depressive reactions with a great deal of self-blame and self-accusation, I would express an opinion that the evidence in the literature is strongly indicative that electroconvulsive therapy will relieve much of his symptomatology of depression.

METTLER: I would then ask you how you

would document the statement that psycho-analysis in the first case, and shock therapy in the second case, would each give better results than routine, general care. How would you direct a house officer to the literature?

WHITEHORN: The first move would be to direct him to some of the monographs which discuss this matter, to indicate what other literature is available for further study. In actual practice, he is likely to ask, "Tell me something of your own experience. Does it fortify this judgment which is abstracted from the publications?" I would then draw upon what limited experience I have had. In regard to the electroconvulsive therapy for the symptomatology of depression, I would say that out of my rather limited experience with the classical agitated depression seen in state hospitals, they are patients who almost invariably will respond with a marked improvement in their depressive mood after three or four shocks; maybe up to 85 per cent of these patients will in a brief time be better. In contrast, less clear-cut, self-blaming depressions are considerably less likely to manifest improvement.

METTLER: We are concerned at the moment with an inquiry as to how the psychiatrist evaluates a clinical situation and how he communicates his conclusions to others. It is interesting that difficulty in designing a multidisciplinary approach arises when the laboratory scientist comes into contact with the clinician. They are unable to communicate.

WHITEHORN: By that do you mean that the clinician seems to retire into an authoritarian roadblock, where he has a machine gun that dominates the scene and prevents the laboratorian from getting around it to know what he is thinking about?

METTLER: No. Let me give an example. The psychiatrist gives the laboratory scientist a listing of prognosis on a group of patients who are to be submitted to an experimental therapeutic procedure. Here we are not considering the disagreement between the psychiatrist's and the psychologist's listings, or the clinical problem of how improvement is judged, or the criteria of improvement. Rather we are concerned with how the psychiatrist reaches his decision on prognosis.

What happens in practice is that there is actually a very high degree of correlation between what the psychiatrist says will happen, and what does happen. Thus he has a good performance record to back up his statement. Of course, the laboratorian knows that the psychiatrist in his judgments relied on his own experience, as you indicated, and that this provided a variety of clues. But this procedure does not seem to be susceptible to analysis. It is not reduced to scientific terminology; hence, communication between them fails.

WHITEHORN: Let us suppose that the psychiatrist is to have an interview with a patient being considered for discharge. The question is, Should the patient go home? The requirements for discharge which the psychiatrist sets may be compared with those of the clinical psychologist from the application of tests. Both are pertinent to the same question. After applying his tests on a patient, the clinical psychologist says, "I can't see that the result is any different than it was before." The clinical psychiatrist will give as his opinion about the same patient, "I think he is ready to go. I think he would make good, all right." How does the psychiatrist justify discharge of this patient? About another patient, he might say, "No."

It is true that the psychiatrist has, as you say, a fair record in predictions. How does he make such predictions? I should say that it would depend a little on the following consideration—and I am talking now, not on the basis of the large literature which could be quoted, but more to illustrate how one clinician will try to form his judgments. Here is a person who is being considered for return to his family and to living with the other members of the household. In the interview I am concerned with forming a judgment as to this patient's interaction with other people. He is interacting with me. Through my own personal reactions, I, therefore, become an instrument by which I test this person.

If I encounter sudden violences, or scowls, or certain other phenomena, or a certain turn of phrase, I would automatically interpret those in part in terms of reactions. I would probably express the interpretation in some fancy language of symptomatology. But this would in part depend upon whether I am somewhat shocked that this person does not seem to understand me, or says something that I do not understand; and whether I perceive that there are going to be difficulties with the patient and occasions for sudden resentments. Such observations and responses enter into my calculations as to what chances that person is going to have at home.

Even though the results from psychological tests on patients A and B might be just alike, the interview may reveal a big difference between them.

METTLER: Your description indicates that the clinician is using multiple clues for his judgments, whereas the psychologist would be using a limited approach to the patient. He is studying only one aspect of the patient's behavior. However, it also points out another very interesting thing; namely, that the clinician has left the area of clearly demonstrable evidence. The minute he does this, he now opens the door wide for a situation in which possibility rather than certainty prevails.

KRUSE: What the clinician, whether he is psychiatrist or internist, does with observations in reaching a judgment on prognosis is of interest. He relates his own experience and that of others to these observations in deciding what is going to happen to the patient when he is discharged. To use the parlance of baseball, he seems to go by the book and play percentages. Statistics have entered in, perhaps by an elusive process.

WHITEHORN: Certain matters of probability.

METTLER: Anything that is not objective cannot be fed into statistics.

WHITEHORN: That is the point Dr. Kruse is making.

KING: For a long time we have known of people who act intuitively, who can, furthermore, demonstrate success in the process, and who have never been adequate in defining and explaining how they can act that way. A good "leader" finds difficulty in explaining why he is a good leader. It has

also been known for years that clinical practice, including clinical prognostication, has a large element of art in it.

What Dr. Mettler was asking was, "Can some of the art be taken away and objectivity added?" The psychiatrist is put into an authoritarian role when he cannot tell the scientist anything except, "This fits my experience."

At the Ochsner Clinic in Tulane University a statistical study is in progress in an attempt to ascertain how the clinician makes his judgments. He himself wants to know, and it would be a forward step if the process were clear to others.

WHITEHORN: That was one reason why I went into some detail about transactions that go on in the clinical interview.

KRUSE: I think also that some clinicians operate by the process of getting the remote derivative. They feed in data and then finally come out with an answer by a process of which they themselves are not conscious.

WHITEHORN: This point I would like to relate to one of the first points we took up. The clinician is primarily oriented to take care of the patient. The intervening processes in the judgments have less weight on his conscience than doing the right thing about the patient. This concern with the patient distorts his viewpoint somewhat when he comes to collaborating with his scientific colleagues. The scientist's interest lies more in the nature of the processes concerned.

METTLER: That suggests another point. In dealing with the psychiatrist, we are talking at one moment with a person who has one hat on, who is speaking, for instance, as a person who is interested in the cause of a disease. And then, before we know it, we are confronted with a protean individual who has metamorphosed into something else. But this process of metamorphosis is not obvious to us. It has occurred internally in him and he is speaking in a completely different capacity. There ought to be signs hung on psychiatrists, "I am now speaking as this" or "I am now speaking as something else."

WHITEHORN: Some do. I must say that I attempt at times to indicate in what capacity I am speaking. Psychiatrists differ in the way in which they indicate by sign what kind of a function they are performing.

KING: Apparently a hypothesis means quite a different thing to the clinician than to the research worker because the clinician, not just the psychiatric clinician but every type, generates and abandons hypotheses at a rate of speed that makes the researcher's head swim. In most sciences a reasonably good hypothesis lasts for a few months because considerable thought has gone into its formulation. But the clinician knocks them down so fast that it is difficult to keep up with him.

WHITEHORN: I would relate that to the differences in the scholarly responsibilities for the implications of hypotheses. The clinician does not have this on his conscience to anywhere near the extent that the professional scholar does.

SCOTT: These comments seem to indicate a need for improving diagnostic methods, particularly if the psychiatrist is going to use the multifactorial approach. He has to be able to recognize all of the different symptoms and their significances. The question that you have been raising, Dr. Mettler, is simply, When the process becomes as complex as has been indicated, how can he really tell?

METTLER: I should like to make clear that I do not want to be cast in the role of questioning the clinician's abilities. I am not arguing for an improvement in his performance, which really is very good indeed. My point bears upon his communication with others.

WHITEHORN: Literally Dr. Scott asked, "How can he [the clinician] tell?" That is a very good question. But the intonation implied that it was a rhetorical question.

METTLER: He was implying that the clinician could not tell. That was exactly what I wanted to avoid. The clinician can tell all right; he knows.

SCOTT: Does he? That is what I want to know. Let me give an example which has a bearing on the question. A middle-aged mail carrier had various symptoms and signs. He complained of feeling very tired; and also of pain in one shoulder, which he attributed to carrying the mail bag all day long. The government had put on an extra mail delivery, so he had to carry more mail. Both complaints might have been the result of carrying a heavy load of mail. He showed considerable nervousness and signs of anxiety.

He was not making a good salary, and as a result his relationship with his wife had deteriorated; he was on the verge of divorce. Thus, there were conditions of stress from his work, economic status, and domestic discord.

He went to what he called a "nerve doctor" who diagnosed his condition as nervousness and prescribed sedatives. A few months later the patient died of an acute heart attack.

This is an example of multiple pathology and multifactorial causation. Along with his psychological difficulties he had heart disease, which apparently was not recognized. Some of the factors were environmental, some were organic.

The psychiatrist, specializing as he does in the psyche, would have to depend heavily upon the acuteness of his diagnostic skill and judgment to know whether to refer such a patient to someone else or to broaden his own treatment.

METTLER: That is a general medical problem which is not peculiar to the psychiatrist. It is part and parcel of the production of our civilization.

If you had said, on the other hand, that the psychiatric condition had been overlooked or misdiagnosed, your statement would have been more closely related to the problem under discussion. It would then have brought up this point: When we are unable to tell how a psychiatrist arrives at his prognoses and estimates of improvement, the door is open to authoritarianism and mere opinion. We are then in a position in which it is very difficult to control a field of knowledge because one psychiatrist who has perhaps a better front than another is able to move in and dominate a situation.

This cannot happen in a scientific field for long because such a situation is controlled externally. The scientist must describe how he can tell; he must support his judgments and conclusions. Repetition in other hands soon reveals any authoritarianism. The goats are separated from the sheep. Absence of this control is one of the difficulties in the field of psychiatry at the present time.

KRUSE: Would you say that the sheep and the goats are skillfully separated in the scientific field?

METTLER: More effectively. I grant you that there are fakes in science; no question about it. But at least there are external controls. It is a self-controlled situation. A scientist who is a fake soon will be discovered.

KRUSE: Not necessarily.

WHITEHORN: Dr. Mettler points out a feature of the situation which seems to make it easier for chicanery to creep into clinical psychiatry than into biochemistry. However, this does not mean that there are no basic scientists who are getting by; or that every clinical psychiatrist who seems to have some degree of success is a quack. There is a difference of degree there.

METTLER: It is an area of danger.

WHITEHORN: I would say we view it here more as the danger of misleading serious students. The public views it as the danger that the patients suffer thereby.

METTLER: And it is disadvantageous for the pursuit of knowledge.

WHITEHORN: That is what I meant by the serious students.

METTLER: I meant disadvantageous for research rather than for training or education. For example, with three psychiatrists in a multidisciplinary program, there is no way to pin them down. When one of them insists on a point of view which is at odds with everyone else's activities, he can hang up the whole works.

KRUSE: Are you intimating that the majority in science are necessarily right?

METTLER: No. But in psychiatry a situation may develop in which one psychiatrist, because of personality factors, may obstruct the development of multidisciplinary activities. Now, we have admitted that we need a multidisciplinary approach in the field of psychiatry. We have also admitted that we cannot tell by objective technics in what way the psychiatrist arrives at a valid opinion. Having admitted those circumstances, it is impossible to resolve a situation in which

one member says that his opinion is just as good as the next member's. This obstacle defeats the team approach.

In the scientific field there are external means to bring a difficult or unsound investigator to heel ultimately. It can be shown that his performance is not good in some respect, or that his judgments are even worse, or that his data are inadequate or false.

WHITEHORN: I think that Dr. Kruse is correct in challenging the proposition that this problem is peculiar to psychiatry.

METTLER: No. It is not peculiar to psychiatry. It is just a great liability, rather than being peculiar.

KRUSE: Probably there is more of it in science than you realize.

METTLER: That could be.

KRUSE: An investigator may make a perfectly good, valid observation and fifty others may be unable to see it. I know of an observation that was unconfirmed and rejected by four or five scientists immediately after it was reported. Twenty years later it was rediscovered and just as unanimously verified as it had previously been rejected. It is now indisputably valid. Why could investigators not see it twenty years earlier? A very interesting question.

METTLER: Frequency modulation was proven to be absolutely impossible mathematically.

KRUSE: The psychiatrist's judgments on a patient's improvement and on the prognosis, including fitness for discharge, answer two separate but related questions. Is the patient better? Is he ready to return home? In a sense the one is a projection, an extrapolation, of the other, with additional considerations.

A judgment in response to the first question implies criteria of improvement; these are particularly necessary for evaluation of treatment. Here scientific methods can be of great help.

Inconclusive results from a therapeutic approach suggest lack of homogeneity in the sample of subjects. Discordant, unverifying results hint at a dissimilarity in sample from that of the original study as one possible explanation. In investigations on therapy it is a prerequisite that the group of patients must be homogeneous in several respects.

First, if the effect of a treatment on a disorder rather than on a symptom is under test, that disorder must be a clinical entity. A mixture of two disorders would not necessarily be expected to respond *in toto* to one therapy. It might, it is true, lead to the separation of two separate and distinct entities and thus answer a different question.

Second, the velocity of the disorder must be the same in all subjects; that is, it must be in either the acute, or subacute, or chronic form in all. For each form differs from the others in its rate of response. In consequence, the length of the study should depend on the velocity of the disorder. Too early termination may give misleading results with the more slowly moving forms.

Third, the disorder should be in the same stage in all patients. Again, the stage influences the kind and amount of response.

Finally, in the study of a disorder with multifactorial causation, it is preferable in one type of study that the predominating factors be the same in all subjects. Furthermore, the therapy to be tested should be appropriate to these factors. One therapeutic approach would be successful against one set of factors; another approach, against another set.

All these factors have a bearing on, indeed determine, the response of an individual to therapy. In practical application in a study, the difficulty is in the sampling; in the selection of subjects who are similar and impart homogeneity to the group. Unless the group is homogeneous, the results are bound to be invalid.

WHITEHORN: This is an appropriate point at which to present one clinical viewpoint that relates to your question of the diagnosis. Where we are particularly handicapped in clinical psychiatry, in my opinion, is in the characterization of persons. This I view personally as part of the over-all diagnostic problem. In our work with the patients, we make two kinds of diagnoses: one, the statistical diagnosis for reporting purposes; the other, a personal diagnostic formulation.

Both of them are heavily loaded on the psychopathological side. But the personal diagnostic formulation represents an effort on the doctor's part, as far as he can carry it in that direction, to see the patient's reaction as a bit of human behavior; to consider in what sense it can be understood, in what way the situation offers an approach as a kind of human behavior, and what potentialities there are for alternative human behavior that might work better.

If I could work other factors into the system, I would go even further. But let us take a system at that level and consider the diagnostic and prognostic problem brought up by Dr. Mettler. Then I spoke about the prognostication on two patients, the basis for the decision that the one could go home and the other should not. Much of the judgment there had to do with judgments of the person, aside from the disease.

In my opinion the improvement of the diagnoses for purposes of prediction and scientific study would be achieved by a better characterization and classification of the person. This is of more pertinence probably for psychiatry and for human adjustment than it is for cardiac disease, although there is some pertinence there. Hence, if we attempt to work toward a solution by dividing disease categories more finely, we might work a long way and miss the boat.

SCOTT: I seemed to notice in many of the preceding statements a recurrent common theme: that of individual differences, which are, I presume, caused in part by genetic factors. One of the basic characteristics of the human, as opposed to many other species, is enormous genetic variability. There is nothing like it in any other species except possibly the dog. After long experience with different breeds of dogs, we have come to the conclusion that there can be no generalization about dogs unless the breed is specified. Even then within the breeds themselves there is great variability, which must be hereditary. These differences between individuals occur in their anatomy, physiology, and behavior. The only species that exceeds the dog in individual variability is the human.

Abnormal behavior is an essential research problem that needs to be attacked from all scientific viewpoints. Among others, it should be related to the problem of describing an individual in terms of his basic characteristics; for they are likely to influence what disease he will get and what the prognosis of it will be.

WHITEHORN: Would you be willing to relate these characteristics to how the animal reacts rather than to disease? But then, maybe you want to adhere to the idea of diseases. I mean that if his behavior goes beyond a certain line, then it would be said colloquially that he has a disease.

KRUSE: Disease is the result in part of the person's reactions. The person is the battleground; the action upon him and his reactions to it constitute the disease.

METTLER: This points up one of the big differences between the worker in the field of psychiatry and in a laboratory discipline. The description of the experimental situation is usually made in terms of a laboratory. There is so much of such-and-such, which one analyzes, as best one may, into its component parts; then the parts are measured or weighed. But, in the area of personality, the laboratorian is confronted by the psychiatrist with yards, and yards, and yards of verbiage, all of which has special semantic value. The P.D.F. [personal diagnostic formulation] in this instance, I would hazard a guess, is full of words which have specific meaning in the locale in which they are used.

This becomes very difficult to deal with as a scientific document. It has great informative value to the individual. But it is very much as though we were pushed back to the Stone Age and our records had to be chiseled out on cumbersome pieces of rock. This material is not easily handled. Each case has an inertia of its own.

What happens? The attempt is made to categorize. If the material is too long in one place, it is lopped off in the process; if it is too short in another place, it is filled in to fit. In consequence, Dr. Whitehorn would be very much concerned over such a situation, and say, "You can't do this. These people are not susceptible to categorization."

WHITEHORN: I would not be likely to say that belligerently, but regretfully. We have not gone far in this categorization.

METTLER: Then a rating scale is de-veloped. Again, I know Dr. Whitehorn's reaction to a rating scale because on one occasion on which this point was brought up, he said that he had a rating scale. It was *Webster's Dictionary*. But that is just the piano on which the tune is played. The investigator who is trying to work with this mass is attempting to find a device to lighten each one of the P.D.F.'s so that he can manipulate them in an experimental or scientific situation. Here indeed is an area of great difficulty in psychiatry, the description of the individual's personality.

SCOTT: It is a problem which also confronts the experimentalists. On our experimental farm a large number of dogs are raised every year under uniform conditions; e.g., all are put through the same kind of training. In studying the relation of heredity to the animal's behavior, we try to assess the effects of heredity by measuring differences under what are presumably uniform environmental conditions. For this purpose a series of tests, in which we try to describe the variability of behavior as seen under these uniform conditions, have served fairly well.

In a special experimental project of a colleague, fox terriers were subjected to brain surgery and then were put through the same series of tests in order to find out the result of surgery. Interestingly enough, the results of the majority of the tests showed either nothing or only slight effects. However, it could be observed, just by a look at these animals, that they were different. An apt description of their most obvious peculiarity was that they just stood around all the time, apparently waiting for something to happen. This behavior was significant because the series of tests for the most part required doing something to the dog and then observing its response. When something was done to these dogs, they would respond; but they would never seem to do anything spontaneously or to anticipate anything. It was concluded that the tests which had been devised to measure normal variability did not measure the kind of variability that resulted from surgery.

I suspect that this outcome also occurs in human situations. Most of the psychological tests have been designed to detect variability of behavior in the school situation; and for that, they are very good. In devising tests, the psychologist has learned that the closer the test is to the real situation, the better are the results. That is probably one reason why the intelligence tests are better than fair; they are very close to the school situation.

On the other hand, most of the problems which the psychiatrist faces are in the area of the interpersonal relationship, for which these tests are not appropriate or revealing. Attempts to devise tests that would be useful in the interpersonal area have thus far met with something less than complete success. What we need, I think, is a new kind of test that would not be a pencil and paper test but would actually come close to the interpersonal reaction. Probably that is what is being obtained in the psychiatric interviews. But it has not yet been reduced to formal procedures.

KING: The field of education had its own criteria, and tests could be designed to produce results that would correlate with them. It is true that the closer the tests approximate the real situation, the more specific they are. But then the psychologist may not be applying psychological traits as criteria. If he adopts the technics and criteria of the psychiatrist, he is abandoning his own field and stepping into the psychiatrist's domain. For this reason I have an aversion to the hue and cry for more and better tests developed in this manner.

WHITEHORN: We have already emphasized the focus of the clinician on the care and treatment of the patient. This bias is evident when it comes to trying to make something etiological of the clinician's observations and reflections. If he sees favorable changes occurring in a patient, he is under a strong temptation to think that therapeutic benefit has been obtained and that it is because of something that he has done. The person who does not carry that weight of therapeutic responsibility is relieved somewhat of that temptation and he is geared to getting the control case by which he can reach a conclusion. But the clinical psychiatrist, by the nature of his responsibilities, is inclined to be hopeful about his work and is almost as eager to believe

that his conclusions are true as he is to get a control. Individuals, of course, come to be clinical psychiatrists by various routes and they differ in their temperaments. Hence, not all clinicians succumb to this temptation. Nevertheless, the clinician's responsibilities are a source of bias to which he is subject and for which I would bespeak a charitable forgiveness.

I might illustrate this by personal experience. Early in a transition stage of doing laboratory work and clinical work, I was conducting experiments on glucose and phosphate metabolism by administering rather heavy doses of glucose and of sodium acid phosphate and observing the changes in blood sugar and blood phosphate. There was indication in the physiological literature of the World War I period that this combination of substances might reduce the sense of fatigue. This investigation brought me into repeated close contact with patients, including a number of schizophrenic patients. The clinicians who were in charge of the service began to comment upon improvement in these patients. They were doing better than had been anticipated. Was this on account of the phosphate? Of the glucose? Or something else?

I began to spend somewhat more time on visits with the patients. I found myself in a fairly good position to become personally acquainted with them because they looked on me as a different kind of creature than the officious doctor who left orders on the board.

Before accepting a proposition that either the glucose or phosphate was curing them, it seemed useful to set up a control group who would receive personal visits with animated conversations, but neither glucose or phosphate. These patients, too, improved.

It is beside the point that the weight of evidence is now preponderant that the nature of the personal relationship between the patient and the physician does have a bearing on recovery, and that there are ways of cultivating relationships which are conducive to recovery. I would therefore record that as part of the material which I consider to be facts. But my point is that because of a desire to be personally useful and significant, I found it easier to believe then that my ministrations had more effect than did the sugar. Indeed, I must confess that I was inclined more to believe those patients who expressed their personal gratitude to me for helping them get well than those who attributed it to my medicine. Inherent pressure influenced my judgment. I do not believe that this characteristic is peculiar to me. This personal credulity is a factor which has a marked influence on the development of beliefs in many clinical psychiatrists. Their desire to be helpful accounts in very considerable measure for their readiness to believe that what they think, do, and say is somewhere at the center of the therapeutic process. This perhaps is worth noting as a point affecting the clinician as a scientist trying to draw conclusions from his observations and his methodology. It does not exclude him as a reliable witness, but it does indicate a kind of a bias in him which is likely to affect his conclusions and judgment.

METTLER: The difficulties, which have been pointed out, arising from the preconceptions with which psychiatrists approach the problem are also true in the laboratory. It is perfectly well known that the laboratorian gathers his data in some frame of reference.

chapter *21*

Additional Clinical Psychiatric Principles

◆ ◆

WHITEHORN: Dr. Betz and I have just prepared for publication the results of what I think is an interesting and significant study of the differential recovery rates of schizophrenic patients with different members of the staff. Among other things we looked for the prognostic indicators to see whether the members who had good results were just lucky in their patients, whether they had patients who were going to get better anyway. This possibility was shown not to be statistically significant. In the analysis of the data, various other factors which can be characterized clinically were taken into account; e.g., the character of the relationship between the physician and the patient in terms of whether the patient confides in the doctor, whether the patient discusses with the doctor how to solve a personal problem. Within the range of judgment this is a *yes* or *no* matter. Also the personal diagnostic formulation, re-examined by another person, now gives some notion of whether the doctor perceives in the patient some personal problem, whether his imagination or his contact with the patient leads him to see a personal issue in the patient's life which makes the reaction meaningful; or whether he perceives in the patient only such-and-such a descriptive reaction pattern, such-and-such a disease.

One finding that came out of the study was that those patients whose physicians initially make a personal diagnostic formulation which in a large measure sees the re-action as a meaningful personal one, or at least sees the patient as participating in it significantly to a personal degree, are the ones who become more confidential with their physicians. By and large, they are also the patients who recover in larger proportions and who have a better social adjustment upon recovery. Not only do they have a remission of the specific symptomatology of illness, but also they are more amiable companions and get along better. Indeed, those patients whose therapists formulated personal problems as well as descriptive categories did better even if the patients did not establish a more confidential relationship. These results fortify the assumption that the nature of the personal contact and personal interaction between psychiatrist and patient makes a difference in the outcome.

Furthermore, the evidence was obtained in second- and third-person, rather than in first-person terms. To some extent the methodology controlled one source of the personal element entering into the analysis. If a psychiatrist having this personal relationship were himself to analyze the data out of his own experience, he might be tempted to reason and conclude as follows: "This is my patient. I did something; it must have been good for this patient." But here the investigator is analyzing the records of a colleague, and it was the latter who had the personal relationship. This procedural point gives weight to the conclusion that the factors determining the establishment of a personal relationship also determine in some measure the kind of recovery.

This inference prompts the question, Was this relationship efficacious because it had an influence on the patient or because it had an influence on the disease? The answer would seem to be that it had an influence on the patient. For, upon weighing the question, What is being affected—the patient with all his complexity or just the psychopathological events? It seems more likely that the patient as a person is being affected. It might be said in characterizing the situation that the doctor was establishing a relationship with what remained that was normally reachable and transactable in the patient rather than being in touch immediately with what were psychological limitations.

Next comes the question of how these transactions between doctors and patients have an effect. Here people tend to divide into two general groups: those who assume automatically that it must be the doctor who did something to the patient that made the patient get better; and those who assume that the patient had certain potentialities to get better which were somehow effectuated by contact with the physician. According to the former, the physician brought about the recovery; according to the latter, he improved the opportunity for the patient to make it happen. In essence, by one group it is viewed as a curative process; by the other, as an assisted recovery process. Consequently, to any research on the subject there are two approaches. Or a combined approach might be conceived in which the patient and doctor devote themselves to the consideration of a life situation with its problems and reactions and come to compare views on how that life situation might be met otherwise than as the patient is meeting it.

This latter proposition raises the question that is sometimes put into words by patients: "Are there other ways? Is there any meaning to the word 'possibility'? This is the way I am, this is the way the situation is, and what do you mean, there is some other possible way?" It is, in a way, a statement more or less of a fatalistic position, "My mother was this way, my father was that way, my sisters were such. How else could I act?" The doctor is sometimes hard put to it to make any reasonable statement of any matter on which the patient really now has a choice.

But in a cafeteria, for instance, there is one such opportunity for a patient to choose this or that salad. And no matter how mother and father were, or all the circumstances making for a fatalistic outcome, in reality there remains a little crack in fate where he can choose this or that salad. It is a small crack, but still it is something. From this tiny crack of choosing which salad, the psychiatrist can move on to other choices. Some patients will introduce possible courses of action which had occurred to them earlier in life. They chose one rather than the other, and a train of consequences followed from the choice they made. But they might have made another choice.

This consideration introduces the assumption of determinism. Several of the statements of position on the causation of mental disease contain this assumption. Most scientists with whom I have talked about human beings have made either an explicit or implicit assumption that whatever happens is determined by prior events, by what is in the patient and what happened to the patient. The character of my preceding remarks leads me logically to assert that I believe in incomplete determinism. It amounts to a statement that I believe in determinism but with the qualification that it is not quite 100 per cent. There does remain a region of choice; some possibilities do exist. This is a proposition that is practically impossible to test, because if one possibility is chosen, the other one is not.

When I express this view of incomplete determinism, I am told that it runs counter to all scientific philosophy or method. To this statement I have recently begun to answer that I do not find it so. Most of my scientific friends are experimentalists rather than pure observers; and they seem to act as if they believed that they could decide to do this or that experiment, two possible things. If this is not choice, what is? The experimenter who approaches a psychic problem with the attitude of setting up an experimental design implies, or else there is no sense in it, that there exists a possibility of making a choice about it. He thinks over the problem, imagines this and that possibility, and then makes his choice of design. Hence, experimental scientists, as contrasted with astronomers or observational scientists, do seem by implication to exercise as scientists a choice between possibilities.

If experimentalists are thinking of patients as subjects, many of them find it more comfortable to assume that the patients will behave like other objects of scientific study and that they will not confuse the matter by exercising choice. But this is to put the subject of the experiment in a different category than the experimenter. If the experimenter claims that as a human being he has a choice in the design of his experiments, but he denies that the patients as human beings have any choice, he separates his universe of human beings into two categories: one, experimenters; and the other, patients. Of course, occasionally, the experimenter becomes the patient. I have not had any success at all in discussing this point with scientific friends who have become my psychiatric patients, so I do not know what they would do about it in that stage. My presumption is that they might then become aware of the fact that they are human beings both ways.

The psychiatrist has another belief or principle that relates this matter of choice to mental disorders. It is that in the wide range of behavior in mental illness, the range of choice seems markedly diminished. This is to say, if the patient behaves in such-and-such a manner that can be described, he seems to do it with a consistency and a regularity, despite some contrary motivations, that would seem to indicate that his choice of behavior is much more limited with regard to those matters that are immediately pertinent to his illness.

Accordingly, I have developed a view regarding what it is that is occurring which is of therapeutic value in the transactions between the doctors and the patients. I am inclined to view it as representing a kind of conversational relationship, interpersonal transaction, or friendliness, which, through the discussion of matters of mutual interest, calls attention to an area in which it is possible to make choices, where determinism does not reign completely. By this means the clinician is able, with quite a number of patients, to enlarge this gap in deterministic fate so as to include some of the behavior which in time preceded the obvious illness and which may have had a bearing on the development of the illness. It might be said that the patient worked himself out on a limb in respect to attitudes, beliefs, and antagonisms; and there he had a very limited choice of directions in which to move. Many get further out on the limb. In this way the patient's freedom of action is limited by the choices of action that were made. As part of a psychiatrist's relationship with the patient, there is some enlargement of current possible choices of behavior, and a more enlarged view of what might have been possible in the past.

Apparently there are two kinds of beliefs by which people who become patients markedly restrict their conscious choices. One of them is the kind of consideration which would lead to punishment or a sense of guilt. They think: "This just isn't done. There's only one right way to look at this matter, so that there is no freedom of choice. A decent person would not do this." The concept of decency and propriety propels them along a restricted line. The other consideration is closely related; it is the sense of shame. The patients themselves would not choose to do something; and so, in a way, they limit their own choices.

In these two territories the psychiatrist has the opportunity to generate in the patient an increased sense of freedom of choice. Discussion of the family background may bring out that various relatives and friends differed quite naturally in their notions, and may bring the patient to realization of it for the first time. For example, the patient may say, "Mother thought thus-and-so and insisted on it; Uncle Joe had different ideas about it; and Aunt Mary, still different ideas. And, you know, Aunt Mary's ideas might have been just as good as the others'. I never thought of that before." Thus, possible modes of conduct which had not been recognized as being within the range of practical potentiality at one time are now seen as conceivably within the range of what might have been done. As a result, if a new critical situation confronts the patient, his range of possible, or at least of acceptable, choices is now enlarged. This is an important consideration in psychotherapy.

As far as I know, this rationale has never been made the subject of any systematic treatise of psychotherapy. What is much more likely to happen is that a clinician, in pondering over his transactions with the patient in retrospect, will hit on some specific topic of conversation, some statement that occurs, and say, "This is what made the difference." Actually it may be that the different propositions that he enunciated, or the different thoughts that were in the back of his mind, did not, in themselves, have a thing to do with the patient's favorable reaction. But the psychiatrist's general approach, and the possibility of his opening up a wider range of potential choices—these may have made a difference.

I would relate this line of thought to the discussion earlier, on the asylum. It is a place where people can be taken to be cared for when they are unacceptable to society, or when society is intolerant of them. It may also relieve these people of certain restrictive factors that exist in the society. Put into other words, it may open for them potentialities for choice in behavior which did not exist before; and this opportunity may restore to them something more of their humanness, their sense of dignity and direction. I have had patients who said, "I like the life here in the hospital. It's the only place I have lived where I can be independent." That sounds startling when first heard because it seems so contradictory of the common view of the situation. But it is a very meaningful statement for many patients who in that situation really do have choices of alternatives, ways of behavior, which they did not have in another situation. It may have been physically more possible in the other situation than in the hospital, but emotionally impossible.

METTLER: It has been interpreted that asylum provides enlarged opportunity for choice, but it also has an opposite phase. There is, for instance, the patient who wishes to stay in the hospital because it restricts his freedom of choice and thereby creates a situation in which he finds contentment in routine. Such individuals are likely to be panicked by interpersonal relationships that they are not used to; in the hospital everything is relaxed. Furthermore, many of these patients take comfort in the fact that they can display their peculiarities of behavior in an institutional environment because it is expected and no one worries about it. Therefore, limitation as well as freedom may be provided by asylum.

WHITEHORN: Next, I would like to relate this matter of restriction and enlargement of choice to some of the so-called traditional reflex types of experimentation in the production of neuroses. There is something in that technic of producing pathological behavior which means a marked restriction in the dog's behavior, not only in what the animal can do, but in what it can hear. Both incoming stimuli and the possibilities of action are restricted. The factors responsible for the restrictions were not introduced into the technology of such experimentation for that reason. The aim was to simplify the factors so as to have more scientific control. But whatever may have been the reasons for introducing the so-called camera or the harness into the Pavlovian research, one of the effects is to reduce the range of choice.

The technic may reduce the situation to a point where the animal can pay attention to and respond in a very restricted pattern, which is in itself a kind of psychopathology. Or it may reduce the situation to a point where the dog cannot take it any more and breaks out of this imposed system with some kind of uncooperative behavior. The dog becomes restless, irritable, and fidgety; it cannot be used any more. He is then thought to be neurotic. Or he may become so stiff and catatonic as to be manifesting an obviously pathological form of behavior.

What does one do with a dog like that? Sometimes he stays that way with minor modifications. Gantt's dog, Nick, had approximately ten years of neurotic life. He underwent modifications, but he remained still very obviously neurotic. Others of these dogs had responded well to what might be called therapy, which most effectively consisted in gentling by the experimenters. It might be looked upon as a kind of permissive control, or lack of control, of the dog, rather than a measure specifically designed to overcome the highly restrictive character of the previous management. This therapy might have theoretical pertinence to the presumed etiological factor. If the etiology is limiting the choices and the therapy is enlarging the choices, they have an obvious relationship.

KING: Another explanation of the induction of nervousness in the experimental animal is that he is incited to action without adequate cues from which to decide which channel that action shall take. It is his inability to make a choice because too many possible avenues are open that constitutes the difficulty. Numerous parallels occur in man. His disinclination to leave an asylum and return home may be because he fears going back to where he will have to make more choices. What is guilt except berating one's self for not having made some other choice? It is really reproof of one's own limitations. Apparently difficulties arise from either too much or too little choice.

WHITEHORN: These are the thoughts of one clinical psychiatrist struggling to make sense out of a wide range of observations. They have a bearing on the most basic of the assumptions that are likely to be considered: that is, the assumption of determinism. How could I find myself at home and participate meaningfully in a Conference with all the other participants who are committed 100 per cent to determinism? I suppose that emotionally it would be a little difficult. Theoretically, I do not think that I would find it particularly difficult, because I could say, and I think quite honestly, that for a very large range of behavior there is good evidence that what has happened, the kind of a person one is, and what has happened in one's life, settles what remains as a possibility. If the talk is 90 per cent determinism, I can accept it.

If it is 100 per cent, I can make a 3 per cent difference and probably get along with it all right. I would have no difficulty unless someone insists repeatedly on 100 per cent.

METTLER: The percentage makes no difference. It is a question of principle.

WHITEHORN: A 3 per cent principle?

METTLER: It is an "all-or-none" proposition; either you believe in it or you do not.

KRUSE: The all-or-none principle is often carried over from physiology. In modernday logic, it is recognized that there are also gradients with points in between. It is possible that there is 90 per cent determinism, and 10 per cent more or less of indeterminism. Akin to the all-or-none principle is the either-or proposition. The latter is a prevalent fallacy.

METTLER: I do not think that it is. In this particular instance the "either-or" principle is valid because we are dealing with a logical proposition. We are not dealing with an area of demonstrable evidence. That is the crux of the matter.

SCOTT: For a great many years I have been trying to get animals to repeat their behavior under controlled conditions. An animal with known history is put into a situation; then that situation is repeated. But it is almost impossible to get him to do the same thing twice. Nevertheless, there is a certain lawfulness about his behavior. It is observed that upon continuous close repetition of the same situation, i.e., under constant practice or habit-forming training, the animal's behavior becomes highly reliable.

If the psychologist gets a coefficient of reliability of about 90, he is very well satisfied. That is considered unusually good. Errors in measurement or in technic do not account for all the variability.

We have finally come to the conclusion that there is something of a fundamental nature in the nervous system which causes variability. Actually, if there were no variability in the nervous mechanism, there would be no possibility of improvement or adjustment. So there are two opposite tendencies: the one, toward variability; and the other, toward habit formation. The latter blocks or reduces the variability. But if practice and training are stopped for a while, variability in behavior will be increased.

I would therefore consider myself to be a determinist because behavior is predictably determinable.

METTLER: Variation has nothing to do with determinism. They are two different categories, two different things. That is the fundamental point. The objective problem in variation is not a question of free will; it is a question of choice. Choice can be demonstrated. It is a word given to a group of phenomena. In contrast, determinism belongs in the area of philosophy; it is a philosophical concept which is quite independent and distinct from choice. Hence, it is completely unnecessary to bring the concept of determinism into the choice of behavior; indeed, it has no bearing on choice.

In reporting the results of a study, Dr. Whitehorn stated that those patients who got better had a physician who formulated personal problems; and they had a high degree of personal relationship with their physician. The next step in the line of reasoning was that something happened which was either the action of the physician on the patient or on the disease. There is a third possibility; namely, there was an interaction. Those patients who recovered have the capacity for variation in their behavior; therefore, the capacity for variation in behavior may in itself be a factor acting toward the improvement of the individual. By virtue of the fact that these patients possess the capacity for modification, they can respond to the physician.

WHITEHORN: That is a very good statement about those who did get better. Insofar as it implies a negative statement about the others, it is open to some reservation. They too may have had this potentiality, but no opportunity for its development presented itself.

METTLER: On the other hand, it may have been a lack of potentiality which was a personal phenomenon depending on certain organic circumstances in the individual. If that is so, there is no need to introduce any future determinism into the discussion. Rather, the explanation may be that one individual is a physiologic organism with the capacity to react to its environment and another is not.

WHITEHORN: On the other side, our limited evidence seems to indicate that certain physicians are likely to have interaction with their patients.

METTLER: That suggests that with patients of high reactive capacity, their ability to reorient themselves will depend upon their being able to establish a contact with reality. It is the patient's experience which will help him to achieve his contact with reality. Surely the physician who has helped in evoking reactions in a patient—you can call it choice if you wish; but choice is, in essence, reacting to environment—has been part of the patient's environment. Naturally the physician is a more effective element in the environment of the patient who could and did utilize the opportunity, than of the patient who could not or would not. On the other hand, the psychotherapist who was able to establish a greater degree of empathy would also be able to bring the patient back closer to existence. The situation can be viewed not so much as a matter of choice but rather as a mechanism which enables the individual to achieve completion of reality. I am trying to develop an alternative explanation. You say that it is not a particular event in the psychotherapeutic procedure but rather an attitudinal state which is the most important thing by virtue of the establishment of the patient's awareness of choice. Then you go on to build up a situation in which choice becomes the justification of indeterminism and thereby you elevate the principle of indeterminism to be the guiding consideration in the therapeutic approach.

WHITEHORN: That was not my intention.

METTLER: That human beings, as well as inanimate agents of therapy, enter into the situation would not necessarily alter the fact that the principle is the same, whether it be drugs or some other proposition. They are the mechanisms by which the person who has lost contact with reality re-establishes it. The instrument is another human being, since after all contact with a human being is the only way that the patient can find out what other human beings do. If the physician is an inferior instrument, as a human being providing this relationship, it is going to take the patient longer to re-establish contact with reality.

WHITEHORN: This is put very well. It demonstrates that this particular situation can be viewed from a variety of angles.

METTLER: There are several possible explanations of the effectiveness of psychotherapy. One might be, for example, some particular event in the psychoanalytic procedure, such as the Freudians have emphasized as being important. Another would be the rationale which you have elaborated: the psychiatrist's attitude and broadening of choice for the patient. Still another, and perhaps the principal one, is that the patients have a narrowing of their conceptual relationships to their environmental situation and so re-establish contact with reality. Therefore, as a complete determinist, I would say that I could talk imperturbably about your findings by giving them a different interpretation.

WHITEHORN: Suppose that you were the chief of a service with a particular concern that the patient have a favorable outcome. You make a choice of the staff member whom you assign to the patient. You think that you make a choice.

METTLER: I would say that the appearance of a choice in such an instance is entirely illusory. The same would hold for the example of the experimenter developing a choice of method for conducting an experiment.

WHITEHORN: Does the same illusory depiction hold true if we present here a series of possible hypotheses and assumptions, and if we then feel that out of our discussion we are choosing which of these we will experiment with? Is that purely illusory? What is the point of a conference if the assumption prevails that what comes out of it is not in any way determined by the participants?

METTLER: Of course it is determined by the participants. But here "determined" is just a word. Whether or not a choice is involved or whether the matter is determined does not make a bit of difference, except that philosophically it seems indefensible to

me to accept the point of view of indeterminism.

WHITEHORN: It probably is just a word if that particular view is chosen. But somebody else might choose a different view. And he might in his own mind even make it philosophically defensible.

SCOTT: In one of our tests a puppy is led to a partially covered dish of food; he must remove the frame covering, in order to obtain the food. It is possible for him to accomplish removal by pawing the cover or pulling it out with his teeth. Ordinarily he will first run away from the dish; then he will climb up on top of it, look at it, smell it, paw it, walk away and come back, and repeat his maneuvers. He may succeed in getting off the cover with his paw. On successive trials he will go through some of the same maneuvers as before, and will gradually eliminate unnecessary movements.

Not all puppies succeed on the first trial. If one does not, he is removed from the room. On the next trial he will go through the same motions but he will reduce the time during which he makes his attempts by about half. Then, in succeeding trials, the time during which he tries will be very greatly reduced; finally the puppy, without trying, only sits down and waits until he is taken out of the situation. It appears that he has reached a mode of adjustment to this situation, that of inaction, and is just waiting until the situation terminates. Changing the situation or making it easier for him to get the food is of no avail. It looks as if he has lost the power of choice because he has adopted this kind of behavior.

WHITEHORN: Committed himself.

SCOTT: The animal does not show abnormal behavior resulting from experience. It conceivably might disturb him greatly if the situation was rigged so that it was very important for him to get the food.

WHITEHORN: It does limit his reactivity somewhat.

SCOTT: Oh yes, very much. This might be related to human behavior where individuals reach a conclusion about what they ought to do and faithfully do it even though it may result in very much reduced power of adjustment and may interfere seriously with their activities for the rest of their lives.

WHITEHORN: If it is accepted that there are choices other than the one decided, the very exercise of this prerogative of choice in some situations has a significant effect on other choices that can be made. The behavior of the puppies emphasizes the kind of habit-formation that follows from the making of choices.

SCOTT: From the point of view of practical behavior, it is very convenient to assume choice. While in the realm of pure theory, we can assume pure determinism. I can see no real inconsistency in using that point of view.

WHITEHORN: But I would maintain that it does make a difference with some patients. Let us suppose that the phenomenon to which one ordinarily refers when he says he made a choice is an illusion. This is an illusion which has some therapeutic value; it may affect people's moods. And in some situations it is a useful illusion if that is what it is. For example, Doctor A might be better than Doctor B for neurotic patients. But Doctor B might be particularly good in caring for schizophrenic patients.

KRUSE: Are you suggesting a choice on the basis of the physician with whom transference is apt to be best realized? Or, to speak in other terms, would it be on the basis of the physician who might establish better rapport with a patient and bring out all of his potentialities for recovery?

WHITEHORN: I think that the comment is a useful one. I do not know where it is going to take us. If you talk about transference or rapport, I should say that the distinction between them is very important in this connection.

KRUSE: In your evaluation of a physician, would you differentiate his personality from his technical skill, and would that distinction enter into your choice?

WHITEHORN: We now come to a question which I do not have enough information to answer. My impression would be—

KRUSE: Probably you might say that the personality is a very large element in the choice.

WHITEHORN: I would be inclined to say

so. There is evidence from the fact that some of the doctors seem to have good relations with schizophrenic patients from the beginning of their training. This implies that this trait is not so much dependent upon body of knowledge and skills. I suppose that every such observation has to take into account the environment in which the action occurred. Many doctrines and various personified operational models, some idealized, are afoot. But I try to maintain for the staff a fair degree of freedom of choice of their principal source of inspiration and knowledge. We do not promulgate doctrines. Hence it may be assumed that the doctors in training have made a natural "choice" among the various models. Perhaps this is a factor in the degree of the difference that we observe at times.

SCOTT: For the worker in animal experimentation, it is often very difficult to relate what animals do, to what people do, particularly because human behavior is frequently described in terms of what the people say or how they feel. Since there is no verbal communication from animals and since it is not easy to ascertain how they feel, there is great difficulty in transferring or relating to man the body of knowledge on animals. One test of the conclusions from a study on animal behavior as to whether they are sound or generally useful might be whether they can be related to the fundamental theories of behavior. These theories may be listed in relation to the different levels of organization that effect behavior: (1) the genetic theory, that is, hereditary differences; (2) the theories of learning; (3) the theory of social relationships (this is not very highly developed as yet); (4) the theories of social organization and culture. Any explanation or hypothesis that is brought up should be consistent with the germane portion of these four basic theories. I would say that the concept which Dr. Whitehorn has introduced is consistent with what we know about learning. That being so, it can be interpreted and formulated at various levels. His postulate is also related to the theory of social relationships. For example, in animal experiments one individual may react very differently toward different individuals of his own kind. In the domestic goat, there is usually a dominance order; and when food is placed between two animals, one goat will butt the other out of the way and take the food. The attacked goat never fights back; even if he is quite hungry, he will take more of a beating. However, this unsuccessful goat reacts differently to each individual in the rest of the flock. To one, he will respond quite aggressively; that is, he will drive him away from the food and take it. To another, he will be mild.

These observations, as well as Dr. Whitehorn's study, pertain to the differentiation of social relationships. The interpretation of one may be applied to the other. I suspect that the patient gets along well with certain individuals who resemble someone with whom he has had a pleasant association; he gets along badly with other individuals who remind him of a past unpleasant situation.

WHITEHORN: In 1945 or thereabouts Hebb gave a very interesting discussion on animal neuroses, pointing out that a very large catalog of what might be called peculiarities or oddities in animal behavior may have little to do with the problem of human neuroses, although in a global kind of a way they may be called animal neuroses. But he was inclined therefore to alert scientific workers to the danger of too gross identification of the one with the other. I thought that it was a very useful argument.

However, existing information does arouse a desire to have a more careful analysis in order to see in what respects there may be some similarities, in what respects there may be differences, so that one might take an intermediate position and not be overwhelmed by a global similarity or not be so negativistic as to say that there is none at all.

METTLER: Animal experimental work is always plagued by the objection which was brought against Galen a great many years ago in his experiments on the recurrent laryngeal nerve. The question was asked how he could say that the recurrent laryngeal nerve had anything to do with vocalization when all he had worked on was the pig. The point involves a confusion in terminology. While it is true that pigs do not vocalize, they do have phonation. Pi-

geons vocalize. Similarly, the present issue is not that animals do not have behavior disorders; they do. But these disorders are not what are called neuroses in humans.

The experimentalist can only say of his results with animals, "When I do thus and so, this is what happens." He must restrict himself to a statement of the facts as they occur under the circumstances in which they occur. This is a statement which can be made as a verity and, if correct, is to be accepted as fact. Interpretations made on the basis of such facts have to be handled in the realm of hypothesis, as logical probabilities or possibilities. As such, there is room for different people's opinions.

WHITEHORN: What usually happens is that tentative identifications are made and then corrected. People do not operate ordinarily by keeping their data at the level of data; they bring the data together into tentative notions.

SCOTT: I brought up the subject of the transfer of results from animal experiments to man because it seems to me that if clinical findings and propositions are to be validated, for the most part they must be validated on animals. Because the clinician has a responsibility for the welfare of the patient, he is more limited in his use of human than of animal subjects. Yet there is this serious difficulty of relating the findings from animals to man. It arises from the fact that the human observations are almost always reported in terms of ideas or verbal symptoms and seldom in physical symptoms. I would not know a schizophrenic dog if I saw it because I could not apply the symptoms reported for man.

WHITEHORN: Dr. Gantt has a dog with interesting behavior. When the dog's cage door is opened, he runs out into the corridor, takes a few steps, turns around, goes down the hall to the door of a room, goes into the room and becomes immobilized. If Dr. Gantt lifts the dog's forepaw, the dog lets it stay up for several minutes. Then the dog's paw slowly droops a little. It is a behavior which at least looks like examples of psychotic phenomena. If Dr. Gantt gives the dog an injection or if he inserts only an empty needle through the skin, then the dog is alert and lively, runs around the room, and goes back to where he was before. Until the needle is stuck into him, he has this stereotyped pattern. When the needle is stuck into him, he is released from the pattern. This phenomenon is different from catatonia. Unfortunately, we do not have a record of how the dog developed this behavior.

There is no practical way of finding precisely what is meant by catatonia in subjects, what with such a loose, descriptive appellation. The original idea, if one goes back to the historical basis of the term, referred to motor phenomena. Nobody now would dream of restricting the term "catatonia" to those examples where there is good evidence of motor disturbances.

METTLER: We can now produce experimentally a condition in which the animal, when placed in a position, will retain this position. It is part of a phenomenon which may be called catatonic rigidity. It has an organic basis easily demonstrable in terms of damage to the pallidum. When this manifestation occurs, therefore, in the course of a neurologic disorder, we would say that it is due to disordered physiology in the pallidum. But we may find these elements of disordered physiology in any kind of constellation. The problem has therefore been to isolate the irreducible minimum and find out what mechanisms underlie it.

WHITEHORN: Perhaps I can add another detail to the subject. Dr. Curt Richter has some wild rats which in a relative way might be called catatonic, or perhaps even more accurately might be called paranoid. These particular rats had received an almost lethal dose of ANTU. but had survived. It was noticeable that all of the survivors were very difficult to feed. Some of them, at the intrusion of anyone with food, would scurry to the very farthest corner of the cage, climb way up into the corner, stick their noses just as far out of the cage as possible, and stay there, still. The next morning some of them were found in the same place and position. This is an immobile state. By reason of the immobility, it could be said that this behavior might have something to do with catatonia. It is an oddity of behavior that shows up under certain circumstances. Neither this nor what Dr. Mettler reported may be identical with what we call catatonia in the human; indeed, they may not be identical with each other. But it is useful to record the phenomena.

METTLER: A long but interesting chapter in the history of medicine has been the manner in which symptoms and signs have been elucidated as to their causation and their occurrence in a particular clinical entity. The discovery of the causation of a disease has permitted symptoms and signs to be properly associated and located. What has usually happened is that the problem has gradually been worked out by analysis through a fractionation of symptoms. Sometimes there has been division and subtraction; sometimes, addition and combination. A symptom complex may prove to be, not a homogeneous entity, but a heterogeneous mixture. One or more symptoms or signs are found, on the basis of causation, to be unrelated to the remainder of the complex. These manifestations are taken away and ultimately may be placed in another complex with a different cause. For example, various aspects of gonorrhea, syphilis, granuloma venereum, lymphopathia venereum, diseases associated by accident or circumstance, were all once thrown together as one clinical entity and were called *the* venereal disease because they might exist as a constellation and there was no clear way of separating them. Descriptive technics were adopted which tended to separate them but they were not completely separated into distinct diseases until their etiologic agents were discovered.

On the other hand, two symptoms seemingly foreign to each other may be found to be related and are therefore organized into the picture of a single disease. For example, in the early studies on venereal disease, no one had any idea that the cardiac phenomena which occurred fifteen years later were related to syphilis. Because of the separation in time they did not seem to be related. But they really belonged together. They were different parts of the same pathological process. The only thing that ever brought them together was the discovery of the etiologic agent.

In bringing order and organization to

symptoms and signs by the experimental method, it is desirable to find out what elements in a symptom-complex are relatively consistent and what are variable. In the field of psychiatry this has been beautifully done by the dynamicists, who have gradually worked out important basic phenomena. In neurology, the search has been for disordered physiological processes which are separable from the complex and which may appear in various constellations. In a sense, the least common multiple and its underlying mechanism must be sought.

KING: I suspect that the same thing is going to happen in psychiatry.

METTLER: This or that particular physiological system in animals can be studied from a comparative point of view to find out what has been added or omitted in different forms. Stereotypy, for example, is a very interesting manifestation to study from the standpoint of comparative physiology. Stereotypy in birds extends to a point where they continue to attack a space where an object has been after it has been removed. The foregoing, exhibited by young chicks, is seen in other animals when, by removal of parts, their brains have been reduced approximately to the structure of the avian brain. The basic processes remain susceptible to study from form to form, but their combination into constellations is so variable in different forms that it is difficult or even impossible to compare such constellations. It is this criticism which I would like to raise against the study of so-called "neuroses" in animals. Some animals cannot, for example, develop certain constellations of signs because they do not have the necessary anatomic substrate. Paralysis agitans, for example, does not occur in intraprimate forms.

SCOTT: What has to be done is to identify the symptoms on a more than superficial basis in order to impart significance to them. There may be some fundamental similarity, even if it is at first obscure. For example, it may be possible to identify the behavior of Liddell's neurotic sheep and goats with certain human reactions. In tying up a goat and giving it an electric shock repeatedly at intervals of ten seconds over a period of six weeks, he is fundamentally

giving the animal painful stimulation which it would ordinarily avoid. The goat, if he were not tied, would undoubtedly leave the experimental area upon receiving an electric shock; he would move away and never come back. Being tied up, all he can do is to lift his leg. The adjustment is one of a thwarted avoidance or escape reaction, and the eventual symptoms could be related to the human phenomenon of anxiety.

There is a plausible explanation of the goat's action. In terms of Skinner's theory of operative conditioning, a response tends to become associated with any that immediately precedes or follows it. The shock produces first the leg-lifting reaction and then the slower changes in heart rate and breathing. Thus, the lifting of the leg would become associated with the emotional reactions which occur later, and would tend to set them off. Of course, the emotional reactions themselves are unpleasant and tend to produce an attempt at escape with movements of the leg. Hence, there is a circular reaction set off in the animal. The reason that this circuit does not occur under normal circumstances is the animal's immediate tendency to escape from an unpleasant situation whether it is caused by direct pain or by his own emotional reactions. But with repetition the emotional reactions would tend to produce the escape reactions without the . . .

METTLER: You mean without reinforcement?

SCOTT: To some extent without reinforcement. The reaction would tend to reinforce itself. Most of the theories of reinforcement and memory have been developed on feeding behavior. Recently Richard Solomon reported giving fox terriers a severe shock and sounding a buzzer at the same time, while they were in a jumping box. After this was done once, these animals responded every time the buzzer was sounded without ever being shocked again. They reacted hundreds of times. Upon repeating this experiment with a mild shock one of my associates found that a dog would still react after many months. In the meantime there had been no reinforcement.

METTLER: We have found that for an

accurate amount of work, we have to reinforce our animals regularly.

SCOTT: This is a situation which the animal can avoid by staying out of the way. If a wolf has ever been caught in a trap and escaped, it is practically impossible ever to get him to touch it again. Reinforcement is not necessary. It is a dangerous situation for the wolf, and one experience is enough.

There is a need to extend basic research in learning. Experiments on learning have been conducted and theories have been constructed on the basis of a limited type of behavior with a limited physiology; namely, eating. But it should be borne in mind that the physiology underlying sex behavior or fighting behavior is quite different from that underlying eating behavior. If investigation of learning is extended to these behaviors, substantial modification of the existing theories may result. Besides, these behaviors are more important in psychiatry than is eating behavior.

WHITEHORN: By some experiments in which I have participated, I should like to illustrate the difference between the clinician's natural inclination and the laboratorian's approach. The purpose of the experiments was to study the speed of learning, the ambiguity of response, and different intensities of stimulation. A dog was to be taught to lift his foot at the sound of a buzzer; during the conditioning stage the sound was followed by electrical stimulation as the means to get him to raise his foot. After three or four hundred trials, he learned to avoid this tactile stimulation. The buzzer sounded and he lifted his foot. While the apparatus was being set at another level of stimulation, it inadvertently and unfortunately was short-circuited, so that the dog got a momentary but very brisk shock. The dog ceased to be a cooperative subject very promptly, struggled in the harness, could not be gentled, was released in half an hour from the apparatus, and was taken back to his quarters. When attendants went after him the next day to bring him to the laboratory, they could not get him to come. Day after day the attendants tried to get him to come to the laboratory; finally they inveigled him into a trip down another elevator in the animal quarters building, around through another building, and back into the original building. He went with them that way; but when he reached the laboratory, he was just as upset as he had been before and he would not cooperate. Thereafter, the attendants could bring him into the laboratory via this second route; but then he would not cooperate. They could not get him into the box. This consumed some weeks of trials. After a while, by further gentling they succeeded by stages in getting him into the box; and finally into the harness. Everything was all set up. They were recording respiration, heart rate, motor response. He now had a higher heart rate with more panting respirations than during the control period some weeks earlier when he had been a calm animal. He was given the usual level of electrical stimulation. What happened to him? He heaved a sigh of relief, and settled into his position. His respiration got steadier, his heart rate slowed and became steady; he was a calm dog. As a psychiatrist speaking clinically, my thought about the meaning of the situation for the dog was that the accustomed electrical stimulation was reassuring to him. He knew this situation; it was old and familiar. One unpleasant association was in a way removed for him by the familiarity of an old experience.

KING: Dr. Solomon states that after he had trained his dogs to jump from one side of the box to the other, he then inserted glass partitions to block the possibility of their jumping. When he gave the buzzer signal without the shock, the dog crashed against the barrier and set up prolonged howling. The animal followed this pattern to avoid the shock. It required hundreds of trials to steady the dog to the point where it could finally ignore the signal. Dr. Solomon thought that he had it in a state where it could be used as an abreaction dog. But when Dr. Solomon removed the glass partition and gave the signal, the dog instantly leaped back over as he had done originally. Apparently he had not taken any comfort from his extinction. He would not trust the situation; he was not taking any chances on the possibility of a shock.

SCOTT: This brings out a fundamental

theoretical point: A given line of behavior may prevent further learning. As long as the dog escapes he cannot learn that the situation has changed. This idea might also be fundamental to the problem of psychological stresses. Are traumatic experiences permanent or is there a possibility of relearning?

WHITEHORN: Information on unlearning might be useful with the young.

SCOTT: Besides learning, it appears that genetics is another factor that enters into the buzzer-shock situation. Dr. Solomon's dogs were fox terriers that he had obtained from us. In our repetition of his experiments and confirmation of his observations, Shetland sheep dogs were used. Like the terriers they are highly sensitive animals with long-lasting emotional reactions. Dr. Chambers recently tried cocker spaniels in the same test and they would not jump at all. The cocker spaniel is one of the setter group of dogs which were once trained to lie down on command. They were used to set birds for a net; hence, they had to learn to lie flat so as not to get in the way of the net and interfere with the birds. Consequently, this particular type of animal will not ordinarily exhibit an avoidance reaction when threatened; he will simply drop down and freeze. Incidentally, the literature contains many reports of studies in which a small number of animals with special genetic constitutions were used; the conclusions could not, of course, be general.

METTLER: The issue arising from these examples is motivation. If the stimulus is extremely strong, so that the response is not in the liminal region, I should think that it would be an essentially different situation than one in which the motivation had to be strong to maintain the response. A situation which presents a threat to the animal in respect to his security, indeed his very existence, is a very strong motivation. These problems are directly related to clinical psychiatry. But how are they related?

WHITEHORN: The "psychodynamic" clinician, sometimes to an almost fantastic degree, carries out much of his thinking about patients in terms of their presumed motivation. Recently the experimenters have moved more and more in the direction of studying motivation; hence, this is one possible ground in which common territory and common assumptions might be developed. They differ appreciably, however, in their approach. The experimenter usually controls motivation or tries to set up certain motivations by deprivation or accentuation of need. In contrast, the clinician infers motivation (I will not say how; I will say that he does) in trying to come to an understanding of how it exists in a person. Perhaps for special reasons he may do a certain amount of experimentation by trying to set up motivations by one way or another. To some extent this enters into his psychotherapeutic maneuvers and motivates what is social behavior. Some experiments have been done trying to get schizophrenic patients to cooperate in occupational therapy by giving them a piece of candy. By and large, when the clinician tries to arrive at motivational understanding of patients, he does it by means of cues. He infers motivation from cues; he arrives at a tentative notion; he sees where this should lead to types of behavior which would tend to verify or contradict the notion; then he looks for the cues to confirm this secondary hypothesis. By a series of such scrutinies, he considers that he has a good or a bad grasp of the motivation of the patient. Incidentally, I have not described this process as the clinician ordinarily describes it.

I suppose that the psychoanalysts have systematically operated by a scheme of presumed motivations more than any other school in psychiatry. Their process of using cues is complicated by the additional technic of batting these cues back and forth with the patient; hence, they work out a somewhat more elaborated statement which might be interpreted as a confirmation of the "guessed" motivations. The analyst catches his first intimation of the need or motivation from some notion of what some symbol might mean. By classical technic he is not supposed to comment very much on that but to wait for the patient to make further progress. This means that in time the patient will come out with a remark having emotional overtones, such as "I hate my mother" or "I was in love with my father," which is viewed as a confirmation of what was guessed at in the symbolization.

I would consider it something of an advance if the clinical psychiatrist could talk more practically about the cues, the motivations; but it is not done as a rule clinically. He talks about them in terms of interpretation. It has occurred to me that the animal experimenter might shed light on the matter. He has experimental control of the situations and might have an additional means of checking how reliable certain cues are.

SCOTT: When the representative animal experiments are reviewed, one of the factors that seems to be present in all of them is a high degree of motivation. For example, there is the animal with fear which results either from training or from immediate stimulation. It should be possible to identify the motivation much more accurately in animal subjects than in human beings, although it is not always easy. Take one question: Why does a young puppy cry when it is removed from its litter mates? It seems to be a very drastic emotional experience for a young puppy, which is possibly related to separation in human infants. It is not absolutely easy to figure out exactly what is involved in this situation because it might be the separation from the litter mates, from the mother, or from the immediate environment of the nest box. From our present studies it would appear that what the puppy is crying about depends on its age. But it is not always obvious what the animal is reacting to.

To return to the larger subject of the Conference, I believe that the broad approach to the problem of mental disease has merit. Different people coming to the problem with special points of view, trying out different theoretical ideas, and using a different terminology may each produce something new and valuable. They are equally likely to produce confusion in a way that is illustrated by the old story of the blind man and the elephant. A very large subject approached from a specialized point of view may yield particular results which may be valid for that particular point of view. But if the approach is from another aspect, an entirely different set of results may be obtained. Different investigators may be dealing with entirely different phenomena.

Then, there is the difficulty or lack of communication. Two workers in different fields may be talking about the same thing and just not understand each other's language. Finally, in many instances there may be a natural but indirect connection between two apparently different findings; the connection perhaps lies in a basic unknown phenomenon which affects both. From the point of view of basic research, one is impressed by the large amount which yet remains to be done. In some cases there will be no real convergence of viewpoints until the basic research is done so that the true relationship between the phenomena can be recognized.

WHITEHORN: At the Conference last November someone expressed a desire that the person who had presented the psychodynamic point of view might translate it into terms which the experimentalist could check by his methods. This is a reaction which is shared by others.

SCOTT: It sounds sensible but it does not necessarily have to be done by the psychodynamicist. It might perhaps be done in other ways. Of course, there may be certain phenomena that cannot be translated into other fields. For example, animals are capable of thinking without use of words. They can solve quite complex problems; they can form habits and do many things which can only be called intelligent. It is likely that in the course of human evolution, the power to speak and use words is not substituted for the old power of learning without words, but rather added to it. This brings up the possibility that in the human individual there are two kinds of learning: one which has nothing to do with words, and another which is closely associated with words. Furthermore, these two processes may perhaps conflict with each other. That is a problem which can be studied only in an indirect way with animals which do not talk. Some comparisons can be made. The part of the mind which can learn without words might be equated to the "id" of Freud. It is true that it may be impossible to try out certain parts of psychodynamics on animals, but there are real possibilities with other parts of it. For example, the idea of identification would come from the psychodynamic school.

WHITEHORN: Yes, I should think that it would, at least so far as it had to do with motivation.

SCOTT: Identification might be related to a phenomenon noted in basic animal studies. This phenomenon, which is of great interest at the present time in animal behavior, is the process of socialization. In almost all highly social species, there is some mechanism by which the young animal learns that one kind of individual is his kind, that he is attached to that kind; and that other individuals, not necessarily of different species, are not his kind. This phenomenon of socialization, or forming special social relationships with certain individuals, could be very closely related to the phenomenon of identification. Probably it should be studied in various species of animals because the evidence so far indicates that the mechanisms by which it is produced seem to differ from species to species.

WHITEHORN: You have illustrated by your comment what I think is a somewhat different view of the matter. Instead of demanding of the exponent of the psychodynamic view that he do the task of outlining for you the meanings of his terms in your universe, you seem to be prepared to seek to understand something of what he is talking about, and to find there some possible points of correspondence with phenomena in animals. It is indeed an unusual experience not to have the psychoanalyst blamed for not speaking another specialist's language.

KING: I believe that the psychodynamic group is under some responsibility to translate its language into the terms of other groups. It is possible for some scientists of widely different disciplines to talk to one another. No matter how uninformed a psychologist may be about biology or chemistry, when he talks to members of those fields, there is enough basic similarity in approach so that there is no problem of communication. The sociologist seems to have no difficulty in understanding the psychodynamicist, perhaps because of their common problems. Yet they do not seem to be able to talk back and forth with other disciplines, particularly when the language is more in Freudian and neo-Freudian psychoanalytic terminology than in that of one of the other constructs, such as the adaptational framework of Rado. The latter, for example, can be much more translatable for psychology and physiology than are any of the Freudian concepts. But with clinical psychiatry centering more and more in private practice, rather than in university clinics, the psychoanalytic hypotheses and language have come to be vested in a rather special group with a vocabulary of its own. Admittedly it was hard to put Freud's ideas to test by other methods, but at least he made sense. That is not true of modern cults with their jargon. Indeed it is worse than jargon, for their words and meanings do not have firm acceptance among themselves. Take their talk about something reverberating off a cathexis; that is not just the use of a phrase to represent ideas that mean something to a special group. Even among the group that invented it, there is no common agreement about it. Thus it becomes almost impossible for someone on the outside to clear it up.

WHITEHORN: The "naturalized citizen" in the psychoanalytic group with the typical Freudian way of speaking undergoes a very considerable preparatory training to enable him, through personal experience, to know the limitations of the jargon and the jargonic hypotheses. Without this personal guidance and experience, the language might not only be jargon but also very deceiving. That leaves the psychoanalyst in the difficult situation of trying to make meaningful communications with others when the connotations and implications of his verbal terms are so strongly colored by years of individual experience. How can his experience be attached to the words in such a manner as to constitute a meaningful communication. This is, I think, one of the major problems. If it were possible to formulate such a dynamics with somewhat less of the hypothesis and to work out some of the more misleading implications of the terms, this might be a help in making communication more intelligible. For not only would the propositions be understood, but the assumed implications carried by the terms would also be nearer to what would be really acceptable.

KING: The common term "acting out" is a perfect example. What is meant by it? If it is believed that fantasy is the reality, then acting out is simply how fantasy manifested itself in behavior. If it is believed that behavior is reality, fantasy is just another antecedent by which behavior occurs.

WHITEHORN: Then there is also the term "unconscious fantasies" which complicates it.

SCOTT: Particular technics may be effective, even if not theoretically correct. For example, in early medicine certain herbs were found to have beneficial effects on certain diseases even though the reasons given might have been entirely incorrect.

WHITEHORN: On the basis of statistics, the evidence for effectiveness in operation is not very high for the psychoanalytic, as compared with other modes of treatment, for the mental patient. It is something on the order of 67 per cent to 72 per cent, plus or minus 8. It is a brave man who would make a distinction between the effectiveness of 67 or 72 per cent with an ambiguity of 8 per cent.

METTLER: The psychiatrist is under no obligation to translate his material into language which those in the field of medicine and science can understand. It is, of course, his privilege to remain incomprehensible. On the other hand, if he wants to communicate with others, particularly those in the experimental sciences, it is useful for him to separate objective evidence from interpretation. There is no reason why he should not interpret the descriptive material; but his observations and interpretations should be separated and labeled. In practice, the two become easily mixed. And they do have different values. The facts may be correct, but the interpretation wrong. Then the facts are apt to be unwarrantedly rejected. If the facts are correct about a new, simple and effective therapy, few care about the theory.

WHITEHORN: A number of times I have been surprised, the first few times I was astonished, in my talks with neurophysiolo-gists to note the complete self-assurance with which they indicated to me that they too were doing work which undoubtedly had psychiatric implications. Their observations were important in physiology; but whether the phenomena which they had been studying had anything to do with psychiatry, in reality they would not know. The attitude of the laboratorian seems to be that he is obliged to assume that what he is doing is relevant to psychiatry.

METTLER: By and large the average laboratory researcher in medical and biological science feels very unhappy to be forced into a situation of maintaining that the problem which he is investigating has practical application and particularly that it will be a contribution to the understanding and control of a disease. But he is asked, "What is the meaning of what you're doing? What relationship does it have to the general sphere of knowledge?" In our laboratory, we operate with a hypothesis which is becoming more or less formulated. We are looking for phenomena which have a frame of reference which might be medically, neurologically, or psychiatrically oriented, or phrased; but, of course, our fundamental interest is in the phenomena themselves. I do not think that the laboratorian has any business going out of his area, but such a position is untenable because of the way in which it is necessary to finance investigations in science in universities, especially medical schools. Practically every application for a grant-in-aid to support his research, forces the laboratorian to describe the practical aspects of his work. So he explains how his research has a bearing on a particular disease. (He hopes. Who knows? Maybe it will!) I would say that it is a situation into which the average laboratory man is forced.

WHITEHORN: There might be situations in which one or the other of the laboratory investigators might believe that he perceives relevance to psychiatry in his work.

METTLER: If he advances his ideas in a hypothesis, he should keep it distinct from his observations; just as I am insisting that the psychiatrists should draw that distinction. There is no reason why the laboratory man might not offer a hypothesis, clearly so labeled. Indeed, I have been so bold as to do this myself.*

WHITEHORN: There might even be something to be said in favor of it. In order to alert him to conceptual relevancy it would seem to be desirable that he have a somewhat better comprehension of what the psychiatrist is trying to do.

METTLER: He is in the same boat as the psychiatrist as far as keeping up with the times is concerned. However, everyone knows that the minute the laboratory man dares to bring forth any hypothesis about mental disease, he will run into trouble. He knows that he is going to open himself to authoritarian attack. He must either be a little foolish or very brave; the latter, in itself, is a variety of foolishness.

SCOTT: One of the difficulties that the laboratorian has with the clinician grows out of their different occupational training. The laboratorian, at least the psychologist, is a pure experimentalist and he has never learned to observe. The older school of biologists, now almost forgotten, were trained observers. There are still some naturalists who are trained to observe animals in the field. It is such scientists who have the most in common with clinicians. The clinicians are among the few trained observers left in the world. It is rather interesting that some of the work on animals which is most significant has been done by naturalists and observers who were not trained in laboratory science. I was thinking particularly of Konrad Lorenz' work on birds.

METTLER: It is a widespread misfortune. The same thing is happening in the clinic and among clinicians as is happening among experimentalists. The medical students are no longer being taught to inspect and observe. There is strong emphasis on manipulative procedures. Inspection and observation were once justifiable as a part of physical diagnosis. For various reasons they are disappearing.

WHITEHORN: Like other medical practitioners, the clinical psychiatrist faces a troublesome conflict. On the one hand, he makes decisions and takes actions, sometimes serious and basic actions, concerning

---

* METTLER, FRED A. Perceptual capacity. Psychiatric Quart., 1955, 29: 89–111.

patients. In order to perform this task with any comfort, he needs the inner assurance that his decision is right; that it is based on a good foundation. That need puts a high premium on believing what he believes. On the other hand, over the last century or more, medicine has become more and more scientific; hence, the medical practitioner is restricted as a scientist. If he is officially in the position of being a scientist, that is, if he holds a professorship in a medical school, he has a redoubled obligation to maintain the scientific point of view. And the first rule in the code of the scientist is not to believe, but to doubt. That is the dilemma of the psychiatrist. In one role, he has to believe; in the other, he has to doubt.

ADDENDA

METTLER: Diagnosis of disease rests upon a variable base. Depending on the disease, diagnosis is made sometimes on an etiological, sometimes on a symptomatical, and sometimes on a pathological basis. In psychiatry most of the diagnoses are made upon a symptomatological basis, although some are made otherwise.

FINESINGER: Can you give us examples?

METTLER: The diagnosis of general paresis is made on an etiological basis. The first observations are of a symptomatologic kind of behavior, described in terms of the international nomenclature system as a particular kind of reaction pattern. When the spinal fluid is shown to yield a positive reaction, which again might be an extremely remote derivative, the clinical impression is then amended to become a diagnosis, which now is precise. An example of a diagnosis on a pathological basis would be a psychosis due to manganese poisoning, in which definite areas of demyelinization are subsequently found in the brain. The etiology of the disorder might not be known until the evidence was obtained from the brain. A better example is Wilson's disease, hepatolenticular degeneration, in which psychotic phenomena may occur in an acute neurological disease and the diagnosis is based upon the pathology known to be associated with the latter.

FINESINGER: I think that we could reach

agreement over the different ways of making diagnoses. And I think that we could also reach agreement over their differential application. In some instances, the best that can be done is a symptomatic diagnosis. In others, additional bases of diagnosis are available. In short, there are various levels of diagnosis. The ideal situation is one in which a diagnosis can be made at all levels. Until that can be done, the clinician has to differentiate.

LIDDELL: One thing that impressed me at the First Conference was French's methodological point that a physician has a therapeutic task as well as an investigative task. Methodology enters into the consideration of these areas.

FINESINGER: There is always this problem: What is the methodology for operation in different areas?

I should like to emphasize the importance of the existence of psychological mechanisms, whether the person is aware of them or not. I should like to stress the importance of meanings, of taking material in context, of conducting both cross-sectional and longitudinal studies; for one does not take the place of the other. I believe that the term "psychodynamics" is unfortunate and misleading because it is really psychology in a special area of interest. To me it is psychoanalytic theory, and it is the best available theory. Its general models for describing the personality have been productive concepts.

But it has its shortcomings and difficulties. In my opinion the notion of studying the total personality with all of its factors is a myth. I believe that only certain factors are studied. What actually happens is that certain ideas take over. For example, an investigator may wish to study the verbal material taken down on a tape recorder in psychoanalysis, recognizing that it is only a segment of the material. This procedure arouses much opposition on the part of the professional analysts who will cite a number of variables which have not been taken into account although the experimenter is equally aware of them. This tenet that the investigator must study everything tends to inhibit exploration into many fields. It is also an interesting example of how belief in an idea or ideal may blind one in what he does.

To take another instance, a young analyst, in analyzing a patient, reports to his control analyst. The latter thinks that he knows much about the patient by merely hearing the account from the young analyst. If he has the material verbatim, he thinks that he knows more. He would be inclined to believe that he can learn or formulate enough from verbal productions alone actually to operate effectively in a situation and perhaps even obtain results. Yet he will say, "We have to study everything. The movie is not enough, sound is not enough, we must have the complete material." This example shows how adherence to an overall idealistic theory, which is, of course, impractical in terms of experimentation, may tend in the long run to inhibit productive work. Personally, I believe that this is the situation in which analysis is at the present time.

Another source of difficulty is that the psychodynamicist talks in terms of inferences as though the inferences were the raw data. Obviously that is not so. Yet in his defense it must be said that the material is elusive, difficult to record, and not easy to study. From the very beginning the psychodynamicist is engaged in trying to bring out material which is hard to obtain. The problems of working with the raw material of an analytic hour are equally difficult. Transcribing it, reading it, and studying it make it a laborious process. Sampling studies should be done to determine how much of this material, e.g., from free association, one needs in order to draw inferences from it.

I can understand the accusations of cliquishness, cultism, doctrinaire point of view, and rigidity, which are leveled against the psychodynamicists. Yet I think that their behavior is understandable in terms of their being highly motivated. This motivation usually may be traced back to an emotion linked with their own experience, that by knowing about psychodynamics they personally have been helped. It is, therefore, very difficult to have people who have been helped be objective about the subject.

As a result of his training analysis, the young psychiatrist becomes more sensitive, more interested in patients, and more observing of behavior phenomena. It is interesting that during the first years after a training analysis, the analyst sees mostly his own problems in all of his patients. Then gradually he begins to see their problems.

HOLLINGSHEAD: Granted that he might undergo training analysis and even undertake control analysis. But should he go on through three years of seminar and then become a fullfledged member of an analytic institute? In the long process there is an investment of time, energy, and money, and there is involvement of the ego; hence, inevitably, there is a large measure of defense to justify all the expenditure and all that has been done. When it comes to evaluating the effectiveness of analysis on patients it is little wonder the analyst tends to be defensive!

FINESINGER: In my opinion, both personal and control analysis are useful.

KRUSE: Why is it that the psychodynamicist prefers to search for unconscious motivations whereby it appears that he underrates or completely ignores conscious motivation?

FINESINGER: Because he believes that of the numerous factors operating to determine the various psychological reactions and in turn behavior, the conscious factors merely represent a segment of the total. Furthermore, the unconscious factors, unlike the conscious, are not amenable to change through experience.

KRUSE: Is it not possible that he has adopted an extreme position in his approach to motivation?

FINESINGER: I do not know the answer to that. But I know that my bias is in favor of present practice. For it has so often been the experience of a psychiatrist that after he has been able to have his patients ventilate and discuss their material, he has noted changes occurring in their conscious motivation without his ever having touched upon it.

KRUSE: I am not now underrating the unconscious; rather I am trying to have you bring out why the psychodynamicist places so much emphasis on the unconscious to the relative neglect of the conscious. Why does he not practice a comprehensive approach?

If he concerned himself equally with conscious motivation, might he not turn up something there?

FINESINGER: He might, but I would not count on it. There is no large prospect of finding something that would be of help for patients. This is my reasoning: A person who is well adjusted responds to reality situations quite appropriately. In contrast, a patient does not because situations are distorted to him in terms of his own projection. He reacts to these situations with all the meanings which he puts around them; hence, he does not react appropriately or realistically.

There is considerable clinical experience which bears upon both conscious and unconscious motivation. When one person does nothing more than develop a relationship with another, sometimes motivation changes. For example, when a boy falls in love with a girl, he shines his shoes and brushes his hair. Nobody told him to do that. He does it because he is in love. When he falls out of love, he stops combing his hair. In the therapeutic situation, the psychiatrist sees much of that type of relationship. In such instances, probably he is able to modify motivation on the conscious level. In the other kind of experience, the psychiatrist attempts to bring out unconscious material. He finds that when he is successful, changes occur in the conscious motivation. This is not to say that with some patients conscious processes might not be effective. Perhaps it might be worth while to take up the simpler things first and try at the start to modify conscious motivation by conscious processes.

KRUSE: That is my point. Regardless of the order, it would be a more comprehensive approach.

FINESINGER: The analyst would answer that there is enough experience with such an approach in neuroses and the psychoses to indicate that it does not work.

LIDDELL: Yet I know a clinical psychologist who regularly gets referrals from psychoanalysts of patients during their course of therapy. The analyst says that he has no time to invest further professionally, that it would be an unwise investment on his and his patient's part.

FINESINGER: I think that what actually happens in practice is that most analysts prefer to do psychoanalysis and nothing else, and doing psychoanalysis to most analysts means that they do not get involved in the current reality situations. That is the area where most problems come up; so, after having conducted the analysis, the analyst then prefers to have someone else, the clinical psychologist as you mention, take over. The analyst tends not to deal with the total mental problem. He deals with a very limited segment of it in a way which, from the point of view of society, is quite limited.

METTLER: If a theoretical psychiatric elaboration is advanced in a European culture, and transferred to a country like America, would you expect to find that the sociological differences in the communities would have an effect upon the validity of the theories?

HOLLINGSHEAD: I would, yes. It would also create another problem. It creates very definite problems for the sociologists, and perhaps also for the dynamic psychiatrist. If science is viewed as being universalistic, as giving universal principles that will hold in all times and places, the position that the anthropologist and sociologist take on the relativity of culture creates very definite limitations upon scientific generalizations.

FINESINGER: I would be inclined to believe that whether the sociological factors would be significant depends upon what is under consideration. In some of the dynamic mechanisms these factors might be, in others they would not be, significant. It may well be that sociological factors affect the superego functions or formations. In contrast to this, it may equally well be that they make no difference to repression, projection, or other specific psychological mechanisms. There is some evidence in the Korean material that combat increased the number of neuroses but had no effect on the incidence of schizophrenia. So far as the latter disorder is concerned, the incidence in soldiers seemed to be the same, whether they were living in New York or were out on the Korean battlefield.

HOLLINGSHEAD: I am not sure whether the psychological mechanisms and processes associated with superego formation would differ from culture to culture. But I would certainly think that the content would vary.

FINESINGER: I was using the term "formation" in the sense of the concept of the structure, not of what makes the superego develop.

HOLLINGSHEAD: The guilt sanctions, the definitions of shame and the like will vary.

KRUSE: To what extent, Dr. Finesinger, do you believe that schizophrenia yields to psychodynamic therapy? It has been said in the past that psychodynamics is most effective in the psychoneuroses, but is of little or no value therapeutically in schizophrenia. More recently, stronger claims that it is efficacious against this psychosis have been put forward.

FINESINGER: By "psychodynamics" I think that you mean an attempt at modifying behavior by the conventional, analytic method. I agree that it is being applied more and more in schizophrenia.

KRUSE: Are the claims that it is effective well substantiated?

FINESINGER: None of the claims is well substantiated. There are probably four or five psychiatrists in the country who can report on a series of patients. Rosen* has demonstrated that even very severely schizophrenic patients can modify their behavior.

But this issue goes back to Freud's theory that the schizophrenic patient is highly narcissistic; and that the symptoms are restitution phenomena, not defenses. During the last ten years, the thinking has changed considerably, as a result of the work of Fromm-Reichmann,† Rosen, and others.‡ I think that psychiatrists are now inclined to look upon the symptoms of schizophrenia as being essentially the same as those of neuroses insofar as they are defenses against anxieties. Hence, the psychiatrists orient their therapeutic approach in the same way that they would for any extreme form of defense mechanism.

---

* Rosen, John N. *Direct Analysis*. New York: Grune and Stratton, 1953. p. 184.

† Fromm-Reichmann, Frieda. *Principles of Intensive Psychotherapy*. Chicago: Univ. of Chicago Press, 1950. p. 235.

‡ Brody, E. B. and Redlich, F. C. (Eds.). *Psychotherapy with Schizophrenics*. New York: International Press, 1952. p. 246.

METTLER: It is fine to use analytic methods, dynamic methods, to study the processes of personality function and alteration. But even in the field of neuroses, has anyone brought forward convincing statistics to demonstrate that patients are positively and definitely influenced by psychotherapy?

FINESINGER: You are now introducing the subject of evaluation of psychotherapy, not only analytic, but all kinds of psychotherapy. Up to two years ago there were approximately thirty papers on evaluation in the literature. Among them were six follow-up studies of the work done by psychoanalytic institutes. But it would have to be admitted that there are probably no studies which would meet any reasonable criteria. So, to the question whether psychotherapy has been proved to have an effect on neuroses, the answer is *no*. That has not been proved. But there are attempts, at least, to plan studies that will provide evidence on the evaluation of therapeutic results. Recently a national committee of analysts contemplating such a project had difficulty in deciding the following questions: "What is meant by psychoanalysis?" "What are the operational factors?" "What is the type essential for psychoanalysis?"

The analyst, in trying to evaluate the effects of an analysis, may be off on the wrong course. Freud may have been right. He had tremendous faith in analysis as a scientific procedure to learn about things, but he did not have much faith in it as a therapeutic procedure. An analysis can have amazing consequences. I asked myself, What do all the patients who have been analyzed have in common, whether or not they show clinical improvement? In my opinion, they develop more humane attitudes, they are more tolerant of their fellow patients, and they have a greater appreciation of the many factors that enter into the determination of behavior. The big question becomes, Can they achieve this insight without analysis? But analysts have no real desire to test the point; it is almost as if they did not dare put the issue to test. It is not accidental that it took a committee so long to decide on what is analysis. Every analyst knew what an analysis is. But he was reluctant to subject the effectiveness

of the procedure to scrutiny. I believe that the effects of analysis could be evaluated. If the criteria were not disappearance of symptoms or changes in behavior, but rather changes in attitude, I would predict that a high correlation would be found between analysis and changes in attitude. I do not believe that such a positive correlation would be found with shock treatment, hypnosis, or efforts with conscious motivation.

At the present time the American Psychoanalytic Association is sending around to every analyst a questionnaire asking for detailed data on patients in analysis: the patients' symptoms, what the analyst did, what dynamics were involved, the nature of the follow-up and what it revealed.

As I go back over the list of patients whom I have had in analysis, I can think of three who, so far as could be judged by all applicable criteria, such as symptoms of intrapersonal and sexual adjustment, became really different persons.

METTLER: As you well know, that happens sometimes without therapy.

FINESINGER: No, it does not. That is the point. What happens in other situations is different. These three patients not only are better as judged by symptomatic criteria, but also have understanding and insight. They are now able, as a critical situation arises in their lives, to inspect the circumstances, to see what the precipitating factors are, to link the present with previous situations in their past history, and to find similarities or differences. That, the person who is cured by hypnosis cannot do; the person who is cured by shock therapy cannot do; or the person who spontaneously recovers cannot do.

METTLER: A considerable number of individuals forming a large proportion of the normal population have feelings of unreality, which are quite common at one period or another in their existence, especially in adolescence. Why is it that these people have not gone on to become psychotic?

FINESINGER: Nobody knows the answer to that. A schizophrenic mother may have one child who develops schizophrenia and another who remains normal. Why? There probably are two sets of factors operating in the social setting, those which make for stress, and those which tend to relieve the stress. It may well be that some people are fortunate enough to be in a social setting in which supporting factors are always operating to keep the reaction to stress from becoming pathological.

That is just a theory. But the fact remains that there are these episodic phenomena of a person becoming sick and then without any therapeutic help becoming better. The explanation would be that there are other factors operating in the social situation which in some way have supportive value and which inhibit and minimize the pathological process.

LIDDELL: I think "counterbalancing" would be a good word for this reaction.

FINESINGER: What happens in relationship therapy is that the relationship is a counterbalancing factor.

METTLER: You have been speaking to the question: Why does one person develop, and another not develop, schizophrenia? I asked: How does it happen that some people who are functioning in a normal society have had, up to a certain point in their lives, all the background history of a schizophrenic individual, but then have ceased to have any further symptoms or signs? These people are not discovered by the psychiatrists, as a general rule. It is my impression that there is a large number of them.

We find them in our studies under the following circumstances: In tests of illusion, such as the one which asks the subject to decide which arrow is longer, we found that the normal person usually makes a mistake; the frankly schizophrenic usually does not. When we had this information, we tried to check its validity by conducting the same tests on the staff personnel. We found that some of the personnel were not fooled by the illusion tests. As we went into their backgrounds, we found, furthermore, that at one or another time in their lives they had had impressions that the heads of other people were expanding and contracting, or they had had strange dreams. These episodes do not bother them. Perhaps the process has not gone very far. In some cases these aberrant experiences had occurred

when these people were much younger and in the past fifteen years had not recurred.

Obviously there are a number of people who have traveled just so far down the road to imbalance and have gone no farther. This is a different phenomenon from the question you have been posing, notably, "Why does mental illness occur in one person and not in another?"

KRUSE: Your account of abortion, arrest, or spontaneous reversal of mental pathology is an example of a general biological pattern, because it happens in many other diseases. Furthermore, frequently the disease does not emerge above a subclinical level before it later disappears.

FINESINGER: Sometimes the reversal or abatement comes overnight, like a crisis with lysis. For example, I had a patient who attached sexual significance to rubbing his hands, and thought that the other patients were plants put there to observe him. One morning, after two weeks in the hospital, he said: "I am all right now. Last night, all of a sudden, it occurred to me that this is all nonsense. Now when I rub my hands, it is just that. And now patients are just patients, not plants." His attitude toward many things had changed overnight. I told the resident: "If you could find out what happened last night, you would be a leading candidate for the Nobel Prize."

METTLER: In the history of medicine it may be noted that symptoms are often only loosely and uncertainly associated with one or more diseases, until an apparently irrelevant discovery pulls them together into a unit and provides perspective. For example, in the past there was considerable question whether cardiac dysfunction belonged among the symptoms of syphilis because it occurred at such a remote period from the initial infection. With development of a test for syphilis, its symptomatology was more precisely organized and the etiologic significance of the spirochete in many cardiovascular disorders was firmly established.

This is my point on the subject of value. When those of us who are not primarily psychiatrists talk about mental disease, we are not so concerned with the organization of the personality of the individual. We are really concerned with the possibility of whether we can find a quick, simple and inexpensive method of maintaining people in a state of mental efficiency, if necessary by means of a drug. Our interest is to find some effective way to manipulate the processes of psychosis so that they cease to be practical problems.

Let us suppose someone got up during the coming Conference and said: "Now look, gentlemen, all of this is a waste of time, because I have recently synthesized a drug which can be marketed for fifteen cents a vial, and everybody to whom I give this drug becomes completely *compos mentis*. Furthermore, those with subnormal mentality can go to school and produce a uniform type of performance." That would be the end of the Conference.

Lacking such a fifteen-cent remedy, we are forced to think about, and work with, the problem and ultimately find ourselves in much the same position as does a psychoanalyst. The investigator ponders over what has been happening and undertakes an independent evaluation of the processes in which personality shifts and enters into interrelations. Momentarily, at least, the investigator is no longer concerned with, and is forced to lose sight of, his original goal of a quick, simple, and inexpensive remedy. He becomes a descriptive scientist, much like an anatomist dissecting a body, and has to describe where this part goes and what happens to that part. There has been a shift in values.

I do not know anything about psychoanalysis. The whole thing is a mystery to me. I perceive only that there are specialists who are trying to discover the way in which things happen to people. Therefore, I can only believe that insofar as these analysts are serious, industrious, and reasonable, they bring forth independently valuable and valid data.

However, if what is important depends only on the individual person's frame of reference, it greatly narrows his field of authority and may lead to unfortunate consequences. To an administrator it may be important that mental patients be discharged from institutions in the interest of saving money. He may little realize the difficulties that will be created for their families. Likewise, the notion that the chemist will solve dementia praecox presupposes a personal judgment of values.

LIDDELL: Perhaps the concept of reductionism should be introduced. It expresses the value judgment that as the more basic level is reached, the problem becomes more significant.

FINESINGER: It is true that an administrator may want to get mentally ill people out of the hospital without knowing very much about what has been taking place inside them. But surely there should be an opportunity for study, to try to understand what the processes are. With that understanding, the probabilities are that much better ways would be found to accelerate the recovery of the mentally ill, if not to prevent the illness.

Without doubt, we have to clarify our values. It seems to me that as a representative of the psychodynamic approach I have a certain value as a scientist. I want to find out what is going on in the schizophrenic patient: the psychological and physiological or chemical factors. My desire arises from the belief that I will then be able to treat the patient much more effectively, perhaps prevent hospitalization.

METTLER: What you are saying, then, is that you are doing as much in solving dementia praecox as is the chemist. What I want to abolish is the notion that in some way or other the activity of the chemist is a priestly one.

HOLLINGSHEAD: You are opposed to the idea that there is a single cause and cure, and that it is chemical!

FINESINGER: There is a difference between curing and solving the problem. In order to solve the problem of the schizophrenic patient it is necessary to explain his thinking and behavior. For example, why does a patient say that all the other patients in the ward are trees? Until that can be explained the problem is not solved.

HOLLINGSHEAD: My earlier comment is relevant, that we are really considering disordered processes rather than diseases in which there are observable lesions.

FINESINGER: Are lesions the distinctive and qualifying characteristic of a disease?

The present trend in psychiatry is away from the idea of disease and toward reaction types of behavior.

METTLER: To return to the belief of some investigators that a chemical is going to solve or cure schizophrenia, I would agree with Dr. Finesinger that it will not solve the problem. That will be solved only when it is understood and can be manipulated.

HOLLINGSHEAD: What you are saying, then, is that to solve the problem would be to know the origin, the processes of development, and the cure; to be able to explain all the details.

METTLER: That is the scientific attitude.

FINESINGER: To find a cure for mental illness would be a wonderful contribution. But it would not be the solution to the disease. To cure the disease is, of course, the primary objective. That it may not be worth the time and money to find the solution is a legitimate point of view. But surely finding the solution would allow a more intelligent and broader approach to the prevention and conquest of the disease.

chapter 22

Outline of Critical and Decisive Studies with a Multidisciplinary Approach on Causation of Mental Disease

• •

KRUSE: In the three previous team meetings, the first covered areas of acceptance among the different disciplines; the second, areas of unacceptance; and the third, clinical principles in the practice of psychiatry. The topic for today is the outline of critical and decisive studies with an interdisciplinary approach on causation of mental disease. In the language of Churchill, Where is the "soft underbelly" of this problem? How can the different branches of the forces be unified for a combined attack? Dr. Gerard, how do you visualize that a multidisciplinary approach might be made?

GERARD: The most important dichotomy in approach between the natural scientist and the mental scientist is in the difference between energy theory and information theory. The neurophysiologist and neurologist as organicists have approached the problems of the functioning of the nervous system from the standard matter-energy aspect. What is required to build a new impulse? What are the substances formed or used? The mental scientist has been concerned with the nervous system and its manifestations in terms of information or communication. He is interested, not in what the mechanism of nerve impulse

propagation or synaptic transmission is, but in how information is carried and what kinds of networks are involved. Indeed, cybernetics is the contribution of special interest for psychodynamics.

These two phases are obviously in no way mutually contradictory or exclusive. They are both perfectly valid facets of an approach to a total problem. The reason that there has been extremely little cross-over at more than a superficial level is the basic differences in language. If the problems of the nervous system were to be considered in terms of both communication and energy theory, it would be an extremely useful and fertile approach for the future.

WITTKOWER: About nineteen months ago we started an interdisciplinary group at McGill, with representation from the Departments of Psychology, Sociology, Social Psychology, Medicine, Social Work, and Psychiatry. At first we simply could not understand each other. It was quite impossible to find a common platform on the basis of semantics; hence, we just came together and talked to each other. As time went on, we gradually understood each other; and we have now reached a point where we can discuss problems. For several months we have discussed the problem of family from each representative point of view.

I want to ask Dr. Gerard whether he agrees with the following statement in Dr. Jasper's exposition on "The Organic Viewpoint on Mental Disease": "Immediate and repeated environmental stresses of sufficient severity, depending upon the constitutional stability and past history of the organism, may be sufficient causes for what is termed neurotic behavior, though definitions of what is to be called neurotic behavior may vary and may be conditioned by social standards. Experimental neuroses in animals under controlled conditions make it possible to investigate such phenomena by objective 'biological' methods."

GERARD: I would think so. Would you disagree?

WITTKOWER: I could not accept it.

The definition of behavior, as formulated by the psychologist is likewise unacceptable. B. F. Skinner* states, in essence, that behavior is what an organism is doing or what it is observed to be doing. As an analyst, I find it very difficult to accept this definition, that behavior is what can be seen.

SPENCE: The process is fundamental with behavioristic psychologists. Dr. Skinner and I are fairly close in this respect; we agree that the only thing that the scientist can talk about is something he can observe, measure, and record by objective means. This, of course, includes the speech of the organism. He specifies what behavior is in terms of his operational definitions, which include his measuring devices. What else is there for a scientist to observe?

WITTKOWER: The basic difference between the psychological and the psychoanalytic groups is over attention to emotions. I was glad to hear that you include speech, because my impression was, on the basis of Dr. Skinner's definition, that he does not include speech.

SPENCE: That is observable. I can record it and listen to it. I do not look at it, but I do hear it through a sense. From my point of view, all science begins with the sense

perceptions of the observing individual scientist; these are observable and recordable phenomena. In the case of emotion there are overt symptoms, overt aspects of the behavior; and there are recordable, neurophysiological phenomena.

SCHNEIDER: Can the point be put this way: You can hear what the subject says, but sometimes you cannot see what he says?

SPENCE: All I do is record what he says, merely to discover relationships between the observations.

WITTKOWER: That is the difficulty, because the psychodynamicist would say that emotions are not synonymous with the vegetative activity, central or peripheral mechanisms.

GERARD: Over this point there really is no difference between the different disciplines. I am sure that the analyst, just as the psychologist or physiologist, deals with observables, as far as his information about the subject is concerned. He knows nothing about the person on the couch except what he can observe. The analyst does much inferring from his observations. So do all of us. And in these inferences we may get to different places; but you, no more than anyone else, can go beyond sensory experience as the starting point.

WITTKOWER: That is true enough, but we take into account intrapsychic processes. That associative word "feeling" connotes to me "feel," which is something subjective and is not necessarily observable and measurable.

SPENCE: You are referring to the feeling in the patient?

WITTKOWER: The feeling in the patient.

SPENCE: He, of course, conveys this to you through some sense channel of yours, which typically is verbal processes. I assume that the verbal statements of the patient are primarily the source of information for the psychoanalyst or psychiatrist.

WITTKOWER: That is right.

SPENCE: You begin with them, then you start to build inferences, or introduce theoretical concepts, or—in my terminology—interrelate the observed verbal processes of the subject.

I must say that in reading through the four papers presenting the different view-

* Skinner, B. F. "Descriptive Behaviorism," in *Psychological Theory*, M. H. Marx (Ed.). New York: Macmillan, 1951, p. 439.

points and approaches, much to my surprise the only one with which, I thought, the experimental psychologist had much in common was that of Dr. Alexander on the psychodynamic position. For example, I was amazed to see the extent to which psychoanalysts have suddenly discovered the field of learning. At least, Dr. Alexander has an excellent discussion of it. I disagree about many of the details; for instance, as to the motivations and reinforcements. But that the particular things in which the experimental psychologist is especially interested should receive much attention in the psychoanalytic presentation indicates rather remarkable progress.

GERARD: Dr. Wittkower seemed to suggest that one difference between the analyst and the psychologist is that the former is willing to look at the internal aspects, the feelings, in addition to the observables. I question whether this is a difference. I think that the psychologist looks at these phenomena just as much as does the analyst. But the psychologist may be a little more skeptical about how he uses these observations. The psychogalvanic reactions, the vascular changes, the hair erection, or any one of the motor manifestations that a rat gives in the presence of a cat, these he would not call fear reactions or emotions, except as he, like the analyst, is extrapolating from his own inner awareness of what his experiences are when these things happen to him.

WITTKOWER: Dr. Skinner specifically states, " . . . psychology is concerned with recording and measuring human behavior and its various aspects, and with relating the quantities so measured to variables in the past and current environment." According to this definition, the psychologist is predominantly concerned with recording and measuring.

SPENCE: Dr. Skinner is known as the empiricist of psychology, and I agree with him that observation is the beginning point. All science begins with observed phenomena; then, as it develops with technics of quantifying and specifying these phenomena, it begins to attempt to discover empirical relationships between the factors, the variables. Dr. Skinner has a tendency not to

want to introduce any kind of theoretical concept.

I would thoroughly agree with the statement which you read from Dr. Skinner's exposition, except that it does not go far enough. I believe in being a little rash about introducing hypotheses. However, my feeling about many of the psychoanalytic concepts is that they bring in words, terms, and ideas which are not grounded in empirical definitions. The analysts tend rather to introduce ideas in terms of their own phenomenological experience. This practice can oftentimes become highly biased. In the particular culture in which Freud was operating, he greatly overexaggerated one particular motivation system. Many of the more recent psychoanalysts have been tending to correct that overemphasis.

SCHNEIDER: When we consider the extent to which there is a recognition that measurement in certain respects has more limitations than do perceptions, which many psychodynamically oriented clinicians claim to experience; and when we take up the question of whether these perceptions are or can be empirically verified, it is precisely at this juncture that we tend to go on the rocks. I agree with Dr. Gerard that there is every reason to keep the peace among us. But I am not certain that I would like to sacrifice communicability for peace.

SPENCE: When you say that there are considerations other than measurement, I am not quite sure of your position. I recognize that everything does not have to be quantitative, and that we can deal with a scaled set of values—I mean values in the sense of numerals for which we have a fine measuring scale. But as a behaviorist, I could not agree that there did not have to be some specification of the conditions of observation.

SCHNEIDER: On that there is agreement. We all try to specify the conditions. But what some of us will accept as satisfactory specifications, at least for the time being, others will simply refute. The latter will say, "There is no place to start. There is not sufficient specification." Very different action consequences flow from the different standards which we would accept as sufficient to enable us to go ahead and act. That is, the experimental psychologist will not go ahead and act on a variable that the analyst says is important.

GERARD: The limitation on acceptability of specifications is not philosophical or basic. For example, everyone will at once admit that he can recognize a friend a block away. Everyone will also admit that it is quite impossible for him to specify the sensory clues whereby he makes the identifications. Isn't this essentially the issue? This is not a theoretical difference between disciplines; rather it is a matter of practical intelligence, of what the investigator is willing or unwilling to stand for.

But this point is quite different from what you said prior to it. That was exactly at the center of a possible serious disagreement. May I phrase my understanding of the two statements which you made so that we may be sure that we are talking about the same thing? The one was that certain phases of nature are not and cannot be practically quantifiable. The other was that they are not potentially quantifiable. Do any of us really believe that there are certain parts of nature that are inherently not quantifiable, that is, therefore outside the scope of natural science?

WITTKOWER: I would find it very difficult to visualize the libido or the unconscious processes as quantifiable. They are not measurable. This does not in any way repudiate the very valuable work which has been done by experimental psychology in the borderline fields.

GERARD: That is going to get us right to the heart of the issue.

SCHNEIDER: The question of decisive experiments turns on this issue; the decisive studies should be in the area where measurement is least relevant. We have only a very vague idea of what the critical variables are. We now seem to be in the stage of agreeing that we ought to work together, but not knowing what precisely to do. To the extent that some of us would be willing to work on potentially measurable but at the moment impracticable variables, to the same extent others are simply unwilling to start from this point. On the crucial problems now facing us, we have some

vague ideas that both the kinds of symptoms and the rates of symptoms differ from culture to culture and from subculture to subculture. Whether the fundamental dynamics are the same for a very specific symptom is a fundamental question. In my opinion the analyst and the anthropologist are quite willing to collaborate to some degree on problems of this sort. The experimental psychologist says, "You give me a measurement on which I can lay my instruments, and then I will tackle it." But he is rather unwilling just to take the mud in his hands and feel around for something.

SPENCE: I would not agree with that. But I am now talking completely out of my usual field of discourse because what I deal with is measurable. Here I am trying to take the role of the clinical psychologist as he would enter into this with his traditional training and experimental approach.

I would put it this way: There are scaling and measuring devices. The investigator can identify patterns by names, and then he can count. Counting is a fairly simple procedure. What I would insist upon is that there be a specification, so that one counter can be sure that he is counting the same thing as another counter.

SCHNEIDER: It is precisely at the level before counting that I meant. I am not sure whether we really know where to start counting, or what to start to count. We are at the level of just simply trying to make as shrewd a guess as possible of what the variables are like.

SPENCE: At this point, you must specify what you mean by variables.

SCHNEIDER: It is at this point that we always break.

GERARD: I had the pleasure of participating with a multidisciplinary group which met one day every week for two years. Its composition was broader than that of the group mentioned by Dr. Wittkower. Having spent the first year learning to talk with each other, we spent the second year really seriously trying to learn how far we could go in formally creating an intellectual approach which hopefully would be valid across the disciplines which are dealing with basically similar phenomena.

Most of the participants from the social

area had trouble with the rigorous formulations. When the formulations were reduced to the symbols of mathematics, they began to have trouble with the language; but most of them overcame all that.

Having formulated the logical models—what would be the consequences of this or that assumption, of logistic growth, of a fixed ratio of interaction—we then got exponents from the various disciplines to provide examples to which these might apply. It was easy to find examples in all the areas, but when it came to specifying how one would attack a situation operationally, it became clear that there was a great amorphous mass and a great obscurity.

A specific example in the sociological realm was to follow the interaction of a man and a woman, a husband and wife, in a primitive society where the wife controls the property but the husband normally is the boss. The question was, What would be the change in their interrelations if the property rights of the wife were suddenly abolished? What things would be looked for to identify the dynamic changes?

What distressed me was that in every one of these cases, even in the sociological area, it was not the social scientist but the natural scientist who came up with the suggestion of concrete observations for variables. I submit that this indicates, not a difference in the inherent character of the subject, but rather a difference in the kind of approach which is customary in the different areas.

SCHNEIDER: The problem here is really the question of strategy. We all say that what we would like to do is to start with a problem. We try to specify that problem as explicitly as we can. It is at this point that the strategy becomes apparent. We can start with the given problem; assume that we know something about it; bring forth a series of more or less loose, unsystematized, crude ideas; and then proceed to pick out the measurable, the operationally defined, what we presume to be the critical variables. It is precisely in this area that we really know least about mental disease. We have not been able to establish any kind of systematic, effective scheme of classification of mental diseases that has lasted for more

than ten or fifteen years. Also, we do not have the faintest idea whether schizophrenia is the same from city to city and from culture to culture. No one has really given any careful attention to this problem. Once the initial hunches and guesses, which have to be recognized and accepted almost at the level of intuition, can be worked through to some extent, a systematic attempt at verification can be made.

If this is basically accepted strategy, the problem is not to bring four of us together, but rather to ascertain at what point in any experiment each discipline becomes critically relevant. I think that the anthropologist and the analyst would be very happy to go ahead and explore, each in his own peculiar way, such borderlines and phenomena.

SPENCE: You mention intuition and hunches. The investigator has to start with something. I am talking about the something that the hunches and the intuitions play with. I am talking about what the investigator sees with his eyes and hears with his ears, and his ways of bringing some kind of organization into that. To bring about organization, he has to begin with everyday language; he has the concepts of everyday language. He begins to observe that one thing is related to another—he does see these relationships to some extent; and he begins to form new patterns of things that go together. Long before the intuition and the hunches come, there has to be organization of observable events identified as a concept. At that point the investigator does not have to be quantitative; he can count, and measurement is nothing but complicated counting.

SCHNEIDER: It seems to me that you are squeezing the time periods very closely here. I am trying to spread them out. At this point it seems to me essential that psychoanalytic psychology ought not to be asked to do what you are asking. For it takes more than six months, perhaps two years, to begin to establish even the hunches. I am talking about a far earlier period.

GERARD: That is where I would disagree. To make this a very sharp issue, I would suggest that psychoanalysis has begun to sin within the last decade or so in that potentially it now could go beyond the "hunch" stage; yet most of the practitioners of the art and the very few investigators of it as a science are on the whole not only making no effort to make the next step, but are perhaps even convinced that it is unmakeable.

I would like to come back to Dr. Wittkower's statement that the psychic forces potentially cannot be observed and quantified.

WITTKOWER: To clarify that point, I thought that I said that certain psychic forces cannot be objectified and measured; of course, others can be.

I feel that there is a marked overlap of the psychodynamic field with learning theory, and that a very useful cooperation can be brought about. At McGill, the Department of Psychiatry has very close contact with the Department of Sociology; the very fact that a project has emerged from the cooperation indicates how close it has been. In fact, I would say that psychiatry in the past has underrated, or even disregarded, the importance of social forces; and I am convinced that close cooperation with sociologists will enlighten psychiatry.

As regards physiology, I am all in favor of cooperation but I feel that the time has not yet come to bring about what Rohrer calls a coordinating definition. I do not think that we have reached that stage. But that time may well come; Freud actually forecast its occurrence.

How to go about cooperation is a practical matter. There are several ways of doing it: The principle of the Leighton study is that two disciplines work in parallel and never meet. Personally, I do not regard this as a very helpful procedure. The second possibility is a parallel study with continual intercommunication and exchange of observations, which is difficult.

We have decided on a study in which the two disciplines go ahead and meet at nodal points and interchange observations, and it is still doubtful to us whether this is the wisest procedure.

GERARD: May I press you to discuss further this point of unmeasurables? I regard it as a critical point.

SPENCE: It is to me, too. Let me give an example in a learning theory. Dr. Wittkower has said that there is no possibility of quantification of the libido. In the formulation which I seem to have inherited from Hull, there is a concept known as D for "drive." Hull has likened D to the libido. We quantify D by means of the equation: $D = f \ Td$ where Td is time of deprivation, e.g., food deprivation. Combined with the learning factor, H, which is defined as a function of number of trials $(H \propto fN)$, the concept of excitatory potential E is introduced, i.e., $E = H \times D$. I should have identified this concept of E with libido. Thus, E is quantified. It is not measured but it is quantified.

This operation is typical of physical science. Physicists deal with energy, which is equal to MV^2. Nobody ever measures energy directly; it is calculated by means of a formula. Similarly, by calculation D is quantified in terms of the number of hours of deprivation and number of experiences in that situation. From this we go on to make predictions about quantified behavior by means of another functional relationship. I have entered into detail about quantification without measurement of a particular item because I felt it was not being understood.

I would insist that libido could be quantified in this sense. Let us say that we could begin to specify certain early childhood influences, e.g., parental. At least we could talk about them in terms of "more" or "less"; we could think of more and less of three or four properties. Then, taking a combination of A, B, and C, we could say that here is an individual who has more A, more B, or more C, than that possessed by some other individual. With different amounts of these influences in the past history, we could say that there is more of this or that now in one individual than in another. That is all I mean by "quantification."

WITTKOWER: In talking about this, we talk about strength of ego, and strengths of impulses.

SPENCE: That is right.

WITTKOWER: But when it comes to actual quantification. . . .

SPENCE: This is all I mean by quantification.

GERARD: On this question of measurables and quantification, I would agree with Dr. Wittkower that just putting measurement in terms of more or less is not good enough.

In my opinion Dr. Alexander has made a good, clear presentation of the psychodynamic position. But the part of it which I would criticize is the very point that has now come up. Dr. Alexander makes a nice equation, and it looks as if he is quantifying something. He states that there is metabolic energy which is used for maintenance and growth, and what is left over is for activity. When there is much left over, it makes for play and libidinous energy. Then he goes on to say that the greater the surplus energy, the more there is for libidinous activity. In the sense of seeming to be an equation, this is, to put it bluntly, nonsense, for the following reasons: In the first place, every organism adjusts its intake to its needs; it does not have any kind of a fixed intake, which then spills over with excess energy. Secondly, the energy involved in physiological activity, such as the physical energy of exercise or work, is primarily in the muscles. This is physiology, not psychiatry or psychoanalysis.

If the term mental energy is to be used, then I think it is highly desirable to see exactly what is meant by that concept of operation. For the term has been taken over with many of the overtones of physical energy, and they do not belong there. Energy in the sense that the physicist or the biologist would use the term would not have cathexis associated with it. Energy does not become bigger and bigger because it is not expended. Physiologically, this is not happening in the nervous system. There is not a piling up of glycogen as an energy source. There might be a piling up of impulses running around re-entrant circuits and therefore building up excitation until something explodes; but there is no evidence of this and, if it does exist, it is very different from energy.

Actually the psychodynamicists have a perfectly meaningful concept in the building up of excessive energy, but what they refer to is not energy. It gets us nowhere to say that this phemonenon is something

measurable; therefore, let's call it "energy" and be done with it. We are going to make real progress in characterizing this concept if we will get together, as we are doing here, and discuss it until we can find out exactly what is meant. Then maybe I can say, "Look, the word you want for this in terms of my discipline is so-and-so." Maybe energy means active circuits or synchronized neuronal beats.

SPENCE: I think that I could trace through Dr. Alexander's exposition and find what is related to what and be able to make statements about something which is varying in a rough manner of "more or less." It is the words that he uses which mislead us; the metaphors lead us astray because we have our connotations for them. We go off the track at this particular point.

GERARD: I am sure that you are right, for I have often talked with Dr. Alexander and did not find myself reacting in this way. He has used a different framework for expression here.

WITTKOWER: It is true that the experimentalist is observation-minded and the psychiatrist of necessity is action-minded and therapy-oriented. Therapy is part of the latter's job.

As for the hunches and guesswork, I should like to raise the question, What is meant by verification? To give a concrete example, an obsessional patient is found to be afraid of doing harm to anybody and is afraid of contamination. True enough, our preconceived idea is that behind this defense is a streak of cruelty, to put it into simple terms; and that sooner or later she will bring out these hidden impulses, which she covers up by her defenses. Later, this patient, on the couch, brings out sadistic fantasies with tremendous anxiety. In our opinion this development is verification of our theoretical concept. Would you regard it as verification? Or is verification only what can be seen?

SPENCE: You saw this.

WITTKOWER: So you would accept it as verification?

GERARD: But not proof.

WITTKOWER: Proof of what?

GERARD: Not proof in the sense that we never prove any of our positive assertions.

SPENCE: It increases the probability of the theory.

SCHNEIDER: There is a point at which the question of verification becomes relevant; but it is not at the starting point, it is even later than most experts would place it. For example, it seems to me that the question of verification of the psychoanalytic assumptions is only beginning at this time to become relevant. Ten years ago when people started questioning the veracity of psychoanalytic assumptions, it was far too early and really in a sense constituted an attack on psychoanalysis almost irrespective of the questions at stake.

In respect to measurements, I believe that there are functional consequences of introducing notions of measurement—even such an elementary notion as simple counting—at too early a point. Insofar as it is rigorous, it tends necessarily to narrow the field of observation and consideration; and to focus upon a relatively more limited set of conditions and events at precisely the time that the widest horizon and field are desirable.

The anthropologists have been fascinated for many years by the relatively different rates of mental illness in the different societies. Actually, they have gone along assuming that there are different rates. There has been some empirical work which tends to support this assumption. If, at this point, they start measuring in very careful terms, they will immediately run into the problem of the diagnosis. Out of that will come the necessity to enforce again a set of rigorous conditions of measurements.

GERARD: But you have already introduced measurement, right at the start.

SCHNEIDER: In a very loose, vague, and generous way.

GERARD: No one is asking for more than that.

SPENCE: You have to specify at what you will nod your head "yes" or "no"; otherwise you will not nod.

GERARD: I would certainly agree that one could stultify the broad advance by getting too narrowly concerned with detail over measurement. This problem is really not too serious because most of the people who purport to do research, like sheep, follow fads, anyway; and they might as well be counting decimals. That fact is, I am sure, none the less true of psychiatrists than of physiologists.

In turning to the question of verification, I can put the matter in an antinomy. Freud's theories have, after a relatively long period of rejection, achieved very widespread acceptance. It seems to me that this acceptance must have been on the basis either of satisfactory verification or of religious conviction. Which was it? There must have been some basis that began to be visible to people who favor the theories.

WITTKOWER: That is what I was after. There is verification in clinical practice; that was why I gave the example of the obsessional patient. There is also verification in the experimental situation. I am extremely interested in these experiments; yet I believe that at the present stage they have not gone very far beyond what has been verified on the couch.

SPENCE: Miller's displacement study.

WITTKOWER: That shows something which everybody knows.

SPENCE: He considers it literally a verification of the hypothesis. But there is a distinction.

GERARD: I drew the distinction that this was verification but not proof because it seems to me that a very important next step has to be taken. The psychoanalysts were faced first with the necessity of convincing people who are not familiar with the field about the reality of the phenomena. This is now almost universally accepted.

They next have to convince people of the general validity of the interpretations. Perhaps the most convincing single bit of evidence that I know as justification of symbolic interpretations, as of dreams, is the well-known hypnosis experiment. A girl under hypnosis was told she had wet the bed, was now asleep and dreaming, and should describe her dream. The symbolic dream was told to another hypnotized girl and she promptly said it referred to bed-wetting. I believe there was no possibility of sophisticated acumen, in which case there would seem to be no way of accounting for this occurrence other than in terms of the psychoanalytically proposed meaning of dream symbolism.

Beyond that, I think one cannot go very far at this stage, because even so well and truly tried a mental construct, a theory, as Newton's picture of gravity can be shown to be a completely inadequate picture of the universe, when one or two more observations come along and Einstein's relativity concept supersedes it. Consequently, I would be extremely surprised if the present psychodynamic formulations, much less the original ones of Freud, remain for any great length of time the accepted theoretical concepts in this field. I think that there has been a certain unwillingness and failure on the part of analysts to make that examination and revision, to go back over the very basic intellectual constructs or hypotheses, and see whether there are other ways of putting the observations together.

WITTKOWER: It seems to me that you do two things at the same time: One, you say that many of the concepts have been so generally accepted that it is hardly necessary to prove them any further. Perhaps I am overstating that point.

GERARD: The phenomena.

WITTKOWER: Then you say in the next sentence that you believe that these accepted concepts and constructs will not stay, that they will be replaced. Unless I misunderstood you, this seems to me to be a contradiction.

GERARD: May I restate that point to be sure that my position is clear? The phenomena, I think, are accepted, and they are going to remain. New ones will be discovered. That certain experiences will be translated symbolically in the unconscious is, I say, a fact which I am perfectly willing to accept. The interpretation of why that particular translation occurs, for example in terms of dream theory, may or may not be valid; for out of my great humbleness as a scientist, I suspect that a full-grown answer has not successfully leaped Minerva-like from the human mind. Indeed, I suspect that whatever the exciting formulations, they will probably turn out later not to be valid. I do not see any contradiction in what I have said.

It appears that a considerable number of analysts are inclined not to be worried about this; they give lip service to it, but are quite content to go along using existing concepts. I would suggest that only a very small fraction of psychoanalysts today are experimentally minded and are really trying to do anything about the problem. Most of them who were successful in experimentation are now, I believe, called "sitting analysts."

SPENCE: We have been discussing some of the difficulties of beginning to categorize too early. I recognize these difficulties. But I hold to the belief that anything that can be observed, can be quantified. We have to begin somewhere and I am not fearful of making mistakes. There will always be someone who will come along and take care of them. Whenever an error is made, it is always detected and published very soon.

GERARD: You know the definition of a scientist: one who regards the work of his colleagues with quarrelsome interest.

SPENCE: In addition to being an experimental psychologist, I have had an amateur interest in methodology and the philosophy of science. But I must confess that my reading in the fields of clinical psychology and psychiatry is very limited; hence, I have no awareness of the problems there. Nevertheless I should like to introduce a diagram which might help to bring out what the relations are between the dependent and the different kinds of independent variables, and which might present a framework to this discussion (Figure 1). This diagram contains the following factors: time; the organism (O); the observed behavior (B); and all the various past events $(S\ past)$, such as family, social, and religious history. We first observe and identify the behavior phenomena (B) and empirical relations in the present situation $(S\ present)$. Then the psychoanalyst, the sociologist, and the anthropologist look into such past factors $(S\ past)$ as the structure of the family and groups in an attempt to discover relationships. The psychologists, whether they be sensory perception or learning psychologists, observe and measure the empirical phenomena and state the relationships among them. Behavior in a particular situation would include not only what the organism responds to but also what happens when it responds. These phenomena can be left at an empirical level where we discover relationships or laws.

Now comes the theorizing, for I have not put in the neurophysiologist. He is interested in a chain of events that are going on, particularly inside the organism (O). I am interested in the problem of etiology of the behavior. It seems to me that the problems are primarily of this sort.

The early analysts, the early Freudians, tended to ignore the social factors and to relate the organism and behavior. They

at and talk about empirical observed relationships much more than before. Even as a theorist, I am much more interested in beginning with an empirical relationship and then introducing my theoretical constructs later.

SCHNEIDER: The standard for whether or not that is a good procedure appears to be, essentially, what turns out to be most profitable in the end.

SPENCE: I am not so sure.

WITTKOWER: There has been a shift of emphasis from the id psychology to ego psychology in analysis. In the early teaching around 1904, Freud tried to discover im-

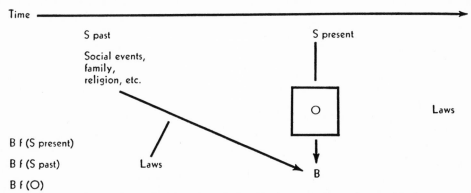

FIG. 1. Diagram indicating the relationship between dependent and independent variables in behavioral phenomena.

started to put things into this organism from the observed behavior, postulating the various entities, e.g., the ego, the id, the superego, and the libido. Much of this was done primarily in terms of the phenomenological experiences of the psychoanalyst himself; that is, in terms of his own past experiences. He did not really relate the formulations too much to a particular individual's past social history. That influence came later. My main complaint about the early psychoanalytic theory is that it was circular. It tended to leave out a great many factors.

SCHNEIDER: It was all circular; it was all imagery; but it was helpful. Why complain?

SPENCE: The early analysts never got out of the circularity. Something was put in at one point, and it came right back. Later psychoanalysts, through the influence of sociology and anthropology, began to look

pulses by doing away with ego functions by hypnosis. He wanted to have access to the instinctual life of the individual. Within recent years, however, we have learned that to concentrate on impulses alone does not do justice to the individual. We have to deal with impulses and events as a basis. But this approach is still within the intrapsychic viewpoint; because when the analyst thinks in terms of id impulses and ego defenses, he is still dealing with individuals. It is also true that environmental, i.e., extrapsychic, factors have to be taken into account.

SPENCE: Therapy centered on the ego, then, is treatment, not so much of the motivational forces, as the psychological processes which have entered into relation with them.

WITTKOWER: Exactly. That is a very good formulation.

GERARD: Or, if one dares to make a very rash, semimorphological statement, the attention has shifted from the hypothalamic drive to the cortical suppressions and controls.

SCHNEIDER: Do the psychiatrists have any advantage over the psychologists or analysts in ascertaining the causes of mental disease? This is a subject that we are here to discuss.

GERARD: I think that your question is meaningless unless you specify it in terms of what has which field of advantage. In terms of understanding the etiology of mental diseases—primarily schizophrenia, which is the great mental disease—I think that the psychoanalysts are not going to make the important contributions; I think that the biologist is going to solve that. But in terms of understanding why whatever etiological factor, or whatever pathogenic mechanism, brings about this or that symptom, I think that the psychiatrists and the sociologists are going to be far superior to the physiologists or the psychologists.

WITTKOWER: Rohrer,* in the American Journal of Psychiatry, puts down this formula: Intensity of anger feelings is a function of the amount of frustration.

The second formula is: The strength of the emotional response is a function of the amount of hypothalamic discharge.

What he has in mind is to bring about a coordinating definition which links up the various disciplines.

SPENCE: In terms of etiology, I would criticize most psychological theorists for the same thing that I do the psychoanalysts. I do not share Dr. Schneider's point of view that circularity helps. The theoretical constructs which are placed in the organism in the formula have to be tied up not only with behavior but also with the antecedent conditions.

I would rather approach our topic for today by asking: Where are the problems? Are they in terms of specifying the cultural factors or behavior, or what is inside the organism, neurophysiology, or the immediate present environment? I am trying to focus on them. The associated methodological problems must be somewhere in the four or five foci that I have indicated. Where do we think the problems are? I gather from Dr. Schneider that he thinks that the specification of the various types of behavior disorder is not in a satisfactory condition.

SCHNEIDER: To my mind, that is one of the really crucial problems.

KRUSE: In the history of medicine it can be shown that constantly the clinician is trying to find a distinct clinical entity, which contains no foreign elements. For example, pellagra of the nineteenth century contained signs and symptoms of beriberi and ariboflavinosis, two other diseases, as well as of pellagra as it is known today. The fact that pellagra was actually a mixed clinical entity at the time its causation was revealed did not in any way prevent that achievement. I realize fully the dangers of reasoning by analogy; but perhaps we should not wait until the mental disorders are classified and recognized in pure form before we are willing to begin the quest of causation. We might approach the problem by observing, reporting, and quantifying in terms of symptoms and signs rather than of disease.

GERARD: Isn't there a difficulty with that approach? If beriberi and pellagra had not been successfully recognized as separate entities before thiamine or niacin were tested therapeutically, the outcome might have been misinterpreted and misleading. Where there is neither the chemical, symptomatic, nor logical clearness of these deficiency diseases, we face obstacles. Isn't it highly desirable to get the mental disorders separated?

KRUSE: Now you are saying something different. I would agree, of course, that it is desirable to get pure clinical entities. That is always a paramount objective. My point was that it is not necessary to hold up research on causation until the final separation of a disorder in pure form is achieved. Actually a therapeutic approach on signs and symptoms aims toward both objectives concurrently. Improvement in some, but not all, signs may indicate a mixed disorder, the

---

* Rohrer, J. H. Research team concept and cultural patterns of science. Am. J. Psychiat., March 1953, 109: 677–883.

lines of separation, and the causal mechanism of one entity.

WITTKOWER: I endorse Dr. Kruse's point. At McGill we always ask for labels. But in my opinion, labels are not of much help in psychiatry, because they mean little. The patient may fluctuate, may present one picture today and another tomorrow. Then we are dealing with complex things; a patient with a schizoid background may show anxiety symptoms. To give a label to this is very neat on paper, but of little use.

SPENCE: By a label you mean a gross designation such as schizophrenic?

WITTKOWER: Yes.

SCHNEIDER: We need exhaustive and careful studies, on a cross-cultural basis, of the people who are called schizophrenic. The intent would be incidentally to help them, but primarily to get some kind of triangulation on that very rough, general, amphorous, mixed category that we still call schizophrenics. It seems to me that this is one of the areas in which a decisive study needs to be undertaken.

KRUSE: I should like to set forth two concepts which may have relevance for the study of mental diseases and their causation. These are concepts of deficiency states and their causes, but their applicability extends to other diseases. It is not so farfetched as it may seem to cite concepts about nutrition in a discussion of mental health. For nutrition and mental health or behavior have several striking points of similarity. They are lifelong processes; they are dynamic; they have multifactorial causes.

The first concept describes the natural history of a deficiency disease. Actually, it is applicable to all pathological processes. Diseases have three characteristics: velocity, intensity, and duration. Each of these variables is quantifiable. The rate at which a disease may progress, including its acceleration or deceleration, may be rapid, medium, or slow; these may be recognized as the acute, subacute, or chronic forms. The second characteristic, intensity, may be conveniently graded as marked, moderate, or slight. The third is duration, in which the total span of the deficiency process may be demarcated into early, intermediate, or late stages. These characteristics of the process are imparted to and recognizable in the pathological manifestations, whether they be symptoms or signs. Hence, a deficiency disease may differ in appearance and form, depending on its velocity, intensity, and duration.

Deficiency states appear most frequently in a chronic form, in which they progress slowly and usually go unrecognized, especially if they are in an early stage and of mild intensity. Under sufficient provocation this chronic process exacerbates into an acute form which is, of course, readily detectable. This acute form may take either of two courses: Inasmuch as a prolonged acute process is incompatible with life, it may spontaneously slacken to the chronic form; or treatment may be instituted to bring about abatement. In neither instance is there a complete reversal of the disease and its pathology; rather it decelerates and subsides to a slowly progressing chronic state. The latter is frequently regarded as normal.

Nutrition is a lifelong bodily process; and pathological alterations, unless reversed, are cumulative. The slowly progressing chronic form is rarely completely reversed; hence, at any given point in life, the pathology represents the accumulation of the entire past nutritive changes.

This concept has significance because it has consequences for the effects of therapy and for the elucidation of causation. If a therapy is administered to a group of patients who have the chronic form of a disorder, immediate improvement would not be expected. Indeed, if the study were of short duration, any potential improvement might not appear before termination of the study. Or, if the patients have a deficiency state predominantly in the acute form, the invariable spontaneous recession, especially upon bed rest, may occur with no therapy, or whatever the therapy. All of these eventualities may give rise to misleading conclusions.

The second concept is that of causation of deficiency diseases. It likewise holds for many other disorders. In understanding the etiology of deficiency diseases, it is necessary to differentiate between diet and nutrition. Nutrition is a bodily process. Diet refers to a regimen of food which supports nutrition. The nutritive state is determined by the ratio $\frac{supply}{requirement}$. When this ratio is one or higher, it conduces to satisfactory nutrition; when it is less than one it tends toward unsatisfactory nutrition. This nutritive process, with its ratio, is in operation throughout life; it is dynamic; and it may be constantly changing. This dynamic ratio is not self-propelled. Both members of the ratio are subjected to influences and conditions which have different effects. Some will increase supply; others will diminish it. Some will increase, others will diminish, requirements. Some conditions operate on both factors of the ratio. Some conditions act throughout life; others are temporary and come at different periods in life.

These conditions constitute all of the influences to which man is exposed throughout his lifetime, both in his external environment and within his body. For convenience, it is possible to classify them as follows: In the external environment there are three broad categories: socioeconomic, physical and chemical, and dietary, each of which contains many factors. In the bodily environment there are two categories: digestive and metabolic functions, and bodily functions and reactions, each again containing many factors.

Many of these conditions are continuously in operation. Never is nutrition affected by just one condition. It is influenced by the composite action of multiple factors. Two persons, each showing a nutritional disorder, may have a different combination of conditions responsible for it. Indeed, one person having nutritional disorders at different periods in his life may have changes in the set of conditions and in the degree of influence of any one condition from one time to another.

One condition may be preponderant in a disorder and therefore more responsible quantitatively than the other conditions. But curiously, a precipitating condition, as the final straw, so to speak, may be of little magnitude; yet because of the timing, it may have a disproportionate amount of responsibility attributed to it.

Nutrition and mental health have broad points of similarity. Both are lifetime processes. It would appear that mental disorders, like most other diseases, also show velocity, intensity, and duration, which, I suspect, are revealed in their manifestations. Furthermore, it is my belief that the psychiatric status of a person, as well as the nutritional status, reflects the accumulated changes of his entire life. Then too, a psychiatrist thinks in terms of the needs of the patient and sources of supply. He likewise recognizes that both the needs and the supply are affected by many influences. Thus, both nutritional and mental diseases have multifactorial causation. Finally, it may be noted that when the factors or influences are arranged under disciplines, the same four approaches emerge in both types of disorder: socio-cultural-economic, psychodynamic, experimental psychological, and organic.

GERARD: A sports writer wrote that Carresquel's homer won the game. He knocked in two runs in the first inning, and the game was 17 to 16, after twelve innings!

KRUSE: An apt simile.

GERARD: I should like to ask Dr. Wittkower about your inference that mental disease is cumulative, and presumably that the symptoms are cumulative. The psychiatrists whom I know seem to be in fairly good agreement that schizophrenia is rather an acute insult to the organism, a primary disease process in which there is separation of emotion and reason, and confusion of awareness. But most of the symptoms ordinarily associated with schizophrenia, such as hallucinations and the paranoid reactions, are compensatory reactions. They are not progressions of the primary disease.

KRUSE: The pathology of deficiency diseases is also compensatory. The enlarged metaphysis in rachitis represents nature's piling up an inferior substance.

WITTKOWER: Schizophrenia is a difficult example because most psychiatrists believe that there are marked constitutional factors. There are cases of schizophrenia which are ushered in by acute precipitating circumstances; but there are others which are related to long, cumulative stress.

GERARD: At this stage I should like to introduce the following recommendations for further research: (1) To identify mental disease in the population. (This is the nosology of disease.) (2) To determine the type and range of individual variations. (3) To develop adequate criteria of change, including the change of cure. (4) To identify, and particularly to quantify, the etiological factors. (The quantification will be specific for each case, of course, and perhaps for each symptom of each case.) (5) To locate the time of the pathogenesis, whether the factors are operating early or late. (6) To analyze the mechanisms of pathogenesis.

To expand briefly upon the first three points: First, to identify disease we would separate the types of mental diseases as well as possible and then break them up into groups, say, schizophrenia A, B, and C. Second, to determine the type and range of individual variation, we would ask ourselves, What phenomena shall we observe? What are the behavioral capacities, the frustrations, and their mean in a given population, whether that population be the whole human race or a small cultural group? What is the variation within this population? In other words, we would try to identify the range of normality and we would attempt to define what we would term "abnormal," i.e., we would try to define our unit of error. Third, to develop criteria of change would imply measurement beyond that implied in the variation noted in the first two recommendations. It would imply, for example, measuring what has happened to a given patient or group of patients under study when we have instituted such steps as modification of environment, exercise of authority, medication, or whatever. Measurement of these changes would necessitate the use of methods and criteria with rating scales, such as blood pressure determinations and van den Bergh's test. Indices of change in the patients' states would have to be worked out.

In considering the last three recommendations, I suggest that we make a very sharp distinction between etiology and pathogenesis. The etiology of schizophrenia, for example, would be whether it is caused by a genetic defect, by a rejecting mother, by stressful life experiences, or something like that. The pathogenesis would be what has happened in the functioning of neurons, in my terminology, or in the balance between id, ego and reality functions, superego, in psychodynamic terms, to produce the particular symptoms and manifestations of the disease.

They are quite separate problems, but neuron breakdown might be the result of an infection, or of a genetic defect, or of overstimulation; so all etiologies might fall into a given pathogenesis, or any one etiology might produce different pathologies. Most of the arguments have been in terms of etiology, and this, I think, is well towards recognized resolution and quantitation. Pathogenesis is quite different; and by all means this, I think, is now the most interesting phase of the problem.

SPENCE: I was a little taken aback by the word "causation"; I had thought that it was out of date completely in science, and that the talk instead was in terms of functional relationships. I know that it is used much more in medical circles than it is in psychology, and sociology, and anthropology. Does the word occur frequently even yet in neurophysiology?

GERARD: Biological scientists who have any philosophical flair or interest, of whom there is a considerable number, would recognize at once what you say. But still, as a simple term, expressing what we mean by antecedent-consequent relations, we would use causality all the time and not worry too much about it.

Here we might profitably return to the difference between etiology and pathogenesis. As I am using the term "etiology," it starts in the total universe with factors operating in a system, and comprises those factors which can be identified and which will be weighted causally. In contrast, in pathogenesis the variables are isolated, their modes of interaction are ascertained. The mechanisms of interaction are the pathogenesis. For example, it would be the way in which the favorable or the adverse influences operate to bring about the swelling of the tissues at the joint in rickets.

I should like to draw another example from the field of nutrition. The dentists have studied the distribution of dental caries in relation to different racial groups, such as the Italian and German, not only in their own countries but also among the foreign populations in metropolitan areas like New York City. They find marked differences in the incidence of dental caries in the different ethnic groups. Etiologically there is no question that it makes a difference in the incidence of caries whether one is a German, or Italian, or Swede, or Englishman. When we consider the pathogenesis, we ask: How does this ethnic difference operate? The first inclination would be to say that this is an inborn genetic difference, a difference of susceptibility. It could be that, perfectly well. Another thing that it might be, however, is purely cultural, e.g., the kinds of food which the different groups eat.

KRUSE: And that influences the kind of bacterial flora.

GERARD: To shed light on the pathogenesis, a very simple experiment can be made. In mixed marriages, the incidence of caries follows rather precisely the ethnic character of the mother. The father has nothing to do with it. Since genetic factors would be mixed, this evidence is pretty conclusive proof of a cultural, not a biological, pathogenicity. Thus it could be shown by a very simple analysis that what was responsible was the mother's culture (the kind of food she fed) and the kinds of bacteria that developed in the mouth, not the kind of genes that were contributed. Isn't this just exactly what we are up against?

SPENCE: The psychologist uses the words "network of interrelated factors"; then comes the tracing of their sequences. The study on caries, just cited, serves as a clear example. First were the ethnic differences; next was the fact that the females in the particular groups preferred different kinds of foods. To talk about "cause" is just out of fashion, as far as science is concerned. In the physical sciences, the tendency is to speak in terms of functional relationships, or the network of interrelated factors. When you mention the tracing of them, I gather that what you are talking about is the psychogenesis.

KRUSE: In some of the biological sciences, the term "cause" still has currency.

The important thing is its meaning. The concept which I have outlined and the psychologists' formulations have points of similarity. I use the term "network of interrelated conditions" and "factors" interchangeably. In nutrition the network of interrelated conditions with their effects is viewed as converging upon the ratio. In a broad, loose sense an adverse ratio and the combination of conditions responsible for it, comprising a complex, can be regarded as the cause of the ensuing pathology. But it is also desirable on occasion to differentiate and designate the principal parts of the entire constellation. The adverse ratio may be regarded as the primary, direct, immediate cause of the pathological process; while the combination of conditions influencing the ratio are secondary, indirect, mediate causes. According to this view, conditions are necessary to the occurrence and existence of pathology; but they are the secondary, not the direct, cause. Nevertheless, a condition is regarded and defined as a cause. Another view is based upon a distinction between cause and condition. In it the state expressed by the adverse ratio is the cause; the factors responsible for the unfavorable ratio are adverse conditions. In this sense, a cause is the agency producing a result; whereas a condition is something that necessarily precedes a result but does not produce it. It is a prerequisite to fulfillment.

There does appear to be one difference between the psychologist and the biologist in conception of etiology. In the network of interrelated factors and the sequence of antecedent conditions and their effects, the biologist would draw a distinction between causation and pathogenesis. In order that it may be sharp, I would raise the question: Where does the former stop and the latter begin? When there is a constellation of adverse factors predominating but no pathology as yet, whether morphological, psychological, functional, or chemical, is that the beginning of pathogenesis? When forces, conditions, and influences are operating toward and conducing to pathogenesis but not yet producing pathology, is that point a part or a stage of pathogenesis? It should be borne in mind that an adverse situation evokes counteracting influences which attempt to forestall or mitigate unfavorable effects. Or does pathogenesis begin when pathological changes of any kind first start or appear? If the criterion is demonstrable pathology, that is of course determined by the limits of observation. It may seem as though I am trying to draw an overly fine line. There is little difference of opinion over the interaction of conditions or factors and the sequence of the process; but there is much vagueness and loose usage of the term "causation" in comparison with the term "pathogenesis." It creates confusion. If we are to discuss causation or any of its synonyms, clarification by definition, demarcation, and distinction might make for progress.

GERARD: The latter point which you raise has to do with what I call the limits of homeostatic tolerance. The equilibrium position of a particular attribute of an organism is the physiological norm. Any one thing can be displaced in only one or the other direction, but the whole organism, the constellation of these norms, can be displaced in a variety of ways. Any influence acting upon a particular entity can change its quantitative level or character. This may be the level of calcium in the blood, or it may be the blood pressure, or it may be the anxiety state of the organism. "Load" is what is placed upon the system, that tends to displace it from its equilibrium level. Stress or strain is the disturbance produced in the system. All the homeostatic mechanisms tend to bring the systems back toward the equilibrium.

There is an area of homeostatic tolerance. The variable can be displaced to some critical extent, of which the parameter will vary quantitatively in the different directions; and up to this point the action is reversible. Ordinarily a disturbance is not spoken of as pathology until it has crossed that zone; it would be called "physiological play" of the variables. Man becomes hungry, he is depleted, he needs more food; but nothing irreversible or damaging has happened if this is only between meals or for a day or two.

When the impact of the outer world has displaced the variable, has produced a sufficient stress or strain so that the disequilibrium has gone outside of this area of homeostatic tolerance, then irreversibility will begin. The further it goes and the longer it stays, the more the permanent, and usually adverse, effect. When there is pathology, when that line has been crossed, that is pathogenesis. Etiology would be whatever is the displacing load.

KRUSE: An attempt to preserve homeostasis when adverse conditions predominate is another way to say that a set of counterconditions come into play. Certainly, a pathogenic situation, unchecked, is going to lead to pathology.

GERARD: Another point that might be worth discussion is the question of terminology: the working out of common concepts which we are now using under different words; or recognizing different concepts that we are now using under common words.

As a very desirable step—and this is a different kind of research approach—there should be a really strenuous effort to formulate each psychological or psychodynamic concept in neuronal terms. I would equally say the reverse of that, that neurobiologists should pay attention to the phenomena presented by the mental scientists.

Also to be considered are: the role of spatial organization, that is, the structural location of various processes (Is the id, for example, in the hypothalamus?); and the role of functional mechanisms, nerve nets, potential fields, and reverberating circuits. Furthermore, we should recognize the different levels at which we are considering these problems, whether it is the cellular or the organism level.

The most important thing to overcome is something which we all agree to curb but in regard to which we sin perpetually; that is, mixing causality between the physical and the psychological realms. An impulse, an idea, an emotion, never causes an action. The only thing that causes an action is a neural discharge, which comes from neurons that are being excited. Causality has to be explained either in the material mode of discourse or in the psychological mode of discourse; in the latter, by a repression, or a compulsion. But they cannot be mixed.

Compulsions do not make neurons discharge. This understanding, I think, is one of the most important things to achieve. It is because we do not observe this verity that we get into so many meaningless arguments and fail to make significant approaches in research.

SCHNEIDER: Compulsions cannot make neurons discharge?

GERARD: What happens is that an environmental situation interacts with a given set of the neurons in the brain.

SCHNEIDER: Emotion, as a concept, is not going to affect a concrete neuron.

GERARD: That is right. In the same way, I would say that ether does not produce anesthesia, although we use this expression all the time.

SPENCE: We have to speak of functional relationships because of just the problems that you raised, psychological and physical.

GERARD: If I were to express my view of this, which I dare say you would not agree with, the psychological is the internal view, the material is the external view, of a given reality. An antecedent event has a consequent event related to it in some way, and there is always both a mental and a physical attribute to each event. Confusion arises when one forgets that he is merely taking one half of the event and applying it to the alternate half of the other event.

SCHNEIDER: In talking about expressing psychodynamic concepts in neuronal terms, you mentioned that you prefer to start with the psychodynamic concept. Insofar as the problems that we are going to be concerned with start at a gross observational level of overt behavior, as distinguished from neuron phenomena, it is in those terms that problems have to be defined at the beginning. Your assertion makes no sense.

GERARD: It takes far greater wisdom and prescience to go up the levels than it does to go down. All that I am saying is that biology hopes to explain or reduce, if that is not an objectionable word, its phenomena and problems to the phenomena and laws of physics and chemistry; and only when we begin to express them in terms of the interactions of molecules and structures, do they take sharpness in the same way. Some day the behavior of psychodynamic phenomena has to be expressed in terms of the interaction of neurons.

SCHNEIDER: I am thinking of how to get the problems defined, and where to start. I believe that we are in agreement that the statement of what conditions we are going to be concerned with in mental disease must initially be made in fundamentally emotional terms before neural.

GERARD: Except on the nosological side. One might pick out the specific entities of biological practice.

SCHNEIDER: I should like to ask to what extent there can be a cumulative effort as to the relevance of psychosocial factors to mental disease, and to what extent we can expect to go ahead in specifying where, and when, and how, and under what kinds of conditions, they will be relatively more or less relevant, and relevant in what ways?

SPENCE: This is at the level of the statement of the observed behavior of the phenomena, and the social and environmental factors?

SCHNEIDER: Yes. In phrasing the problem at that level, which is where both social and scientific problems arise, we could then move into the organic and psychological fields.

GERARD: I am not sure that I understand what you mean. My conception of the social factor—to give a paradigm—is this: When a person has hallucinations under mescaline, exhibiting symptoms which are organically accountable, they represent something that happened to the chemistry of the brain. The fact that the hallucinations lead to English or Chinese verbalizations is clearly not dependent on the mescaline, but on the residue of social factors.

SCHNEIDER: I am trying to consider the question of where to begin on such a problem and how to proceed. Perhaps we begin at the level of seeing sick people who are problems to society. It is at this point that we have met together. Here we begin to state the critical kinds of distinctions to which we hope that the organicist can make some contribution rather than simply do organic work and come up from time to time with, "Look, this happens to be relevant to some of the sick people."

SPENCE: The approach of such a psychologist as myself is the same as yours. I have little or nothing to do with neurophysiology any more. Our psychological laws, empirical relations, pertain entirely to observable and measurable—sometimes fairly precisely measurable—response changes and environmental conditions, immediately past, or certain other environmental conditions, such as modification of the state of the organism. But we do not talk about what is going on in the organism. In these laws between the observed behavior, the described phenomena, on the one hand, and the manipulated or, in the case of behavior disorders, the environmental phenomena, on the other hand, we have no reduction at the present time.

GERARD: But you would hope to.

SPENCE: Certainly. I hope that somebody is attempting it. Perhaps it is more accurate to say that I would not preclude somebody's attempting it. But in my opinion the pressing problem right now in the field of mental disorders is describing a behavior disorder and cataloguing, relating, and correlating the social conditions which bring it about.

GERARD: We are not in disagreement. Reduction is rather far down the list. It happens to be one of my own special interests.

KRUSE: Aren't all the social studies at the present time actually at the level of attempting to demonstrate an association between the social environment and the occurrence of mental disease? Then it is hoped that clues will be obtained on what are the specific social factors or influences which bring it about.

SPENCE: To what extent has there been an attempt to do more than enumerate social variables, to organize or classify them?

SCHNEIDER: None. The starting point was the question, Are they relevant? The immediate research problem was to demonstrate their relevance. This has been done by showing the differences in manifestations of a disease in different cultures or within cultures over a long time period; for example, the very different manifestations of hysteria from earliest times, through the Middle Ages and Victorian period, to today. Are the differences that are found due only to the fact that some people speak one language, some another? Or are there phenomena that are functionally equivalent within the same fundamental structure of an illness? This is one of the focal points of decisive research at this time.

WITTKOWER: We have drifted to a discussion of the psychosocial position. Some statements of that position are merely an enumeration of observations without an interpretation of what they mean. Predisposing and precipitating factors are described; and all the various points about life in metropolitan, urban, and rural areas are set forth. But, after I have read it, I ask myself, "What does it all mean?"

SPENCE: Isn't it a matter of an empirical discovery as to whether or not this material is a relevant variable? These, after all, were observations. You desire to learn more about them. I am very empirical always in my approach. First, I want the discovery of the relevant variables; then I want the discovery of some functional relationships between them.

SCHNEIDER: Now we are back where we started. We are still trying to find out what the relevant variables are. We are still stating the conditions of relevance in such terms that they are essentially communicated by almost unmeasurable and uncommunicable feelings.

I can describe Zulu hysterics to you. But beyond that, the stipulation of both what the relevant conditions to hysteria in general are, and what the relevant conditions to the etiology of hysteria among the Zulu and among us are, is a problem that will come up within the next ten or fifteen years. Nevertheless, it is not directly relevant at the moment.

SPENCE: At the beginning, these things have to be specific. We would have to specify the different types as "Hysteria 1," "Hysteria 2," "Hysteria 3." Any common factor will come out later.

SCHNEIDER: Surely. That is just what we are doing.

KRUSE: Are there not two relationships here? In some cases the variables may influence each other; in other cases, they may not.

SCHNEIDER: That is right. This would be the end result.

KRUSE: An example of a situation in the physical environment might be of interest. In the Far North some persons, particularly the natives, develop snow blindness. Bright sunlight and a vast expanse of snow in every direction, acting as an infinite number of tiny mirrors reflecting light in many directions, produce an unbelievable intensity of light coming to the eye at every conceivable angle. Long exposure to this is a severe experience for the normal unprotected eye. The potential victims of snow blindness usually have a moderate to severe, advanced, chronic ariboflavinosis. Thereby they are particularly sensitive to light. In turn, the light brings about exacerbation of the chronic to an acute process.

It can be treated in two ways: One is to protect the patient from the irritating focus in the environment. Extinguishing the sun is impossible; and confinement to a dark room is impractical, except as an emergency or short-term measure. But dark glasses, with a shield to keep out strong light, bring prompt and great relief.

The second method of treatment, administration of riboflavin, is designed to overcome the patients' deficiency and susceptibility. Both measures should be instituted. One mitigates the precipitating environmental condition; the other abates and reverses the pathology responsible for susceptibility. This is an example of multitherapeutics based upon cause and condition.

SCHNEIDER: That is exactly what has been done in some hospital research.* There has been an attempt to reproduce what are presumed to be critical elements in a therapeutic situation by manipulating the hospital ward environment almost as if it were a simple central dynamic relationship, though with recognition that it is not.

SPENCE: To return to the first four items

* Stanton, A. H. and Schwartz, M. S. *The Mental Hospital; A Study of Institutional Participation in Psychiatric Illness and Treatment.* New York: Basic Books, 1954.

on Dr. Gerard's list of recommendations for future research—(1) nosology, i.e., description of the behavior phenomena: (2) type and range of individual variations; (3) adequate criteria of change; (4) identify and quantify the etiological factors—I believe that the first three have to precede the fourth in the sense that it is necessary to know what to try to relate the fourth to. I would ask Dr. Wittkower: What are the major empirical problems?

WITTKOWER: Will you specify the question more definitely?

SPENCE: I do not like to speak of mental disease; I would prefer to speak of behavior, the behavior phenomena, the observable behavior symptoms. Since you are concerned with these problems, and since you are interested not in a particular theoretical viewpoint, but in terms of the determined variable and the determining or independent variable, let me ask you these questions: In the classification of these different behavior disorders, has anybody ever counted out the number of different items of behavior that have been listed in all of the psychoneurotic classifications? How many different observable items of behavior are in anxiety states? How many are in conversion reactions? How many and which ones overlap? I believe that something like this has to be done.

SCHNEIDER: Such a count would run for the next twenty years.

SPENCE: But this is the kind of study that is most pressingly needed.

WITTKOWER: What would we count?

SPENCE: The individual items that go into an anxiety state.

SCHNEIDER: That is the crucial problem: What are they?

SPENCE: Which ones have been described in the books?

SCHNEIDER: This is the problem: What are they? We feel fairly sure that we know some of them. But we are not very sure that we know all of them; or that the final count is relevant in every case; or that we are getting relationships that are the same in each case, though we suspect that we are. Before we can start counting, we encounter difficulty. If we submitted a list to seven psychiatrists or psychoanalysts, they would not agree among themselves that the items enumerated were the relevant countable items.

SPENCE: But there are some existing items. Let's not be worried about the ones that the psychiatrist has not yet noted. He is diagnosing patients. He sees a person in an anxiety state. What are the specific things that the psychiatrist observes that lead him to say that this is an individual with a psychoneurotic manifestation of behavior which he designates as an anxiety state. Upon looking at the patient, he does not find on the person's shoulder a sign, "Anxiety State." It is the individual's behavior on which the psychiatrist bases his diagnosis.

GERARD: Dr. Grinker rates the anxiety level in a subject from 1 to 5. This is a quantitation. What are the criteria upon which he does it? He does not even see the subject. He uses the material from an interview of the subject with another psychiatrist. From the reactions, the verbal behavior, and the statements, Dr. Grinker analyzes and classifies the material. He can define more or less satisfactorily what his indices are. He has not done what some day will have to be done—to see whether two or three psychiatrists, after checking their criteria, could make the same ratings independently—but he looked at the same record a year later, and he came out with the same rating.

WITTKOWER: Dr. Grinker places his main emphasis on what the patient feels and says.

SPENCE: Observable phenomena.

WITTKOWER: Yes. We are in agreement on this point. You ask: In the patient's complaint of anxiety, what various items in his statement—for the anxiety is something that the patient describes and reports— form the basis of deciding the nature and degree of the anxiety?

GERARD: What does he say that makes the analyst call it "anxiety?"

WITTKOWER: It can be on a descriptive level and broken up, as has been done.

SPENCE: How many items would come in? How many are there in the current listing of the American Psychiatric Association?

WITTKOWER: Let me answer the question, Would all psychiatrists come to the same conclusion? I would say, basically, Yes. But the material would still be very much on the descriptive level.

I know of an instance in which subjects were examined for a personality assessment. Just by chance the same subjects were sent to two psychiatrists, who wrote up independent reports. The findings of the two psychiatrists were practically identical. But the psychiatrists had undergone similar training. Hence, I would add a necessary proviso to my answer.

GERARD: Your illustration proves that there is more than fantasy in the diagnosis. But that still is not answering Dr. Spence's question.

SPENCE: Dr. Wittkower has given an index of the reliability or the consistency of a particular schema of ways of receiving, perceiving, or responding; and it indicates consistency.

GERARD: There is a set of behavioral attributes which the psychiatrist calls "conversion hysteria"; another set which he calls "compulsion neurosis"; and another set which he calls "schizophrenia." To a large extent, the same blocks go into each of these. Dr. Spence is asking Dr. Wittkower whether he can identify some of the blocks. Or, let me put it another way, with a thousand words made of letters from the alphabet, can he tell us which letters go into which words.

KRUSE: Components.

SPENCE: "Elements" is another word.

WITTKOWER: It can be done. But the difficulty is that you think in descriptive terms, whereas we think in dynamic terms. Whether in descriptive or dynamic terms, one can specify what the psychiatrist sees or observes. It is more important to come to dynamic conclusions about mechanisms.

SPENCE: When you use the word "dynamics," you are really getting into theoretical terms. But your theoretical inferences start from something.

WITTKOWER: From the observations. So, on the observational level, the answer to the question is definitely that a number of psychiatrists trained in the same way are able to draw up a list of items on a number of individuals examined by them.

SPENCE: I would certainly believe it to

be so, disregarding now whether they would agree that particular blocks really belong in this or that category.

GERARD: You are asking the names of the items. You would like to count them.

SPENCE: How many such items, do you think, would be associated with the psychoneuroses? Admittedly, we do not have all the items; on the other hand, we probably now have some false items. Is my experience unique? I recall that in a number of case conferences, three or four different psychiatrists, all presumably with very similar, if not identical, training, disputed with some heat over whether the patient had schizophrenia, or manic-depression, or perhaps a hysterical episode. It was as if they were debating, "Is this a cow, or is this a calf, or is this an elk?" This happened a significantly greater number of times than one would expect by chance.

GERARD: What arguments did they use with each other? That will help answer the question.

SCHNEIDER: I agree in the main with Dr. Wittkower's answer that in a significantly large number of cases such agreement is not only possible, but is actually achieved; but with the qualification that there is still a large block of cases in which such agreement does not arise. It can be stated in terms of probability levels, that the probability of agreement among a group of psychiatrists about entities like compulsion neuroses or anxiety states is at a relatively low level.

WITTKOWER: All the time that you are talking about labels, I would rather think in terms of mechanisms.

SCHNEIDER: We would have to have a common understanding that none of us is going to use labels without reference to actions.

GERARD: Granted that there will be considerable disagreement in many cases in giving the final label or diagnosis, the significant question now is, When Dr. A tries to convince Dr. B that the patient has schizophrenia, and Dr. B tries to convince Dr. A that it is a cyclothymic state, what facts do they hurl at each other? These are the blocks on which the collective diagnosis rests.

SPENCE: Do these differences come out on the basis, not of what they see and specify, but of their theory?

GERARD: They start with the history and their observations. Then one will say to the other, "This is schizophrenia, because this boy showed such-and-such a symptom at such-and-such a time." The other will argue for a different diagnosis.

SPENCE: Where did the disagreement come in?

GERARD: In weighting the symptoms.

KRUSE: Disagreement may arise on two grounds: (1) One clinician makes an observation and the other does not. (2) They weight their observations differently.

SPENCE: I want to consider the components of a disorder rather than its label. I want to begin work with the more specific behavior symptom, to be able to describe in a sufficiently precise manner the various kinds of verbal statements and observable behaviors of the individual: that he cried, that he laughed, that he did something else. Would Dr. Wittkower be able to specify a large number of the components of behavior?

WITTKOWER: It could be done, but it is more difficult than it appears. Usually the psychiatrist takes in the whole patient and does not break up complaints and observations into factors.

SPENCE: As a scientist, I am highly skeptical of that.

GERARD: It is like recognizing a friend, and not being able to say how it is done.

WITTKOWER: I can give my reasons why I regard a particular patient as an anxious individual with schizoid features. A student has not had the same experience and naturally has fewer criteria; hence, in carrying out the same investigation, he may be mistaken in his observations. So the element of experience and training comes in.

SPENCE: I would grant that the psychiatrist has learned certain ways of proceeding, and that he integrates his material as a calculating machine does. I wish that you could give us the laws of his integration.

SCHNEIDER: That is why I raised the point that there is not a consensus among psychiatrists and analysts such as could be obtained among automobile mechanics; psychiatrists are in a rather different state of development than automobile mechanics and are concerned with human beings rather than machines. We will have to wait for some time for what you ask.

GERARD: I do not think so.

SCHNEIDER: Look at the kinds of data that have been rigorously excluded, but are still of some significance to the analyst and to the psychiatrist. He uses his own perceptions as tools, although he cannot invariably stipulate explicitly in what way he is using them. That is why he cannot specify and count items, and give his method of integration.

SPENCE: You say that this is still to come. Could somebody be put at the job?

SCHNEIDER: Surely. The psychiatrists are all aware of the fact that they ought to be at the job eventually. But they are still at the level of sorting.

SPENCE: When do we start? I am in favor of describing the phenomena in which I am going to be interested.

SCHNEIDER: Give them time.

WITTKOWER: I suppose that you would undertake a factorial analysis.

SCHNEIDER: That narrows the range of interests.

KRUSE: Perhaps by the very nature of his preoccupation with the care of the patient, the psychiatrist finds justification for not analyzing his own procedure.

SPENCE: His preoccupation with his theoretical concepts may keep him from doing it.

SCHNEIDER: That remains to be demonstrated.

WITTKOWER: The analysis of procedure should by all means be attempted. But the result may well be an agglomeration of disjointed factors instead of the comprehension of the total individual. Nevertheless, let us try it. Say, while I am examining a man who is undressed, he perspires and feels embarrassed. I have a hint that he is embarrassed by my person as a male.

GERARD: This is item one that can be written on a list.

WITTKOWER: He tells me that he is afraid of contact with women. I now have additional evidence which goes in the same direction. So it goes on and on until I have an agglomerate of observations which allow me to say, "This is a latent homosexual."

SCHNEIDER: What you are doing is introducing the notion of configuration, before you have even begun to get near it with your list.

SPENCE: It is impossible to state configurations quantitatively.

SCHNEIDER: Quite so. But first you have to be able to perceive the configurations.

SPENCE: The history of physical science would not bear that out. Maybe we have something different here.

GERARD: We are getting away from the issue which started this line of discussion. The question was, How do we make research progress? The suggestion is: Let's see to what extent we can pick out individual observables, and then we can begin to worry about how useful they are. Until Dr. Wittkower stated a moment ago that he could see that the patient was sweating, and that he heard the patient's statement about his fear, not one observable had been mentioned.

Both Dr. Wittkower and Dr. Schneider have been saying that there is no point in trying to mention observables, because they are too intangible. I do not agree with this. I am perfectly willing to agree that the observables are amorphous, crude, and hard to describe. But something is observed and it can be described in some kind of words. These are some of the variables that are being looked at. This is the first step.

Let me give you two instances of attempts at research on the psychodynamic interview situation. One is a study made by a psychologist, in which he got complete recordings of interviews under various conditions. He was trying to learn what happened in the interview, and paid attention to such phenomena as loudness of voice. Therapists of five different schools reviewed the material. They differed in their interpretations; even two in the same school did not agree. The picture of the patient that each got from listening to the recording of the interview differed from one to another. The variables that were being examined proved to be not very useful for operational criteria.

In another study psychiatrists were getting nowhere in attempting to agree on their interpretations of interviews. Finally they said, "Let us decide simply whether we can define when there has been a change in the patient's attitude, a change in the therapeutic situation. We will say there is a change when two out of the following three things have happened: a change in the topic of discussion; a change in the time-period discussed; a change in initiative between analyst and patient." They also sought to ascertain how often such a change occurred following a patient's statement, and how often it occurred following the analyst's statement. When the problem was put into these terms, the whole thing snapped into position, and even a clerk could go through and quantify the interview. What you are saying is, "You have to find the right variables."

SCHNEIDER: This was done around the decade of the fifties after many years of work in this area; it was done at the same time that a number of unsuccessful experiments in attempting to stipulate and specify were being done. My argument really comes down to this: In a sense we always have to be aware that eventually we are going to have to make some kind of statement that any automaton would be able to sort. This is at the level of being able to get a real consensus on whether what you see is this or that, to be able to sort it into one variable or another. We are all imperatively aware of it. But my continual point here is that there is a time and place for this kind of imperative to become operative. And I am not sure that now is the proper time and that psychoanalysis is the proper place. I say this essentially because there are certain action consequences which follow an attempt to become rigorous, and one of the most important of these consequences tends to be a sloughing off of uncertain variables. I am not sure that we are ready to sacrifice variables which we are uncertain about at this moment, which might, in fact, later prove to be crucial; rather than to try to juggle an enormous number of variables, many of which will turn out to be totally irrelevant, on the chance of catching a few of the critical ones, when we are not yet

certain either of their relevance or of how to seize them, communicate them, and define them.

GERARD: But it is not "either-or."

SCHNEIDER: I really think that it is "either-or," precisely because of this important consequence of becoming rigorous, of sloughing off uncertain variables. The researcher who becomes rigorous literally narrows his field of research.

GERARD: But somebody else does not. "Either-or" applies to the collective action.

SCHNEIDER: At the present time in the United States there are not that many researchers. Where are you going to put them that they will be most useful?

GERARD: Here is a psychologist who wants to contribute to the solution of mental disease. You might say, "Come to me and give me your variables and I will see what I can do." Why not?

SCHNEIDER: I would rather put his brains to work at another level. I think that they would be more useful.

WITTKOWER: I do not agree with that at all.

GERARD: This is coming out very clearly. It is important to get to the ultimates of agreement.

SPENCE: I have had a considerable amount of like experience with a social psychologist working on the problems of describing the socially important behavior of children. We used to encounter this same problem over and over again; I tried to reduce it to my procedure. I am engaged in employing the conditioned reflex, substituting the human eye blink for the traditional salivation of the dog. Perhaps it is because we are so far beyond the stage that you are just approaching that we have never had to contend with it; hence, we literally do not understand it.

SCHNEIDER: You have done this by very drastically narrowing your field of observation to the eye blink.

SPENCE: Now we find that the laws that we are getting out of the eye blink, we are able to transfer to all other kinds of behavior.

SCHNEIDER: It is at that level that your case remains to be demonstrated to the analyst; namely, the relevance of the studies of the eye blink to the schizophrenic patient. This is our problem. This is what we came here for.

SPENCE: I have been extending results by analogy.

WITTKOWER: I am not so pessimistic as Dr. Schneider. I think that there is plenty of room for what has been called "experimental psychoanalysis." Many extremely valuable experiments can be carried out. But I am not so sure that it is wise to concentrate on isolated phenomena because, as I tried to demonstrate to you, we try to take in the total situation; nevertheless, there are many experimental situations which can be used. For instance, it would be extremely interesting to record psychoanalytical sessions from the beginning of the treatment on through the whole of analysis; and then to analyze the records in order to find out what differences they show.

Another experiment suggested by Malmo comes to mind. It should be possible to demonstrate transference by recording the physiological reactions of both the analyst and the analysand. If the interviews were recorded, the phenomenon could be objectified and demonstrated. It can be done; therefore I would certainly not agree that one simply should leave it and say, "We are not ready yet."

SPENCE: What is the present problem then, Dr. Schneider, as you see it? I mean the major task immediately facing, not the practicing psychiatrist, but the research psychiatrist? Could you formulate that?

SCHNEIDER: I suppose I should have expected that this would be thrown back in my lap. I am not dodging the question, I hope, if I say simply that it seems to me that one of the things that is crucial now in the development of research on mental disease is to take drastically contrasting cases from other cultures, not from subcultures within our own; and to study them by the same technics as have been used in our culture. So far as I know, Devereaux working with acculturated Plains Indians, is the only one who has done this.

SPENCE: What are you going to look at in the two extreme groups?

SCHNEIDER: We would look at everything that might conceivably be relevant.

SPENCE: But how are you going to record it?

SCHNEIDER: First, in my head—remember it, perceive it, and be able to recognize it again the next time that I see it. When this has been done sufficiently, I am eventually going to reach the point of being able to stipulate precisely what the criteria of change are so that they can be measured relatively objectively.

WITTKOWER: If you go through the research which has been carried out in this field, you will find that much work has been done; but, to use Talcott Parsons' terminology, the studies have all been concentrated on large social systems, and no real attempt has been made to concentrate on small social systems.

SCHNEIDER: And individual systems too.

WITTKOWER: My main interest at present is the study of family, with a reduction of variables as far as possible. Moving into new cultures introduces a large number of variables which cannot be controlled. That is equally true in a study of families; but by taking a group of families culturally alike in one or more respects, for example, all of one religion and all Canadian for generations, it is possible to reduce the number of variables to a minimum and thereby carry out basic research.

SPENCE: You are talking about the causal variables?

WITTKOWER: Yes.

SPENCE: The determining variables. We are on the topic of what is observed. You are bringing in something else.

SCHNEIDER: No, I think that it is very closely related. I would argue that the grossly contrasting situation is not a loss of control of the variables, but rather a critical control of the variables; because instead of demonstrating differences, it tends to demonstrate fundamental similarities. Naturally, the standards under which the investigators work have to be coordinated. Both the total group, and the individuals within the group have to be studied. If possible, they are plotted along some kind of very crude, very rough scale, in terms of their deviance from whatever has been stipulated. The attempt is to get people on the norm just as it is to get people in different quadrants off the norm.

SPENCE: Now you are beginning to get at what I have been asking for all the time: the norms and quadrants.

SCHNEIDER: But I use these words with somewhat different referents. I go into a society that is made up, let us say, of two or three thousand people. If I am asked to define "aggression," I could describe it in very gross terms that might not even be reproducible or completely communicable between us. And I could describe my deviants likewise in very gross labels. Nevertheless, I think within the same frame of reference as you do.

SPENCE: Sometimes it has to be that kind of definition or description because if it is not, it is not going to be public knowledge, and it is not going to be science.

GERARD: Dr. Schneider's attitude reminds me of an investigator putting in a proposal for research support who is fearful of specifying anything lest he be held to it; so he tries to make the description as vague as possible. You are afraid that if you admit that there is any isolable characteristic that you could describe in sentences, if not in numbers, that we are then going to clamp down and say, "Now, this is what you have agreed to work on the rest of your life." This is not so. We say, "Give us your thoughts as fast as you can put them into words, and we will see what we can do, coming along like geese gleaming behind you."

SCHNEIDER: That would all be fine if in fact the scientific operation did not take place in a social setting, and therefore none of man's mistakes that was ever published could catch up with him. That is to say, the whole activity of science is one in which either an individual or a team of investigators performs an operation and reports on it. Part of the procedure of receiving that report is literally to pick it to bits and to criticize it. If the scientific method, in fact, operated within a very rigorously controlled set of criteria so that people did not pick people to bits, I would be happy with it. It is an important factor to weigh.

SPENCE: That is a thing that has never bothered me, and I am picked to bits all the time.

GERARD: You are being defensive in terms of the personal relations. I could sympathize with you there.

SCHNEIDER: No, there are two sides to this. One is what I think you interpreted my statement to mean; namely, the fear that someone will become annoyed and not give a grant, or another investigator will make the first look like a fool. This, I think, is important; but it is not the paramount point. The second phase is the question, Will someone pick up and follow the lead that has been given? It is at this point that the group tends to throw out, not an idea in a paper, but the whole paper, and, in fact, whole people.

GERARD: This is correct. You are now talking about the sociological aspects of science and the limitations of scientists as human beings. This is what I have often called the "sheep factor." It is really extraordinary how extremely few instances there are in which somebody has set the pack off on a new line. When an experimenter puts out an idea, it may be wild or it may be ridiculous; but if he is a serious enough scientist, it is read. Then for ten years others come along and test it. Finally they may say, "Well, that's too bad, it's wrong!" But this is happening all the time. The great virtue of science is that each of these little pseudopods gets out sooner or later; then it is retracted, or cut off, or develops into a fixed organ. All that we are saying is, "Let's get them out into the open as fast as we can."

SCHNEIDER: Perhaps the classic example is that of Freud, who got pushed out of one hospital. He did not get a job that he had every reason to expect and should have gotten. If Freud had been another man, he would have accepted the incident and taken another job at a hospital. I argue strongly that this is essentially the same operation as that of increasing and implementing rigor in analysis.

By and large, what is going to happen if you insist upon your procedural steps at this stage is that at two different levels a series of potentially critical variables will be either disregarded or ignored; either through the rigor of the social situation operating to conformity, or through the rigor of scientific endeavor attempting to quantify and objectify *prematurely*. Yet I think that they are structurally identical phenomena. This seems to me to be the danger, particularly in the almost pre-infantile field, if you will pardon me, of psychiatry and mental disease. I think it is really at the level of polymorphous perverseness, and ought to be accepted as such. There should be exploring around for everything to find out what is what.

chapter 23

Further Thoughts on a
Multidisciplinary Approach

◆ ◆

KRUSE: We have frequently alluded to science and its method. Just what does it mean? Does each of us have the same conception of science? If we have mutual understanding of science, we will have taken another step ahead.

SPENCE: I always like to think of science as beginning with the observations or sense perceptions of an observing individual called a scientist; then on the basis of these observations, he attempts to formulate by operational definition what I call low order concepts—variables, if they are quantifiable; and factors, if they are not; next, on the basis of these factors, he discovers functional relationships between them, which constitute the level of laws; and then out of these, he evolves more abstract concepts called "theoretical concepts," which begin to tie together what had previously been isolated realms of relationships. There are many degrees of the integrating or theoretical concepts, the most highly developed of which are the Newtonian theory of the pre-Einsteinian period, and more recently the relativity theory.

In psychology we do not have anything much above the level of what I call the empirical laws. We have much of what I would call speculative theory, in which I would not engage to any extent, and which I would not condone. There are great individual differences in this regard in psychology. Then there is the pure empiricist,

the man who wants to do a little thinking.

GERARD: This, I think, is a matter of personal trait, not of field.

SCHNEIDER: My definition does not differ in any way. The investigator may start with something that sounds like a problem, even simply an interest in a phenomenon without even being able to define its boundaries. Or he may start out with a relatively more or less clearly defined problem. The sets of rules by which we work are reasonably clear. But a certain latitude that is exercised both in different disciplines and with different problems begins to make the break. That is, the humanist who is interested in the *why* of Coleridge's poems or what they really mean treats the rules and laws of science relatively more elastically and gives them more latitude in which to work. It is precisely this sort of latitude that is needed in the early development of the social sciences and the sciences of the emotions. It is for this reason that the definition of the social sciences, as sciences, was to some extent a pity. They should have been left among the humanities to develop as sciences when they could and when the time was opportune, not rushed into adolescence right away without giving them time to develop, expand, and grow.

I think that we are really in agreement on what science is. But there may be some difference on the question of how to conduct science with respect to certain kinds of problems and how, in fact, to phrase the problems, to deal with the problems, to specify the problems; a difference in strategy of research, rather than a fundamental difference in the frame of reference in which we work.

KRUSE: Do I understand that as a corollary of your belief, Dr. Schneider, all the approaches in the multidisciplinary approach should preferably be at the same stage of their maturity so that they may be used concurrently? Or would you grant that there will be different stages of their maturity, and that you will use them as you find them?

SCHNEIDER: It is the latter proposition. It is clear that neurophysiology—with respect to certain problems anyway—is far more advanced than either psychiatry or anthropology.

WITTKOWER: I subscribe to S. S. Stevens'* definition that science is a set of empirical propositions agreed upon by members of society. This definition contains in it the word "propositions"; on the other hand, it does not contain the word "knowledge." It leaves the door open for modifications. And I would only add that the definition applies to analysis—if you will read Freud's writings. He always started from the observational level with the clinical material, and drew his conclusions and formulated his concepts on the basis of these clinical observations.

GERARD: I like to define science as simply cumulative, organized, and tested common sense, and I do not care whether it has been done in a laboratory or elsewhere. But those words, I think, are important. I will not accept any limitations to the scientific mode of approach to the universe, except this: As long as we are attempting to understand, we are using the scientific method, and I can see no other approach; but when we are trying to enjoy or use, we are in different modes which need not be, and in fact are not, scientific. So if one is enjoying a literary work, one is functioning nonscientifically. When one tries to account for

his enjoyment, or to account for the processes on the part of the creator of the work that led him to create it, then one is functioning as a scientist. Reading Coleridge's *Ancient Mariner* is literary enjoyment; analyzing it is attempting to apply the same criteria and procedures of all scientists.

The stage in which we try to identify the variables of interest—I have called it the taxonomic stage—is like that of identifying the nouns of the language and the entities under consideration. The static stage is getting the simple static relations between them. The dynamic stage is the one where some of the verbs of existence come in. In it we enrich the language and we see how the variables interact in time and with changes. Finally, there is the holistic stage, the putting it all together with a certain amount of "Eingefühl." In fact, I think at the very end we come back to the kind of amorphous in-feeling which is a deep understanding of the situation, which goes beyond the analytic, beyond the verbal, and beyond the definition. Then we really know it. I suppose that this is a Bergsonian kind of statement; but to the extent that we are vague and limited at the beginning, we are suffering from failure rather than from the recognition of success.

KRUSE: What happens to newly discovered scientific evidence is a matter of considerable importance. Let me cite two eventualities. Both point up the uncertainties and vicissitudes inherent in the scientific method. A finding is not accepted until it is confirmed in other hands. Every now and then it happens that a piece of work is not repeated. It is left in limbo, neither confirmed nor outrightly denied and rejected because there has been no independent repetition.

The other eventuality is that a study meets with a veritable wave of inability to reproduce its results. Then after a time, sometimes as long as several decades, an investigator takes it up again, and confirms the results. That sets off an equally large wave of confirmation. What is the explanation of this course of events? In view of it and other considerations, should not a positive finding be weighted more heavily than a negative result?

---

* Stevens, S. S. "Psychology and the Science of Science," Chap. II in *Psychological Theory*, M. H. Marx (Ed.). New York: Macmillan, 1951.

Both events are unfortunate weaknesses in the use of the scientific method, at least in its aspect of verification.

SCHNEIDER: The weight of a positive finding depends partly on its relevance to the questions being asked. During the War certain kinds of questions became imminent and crucial, and almost any kind of methodology was admitted if it might even remotely bear on what was imperative to the national health and survival. On the other hand, when the investigator does get a positive finding, he may not infrequently find that the question is no longer asked. Furthermore, for him to keep going on the kinds of questions in which he is interested means all too often that it is necessary to accept half-findings, findings that cannot really be verified, but have to be taken on faith.

WITTKOWER: Now you are introducing one of the basic concepts of analytical thought that bears upon the point of nonacceptance. A basic principle of the analytical theory is that of economy of minimum effort, which Alexander has already described. This principle states that the organism functions, if possible, at a minimum of effort. Consequently, if a new view is presented, there is a disinclination to effect change. Thus the nonacceptance of ideas is based on the principle of economy of minimum effort. I accept what is there. The baby, for instance, wants the story told in exactly the same way with no modification.

The opposite of the principle of the economy of minimal effort is the principle of surplus energy. In Alexander's vector theory, energy is not saved, but expended; it is expended in playful experimentation.

So there is a balance in research, in science. The principle of the economy of minimum effort means no change; what is there, is right. Opposing it is the principle of surplus energy with desire to experiment, to change, to bring about improvement. According to the balance between these two forces, there is progress or stability in the state of affairs.

SPENCE: I have approached the topic differently. I have taken it up in terms of the particular problem that Dr. Kruse raised; namely, the acceptance of positive results. I think that there has been much too much tendency, at least in psychology, to follow what I call the empirical statistical point of view, which says that a particular result should be accepted with such-and-such confidence, say, a 5 per cent level. Let us assume that I find a relationship, a difference between two groups, and that the only confidence that I could have is that if I repeated it a hundred times, it would happen by chance only five times. This practice would be all right if the relationship under study were the only one that I knew.

But this is not the situation in which an experimenter in a fairly well-developed area of science finds himself. He knows a great number of other relationships. He also is in an area, I assume, that is sufficiently well-developed so that it has a theoretical structure upon which to make predictions. A theory has worked, let us say, in some seven, eight, or nine other cases, and now it predicts a certain result, and this result comes out with a statistical statement, the confidence statement at a 5 per cent level. I am very much more confident of that positive result because it fits into an existing body of knowledge, an existing structure. Yet statistics books do not in any way reflect the fact that a man is not completely ignorant, except for a particular isolated fact.

SCHNEIDER: As I understand Dr. Spence's point, every experiment has to do with several populations: that of the experiment itself, and those of other related experiments. We are caught up again in something which one knows but cannot measure. Statistics has not yet provided a good measure.

GERARD: It is measurable.

SPENCE: Some mathematicians think that it can be done, but that a new kind of statistics will have to be developed.

GERARD: The worth of an additional bit of information will depend on the probability of its being that way anyhow. If you know perfectly well that this die is always going to fall *1* because it is a loaded die, then it is of no value to you at all to have somebody peeking over the table and telling you that it is falling *1*. But if it is an honest die, then you have one-sixth chance of knowing it; and it is very valuable to you, if you are betting, to have a spy there telling you which way that die is falling.

As for the positive versus the negative result, I do not believe that there is a rule on that. I think that it depends in each case on the situation.

SPENCE: The statistician has a rule which the scientist with his additional knowledge does not take too seriously. The statistician will take the negative result much more seriously than he does a positive result. In the case of a negative report, he will say, "This is disproved." Yet, in the case of a positive result, he does not say that it is proved. In contrast, I put very much more faith in a positive result if I have all the additional knowledge.

GERARD: An investigator sometimes finds that a set of results obtained by one technician are not reproduced by another. Here the discrepancy may be solved on the basis of regularity in performance.

KRUSE: When an investigator cannot confirm another's reported findings which ultimately prove to be valid, the failure is usually due to faulty observation or manipulation. He has looked but not seen; or he has introduced something that should have been omitted; or he has left out something which should have been included.

On the basis of chance, it is justifiable to weight positive results tentatively.

GERARD: This I agree with. There are more ways in which the investigator can go wrong and not get positive results than there are in which he can go wrong and get them. Two different workers in two laboratories have been studying the relation of large doses of adrenalin to shock and stress. Working together, they found consistently that adult or young adult rats given adrenalin intravenously would survive a dose of 8.5 gamma per 100 gm. but would die at 9. Since this is an unusually sharp end point of lethality, they did not trust it. Accordingly, they checked it over and over again. But it really was so; hence, they were finally content with it. It was decided that the value could be used to determine the amount of adrenalin released in stressful situations. After an animal had been shocked, the amount of additional adrenalin necessary to produce death would be measured. The difference between the lethal doses for shocked and unshocked animals would represent the quantity of adrenalin endogenously liberated by shock.

At just about that time the controls became irregular. Rats did not live at 8.5 and die at 9 gamma per 100 gm.; they began to die all the way from 5 to 15. And this happened in the two laboratories and with the two groups. At the same time, animals which had been giving consistent results in unrelated experiments began to yield irregular results. The reason was unknown. Sometimes these things will happen.

SPENCE: We have had a very interesting example of that. We had found that human subjects who scored high on an emotionality test showed a higher level of eyelid conditioning than did those who scored low. We had obtained this result in a number of experiments. It raised the question, What accounts for the difference between the two groups? Were the subjects who yielded high test values chronically emotional? Or was it the noxious character of the air puff that induced different amounts of emotionality? When the strength of the air puff was reduced to a point where it was phenomenologically pleasant, we got no difference in the level of conditioning in these two groups of subjects. That appeared to settle the matter. Then we remembered that we had not tested the effects of both the weak and strong stimulus. When this was done, again there was no difference between the two groups. For a while we were really puzzled; but the explanation turned out to be very simple. The experimenter conducting the tests had a very different cultural background from that of the subjects. They were frightened by him; they were merely responding to him. This experimenter who did not get the difference between groups produced a high level of conditioning in both because he frightened both. When we installed another experimenter with whom the subjects could feel at ease, the usual difference between groups reappeared.

KRUSE: You have brought out the point that an investigator affects the subject. Your experience would indicate that psychodynamic factors do enter into the experimental approach and must be taken into account.

WITTKOWER: It is an important point. Here we are concerned with behavior, with what the research worker or scientist does or does not do. His personality and his effect on the subject come into consideration. Does he have the curiosity that is so necessary in an investigator? To a certain extent whether he gets positive or negative results depends on his personality. Dr. Spence has just cited an excellent example of the extent to which the experimenter influences the experiment. I should like to add another.

In working on gastric fistula Margolin had a patient who always produced increase of acidity whenever the experimenter came near her. He found out that the girl was sexually stimulated by the presence of the experimenter, and had libidinized the opening in her stomach. Consequently, the results of the experiment, as far as the objective observer was concerned, were completely falsified by the personality of the experimenter and the relationship between them.

SPENCE: These things, I admit, have been neglected a great deal in experimental psychology. But we are not blind to them; we are discovering them.

I can give another example showing the effect of the sex relationship. We have a whole set of experiments on verbal learning with a memory drum. The subjects have to learn to associate word A with word B, C with D, and E with F, and so on. As they always are in verbal learning, the women were slightly higher than the men in this test. Suddenly this sex difference in the results between the men and women became accentuated to twice as great. When we looked into the situation, we discovered that a young and rather good-looking male investigator had conducted the series which gave the magnified sex difference in results. It was clear that he inspired the women to do very well. In contrast, since he was aggressive toward men, he antagonized them; consequently they did very poorly. We now systematically rotate male and female experimenters.

WITTKOWER: Not only that, an attractive girl is, of course, different from an unattractive girl. When a very attractive female clinical psychologist conducts the Rorschach, the male patients do not give sexual responses because they feel inhibited to present her with them.

SPENCE: Such things are expected in clinical psychology; but not in the laboratory, the human laboratory, where experimentation has been going on for years. The psychologists have just missed these points completely.

GERARD: While working on learning, Dr. Spence has found a technic which would enable him to get at sociological factors. Why not go ahead and use it? There is something entirely comparable, the use of the placebo control, in nearly all psychosociological experiments.

SPENCE: We have turned over this problem, the role of the experimenter in laboratory experiments with adult human subjects, to our personality psychologists who are now studying it systematically. I believe that they are going to turn up relevant variables in relationships that the experimental psychologists, working in a laboratory, have just completely ignored. And I am sure that many of the laws either are going to be changed or are going to disappear when these relationships are discovered.

GERARD: This illustrates a point which we have discussed. You went ahead, obtained data, and formulated detailed laws, some of which were invalidated because you neglected some variables. Your reaction is that when you go back to the problem, you will know what you are doing; that you will have something manipulative which you would never have had without the initial study.

WITTKOWER: I do not see that it is quite so manipulable. How are you going to control it?

SPENCE: We do not control it; we actually introduce it; we put a man with a man, a woman with a man, and a woman with a woman.

WITTKOWER: Suppose something goes wrong between the man and man or the woman and woman? You do not control it.

There are innumerable factors, such as differences in tone of voice.

SCHNEIDER: Again we have our roles reversed. Here I am arguing for you to become much more rigorous, and you think you have sufficient control to go ahead with the experiment as it is.

SPENCE: What changes come about in the experimenter's laws as he discovers more relevant variables is a matter of the development of the body of scientific knowledge.

GERARD: In our discussion earlier of non-acceptance of new data and concepts, Dr. Wittkower pointed out the parsimony of ideas and the tendency to go on repeating the same ritual, like the baby wanting the story told the same way, rather than to try a new tack; to accept the current theory rather than to get a new one. This is, of course, perfectly true. For that reason the need is to find someone somewhere with enough originality to restructure the problem and its issues from time to time.

Natural science and biology have been concerned largely with the matter-energy relationship in which the interaction of observer and observed, or entity and environment, is relatively negligible. The experimenter can therefore go ahead and operate. It makes mighty little difference whether a man or a woman is reading the instrument, say a spectrophotometer; he or she simply marks down pointer readings. On the other hand, the mental and social sciences have been concerned, without being aware of this basic difference, with information and communication. But communication involves an interaction between the sender and recipient; so, obviously, the roles of the experimenter and subject, the interacting members, here become highly significant.

Since these interactions almost always have some element of purpose in them, that is, the system has a utility and seeks a goal, there has been the great problem of translating from mechanistic to teleological language. I feel very much encouraged by the growing attention to the theory of information and communication.

I have thought of a fascinating problem that, I believe, could be worked up. One can quantitate the degree of determinacy or indeterminacy in the processes, the forces, that generate structures. Every structure is the result of a process. To the extent that the resulting structure has high regularity, like the cells of a honeycomb, it is very certain that the process which produced it was highly determined. In contrast, to the extent that the resulting structure shows statistical variation, it is equally certain that it was produced by a stochastic or chancy, rather than a highly determined, process. It is worth noting that the polygonal shape of epidermal cells is highly variable although its formation certainly involves no volition, planned action, or behavior in the usual sense; whereas the honeycomb, produced by the action of living entities with some kind of individual volitions, shows great regularity, and so determinism, in its formation.

Thus, structure is a residue of information. How much information is needed to reproduce a structure? The more chaotic it is, the less information is needed; the more precise it is, the more information is needed. Here the information may indeed be viewed much as is negative entropy. I think that one could develop this approach to organic structure very profitably.

KRUSE: Another area, the proper use of statistics, should not be neglected in studies. Too often the course of events is: The biological or medical investigator sets up a study according to his own notions. The statistician is not consulted during this stage of planning. At the end of the study the investigator has a large amount of data. He knows very little about statistics; hence, he dumps the material into the lap of the statistician with the polite request, "Please give me an answer." It is almost as though he regards statistics as an automatic machine. But whether it be statistics or an automatic machine, one has to ask the right questions in order to obtain appropriate answers. The statistician cannot be expected to know all the fine and detailed points of the biology of every disease; therefore, he is not in a position to ask the right questions. On the other hand, the biologist is apt not to understand the technical points about sampling, coding, and such statistical methods as correlation. Not a few studies planned and conducted without consultation with a statistician have produced jumbo-sized headaches when the time came for analysis of data. Essentially it is another variation of the same problem; that is, the necessity of bringing together experts from different disciplines who do not have the same language or the same technics. Unless the investigator is versed in statistics, it is highly desirable that he consult the statistician at the very beginning of a proposed study, and that they confer about it, with each instructing the other. Then, and only then, is the time to begin the design of the study.

SPENCE: Psychologists do use statistics much more than do the biologists. This is what is known as a compensatory device. Yet it is interesting that the most modern technics of statistics come from biological statisticians, rather than from psychological statisticians. I am thinking of R. A. Fisher.

We always get careful advice from the statistician on the design of our experiments.

KRUSE: If there were a closer association between clinical investigator and statistician, even more rapid progress might be made on quantification in biology and medicine.

SCHNEIDER: On the other hand, I do not believe that the investigator ought to accept unquestioningly that the statistician can do everything. The experimenter can think of things to be done in which the statistician literally can be of no help.

GERARD: The statistician cannot formulate the problem.

KRUSE: I did not say that the statistician alone should plan the experiment. As a matter of fact, I said quite the contrary. I emphasized the need for joint effort of the biological or clinical investigator and statistician.

WITTKOWER: In our Department we write up a research memorandum and send it to a statistician, who tells us whether the experiment is feasible. He is consulted several times in the course of research and helps in the actual drawing up of the final results. This arrangement has worked moderately well.

We recently had a long Departmental meeting on the value of controls. After many hours, agreement was reached that controls are of limited value in psychiatry because—and here I come back to our bone of contention—certain things are simply not codifiable. For instance, love or aggressiveness cannot be measured.

GERARD: Aggressiveness has been measured.

SCHNEIDER: But the way in which it was measured does not help the psychiatrist.

WITTKOWER: That is just it. It can be done in the experimental situation. But the animal experiments, although extremely interesting, are not applicable to the clinical situation of a patient.

SCHNEIDER: The statistician is behind the psychiatrist and all too often the social anthropologist and the sociologist. The statistician's technics have not yet caught up with many of the problems which the social scientists are able to formulate at least.

GERARD: I agree. As Dr. Spence said earlier, statistics are a crutch. Statistics are used when there is nothing better. It takes no statistics to know that hitting a man on the head with a pickax is going to kill him. It has to be done only once to be very convincing, twice to be absolutely certain. It is not necessary to see how many times the association happens.

KRUSE: To get back to the components of clinical psychiatric observations, I do not believe that the statistician will ever furnish them. He has to depend on the psychiatrist to break down the components.

WITTKOWER: But only to a limited extent actually. For example, it is possible, to a certain extent, to assess overt anxiety. But as for unconscious anxiety, there is no method available to quantify it.

GERARD: Don't you talk about a patient's being more anxious, or less anxious?

WITTKOWER: Well, yes, but . . .

GERARD: Then you are quantifying it.

WITTKOWER: Yes, but very roughly.

SPENCE: What about electricity? It is quantified by the movement of the pointer, by the solidification of an electrolytic substance, by the heating of a light. Electricity itself is something else. Anxiety is in the same category as electricity. Why cannot this unconscious motivation, unconscious anxiety, or fear be quantified by something related to it, such as the intensities of certain kinds of mechanisms.

WITTKOWER: There are so many. One could say that tension may be a criterion of unconscious anxiety. But there are many others. I feel that you are trying to make something exact.

GERARD: All I mean by "quantify" is the ability to say "more or less." It is all that we are asking.

WITTKOWER: Well, if you leave it at that—

SPENCE: I am quite happy to do that.

GERARD: This is all we want. If you can say, "I can tell whether it is more or less," you are quantifying. It is objective, it is reproducible. From there we will undertake to guarantee that in this year or this century, I do not know which, we will be able to measure it and get indices on it that one can quantify numerically.

WITTKOWER: If you pick up a child and ask, "How much do you love me?" and the child puts his arms around your neck and demonstrates his love, can you measure the amount of love by the pressure exerted on your neck?

GERARD: Probably not. But it is not so long since time was judged in terms of subjective experience, "It's a long time or a short time." But then Galileo came along with his pendulum and invented clocks; now we measure time by billionths of a second.

In our laboratory we are measuring love. The pediatrician working on this reports that a newborn baby can tell whether the person who picks him up loves him or doesn't love him. How does the baby tell? And how does the pediatrician know that the baby tells? When the baby is picked up understandingly, and the pediatrician makes a confirming judgment on the handling, the baby relaxes, flushes, its skin temperature goes up, it acts as if it is content. When the baby is picked up un-understandingly or roughly, the opposite changes occur.

SCHNEIDER: These are the rocks on which studies founder. It is said that a baby knows whether the person who picks him up loves him. It is measured in terms of skin temperature. What happens then is that skin temperature tends to be identified as the essential, concrete, and real measurable effect in love.

GERARD: This is not a bad direction but a bad experiment. Let me at once reassure you that the skin temperature is only one of a dozen different measurements that we are trying to apply. Actually we are not trying to measure love; we are trying to measure autonomic reaction. We are trying to find out, first, the extent to which the different autonomic responses do or do not go together, and therefore the extent to which we will be able to use them as a measure of mood. We are also measuring rate of salivation in older subjects, the shrinkage in the nasal mucosa, the heart rate, and other phenomena. We are saying frankly that we are simply starting to get the measurable experimental variables. We will hope, then, that we can develop some kind of an interrelation.

One of the hopes with which we started was that perhaps we could get an objective test of psychoanalytic dynamics. With the shift of the erotogenic zone from the mouth, to the anus, to the genitals, we would see whether autonomic responses from these regions occurred at the predicted times. Stated that bluntly, it is obviously too simple, but a more sophisticated relation might work out.

KRUSE: One way of measuring such entities as love and anxiety is the use of an index. Another procedure is to ascertain whether the entity is divisible into components. It may be that the entity may not have been examined in this light, and that it proves to have components upon a search for them. If components are found for anxiety, for example, another way is opened to measure it.

SPENCE: I have an operational definition of anxiety. I have a particular set of items, and the nature of the response to them is what I mean by anxiety. That is all that I mean by anxiety.

Given a variable which can be ascertained, the first step in measurement of it is to study its reliability. If I repeat the operation, will I get the same result? Let us assume that I obtain a consistent measurement. Then comes the second question, Does it have any significance? As a model,

I may cite the so-called Bergmann index: It is the number of hairs on Dr. Bergmann's head, divided by his weight, multiplied by the square root of his heart rate. This is a perfect, precise, operationally defined concept; and the likelihood that it will bear any relation to anything else is probably close to zero. I can, of course, take any measure. Whether it has significance or not determines whether it continues to exist in science, and vice versa. If we continue to discover relationships between it and other defined concepts, we are satisfying the requirements of science. This is all that science looks for: relationships between concepts. Thus, there are these two aspects of any operational definition of a concept: one is its reliability, and the other is its significance.

WITTKOWER: My definition would be entirely different from yours because there is a basic difference in concept. You define anxiety as what you can measure; whereas I would define it as what an individual feels. A patient may have anxiety now, and half an hour later he may have none. It may have been converted or transformed.

SPENCE: My concept happens to remain consistent. I apply the same measuring instruments to the individual a week from now, and I will get the same results.

WITTKOWER: Are you dealing, then, with fear or with anxiety?

SPENCE: What you name it is immaterial.

GERARD: I believe that you overstate it.

SPENCE: The relationship is very high, about 87.

GERARD: Upon measuring the catacholes in the urine of medical students just before an examination is announced, the level is found to be 1; after the announcement, it is 5. At the height of the examination or just after, the level is 25. This is a highly changing measure, something that corresponds to what I think you mean by anxiety.

WITTKOWER: Fear.

GERARD: Isn't anxiety fear of an internal, rather than an external, danger?

WITTKOWER: The original definition of fear, to go back to Freud, is that fear is objective anxiety. If a lion comes into this room, we are all afraid. That is objective anxiety; that is fear. In contrast to it, there is moral anxiety and neurotic anxiety. What Dr. Spence measured is objective anxiety, that is, fear.

SPENCE: It is a measure of an individual's fearfulness, or tendency to be fearful. Fear is taken into our measure as follows: An individual has been living in the world, and he now responds with an emotional syndrome to different numbers and varieties of environmental events. An individual who responds with an emotional syndrome to many of them is what we call a "fearful person." We unfortunately used the word anxiety." We should have used "fearful," or "fearfulness." I think "emotional" would have been an even better term.

KRUSE: To continue the example in which a lion brings on fear, let us assume that none of us has experience with, or knowledge of, this kind of animal. While we are sitting here, a lion appears; we are fearful— . . .

WITTKOWER: There would be a variation in our reactions according to our personality structures and past histories.

KRUSE: Twenty years later we are sitting here; there is no lion in the city but we are anxious. Is fear still operating?

GERARD: I can cite an actual instance. A panther appeared in our neighborhood in Vermont six or seven years ago. It has not been there since, but every summer there are rumors of this panther's having appeared in one region or another. Many of the people in the area will not go out at night because they are either anxious or afraid, as the case may be, of this panther. That illustrates your question.

KRUSE: Are the people now fearful or are they anxious?

SPENCE: Aren't they fearful of a symbol?

WITTKOWER: Yes. When Dr. Spence tests fear, he tests at the same time fearfulness which is anxiety-proneness. To take an illustration, the blitz in London was most unpleasant. There was danger; everybody could be killed. For some people, on the basis of their past history, the actual experience of the air raid meant something that they could not stand. It was too much for them; they had to clear out of town. In short, objective anxiety became merged with neurotic anxiety.

SPENCE: We say "conditioned fear response."

WITTKOWER: That is really using different terminology, but it amounts to the same thing.

KRUSE: I raised the question about anxiety in order that we might consider possible relationships or components which are more readily or more precisely quantifiable.

GERARD: My psychiatric colleagues and I, in discussing this topic, agreed that anxiety is fear of inner dangers. Fear was accepted as the more general term.

Here, I believe, we may really get down to our area of deepest disagreement; and I shall purposely make it very sharp. When Dr. Wittkower tells me that there is a latent anxiety which determines behavior and which is inherently nonmeasurable, I say to him that he is putting an entelechy or gremlin in the body. He is simply giving a name to something that no one knows anything about. It is utterly worthless as long as it remains in that status.

SCHNEIDER: It is a way of accounting for variance that is measurable, although it is not known what the relevant variables are.

GERARD: Dr. Wittkower stated that it is not measurable.

SCHNEIDER: It is measurable. It is not precisely measurable.

WITTKOWER: It may not be measurable, but it is demonstrable.

SCHNEIDER: Then it is measurable.

WITTKOWER: In the process of repression a word is on the tip of a person's tongue, but the word does not come out. It is not utterly preposterous to assume that the word is there.

GERARD: When you state that latent anxiety is demonstrable but not measurable, I am saying that your position is untenable.

SPENCE: If I am going to postulate something, I must state its relation to something else.

SCHNEIDER: We will. This is, I think, a basically different mode of operation.

SPENCE: If an investigator is going to introduce theoretical concepts from a certain observable behavior—because that is what your concepts are—he has to have a fairly good knowledge of the observations. In my opinion you are not doing what you think you are doing. You are making some very precise assumed relationships between specific behavior phenomena and certain words, which are not just words but are words which have tie-ups with past early events in childhood. You say, "So much of this kind of childhood produces so much of this kind of anxiety." I am not talking about "anxiety" in the sense of observed things; I am talking about just purely a concept. But unless you tie it up with behavior, there is no possibility of getting them together. And my knowledge of psychoanalysis is that it is very nicely tied up.

GERARD: This is very interesting because you and I are insisting that the psychoanalysts can do better than they are willing to admit they can do.

WITTKOWER: We are dealing with the dynamic concept that something is there which cannot be observed.

SPENCE: I would grant that. But you cannot just talk about something there. As soon as you start to talk about it, you start to make statements of what relations it has to something else. These relations are all that I count as definitions or guiding lines that permit you to communicate with other persons.

If I were to say that an "ABEP," for example, is responsible for a particular symptom of behavior, it would not help you in the slightest until I begin to describe in what way ABEP is related to the symptom, what conditions produce changes in ABEP, and what relationships exist between ABEP and other known things. This is all that we are maintaining.

WITTKOWER: I cannot see any argument about this.

GERARD: I simply was trying to make very pointed that when you deny that you can measure anxiety, you are doing yourself an injustice; because if you had no index of its presence or absence, it would be absolutely useless to you.

WITTKOWER: But I did not say that. I

said that Dr. Spence measures overt anxiety and therefore deals with only one particular situation.

GERARD: And I say that you measure latent anxiety in some way also.

WITTKOWER: That is right.

SPENCE: You specify how it comes to be more and less.

WITTKOWER: That is right.

SPENCE: There is a very considerable difference in the GSR (galvanic skin response; also called PGR, psychogalvanic response) of the anxious and the nonanxious subjects. This adapts in the nonanxious, nonemotional subjects; it does not adapt in the highly emotional subjects. We now think that this emotionality is what we call "drive." A fearful person has a lot of drive. A hungry person is a little emotional because of excitation. Here we become a trifle physiological; for we think of it as being the sum-total or the summation of the afferent excitation into the hypothalamic centers. We postulate that this emotionality or drive is the level of activity of certain centers in the hypothalamic region.

GERARD: I am inclined to think that way.

WITTKOWER: Mental diseases are frequently precipitated by frustrating life-situations in response to which the individual withdraws libido from the external world. We call this process introversion.

GERARD: That you can measure in terms of the number of telephone calls he makes, or gets, or the number of times he goes out with people.

WITTKOWER: Yes. Anxiety, in the psychoanalytical view, is a sample re-experience of primary anxiety. This sample operates as a danger signal; the dangers are of unconscious origin. There are two kinds of dangers which threaten the individual: (1) the danger arising from an increasing excitation which occurs when repressed impulses reinforced by charges of introverted libido threaten to invade the conscious ego; and (2) the danger which originally initiated the repression of the unconscious impulse, i.e., fear of punishment for a prohibited impulse.

SPENCE: From my point of view, the anxiety which you describe is inference. What we have are emotionality and the symptom-formation. What we want to do is to classify people in relation to the amount of overt fearfulness that they show. If we went no farther than that, we would have two groups of people. As for those people who do not show fearfulness, we would begin to analyze and study them in terms of symptom-formation.

We have found that those subjects whom the psychiatrist diagnosed as having "anxiety state" gave the highest level of eyelid conditioning. But some individuals do not now exhibit fearfulness because in the course of their personality development, they have developed other reactions, excessive compulsion, or conversion hysteria. Those who have excessive compulsive tendencies show less conditioning because they are less anxious. Those with conversion hysteria showed no conditioning because they are not anxious, they have no emotionality. Insofar as persons can get control of themselves and allow their defense mechanisms to reduce their anxiety in the experimental situation, our theory was that they would show less conditioning.

Those with anxiety states, with no defenses, should exhibit the highest level of conditioning because we think of anxiety as being something that is related to drive strength. In other words, all people who are highly emotional ought to be at a high level of conditioning.

SCHNEIDER: I think that the issue is not that there are statements that can be made about certain phenomena but at the moment they cannot be quantified. The issue is: Where do you want to devote the bulk of your attention? Which direction does the strategy of research take? What are the critical and decisive studies? That is our assigned topic for today. It is really a practical problem. Should research be held up at the level of "A child loves: How much does it love?" or should it be concerned with developing devices and technics for the quantification of such emotions? My position is: Let's let quantification catch up as it can. Although we are fairly sure what we are working with, we are still not quite sure enough.

GERARD: Now you are asking a pragmatic, not a philosophical, question. You are asking: Granted that both can be done, where should I put my investment?

SCHNEIDER: Where to put one's investment is also a question of, "Can both be done?"

GERARD: It is a fair question, but it is very different from your previous question. You are now asking, "Which can be done? With a limited number of people and resources, which line of research should be encouraged?" I would answer that both can be done by the same person at different times, by different people at the same time, maybe even by one person at the same time.

KRUSE: I thought for the moment that Dr. Schneider was suggesting that we draw up a priority list of research topics.

SCHNEIDER: That is what I hoped to do.

KRUSE: Two types of priority lists are possible depending on the criteria. In one, the basis is opportuneness. What can be done readily? What topics are most easily studied? What are the subjects for which there are available technics? The other type of list would be based on the relative importance of the topics. Some of the subjects might even be unapproachable at the moment from the standpoint of methodology. Technics would have to be evolved. On the other hand, it would be most fortunate if methods were available. Thus the closer the two types of lists correspond, the more favorable it would be for progress.

The history of medicine seems to show that knowledge about a disease has its own inscrutable way of unfolding. At one point the clinician brings forth evidence; at another, it may be the experimentalist or epidemiologist. It is always in a definite sequence. That is not to say that only one starting point or only one sequence is possible. But the starting point does influence the course, and one method does influence the next. Accumulated and available knowledge may await integration until a particular interviewing step is taken.

SCHNEIDER: I wonder whether part of the difficulty is that we have started our thinking at too abstract a level; and that actually we tend to choose different kinds of problems, which are relatively more or less amenable to different technics.

SPENCE: I am sure of that. Experimental

psychologists think that their field is reasonably amenable to quantitative technics. I would certainly not want to be in the position of not being able to work with quantification. Methodological preference is one of the considerations that determines what field a man selects for his life work. He becomes a scientist in one area rather than another because he does or does not like to quantify.

SCHNEIDER: In a sense, problem choice is partly a function of the methodology.

KRUSE: The socioanthropological approach in research has the opportunity of working both sides of the street. On the one hand, the social factors which contribute to mental disease; on the other hand, such epidemiological characteristics as incidence and age distribution may be studied. Even an actual epidemic could be investigated to ascertain its mode of transmission; panic is an example of disease in a mass.

The epidemiological approach has undergone development of variations over the years. Originally, disease was studied in its natural social and cultural setting in one locality. Somewhat later, conditions in two localities were studied and compared. Another form of investigation was to compare the situation in the same locality after a lapse of years. Most recently, a new element has been introduced into the epidemiological approach, an arrangement whereby for the test group one variable in the community is changed while adequate controls are provided. These several procedures now provide social scientists with a variety of technical maneuvers.

SCHNEIDER: It is exactly here, in the social realm, that I have been thinking of the decisive problems. Small inbred populations are available now that probably will not be fifty or sixty years hence; for instance, the oceanic island groups with populations that are genetically inbred for ten or fifteen generations. An intensive analysis of mental disease in such a setting would be illuminating. How to control for biology, including genetics, and for culture, and at the same time hold constant a mental disease as an entity, is one of the crucial areas of study.

Another decisive area of study is how to

get a group like this together in the morning, and then end up in the evening having everybody at least speaking with each other. Team research is one of the most difficult operations.

WITTKOWER: In a study based on the libido theory, the subjects selected were the worst patients in the institution. They were the stool eaters and smearers; one had eaten a package of flypaper. Their illness was of long duration, fifteen years or more. They had been given up as therapeutically hopeless; it was agreed that absolutely nothing could be done for them. They were called "burned out" schizophrenics.

On the basis of the libido theory I postulated that it might be possible to do something for these patients if their primitive needs were gratified. The subjects were divided into two groups. The control group was treated along traditional lines, with occupational therapy, which after a short time had to be given up. But on the basis of the postulation, the test group, most of whom were mute, were given dirt to play with. One of the patients plunged into the pile of dirt. She was the only patient in the group who had been speaking, and her speech had been in Yiddish. Suddenly she started to talk in English and from that point on spoke only in that tongue. All the patients began to make little mud pies, and as time went on there was improvement in their personal habits. Whereas previously they had been incontinent, they now developed control. One patient, after two or three months, went about washing continually, as she had developed a reaction formation.

We switched from dirt to asbestos powder, and immediately the patients regressed completely. The incontinence, both in defecation and urination, and destructive actions all returned; hence, we again provided them with dirt. Later we gave them crayons; their choice of color was brown. Then we switched to lipstick, and some of them learned to apply it quite skillfully. Next they were given dolls to play with, and after they had learned to play with them, we introduced dancing. After three months there was disappearance of the anal interest which had dominated the scene at the beginning, and swearing took place with genital rather than anal terms. After five months all patients in the test group, but one, had begun to speak. By this time they had become orderly, played with each other, would sit around a table and read magazines, and showed signs of mutual affection.

At the end of six months we decided to have the one relatively unimproved patient try painting the wall with water paints. At first she threw away the brush and took her hands and smeared the paint on the wall as she had done with her excreta. Suddenly a change occurred. She began to talk, to attend tea parties, and finally she was able to work in the cafeteria.

In summary, with patients who had regressed to a narcissistic organization, we conducted a study based on the libido theory. We offered them some media which corresponded to their level of regression. They responded to it because it was done with the attitude of understanding what they wanted. And they responded to such an extent that animals were returned to the realm of human beings.

SCHNEIDER: In the field of social science, it is difficult to set up experiments of this sort. For example, I became interested in the fact that the rate of hysteria among the Zulus was at first fairly small, but that it rose rapidly, with about 94 per cent of the women giving clear-cut evidence of peak episodes. It is not a simple matter to design a study on this subject that will contain adequate controls and at the same time reveal the crucial variables.

SPENCE: Your problem is not unlike that of Kepler when he was observing the planets; you have to take what is there.

WITTKOWER: Our Department in McGill University is preparing to undertake jointly with the Department of Sociology a research project with school children. Mental health is the dependent variable; but we want to concentrate on the normal, not the abnormal, and particularly the range of normal in the group. Furthermore, we want to include as many psychiatric and sociological factors as possible. The analyst will move into the family and examine every member.

Our immediate concern is the selection of a sample. We plan to study Canadian, Protestant children of the third generation who are in the tenth grade of school. After they have been screened, they will be divided into groups according to their emotional stability; but it should be emphasized that they will still be in the range of normality. We will concentrate on the upper and lower quarters, and compare them in respect to family background and sociological aspects. Essentially it is a basic study in interdisciplinary research.

SCHNEIDER: Is there going to be an attempt to specify types of family structure, not in the simple terms of numbers of members of the family but rather in terms of internal organization and relationships? Besides, as another aspect, the family has its place and relationship in the community. In a study of kinship terminology we have thrown some light on the first point. People who say that their fathers were warm, friendly, and intimate, will always also say that the father was the stronger authority than the mother. But if they are asked who had most authority in the household, it turns out that the warm and friendly fathers do not, on the whole, tend to have most authority. The usual appellations for the male parent form a series: Pa, Pappy, Paw, Pop, Daddy, Dad, Father, and The Boss. If the father is the strong authority, the range of kinship terms used becomes very narrow; the father is likely to be addressed as "Father" or "Dad," but rarely as "Pop." On the other hand, where father is warm, friendly, and intimate, he is often addressed as "Dad" or "Pop."

It could be concluded from the study that with the type of family structure which is in a sense culturally sanctioned, the role of the father tends to be relatively narrowly and explicitly defined. But with the type of family structure that is not squarely sanctioned, the father tends to play more than one role. In consequence there is a real uncertainty about the father-image which is reflected in the frequency of kinds of terms in which he is addressed.

KRUSE: How about first names?

SCHNEIDER: The use of the first name for the parent is very rare in this particular culture, but it is universal in some cultures. It is attended with difficulties. The child refuses to accept the differentiation between himself and his father, and this puts the latter in an untenable position, or at least often makes it hard for him to carry off his role. If a child tends to identify himself with his father, not much more is needed to have the child say, "What authority do you really have over me?"

WITTKOWER: I am sure that the sociologist in our study is considering such points.

SCHNEIDER: The course of the discussion has been surprising. I came prepared with a packet full of concrete studies.

GERARD: We have raised our questions and aired our prejudices.

KRUSE: And we have established tolerance, a common language, and rapport, major ingredients of cooperation.

ADDENDA

SPIEGEL: I believe that it is possible to develop a concept, such as social role, in a manner which will permit integration of psychoanalytical and psychosocial concepts. The concept of social role is one of a number of concepts that need to be developed in order to make the bridge. But once a bridge is established, that does not mean that the whole system of ideas of the structure and the function of the personality which has been developed by psychoanalysis needs to be thrown out. Instead, the system needs to be broadened and integrated.

The concept of social role can contribute to this broadening because it permits human behavior to be described from the point of view of the social system, including its values. The values are one of the elements that go into the structure of the particular role. For example, because of values the mother's role in one culture is structured differently from her role in another. Then too, from patterns of different cultures in their day-to-day activities, persons are located in their social group through the social role. In a sense, it is a finding mechanism. Again, from the point of view of psychodynamics and the structure of the personality comes the pertinent question, What is the motivation of the individual playing the role? Framed in that manner, the question is asked from the standpoint of the superego, ego, and id. The motivation to play roles is governed by all the factors within the personality that are traditionally included in psychoanalysis.

But, when this concept was broached to a group of analysts, their feeling of threat was so great that they saw no virtue or value in it as an aid to integration. Also its unfamiliarity did not enhance its welcome. They have not yet reached the point of appreciating the usefulness of this concept.

LIDDELL: I think that it is important to point out the hazards to interdoctrinal acceptance and cooperation. One lies in the adoption of categorical thinking when attempting research collaboration with those in other areas. For example, Freud's notion of oral stage, anal state, phallic stage is categorical thinking. He did not say what was done, what was observed. He gave categorical terms loaded with meanings, which the other person resists. Pavlov has done this. "Experimental neurosis" is another heavily loaded technical term which has created obstacles to bringing the phenomenon into relation with other areas of dynamics and psychology. All of us would profit by adopting procedural thinking; by saying what we actually do and what we actually observe; and by using as little colored and loaded terminology as possible.

Integration of interdisciplinary evidence presents another hazard. Presently we are interested in the cholinergic and adrenergic blood changes in emotion. Resentment, anger, and anxiety, as observed clinically, can be correlated with the effects of blood samples on a strip of rabbit jejunum. Actually, attempting to reason from specific blood changes, such as the rise and fall of blood potassium, to the loosely characterized types of emotional experience is like taking a lover's leap. But we hope to bridge this gap. With the goat as the experimental animal, we are attempting to correlate his emotional reactions, induced by various manipulations, with changes in the potassium and sodium levels of his blood. With this technic we do not have to read the mind of the goat as to what emotions it is experiencing; we simply report what is done to the goat, his reactions, and his blood changes. Furthermore, our manipulations of the animal are reproducible in any hands. But to make this tremendous jump from blood changes to supposed emotional status in the human is something else.

HOLLINGSHEAD: In an interdisciplinary approach to the causation of mental disease, whether it be in research or in a conference discussion, there is a hazard that in striving for agreement, knowledge will be reduced to the least common denominator. We reach this reduction because we do not understand the other man's field, his methodological procedures, his use of data, and his derivation of inferences. Consequently, we may think we have more agreement than is actually the case.

I would agree with Dr. Liddell that in this type of operation we need to state our point of departure and frame of reference, to make our concepts explicit, and to stipulate what we mean by them. That is, we need to specify so that we can isolate the particular part of a phenomenon with which we are working. Then we have to observe our phenomenon in terms of these concepts, and in such a way that the results can be verified.

METTLER: It appeared to me that when we embarked upon this Conference with its specified objective of a multidisciplinary approach, we were heading for the extinction of the individual investigator. That prospect greatly worried me. But actually it does not happen. What happens is that the individual investigator assumes a new role of tremendous importance because the multidisciplinary approach points up something which only one man can do, but which no one in all conscience would otherwise have bothered to investigate on an individual basis.

FINESINGER: There is no doubt that in psychiatry the trend is to a multidisciplinary approach, a team approach. On the other hand, much time may be wasted by teams trying to do things which one investigator can do much better.

One other point, an investigator learns to operate very precisely in one area. Usually when he moves into another area, he forgets about the use of scientific methodology and criteria. Indeed, the validity of his judgment on matters outside his field may be questioned.

KRUSE: One virtue of the multidisciplinary approach is that it accelerates and increases the collection of data. It also points out associations which are to be pursued. But it is unlikely that it will replace the individual integrator because usually some one person ultimately has to put all of the pieces together.

HOLLINGSHEAD: There is another advantage to the multidisciplinary approach: it shows up weaknesses in any one approach which the individual investigator working alone may not see. However, one of the real hazards of interdisciplinary research is that it tends to make the workers more ego-defensive than they otherwise might be and creates problems of interpersonal relations in the team. Another type of problem is that of communications: whether one learns enough about the other's frame of reference, the way he thinks, and his terminology.

FINESINGER: It is necessary to differentiate between the multidisciplinary approach with representatives from various fields and the unitary team approach with investigators in the same field. Five physicists working together in the same discipline will correct each other. One disadvantage of the multidisciplinary approach in the psychiatric field is that everybody in the project, whether he be a sociologist, psychologist, or physiologist, usually wants to do psychotherapy.

LIDDELL: Dr. W. Gray Walter informed me that the electroencephalographic pattern is simpler in a child than in an adult. Interestingly enough, a child's dreams are frank wish-fulfillments; an adult's dreams are highly elaborate. Possibly the electroencephalographic evidence, considered in conjunction with the age-differential character of dreams, constitutes an actual objective demonstration that the cerebral processes are simpler in the child than in the adult. Here is an instance in which interdisciplinary material can be integrated.

METTLER: It is helpful to the psychologist to know all about the objective evidence that underlies the field of psychology. But just how is he going to get that necessary information? When is he going to stop becoming familiar with all the organic material that underlies psychology and start performing experiments? On the other hand, when he is preoccupied in his own field, how can he be sure he is not overlooking things that he ought to know?

LIDDELL: We are bound to overlook.

METTLER: How does a psychologist decide when he has had enough of excursions and get busy with an experiment in the field?

LIDDELL: When I first left psychology to work in physiology with Sutherland Simpson, he put me on a problem relating to the thyroid gland. Being trained to be a scholar in psychology, I went to the library and prepared a long bibliography on thyroid physiology, which I presented to him. He said, "Do you want to be a librarian, or an investigator? After you work and get some data, then you can look into pertinent literature." In order to conduct experiments which include methods from another discipline it is necessary to obtain training in, or collaboration from, that field. Personal, face-to-face communication is worth more than hours in the library.

FINESINGER: Much depends on the consistency of the results. When they are highly consistent, the investigator feels more secure, even though he may realize that he has not gone into all the variables.

LIDDELL: I find it quite impossible to make common cause with some colleagues in psychology because of their categorizing. You either accept their nomenclature, theories, and corollaries, or else. It is too laborious to make these translations.

METTLER: I recall listening at the last Conference to participants who were working in the frame of reference of clinical knowledge today. I thought then, "They are never going to find out what is going on in other fields; nevertheless, they insist on behaving as though they do know." It is a curious phenomenon. Problems are solved differently in Washington. For example, the Air Force sets up a panel to consider the flight-worthiness of an aircraft. This panel asks for enlightened guesses. Members sitting around the table soon reach a point when they remark, "I don't know anything about this aspect." Then, turning to one, they say, "That is your job." Very quickly the project becomes broken up into pieces. The reason why agreement can be reached so quickly on questions of this sort is that the experts considering them recognize their own limitations. They stick to their own knitting; and on points outside their competence, they trust the opinions and decisions of others with appropriate experience. But that does not happen in the approach to mental disease; here, everybody is a master of everything.

HOLLINGSHEAD: Apropos of your Air Force illustration, there is a difference between the problems of the Air Force and those of mental disease. The Air Force is faced with practical, applied engineering problems; whereas we are concerned with what is essentially a theoretical problem. Very frequently there would be a lot of argument over the theoretical problem behind the engineering problem.

METTLER: Treatment of patients is as much a practical problem as any which confronts the Air Force.

The mere fact that whenever we begin a new line of inquiry, we are bound to encounter a large number of variables of undetermined number and quality, does not take us out of the area of science. This is best expressed in the intention of Claude Bernard,* who pointed out that the clear bright light of science does not always flash upon us but is often slowly developed from a twilight of trial and error or imaginative guesswork (a "ghastly kitchen," he called it). Bernard made clear that the scientist is only a restricted aspect of a man. This man is really only a scientist when he is in his laboratory and when he is dealing with demonstrable evidence. But he does not cease to be a human being. So when he goes out of his laboratory, Bernard says, in essence, he may let his imagination wrap around him as his coat, and when he comes back into the laboratory, he should hang it up as he would his coat.

FINESINGER: What you are doing is get-

---

* Bernard, Claude. *An Introduction to the Study of Experimental Medicine,* H. C. Greene (Tr.). New York: Macmillan, 1927. p. 15.

ting into a rather restricted definition of science.

METTLER: I have recently had an interesting letter from Sir Francis M. Walshe in which he points out that a certain restriction in what we are willing to accept as science is urgently needed at present in the literature dealing with the nervous system.

FINESINGER: I, for one, have many questions about that.

HOLLINGSHEAD: Even in the laboratory there are certain definite procedures which will lead to certainty. What are the procedures which we can apply to this problem of etiology of psychiatric disorders?

METTLER: One way is to make sure that the evidence is demonstrable, that we can show it to a colleague and say, "This is it."

FINESINGER: Show what to your colleague?

METTLER: A phenomenon. A precise phenomenon.

FINESINGER: But you selected that phenomenon.

METTLER: Precisely. And it is controlled and appears in a particular frame of reference.

FINESINGER: You selected that phenomenon and you selected it on the basis of your imagination and other processes. Over that we can argue.

METTLER: True.

HOLLINGSHEAD: What you are saying is that you are going to throw out all the preliminary steps which went on in your head, in which you used imagination, experience, hunch, and what-not to select this particular experiment, which you are going to demonstrate to me again. I could argue that the preliminary is also important.

METTLER: It is important; but it is the coat I hang up when I enter the laboratory. It is not the material of science itself. It is the penumbra in which confusion still lurks. A datum becomes science only when I have shown it to my colleague and he agrees with me.

HOLLINGSHEAD: He accepts it and it becomes part of the fund of knowledge. I will go along with that. While agreeing with you, I still do not want to abandon Dr. Finesinger. For, in the development of certain scientific knowledge, there is always he process of cultural definitions. They are social definitions of the way that one knows that a thing is certain. That is the social aspect. There is also a psychological aspect. Dr. Jasper's opening sentences were aimed at it.

Whenever an organism is under consideration, it is to be remembered that it exists in the world. This world has different dimensions: organic, physical, meteorological, and ecological. Then there is the "knower" who is using principles of knowing, which lead to certainty on his subject-matter. Just as soon as we get into the principles of knowing, which enable us to know things, we are in the area of methodology. And methodology is going to vary from one science to another.

METTLER: I agree with you absolutely.

FINESINGER: I do not think that it makes any difference whether all that area is to be called science. What it is to be called is not the point. To my mind the issue is: Can one differentiate between the various kinds of operations? Are there rules and laws operating in the preliminary area of hunch-getting and selecting as well as in the area of science? I believe that there are rules.

METTLER: Do I understand that we are in essential agreement about this field that we are trying to demarcate?

KRUSE: Perhaps you are ready to set down mutually acceptable principles.

HOLLINGSHEAD: Probably the first principle we might stress is that whatever the etiology of psychiatric disorders, we must approach a knowledge of it by the use of the principles of scientific method. The particular technics that would be used would have to be varied; for there would be a specific application of plans to the particular area in which an investigator is working. The microphysiologist is certainly going to use different technics from the psychoanalyst, the sociologist, or experimental psychologist. But, the methods used should be constant within an area.

METTLER: I would not want to limit psychiatric methodology to scientifically acceptable methodology. I think that would be placing a restriction on it. I would say that psychiatric methodology must not be inconsistent with, but it does not have to come up to, the standards of strict scientific methodology.

HOLLINGSHEAD: What I am saying is that each field has to adapt to its data and material. In microbiology one kind of experimentation can be done; in clinical psychology, another. Dr. Liddell is fairly rigging—to use the term in a broad, uninvidious sense—the structure of his experiments with sheep and goats.

FINESINGER: Everybody rigs.

LIDDELL: I am rigging because I started by using closely related, but different, species; and I am rigging by doing a life-span study.

HOLLINGSHEAD: In more acceptable words, he is controlling his phenomena.

LIDDELL: No, rigging is the better word.

FINESINGER: Rigging is part of the scientific method. It is inescapable.

HOLLINGSHEAD: I should like to go on to another point; specifically, to the organic view. You are going to agree or disagree very sharply with this. We may take the position that we cannot ignore the organic base of human behavior, for a situation may produce a stimulus. That stimulus has to be received and activated by the organism; then there will be some type of response which, coming through the organism, is exhibited in behavior. Clearly there is an organic matrix in which a psychiatric disorder develops. This part of the mechanism is organic. To record some of the behavior of a kid, Dr. Liddell attaches an apparatus to the animal and then gives it a stimulus, which may be a mild electric shock. For the behavior to be observable, the electric shock has to be consummated through the kid's neuromechanisms, physiological, and neurophysiological reactions. That is to say, for the situational stimulus to be translated into behavior, there has to be an intervening variable; and that intervening variable is the organism. It may be a sheep, rabbit, or human being.

FINESINGER: But certain kinds of investigations have been profitable where the inquiry was primarily not in the physiological area; where it was primarily, let us say, in the psychological area. In the field of psychodynamics, for example, much understanding has come about without prying into the physiological area; rather by staying in the psychological or the sociological area. That does not mean that the processes which go on in the physiological area can be ignored.

METTLER: When I hear the psychoanalyst insisting on consideration of the total man, the total personality, it has often crossed my mind that what he really means is, "Let's use my method and to blazes with yours."

FINESINGER: Operationally what he means is the inclusion of all the best available methods.

METTLER: No person can encompass all methods. The psychoanalyst is not really arguing for the inclusion of the best methods but is making a special plea for his own.

Most problems in science present one of three situations, for each of which, methods of conducting experiments are available:

1. The experimental situation in which the number of variables is at least small enough to be watched, certainly not over four or five. This situation is approached by the method of controlled variables. When there are a limited number of variables, for instance in Sanctorius' experiments in physiology, these can be reasonably well controlled. There was a time when this was thought to be the only scientific method. We know better than that now.

2. The experimental situation in which the number of variables is so great that they need not be observed or controlled. For this situation there is the method of infinite variables. Precise evidence can be gathered about the position of a particular molecule in a mixture of an infinite number of molecules. The ideal situation would be, for instance, the location of a molecule of hydrogen or oxygen in the sea.

But in considering the causes of mental disorders, we are moving into a field in which, on the one hand, we have no way of narrowing the variables to a limited number; and, on the other hand, we do not have an infinite number of variables and we cannot use the second methodology.

Problems in psychiatry fall into the area of a small number of variables, perhaps twenty or so, which cannot be controlled. There is therefore another type of situation:

3. The situation with too many variables to be controlled, but not enough variables for the methods of probability and quantum mechanics to be used. This sets up a problem entirely different from that which occupies the experimentalist in his laboratory; it requires that different technics be employed. Here the experimental methodology is that of uncontrolled, limited variables.

If an investigator is to undertake a comprehensive and meaningful approach to a problem, he has to make certain mental adaptations which are appropriate to the methodology which is itself appropriate for the investigation of the type of problem with which he is faced. What then is the methodology which it is feasible to utilize for an inclusive study of this kind of experimental situation?

There are only three ways of dealing with a situation in which the variables are so numerous that they cannot be controlled, but are not numerous enough so that they can be ignored.* They are: (1) the method of remote derivative; (2) the method of factor analysis; and (3) the method of combined operations.

1. By the technic of remote derivative all the variables are fed into a device which will give a factor in the end. Instead of trying to examine instantaneously all the raw elements in the varying situation, the investigator allows them to interact through time and then takes a resulting factor or value. A multiple index is measured. It is the method used, for instance, in the mathematical brain.

The limitation of this technic is that the variables employed must not vary over a large range; and above all they have to be fairly constant during the time they are being fed into the apparatus. One reason why an electronic computer is so useful is that a figure which is introduced has a

---

* Weaver, Warren. *The Scientist Speaks.* New York: Boni and Gaer, 1947.

specific restricted value. Introduction of an individual datum that is itself subject to much variation creates a serious difficulty; for the instrument will not yield significant results when there is fed into it a variable which is constantly fluctuating, such as blood pressure or motor coordination. Hence this method cannot be used in psychiatry.

2. The second method which can be utilized is factorial analysis, in which a situation is analyzed in such a way as to group its variables into clusters, and these are teased out in the search for common elements. This method arises from a nostalgic faith that the experimental situation can be disclosed to be really one in which the variables are few enough to be controlled, and is a sophisticated effort to derive simplicity out of complexity. It is the only method of the three that has been used to any extent in psychiatry. It is used especially in trying to evaluate what a patient is like, a very important point in finding out whether he is getting better or worse. Principal among the difficulties with this method is that for its utilization it is necessary to have a rating scale, with all the troubles that attend the development and employment of a scale.

3. The third method is the combined operations approach, or what is frequently called multidisciplinary technics, a situation in which a number of individuals view the same phenomenon at the same instant. I am inclined to think of this procedure as a Pandora-box technic: the box is the frame of reference within which flutter the unknown variables. Nobody knows what is there; everybody gathers around; at a signal, everybody waves his butterfly net as the box is opened and catches whatever he can, before the situation has become changed by the factor of time. This procedure has its disadvantages. One is that the different methodologies which are used by different investigators tend to work at cross purposes. In his manipulation of the experimental situation, one investigator gets in the way of another who wants to deal with raw data. The other difficulty arises out of its virtue of preventing temporal alteration. It gives a snapshot of the situation instead of a moving picture.

But this method also has its advantages. It might be expected that it would squeeze out the individual investigator. However, by it the psychiatrist and the experimentalist in the laboratory are drawn together. The psychiatrist will turn up with a particular problem. By the method of combined operations this problem is separable and attackable. It is brought into an area of controlled variables, and two or three investigators can study it.

When investigators say that they intend to study the complete man, the total personality, most of them have the notion that they are going to study this total man in terms of business as usual. They underestimate the protean potentialities which the manipulation of study elicits. Those who tacitly assume that it is possible to study total man in an atmosphere of controlled variables, who believe they can arrive at totality by assembling fractions, whether organic or psychodynamic will be disappointed; for the only present available methods appropriate for the purpose seem to be the three which we have mentioned.

FINESINGER: Adolf Meyer* said that unless we study the total man we cannot get to know him. That is a theoretical concept which can be enjoyed. But I disagree with it. We can never study the total personality. We study something about it—ten things, a hundred things about it.

Many of us are interested in this area of study of the total man and have wonderful aspirations to collect all kinds of data. It seems to me that it would be extremely worth while to consider what can and what cannot be done, what can and what cannot be expected. We need to consider the broad concept of methods and the kind of information that each yields. For example, an investigator interested in repression may contemplate using a method. It may yield wonderful information, but is it going to tell him how repression operates? To find that he will have to use another approach. I think that this problem presents itself in every field.

---

* Meyer, Adolf. The rise to the person and the concept of wholes or integrates. Am. J. Psychiat. 1944, 100: 100–106.

chapter *24*

Cross-Criticism
among Disciplines

• •

GERARD: Last year the members of the group went through the incubation stage of becoming acquainted with one another, and of finding out with whom they were eager and dared to tangle. Like feverish patients, they were about to reach a crisis, when suddenly the time for adjournment had come. Here we are again, in a somewhat smaller-sized group, to see whether this time we can resolve the crisis and have the fever drop a bit. We have had a preliminary warmup, what with prepared statements of the four different viewpoints and four team discussions, with representation from each area. I am sure it is too much to expect, and perhaps not even proper to hope, that we can start essentially at the level of information and understanding precipitated by all these previous documents and exercises. But I do hope that we have all been sufficiently preconditioned, sensitized, and immunized to one another's language, viewpoint, content, and even to some extent personality, so that we can start at the level of coming to grips with the problems, no holds barred. It has been suggested that we attempt to stay as much as we reasonably can, on this first day, within the following three areas: (1) various concepts of the causation of mental disease and the four viewpoints indicated; (2) areas of interdoctrinal acceptance; (3) areas of interdoctrinal unacceptance. We will start by allowing differences within disciplines to be brought out; hence, we will have internecine disagreement first, so as to

get into the spirit of the larger areas of dis agreement.

JASPER: I would like to know why Dr Mettler feels that he is not an organicist. . sense that what he means is that it is no a position one can hold as separate from other positions.

METTLER: If progress is going to b made in understanding the cause of menta disease, it is essential for us to make clea distinctions between areas of specializatior and what may be called "areas of opinion." Whether a person is a psychiatrist, or a so ciologist, or an anatomist, or a biochemis makes less difference than do the areas o opinion in which he may be momentaril operating. Insofar as psychiatry has to d with observable evidence, it is possible t deal with it by methods familiar to any de scriptive scientist. In that area there can b no argument because demonstrable evi dence cannot be argued. Generally speak ing, an experimentalist is content to stop with description.

There are many individuals, however who upon one or more occasions feel callec upon to go beyond such reserve. Whethe these persons happen to be psychiatrists o: experimentalists in a basic science makes n difference; for when they do this, they have invaded a new area and cannot carry int it any greater degree of certitude than i naturally resident in it. This region is th area of logic, and material in it is not de monstrable, but reasonable and probable

300

No one can object to such a shift in procedure because we have to act upon problems which lie beyond the area in which we have demonstrable evidence. However, we must be very careful, when we leave demonstration, that we do not introduce into the area of logic anything which conflicts with demonstrable evidence. Furthermore, when we have entered a purely logical region, we cannot assume that the material which we have then to deal with has any greater degree of certainty than the probability of the logical methods which have been brought to bear upon it.

When we have done all we can with demonstrable evidence and all we can with logical material, we still find we are not able to act in all the areas of common behavior because we have to deal with possibilities which lie beyond probabilities. To act upon the basis of possibility where probability cannot be determined is not only necessary but also perfectly permissible, so long as we are aware of the variation which may unexpectedly arise and of the assumptions we are making. Experimentalists usually shy away from such situations; but the clinical psychiatrist, who has to meet the exigencies which arise in dealing with patients, has very little choice in many instances except to go forward into areas peopled only with thin possibilities. Nor can there be any objection to this, so long as the possibilities which are entertained do not controvert logical probabilities and are not in conflict with demonstrable evidence.

Therefore, my point of view would be that there is no such person, strictly speaking, as an organicist. I would not like to be labeled that. There are investigators who deal mainly, if not entirely, with demonstrable evidence, not because of any peculiar virtue resident in their souls, but because that is the nature of the material and methodologies with which they work. There are others who go beyond demonstration because of temperament or necessity. There can be no objection to going beyond the area of demonstrability as long as probabilities and possibilities are clearly so labeled and do not present inconsistencies.

In a Conference such as this, progress can perhaps best be made by keeping the level of information under consideration clearly labeled. Is what is being presented offered as demonstrable evidence, logical probability, or only a possibility? If an investigator is content to allow others the same enlarged degree of freedom within the areas of probability and possibility as he, no doubt, would himself expect, the scope of acceptance is greatly expanded. Unfortunately, however, we all have the habit of demolishing the tentative proposals of others by applying unsympathetic and rigid tests which are out of place in the realms of probability and possibility. In other words, we demolish our antagonists' advances of logic and preference as though they were erroneous observations, while we expect others to accord our hypotheses the acceptance of a demonstrated fact.

From a practical, operational point of view, a good ten-cent fact is worth a vast deal more than a dollar hypothesis. A good fact may be uninspiring in itself, but it is the sort of thing from which solid progress has been made. All the organicists, the pathologists, anatomists, bacteriologists, and chemists have achieved great advances with these ten-cent facts. They have whittled off from the field of psychiatry much unshaped material and presented it for incorporation in what might be called the *corpus medicorum*. This process goes back a long way. They have removed the convulsive complex from the area of what was called "the sacred disease." They have removed dementia paralytica from the area of sexual "excess" and put it on the basis of an infectious disease. They have elucidated the manner in which the nervous system acts under drugs, and particularly under those drugs which are hypnotics, soporifics, and anticonvulsants. They have made considerable progress in the development of a pathology of neuropsychiatry, both in structural pathology and in that dynamic kind that goes by the name of microchemistry. They have contributed extensively in the understanding of those neuropsychiatric entities which involve metabolic disorders which are linked to hereditary patterns; and they have made extensive headway with chemistry in a great variety of areas, especially in those metabolic disorders which have, or are accompanied by, definite psychiatric manifestations. In these ways the small, uninspiring facts which go to make up the area of demonstrable evidence have gradually brought many psychiatric probabilities or possibilities into line with the rest of science. These are accomplishments of organicists. Granted, all this is not enough. But it is no record of which to be ashamed; no one needs to apologize for it. It envisions the practice of medicine in a neat world where all the necessary tests are done and in which patients and doctors are both eminently reasonable and industrious—a world which, in short, does not exist.

POPE: As another representative of the "organic school," I should like to second Dr. Mettler's statement and add that the organicist does not necessarily believe that something like Koch's postulates can be established for various kinds of mental disease. Those expecting that development are almost certainly doomed to disappointment. Surely, however, physical science, insofar as it can describe that complex of events in the physical domain which constitutes a brain in action, does have something to contribute to the total study of behavior, normal and abnormal.

One thing to be avoided, however, is the notion that phenomena describable in physical language are in some manner more basic or more fundamental, as one hears it often expressed, than material that is studied by the psychologist or the psychodynamicist. In fact, the more recondite levels of modern physics show that the relationship must be rather one of correspondence, or complementarity. Moreover, when one moves from observable phenomena into areas where valuation and meaning begin to appear, one has to be very cautious indeed in assertions about the role physical science can ever play because, strictly speaking, these territories are outside of physics, and in them the natural sciences have nothing to say. I realize much of this is a negativistic position to take in relationship to the mental disease problem, but as organicists we have to be careful not to assume that we are the ones who will have all the answers. I do not believe that we shall.

GRINKER: In the team meeting in which I participated, the four so-called schools, represented by individuals who were concerned, in one way or another, with mental health, seemed to have difficulty coming to actual positive statements of disagreement. Disagreement is, of course, plentiful. Yet one of the facts that is obvious to people who have read most of the literature of those working in multidisciplinary activities is the existence of impressive global statements of agreement. The general conceptual schemes that are arrived at seem to be tolerant, broad-minded, and very close to statements made by others. Where the disagreement arises is not in the tolerant global statements or in the general concept. Rather it appears during a discourse which lasts beyond the time that agreements can be continued. Even more, it becomes evident in the operational procedures that each one utilizes. In those situations each states very clearly his area of disagreement.

As an objector to some of the remarks that Dr. Jasper has made in his statement of the organic position, I should like to point out how agreement is not so implicit. The second paragraph reads: "Psychological 'forces,' or even sociological 'forces,' do not differ generically from biological 'forces' . . . These differences lie"—I would insert the word "only"—"in modes of discourse or in frames of reference rather than in difference in basic mechanism . . . " Here is a tolerant agreeing statement of a general nature. But the breakdown comes later.

Indeed, the psychodynamicists are subjected to living in the limbo without a language. Near the end he states that "the 'dynamic psychiatrist' has been forced to formulate practical working hypotheses based upon conceptions and descriptive terms which are difficult or impossible to submit to scientific validation in and for themselves, let alone be translated into psychophysiological processes familiar to those concerned with a more objective approach to the study of behavior." Yet in the next paragraph he says: "We need more *rapprochement* between those concerned with the biological basis of behavior and those attempting to deal with mental and behavior disorders. Less 'mumbo jumbo' of esoteric terminology and more attempt at translation into terms which might be of more general significance for the biologist and the dynamic psychologist alike are of the greatest importance to real progress." So he leaves the psychodynamicists with no position whatever. We cannot be scientific; we cannot translate our terms; and we cannot use our own terms. In effect we find ourselves completely silenced.

METTLER: In paragraph 2 of Dr. Alexander's essay on the psychodynamic position we find: "Although the ego is a psychological concept, it refers to the highest coordinating centers of the nervous system." What is meant by the "highest coordinating centers" of the nervous system? To me this term has a specific anatomical connotation; and to consider a coordinating center anatomically with or without the propounded relationship leads to difficulty. What specifically is the highest coordinating center? I begin to wonder why we have to bring in this anatomical concept at all. What has it to do with psychodynamics?

Dr. Alexander's exposition continues: "It is preferable to speak of ego functions instead of the more abstract concept of an ego. What we observe, describe, and utilize conceptually are ego functions. We assume that they are the functions of an organ system." The word "organ" is used here in a different way than that to which I am accustomed. I recognize that; but it causes me considerable difficulty because I am not clear about just what is meant by it.

Then comes the sentence: "What we actually observe are, however, only the psychological manifestations of this apparatus." I must confess that I am left completely up in the air by this. I do not see how it is possible to subject it to demonstrable evidence. This is no criticism of the proposition; for when I read a statement like this, I know that it has not been put down with any intention of being subjected to a laboratory approach. Hence, I accept it as I find it, as a hypothesis. And as a hypothesis it seems to have value. I must say, however, that from the point of view of my own field [anatomy], I cannot possibly imagine what it means.

JASPER: You are making explicit precisely the thoughts which I experienced when, preparing to set forth the organic viewpoint, I read very carefully Dr. Alexander's writings on psychodynamics. It seemed logical that the hypothesis which he presented must have significance in biological terms because it had to do with an organism and its behavior. Indeed, it seemed impossible that behavior and mental processes could be studied scientifically with a system of postulates that were unrelated completely to what the biologist uses. It was in the hope of stimulating a discussion that I pointed out that the whole structure of the treatment of behavior by Dr. Alexander is full of conceptions that the biologist cannot use in the laboratory or in thinking about actual functions of the nervous system. Nor can the psychodynamic terms be defined in a biological sense. They are therefore useless for an experimental approach. I do not mean, however, that the conceptions are not useful. One function of the assembled group might be to work through these conceptions to seek an interpretation so that we can understand them. If they have an important meaning for the psychoanalyst, they must have an important meaning for the biologist.

When I appealed for less mumbo jumbo of esoteric terminology, I had in mind neurophysiology as well as psychoanalysis. When the neurophysiologist speaks to a group of clinical neurologists or psychiatrists, he finds that he is incapable of describing his experiments to them. The terminology with which he is so familiar in his everyday work in the laboratory is unfamiliar in the clinical field. To the neurophysiologist, his own language is elementary; to the clinical neurologist and psychiatrist, it is so much jargon. The tables are reversed when the neurophysiologist listens to the psychiatrist.

Is it possible, indeed is it necessary, for the organicist and the psychodynamicist to get together? Does the organic experimenter, let us say one who is engaged in laboratory demonstrations of the functional properties of the brain, of the eye, of the nerves (certainly these are properties which determine the reality of the experimental world; man is limited by the potentialities of his nervous organs) have to be an atomic physicist? Or conversely, does the atomic physicist have to be a psychologist or a neurophysiologist? Does he have to understand the perceptual processes that make it possible for him to work in atomic physics? Science has progressed very far without much intercommunication of this type between fields. I think that we can exaggerate the importance of complete teamwork if the investigator proceeds systematically with a relatively narrow problem. Its applications come from contact. Maybe the neurophysiologist does not have to understand the psychoanalyst, but I cannot help thinking that common problems of the nervous system should bring them closer together.

ALEXANDER: I cannot accept Dr. Jasper's statement: "The result is that the 'dynamic psychiatrist' has been forced to formulate practical working hypotheses based upon conceptions and descriptive terms which are difficult or impossible to submit to scientific validation in and for themselves, let alone be translated into psychophysiological processes familiar to those concerned with a more objective approach to the study of behavior." Contrary to that assertion, the dynamic psychiatrist is not forced to formulate anything, any more than a physiologist is forced to formulate certain things according to his conceptual tools and methods. The result is that the dynamic psychiatrist formulates practical working hypotheses based upon conceptions and descriptive terms which can be submitted to scientific validation, just as much as can neurophysiological descriptions. The validation in each discipline is, of course, by its own standards. By validation I mean understanding, describing, explaining, and predicting natural processes which are under consideration or examination. If the latter part of Dr. Jasper's sentence were changed to: "terms which in and for themselves cannot be translated *in our present state of our knowledge* into psychophysiological processes familiar to those concerned with a more objective approach to the study of behavior," I would accept it in its revised form.

Here is what the psychoanalyst can read between the lines. Dr. Jasper quite understandably introduces a hierarchy of scientific validation, in which he considers validation in biology and physiology on a higher level, and validation in psychodynamics on a lower level. Thus he measures psychodynamic statements with his biological standards, which he considers higher. But I cannot accept his hierarchy of values. In understanding, predicting, describing, and influencing mental disease, the psychodynamic approach at present is far ahead of the neurophysiological.

I want to use two very brief examples to be very concrete. A person is afraid of walking in the downtown district of a city. He is not afraid to walk in his own suburban district. But as soon as he comes downtown he is horrified, he sweats, he becomes light-headed and simply cannot function; he must be accompanied by somebody. Considered neurophysiologically, this whole thing is nonsense; it cannot be explained; there is no method presently by which the physiologist can make an intelligent statement about this disorder, which belongs in the category of phenomena in mental disease. The dynamic psychiatrist, however, with his observations, operational tools, descriptions, and logical deductions from what is observed can explain the patient's behavior in terms of motivational psychology. This is in the realm of a scientific discipline. It follows it own rules just as physics or chemistry does. It can be judged only on its own merits, with its own conceptual tools. Working at the level of communication, and utilizing past experiences, general psychological principles, and planned interferences, the dynamic psychiatrist brings about a change in the patient. The patient loses this particular phobia and can now walk downtown. This effect cannot be accomplished neurophysiologically. Phenobarbital might help slightly while the patient is under the influence of it; but tomorrow, without it, he will be just as afraid. The neurophysiologist may attribute a calming effect to it and may advance a theory that the disorder was hyperexcitation in neural processes. The dynamic psychiatrist can do much better in understanding and explaining the disorder, and in helping the patient.

My point is not to extol the virtues of dynamic psychiatry, only to say that the hierarchy of values which Dr. Jasper implies is out of place here. I would say again that in this meeting concerned with mental disease, the yardstick, the correct perspective, should be: How much can knowledge coming from the neurophysiological or organic point of view be used to improve what the dynamic psychiatrist knows about these mental disturbances in his own terms, particularly since the neurophysiologist with his methods knows very little about mental disorders.

In my second example, I should like to show the limitations of the dynamic approach, and to demonstrate the need of multidisciplinary cooperation and teamwork. A person staggers, talks uncoordinatedly, shows disconcern of others, and uses baby talk. It is learned that he has consumed a large quantity of alcohol. He is intoxicated. The psychodynamicist first can describe what he sees and then can reconstruct the patient's mental processes by a technic which is nothing but common sense understanding of human behavior, based on the fact that he and the patient are both human beings. From his own introspective knowledge of what goes on in himself, the dynamic psychiatrist extrapolates into another person. This is just as precise and scientific a method as any used in physics and chemistry. If I observe this intoxicated person, I can predict what he will do next, simply on the basis that I know what I would do next. We both have the same systems. That is the technic of motivational psychology.

As I hear the man talk, I note that he is now less inhibited. After drinking he has gotten rid of certain inhibitions which otherwise influenced his behavior. He is less concerned about others. I would also say that this person has regressed somewhat to infantile behavior; he talks baby talk, plays with words, is incoherent, staggers around, has lost the faculty of balance, and cannot walk any more. Hence, my explanation will

be entirely centered around some coordinating function in him, some kind of control over his behavior, which was lost under the influence of alcohol. I would explain the details of his behavior; for example, he speaks so inanely because the logical control over thought processes is temporarily lost. In consequence he now talks as he talked before he acquired logical control over his words. This is really not an explanation; it is a psychological description of what I am observing.

When we come to explain, we will need the neurophysiologist. He will tell us that alcohol is responsible for the changed behavior. He will assert that alcohol has a particular selective effect on certain portions of the central nervous system. It inhibits the higher, before the lower, cortical coordinating centers. Obviously the functions which were described psychologically in terms of motivation must somehow be connected with the dysfunction of the higher centers. In my presentation of the psychodynamic position I stated that ego is a psychological concept, but it refers to the higher coordinating centers of the nervous system. This statement simply sets forth well-established, already existent, interdisciplinary knowledge. There is good evidence that those functions which come within the purview of the psychodynamicist and which he describes in psychological terms have something to do with the functions of the highest coordinating centers of the nervous system. To me that makes anatomical sense.

METTLER: Specifically, what are these centers?

ALEXANDER: Cortical.

METTLER: What is related to the cortex?

ALEXANDER: The coordination of behavior.

METTLER: Specifically related?

ALEXANDER: Without the cortex it disappears.

METTLER: I would not be willing to admit this at all. Do you mean ability to condition?

ALEXANDER: The conditioning exists.

METTLER: It does exist, but I think that it is unnecessary.

ALEXANDER: I think that it is necessary. We know very well that in alcoholism certain processes in these higher centers are inhibited, at the same time behavior is inhibited. To go farther, if a person is decapitated, it is known that all these processes which we observe will disappear, whereas other processes will not. I do not see why a comprehensive, scientific statement cannot contain a reference to already established knowledge. Anatomically we do not know where the coordinating centers are and what they do. I take humble cognizance of that status. Will you admit that you assume that the central nervous system has coordinating centers by which behavior is coordinated or regulated?

METTLER: I think that the statement has value in the frame of reference in which you are using it. But the minute you take it out of the frame and try to tie it to a particular anatomical or neurophysiological concept, I believe that you weaken the setting forth of your material.

ALEXANDER: What is your answer to the example of intoxication? I can describe the behavior psychologically. You can describe the effect of the alcohol on certain neuroprocesses. Why should we not tie together these two types of observations?

METTLER: I think we can but on an entirely different basis. For instance, I would disagree entirely that the person who becomes giddy upon going downtown is not experiencing a physiological reaction.

ALEXANDER: I agree with you.

METTLER: We know considerable about that phenomenon. We know that it happens for the same reason that a person faints when blood is to be drawn from him. We know that if such a person is able to run while downtown, he is not going to become giddy. These physiological phenomena have been definitely demonstrated.

JASPER: I must have given a misconception. I did not mean to evaluate laboratory data above other data. Certainly I must confess that my first publication was in the *Journal of Sociology* on "Pessimism and Optimism in College Environments." At the time I thought that it was based upon interesting data. I certainly believe that all fields have to be treated and evaluated in their own frames of reference. I do not have any illusions about the value of subjective data, or of what is done in the laboratory, or of what is observed in the field or in the city when the patient gets frightened. The point is that if, in describing the behavior of a man in an environmental situation, the psychodynamicist would use terms that were clear enough so that I could understand him, what he is talking about would mean something to me as a neurophysiologist.

There seems to be some implicit assumption that a neurophysiologist is not interested in the history of an organism, for example, in the nature of the stimulus to which the organism reacts. Attention to these points is just as much a part of the neurophysiologist's job as administration of phenobarbital, to which you seem to reduce him. The neurophysiologist has to understand the stimulus situation in this history and the conditioning processes which give that stimulus situation its potency for a particular reaction. If the psychodynamicist would present descriptions clearly enough, the neurophysiologist could try to translate them and begin to work on them.

ALEXANDER: We did try.

GRINKER: The organicists imply that with great value they can bring the neurophysiological structure into the discussion of such conceptions as ego, provided the psychodynamicists define ego functions clearly. The experimentalist who works with various types of animals is able to see in evolution when these functions appeared in the development of the individual, when they came into maturation, and what areas of the brain have to be damaged either by morphological or functional changes, such as by lack of oxygen or circulation, to result in a dropping out of these functions. These are valuable concepts to bring together; they strengthen the concept of mental activity as being a psychobiological process. The psychodynamicists are fully cognizant that everything that they are studying psychologically in behavior or in group activities must be derived from some function in the individual. There is no question about it. But when the two disciplines discuss individual points, this whole tolerant multidisciplinary, multisystem concept breaks down.

WITTKOWER: I should like to adopt a middle position. It seems to me that Dr. Jasper says that what is seen in the laboratory is scientific and what is not seen in the laboratory is not scientific. That, in my opinion, is going a little bit too far. For example, I had a patient in analysis who said, "I have seen a movie called *Dial M*—" and then he wanted to say —"*for Murder*," but he made a slip of the tongue and said, "Dial M for Muriel." This is the name of his wife. What is going on in this patient is understandable. It is a correct observation. He said it. Nobody can doubt it. It can be recorded. It can be understood and interpreted, but I do not believe that the process can be expressed in neurophysiological terms.

METTLER: There is no reason to.

WITTKOWER: Freud was originally a neurologist; he hoped that a bridge would be formed between psychopathology and neurophysiology or neuropathology. This bridge, however, has not been formed; for there are many processes which simply cannot be explained by such a connection in the light of our present knowledge.

SPIEGEL: Dr. Pope stated in a preliminary session that the organicist works without value judgments; hence, in the fields of psychology and the social sciences, where value judgments come in, the organicist cannot work. I challenge that. Our discussion here demonstrates that implicit value judgments are operating all the time. We could, of course, apply psychological descriptions to our behavior; for example, we could talk about the degree of narcissistic investment that we all have in our particular disciplines. But it is more profitable for each person to keep his eye on the value judgment itself. We do not see our own. Therefore we make statements about the value of work that we are doing without understanding that we are putting a judgment on it. The implicit difficulties which our value judgments introduce are chiefly in the area of operations and methods, not in the area of the concept or the problem which is to be studied. Probably more could be said about why it is that certain types of

values are connected with certain types of procedures, and what the personality structure of the individual has to do with his preference for a particular type of procedure. For instance, when Dr. Mettler said "demonstrable evidence," I had some question in my mind as to just what he actually meant, aside from the holistic value of that term. For it was quite clear, when Dr. Alexander was talking, that he thought that the evidence which he was citing was valid. By "demonstrable" does Dr. Mettler mean something that can be felt, smelt, touched, or manipulated by a physical instrument? Is the kind of evidence gathered in opinion and attitude studies to be considered as demonstrable evidence or is it not? Personally I believe that much profit can be derived from such an inquiry. In general, almost any problem in mental health brings out the need for interdisciplinary contact. For instance, if one really wants to understand fully the development of a phobia in the city but not in the country, it is necessary to understand the neuroanatomy, the neurophysiology, the motivation of the individual, and the impact of the culture of a city versus that of an urban or more rural area, in terms of the symbolic meanings to a person. The problem brings us together; the methods drive us apart.

POPE: I did not say that scientists do not make value judgments, nor that these do not differ in various branches of science. My proposition was that physical science is irrelevant for that aspect of psychiatry which is essentially humanistic, not that physics can have no role with respect to psychology and social science. However, when a scientist makes an assertion about relationships between discernible events in the external world, I am not clear as to just where the valuation comes in.

SPIEGEL: Where the value comes in is in the operations which one worker prefers as against another set of operations; in respect to the degree of certainty which he demands or the tolerance for ambiguity which he is willing to allow, for an individual can give value to ambiguity as well as to certainty. That is the kind of differentiation which I meant.

METTLER: I would agree heartily, Dr.

Spiegel, that the factor of value is inescapable. It is up to Dr. Jasper to clear up any confusion which may exist in our minds about this question of values and hierarchies. We are not dealing here with the question as to whether a person is in a laboratory or a clinic but rather with the kind of material and methods that are used. Just because one is working in a laboratory or using a machine which has many buttons and dials on it does not mean that he is getting accurate scientific data.

With regard to demonstrable evidence, I mean by that the kind of material which one person can demonstrate to others who may or may not be familiar with the methodologies the original observer employed. I would include opinion and attitude studies under the head of methodology, for we know a great deal about how such work must be carried out and something about its limitations. Such studies, properly done, produce evidence which is demonstrable with relative ease, even to persons not specifically trained in such studies. The individual who can demonstrate the validity of his observations only to an individual in his own discipline is less fortunate than one who can also demonstrate their validity to others outside of his own discipline.

ALEXANDER: To my knowledge, every science uses value judgments about theories. One theory is better than another if it accounts better for the observed facts and has superior applicability.

POPE: The role of "value judgments" in science has somehow become inserted—erroneously, I believe—into the question as to how far it is possible for physical science to go in contributing to understanding of the phenomena of psychiatry. Even if we could provide a complete description in physical terms of a brain in action, in complete correspondence with a sequence of psychological events, what more would we then know about the person's feelings and their meaning to him?

SPIEGEL: Implicit in what Dr. Pope was saying is an unstated assumption that it would be nice if neurophysiology could explain everything, if all processes in human behavior could be reduced to the terminology of neurophysiology. But it was a modest admission, wrested from the organicist in recognition of interdisciplinary difficulties, that no one discipline can contribute more than a small portion to the total understanding of human behavior; and that if there is an unstated assumption that all behavior can be reduced to neurophysiological terms, it had better be given up. To that I would certainly subscribe.

FINESINGER: This high-sounding language is all very delightful, but basically there are many disagreements here which come out in the open as soon as the organicist and psychodynamicist begin to discuss a point. One difference really dealt with the problem of information.

As far as I know, one cannot rid a patient of his phobic symptoms by having him run around the street. Maybe his giddiness can be helped by such exercise; but as for other symptoms, they are not changed by it. Apparently here is a bit of information. Out of the total complex, the neurophysiologist picks up a detail with which he is familiar, and tries to explain the whole phenomenon. In the example of phobia it was giddiness.

On the other hand, the psychodynamicist talks about such things as coordinating centers. I suppose that some neurophysiologists do not believe that such centers exist; perhaps others do believe they exist. I think we would have to grant that the central nervous system does have a function of coordination, whether it be explained in terms of centers or otherwise. And even though each school has its own meaning and understanding of "coordination," it is very difficult, apparently, for various groups to take the next step, which is to answer each other's question, What do you mean by coordination? We need to try to correlate our information in these areas.

I can think of many reasons to try to explain psychodynamic phenomena in neurophysiological terms. The initial assumption is that there is some physiological reaction going on in the psychological processes. The natural question is, Why do we not proceed? Instead we get hung up. On such a word as "coordination" we hang many of our disagreements which actually may come from other sources. I wonder whether the fundamental difficulty really arises from lack of information or from lack of clarity. I believe that we understand what we mean by "coordination," but for some reason we do not try to make sense out of it jointly.

GERARD: May I close this period with comment on some of the topics which have come up as major issues, either in the team meetings or thus far during this session? First was the issue raised by Dr. Pope's statement that there are areas in the psychological and sociological fields that are outside the scope of physical science because values come in, which science is not designed or equipped to handle. I personally would not subscribe to that. I think that insofar as there is any content anywhere in the universe, which is to be approached in terms of understanding, the methods of physical, biological, and other sciences are in their broadest sense alike applicable. If an area cannot be approached by these methods, it is not science, not a matter of intercommunication at the rational level. Rather it is a region of art and appreciation which is subjective; here every man's territory is his own castle. I would assume that our dogma must be that the approaches which we collectively represent are potentially able to give us the kind of information that we are looking for.

The second question was whether the physiologist is at the peak or the base of the pyramid, with the other disciplines building up or down, as the case may be. From that arose the question of interaction. The term "basic" as applied to the organic approach was a validity which Dr. Pope was willing to surrender. Some of the other disciplines were eager to accept this offering. I cannot go along with that concession.

In each area of behavioral science, which is what we collectively represent, there are phenomena to be discovered and observations to be made; then an initial coordination of these phenomena is to be found and regularized in a working hypothesis or even in empirical rules which work. This is true in the physiology of the nervous system and in the interaction of large and small groups —in the input-output, stimulus-response reactions of organs, individuals, societies. Observation, analysis, and intelligent, creative

thinking are going on in each of the areas and disciplines. The question is whether these are all entirely equivalent and whether there is some validity to the hope that the phenomena at the more intricate or complex levels will be reduced to an interpretation in terms of interaction of neurons. Although reductionism is not a popular term these days, I submit it is reasonable.

The biologist working with phenomena of irritability, awareness and loss of awareness, sleep, and muscle contraction was not, until very recently and only then in some areas, able to use precisely and with complete effectiveness the material of physics and chemistry; but he profoundly expects that, with the advance of knowledge, all these will be reducible. The reductionism may sometimes not be worth doing, but in principle it will be achievable. The reason for asymmetry is not that it is inherently better or worse to explain behavior in terms of neurons or neural discharges, these, in turn, in terms of the reactions of molecules, and these in terms of the behavior of electrons; it is simply that it is incomparably easier to go downhill than up. For example, a more applied discipline may talk about "area." Area is a composite of the dimensions of length and width. Having defined area, one cannot go from that directly to the definition of length and width. There is an infinite set of widths and lengths of rectangular figures that will give a fixed area. But given a length and width of a regular figure, its area is precisely defined. Hence it is always more useful if one can define the variables in terms of the clearly independent factors which are to be integrated into the larger whole. It is only on that basis that there is a justification for looking towards a reduction.

Thirdly, Dr. Jasper conceded, perhaps too generously in his desire to foster cooperation, that the neurophysiologist talks just as much mumbo jumbo as the psychoanalyst. If so, it is a different kind of mumbo jumbo. The neurophysiologist fails to communicate with other people mostly because of his lack of skill or thoughtfulness in attempting to communicate, not because the material that he has to communicate is unclear or incommunicable. This is not always true in psychoanalytic terminology. A neurophysiologist can make what he is saying completely clear to all his colleagues so that they will know, and either agree or disagree, with what he is maintaining. With a little effort and practice, he can also make the concepts equally and completely clear to the clinical neurologist, psychiatrist, or uninformed intelligent layman. This clarity in concept is less frequent in the psychiatric field. When one psychiatrist sets forth the psychodynamic position, the dissent by other dynamicists might be attributed to incomplete communication or to basic differences in concept; but the nature of the criticisms seems to me to indicate a less precise definition of the concepts.

Dr. Mettler has spoken of the niceness of having a ten-cent fact. But the position of the sociologist was—and I think with some justification—that in the social sciences the problem is to recognize the facts that are worth ten cents. This is part of the difficulty; we operate at the range of precision of the phenomena in which we are interested. In neurophysiology we think our studies have gotten to some of the basic variables; but probably we are wrong and will later find that we are still not examining the right things. In the sociological field many competent people are quite certain that they are not yet grappling with the critical variables. Does this mean, as Dr. Wittkower says, that since the substitution of "Muriel" for "murder" cannot be explained in terms of neurophysiology, no bridge between neurophysiology and behavior is possible? But he did add, "at least with present knowledge." Including the latter reservation, I would agree with him completely; without it, I would as fully disagree. If we learned enough and took enough trouble to analyze the particular discharges from particular neurons in the brain of a particular individual, in principle it would be possible to account for the mention of "Muriel" instead of "murder"— but not in the immediately foreseeable future. It is not now operationally determinable. This is my philosophical orientation.

So, we are back to the basic methodological and ontological dichotomy; it cannot be resolved in an afternoon or two of discourse. Does this mean that it is premature to try to cooperate? Dr. Mettler cited an example of cooperation in industry in which various branches, engaged in a large undertaking, plan and carry out their respective assignments without questioning each other. I would think that it might be helpful if each asked what the other was doing. It might bring about a tremendous short cut and savings. When someone comes for advice, answering the question does not always do the most good. To ask the person why he wants that question answered may reveal that it is not the right question and that he should have put it otherwise. That becomes real help.

In the attempt to understand the causation of mental disease, the various disciplines can cooperate; some are now cooperating. A fundamental prerequisite is for one discipline to be sufficiently informed of the viewpoints and jargon of the others so that all can communicate at a level beyond that of simple technical services. For a worker in one field to say to an experimenter in another field, "If you will make this measurement for me, I will make this observation for you," is good. But it is not nearly good enough.

chapter *25*

Interdisciplinary Differences in Concepts, Values, and Relevance

• •

HOLLINGSHEAD: One of the basic questions for this Conference on causation is what we conceive the phenomena of mental disease to be. Let us start with Dr. Mettler's point of view that over the years, through the achievements in the field of mental disease by the different disciplines comprising the organic approach, a number of behavioral manifestations have been isolated and separated and indeed are no longer regarded as mental disease. We think of them as particular types of organic disease. Epilepsy is, I believe, one of them.

But suppose that by continuing with the best organic methodology, capable of yielding the best demonstrable organic evidence, we finally come to a residual group of behavioral manifestations that we cannot explain in terms of the organic approach with a structure-function type of statement; then we have the problem of explaining etiologically these phenomena with which the psychodynamicist is concerned. This puts a different emphasis upon what we are going to call mental disease. Is mental disease essentially a phenomenon with an organic base, or is mental disease a behavioral manifestation which is a reaction to a complex situation which may have a number of different dimensions? One of these dimensions may clearly be the organic base of the organism, that is, structural, functional inter-

actions that take place within the organism. But there are other dimensions in this situation. Some of these dimensions will clearly be in the area of reactions to situations which may have emotional overtones that may be measured by the psychologist. But there also may be further dimensions in this situation that are a matter of patterned meaning and are learned in the social situation. These are the social and cultural dimensions with which the sociologist and anthropologist are concerned.

It should also be kept in mind that the organism is a living entity. It is a creative something, and it puts meanings upon the experiences that it has. Some of these meanings are learned; for instance, what is good or bad. That is what I meant by the patterned meanings of the social system. If I understand the psychodynamic point of view, there is a certain amount of integration that takes place in the organism. This is what I believe Dr. Alexander was trying to express when he talked about the ego, and the integrative function of the ego, in this meaning world of the individual. It also enters into the consideration of the illustration of the individual who had the phobic anxiety in the city and little or none in a country situation. What is it in the total reactional situation of this individual which gives rise to a high anxiety potential, which

311

is called a phobic reaction, in a city situation; and a relatively low anxiety potential, or the draining off of the anxiety potential, in the country or in the home situation?

There are then, to summarize, a number of different dimensions in this state, whatever it is, which we call mental disease. There are these dimensions—an organic dimension, a psychological dimension, a social dimension, a cultural dimension, and above all an integrative dimension—in what goes on in an individual functioning in this situation. The psychodynamicist is, I believe, attempting to integrate all of these and to give an explanation of the entire process. This view also accords with the concept of different levels of organization.

SCOTT: In my opinion, there is no essential conflict between the various points of view that have been expressed here. As I put it in my prepared statement, the different schools of thought appear to be thinking about the same phenomenon at different levels of organization. The organicist views behavior in terms of factors which are at the genic level, the cellular level, the tissue level, and the organic level; the psychologist considers behavior in terms of factors that operate at the organismal level of the whole individual; the psychodynamicist is interested in the smaller units of societal organization as well as in man as a psychological unit; the sociologist or anthropologist is concerned with social and cultural factors in entire human societies.

The main question is how the factors operating at different levels are related to each other. The most basic factor affecting behavior is heredity. The distribution of the genes is controlled by cellular physiology; that is, genes are handed on to the offspring through a chromosomal mechanism so that the acts of genes are integrated and controlled by factors acting at a cellular level. Beyond that point the distribution of genes is very little affected by factors operating at the higher levels. For example, the nervous system has no effect whatsoever on the distribution of the genes to various germ cells. As a practical problem in gene distribution, let us consider the determination of sex. Thinking about it obviously does not affect the outcome. Nor does a factor at a still higher level, such as language or communication, affect the determination of sex; talking about it will not directly influence it. Thus, factors operating at a lower level may be quite independent of factors operating at a higher level. In many cases they may even form limitations on the factors operating on higher levels.

It is rather difficult to explain all behavior in terms of genes. Theoretically it could be done. If all the different possible combinations of genes (possibly 50,000 pairs) could be ascertained, and if all the environmental factors concerned were known, it would be theoretically possible to work out how all of them together would ultimately affect behavior. But from a practical point of view this calculation would be too difficult to be useful. Many factors which are practically useful in explaining behavior are found at higher levels of organization. Anyone who restricts his research activities to one level of organization ought to take into account that there are factors at other levels which may affect his data. In my own experience I found it necessary to relate sociological thinking to my biological approach. The concept of levels of organization as a frame of reference will include most, if not all, of the facts found in different fields. It may not explain everything, but it is sufficiently comprehensive to include most aspects of behavior without obvious contradictions.

KING: We have argued about who owns the scientific method. We finally agreed that we all own it and practice it differentially. We have also discussed what is meant by demonstrable evidence. By "demonstrable" the organicist or psychologist means that which can be demonstrated, that which can be stated so that those not only within, but also outside, a particular discipline can understand it. Explanation does not necessarily have to be by a process of reductionism or stepping down from the most-organized to the least-organized levels of either behavior or structure. We encounter most of our difficulties at the psychodynamic and psychosocial levels where the workers object, and rightly so, to a hierarchy of values which would require that phenomena with which they are concerned be explained or explainable by terms from psychology, physiology, chemistry, or anatomy. On the other hand, the organicists have tried to say—perhaps not so explicitly as I would like—that they did not object to the concepts of psychodynamics, but did question how well they could be demonstrated.

In discussing the problem of mental disease, there is a great cleavage of opinion at the least-organized levels. Chemists can agree upon a large body of fact. They will, of course, always differ about theory, or about what they will investigate next. As the scale is ascended from the organic level, through the psychological level, to the individual, and then to the level of the group, there is a smaller and smaller body of agreed-upon fact. At present there is no necessity for reductionism in order to achieve an integration. What I am calling for is clarity and demonstrableness at each level as it now exists. If each of us specifies his complaints about the other's thought processes, I think we make a bolder step forward in eventual integration than if we try again and again to put each bit of information into a hierarchy simply because when we have examined some specific problem before, we have found such a hierarchy to exist.

SPIEGEL: I too question the value of setting up disciplines in terms of hierarchies. True, one can arrange pictorially the disciplines, their methods, and their objects of scrutiny in a hierarchical system of levels of organization. It is a logical picture and it has utility for certain purposes, perhaps for a broad, general philosophy of science; but for our purpose here and now, which is to explore how different disciplines can function with each other in terms of mental disease, it has little utility. Indeed, it introduces a multitude of problems which we could avoid if we did not have to indulge in this temptation to set up the hierarchies and try to explain one level in terms of the next lower level in this eternal reduction. It may become possible some day, as Dr. Gerard said, to explain everything on the basis of irritability. I doubt it. As a matter of fact, an explanation can be worked out on any level, a fact which to my mind reduces the value of reductionism even as a

program for the philosophy of sciences. A plausible explanation of everything is possible, including all scientific statements that can be made on the basis of one particular culture; for science itself is a culture and is merely a way of making statements about processes with which everyone is familiar.

But working out explanations on just one level, whatever it may be, is also not of the greatest value. For example, in psychodynamics—and I think this has been one of its errors in the past—there is a temptation to explain everything in terms of psychodynamic principles. It is a temptation to try to explain everything in terms of one level, or finally, in terms of the bottom level; but these operations are not of great utility.

There is more utility, it seems to me, in understanding mental disease in particular, and human behavior in general, as a field, a very complex field; and in trying to understand the contributions that each discipline has to make in terms of the system within the field which is appropriate to the problem that is being studied. So that if we are asked to study a problem in mental disease, let us say, and if certain systems—certain organic systems, certain neurological systems, certain psychological systems, certain social and cultural systems, or small group systems—are involved, then we must include them. We must learn to understand each other's terminology for explaining them; but fundamentally we must ask how the systems interact with each other. That is an entirely different sort of question from that of the validity of value of the organizational levels.

SKINNER: I do not like levels of organization or a hierarchy; but there may be something to that concept in considering causes. However, I would like to emphasize again the distinction between cause and effect or, to put it in more modern terms, the different kinds of variables involved. We are talking about mental disease. Of course, there are ways of getting at what causes mental disease at different levels of organization. But it seems to me that the facts to be accounted for exist only at one level. A person is mentally ill because of the way he behaves. (The analyst might add that the person behaves as he does because of the way he feels.) An individual in society is regarded as mentally ill either because he does not behave as he should or because he behaves as he should not in terms of existing controlling systems. We can or we cannot control such an individual as a member of society. That is a fact at only one level; the whole organism is behaving with respect to a current environment.

In searching for what causes the person to behave that way, it is possible to look in various directions: into the past history, as a psychologist or a psychodynamicist would; or into the constitution, current illnesses, or diseases of the body, as the organicist would. These approaches are at different levels. One way out of disagreement is to realize that we are all attempting to account for facts at the level of the behavior of the whole organism. The many specialties which we represent apply to different kinds of relevant variables which enter into such an account.

In the first paragraph of his statement of the psychodynamic position, Dr. Alexander says that mental disease consists in dysfunction of the ego. I wonder whether he would be willing to modify that to say that it is the *result* of dysfunction of the ego.

ALEXANDER: No. That is a definition, right or wrong, not an explanation.

SKINNER: Then this is a real disagreement. I do not observe dysfunction of the ego. I observe mentally sick people. I do not think these are the same thing.

ALEXANDER: I think that the concluding remarks of the Chairman brought out the really essential area of disagreement in this discussion. I would call it the methodologically philosophical naïveté of the biologists. It came out so clearly in Dr. Gerard's statement that the interaction of neurons is the last word and it must be translated.

GERARD: Excuse me! I did not say that. Let me restate my point.

ALEXANDER: All right. I do not want to do you an injustice.

GERARD: Nor do I to you. What I pointed out was that we had to believe enough in the unity of the different areas so that one could go up or down the ladder. There *is* a directionalism about it so that ultimately one hopes to understand behavior of man in terms of neurons. But to say that as an immediate operational procedure one must work on neurons—obviously not.

ALEXANDER: I see that I understood you correctly. Ultimately you considered this was the state of affairs.

GERARD: Ultimately, one would also understand neuronal behavior in terms of molecules, and their behavior in terms of electrons and nucleons.

ALEXANDER: I doubt whether that would be either probable or useful.

GERARD: I agree it may not be useful but, I believe, it is possible.

ALEXANDER: The naïveté of that view consists in your picking out one part of the complex phenomenon and saying: "If I can describe this part with my operational tools, then all the other observed phenomena should correlate with this central issue. That should be, then, the ultimate goal." I want to point out the naïveté of this position with an example. I am not an abstractionist; I like to think in concrete terms.

In Shanghai, on the street, two people are quarreling. That is a behavioral problem. If I do not understand the Chinese and their language, I never will understand the basis of this quarrel. I cannot account for it. I see only that two people are yelling at each other, and in the end, one hits the other. If I know the Chinese language, then I will understand that the one attacked the ancestors of the other. I will surmise that the latter became angry because his ancestors were attacked. If I am an American, I do not understand that. I think that he is crazy. Why should he care that the other man attacks his ancestors? Here, if our ancestors are attacked, we take less offense. We do not know what kind of people they were before they came to this country. Whatever our ancestors were, we want to be better. What our fathers said is now old-fashioned. So I do not understand. There must be something peculiar about this man. Here is a behavioral problem. The neurologist is called in. He will describe stimuli, neural processes, the seventh nerve, certain complex neural processes in the brain, and finally the motor innervation leading to the arm, all taking part in the action of hitting. He will describe the behavior in terms of neurophysiology.

Then comes the psychodynamicist who says, "I listened to the assailant's talk, and I note that he is very sensitive. Obviously he dreads his parents; hence, when they were attacked, he overcompensated. He was conditioned to suppress all hostility against his own hostility towards his parents. That repression was threatened; therefore, as a defense, he attacks now in the other person what he himself would like to do."

Finally, the sociologist says that to understand this phenomenon, it is necessary to understand China, to know that there people are raised in ancestor worship. When cognizance is taken of that, the man's attitude makes sense. Here is cultural tradition handed down from generation to generation. It explains why the man is sensitive on this subject. But we must also ask why there is ancestor worship in China. For the answer to that we must go back to Chinese history and find out why the Chinese developed it. The anthropologists have formulated an adaptational theory that certain cultural attitudes are adaptations to the specific problems that the group faces. It explains ancestral attitudes from the history of China. In view of all this, is it not naïve to expect, to desire, or to aim to explain this very complex phenomenon in the terms of neuron interaction?

SKINNER: I do not want to prejudge the solution at which we will arrive fifty years from now by saying that there will be a single cause to any entity called mental disease or behavior pattern. On the other hand, we are not ready to assert that the causes are multiple. Possibly they are. We have not, thus far, found out much about causation. All I was asking was that we first agree about what we are defining the etiology of. I was proposing to define the thing to be accounted for as some aspects of the behavior of individuals. In contrast, the psychodynamicists believe that mental disease is in the psyche and that it is a set of feelings or dysfunction of the ego. This seems to be a disagreement that should be cleared up. My own belief is that the analyst has mistaken an explanation for the thing to be

explained; that he, too, is really concerned with accounting for behavior. Dr. Alexander's example was expressed in terms of the patient's phobic wandering in the street and of his feeling scared to death. The patient told of his feelings, and his verbal behavior in doing so supplied the physician with additional *behavioral* facts. For all practical—and in the long run theoretical—purposes, it is better to hold to the observable behavior of the individual and to derive definitions of the Freudian dynamisms, for example, without reference to how a person feels about the world or his own behavior.

SCOTT: The psychodynamicists have defined the problem in terms of feelings; most of the other scientists, particularly the behavioral scientists, try to define it in terms of what is observable. Because of my original orientation toward observable behavior, this discrepancy bothered me until I worked out my own solution. The psychodynamicist talks of the conscious and unconscious mind, ego, and id. From an evolutionary viewpoint, it is known that animals which do not have language are able to solve problems, to form habits, and to do what would be called thinking, all without the use of the kind of words that human beings employ. Human beings presumably came originally from nonverbal animals, and the most likely course of evolution of the brain, when mechanisms were developed for the use of language, was that they were added on to the old brain rather than substituted for primitive ways of thinking. If we assume that there are nonverbal methods of thinking and forming habits left over in the brain, existing together with the newly acquired verbal processes, we have an objective definition or idea which still comes fairly close to the psychodynamic concepts of the conscious and unconscious mind. Objective and psychodynamic thinking are not necessarily irreconcilable. By the use of proper concepts and formulations they can be brought together.

WHITEHORN: We have been struggling to find formulations to fit mental disease, whether it be one state or a group of states, and to ascertain what would be the relevant factors. Fortunately for the clinician, mental disease appears to him as a series of different concrete situations, with factors relevant to one situation, not to one kind of mental disease. That tends to simplify the matter.

SPIEGEL: Concerning causation and system relevance, I should like to raise the question, If we have a culture that describes certain types of behavior as disease, where is the disease? I agree with Dr. Skinner when he says the psychodynamicist too easily locates it in a presumed structure, namely, the ego. But this tendency to attempt to locate the difficulty entirely within the individual, either within the individual as a whole or within one of his part systems, which is held to be at fault, is no more marked in psychodynamics than it is in most other disciplines. Actually one could perhaps picture the trouble better in terms of interaction pattern. Is the trouble really within the individual, or is it within the individual and the system within which the individual is functioning? It is like the question, Is it the problem of one discipline to explain its terminology and concepts to another, or is it a matter of having both find a method of interacting which would make it easier for them to understand each other? It is a mutual system. When a mental hospital which has been in the hands of a jailer, so to speak, comes under a new superintendent who introduces a whole new series of procedures, pays attention to the attitudes of the personnel, and attempts to enforce an environment where the individual is treated as an individual, many of the patients in the hospital who have been sick or held at one level for years begin to improve. The difficulty cannot be entirely within the individual but is rather within the interaction patterns; hence, the examination of patterns that are mutual and reciprocal is as important as the examination of a particular system.

LIDDELL: In his outline Dr. Skinner has formulated the psychological position in terms of practical programs of research. He has emphasized what the psychologist can do practically, and what he cannot do, or is not professionally interested in doing. Fortunately the psychologists are not burdened with principles or definitions of terms. On the other hand, I think Dr. Alexander is far superior to the terms and principles that he introduces in his statement of the psychodynamic position. He is a sensitive and keen observer, a skilled experimentalist. Many of us are not much interested in levels of organization, hierarchy, or naïveté. What is important is that we all have special divisions of labor in the observational skills which are centered upon behavior. I have wasted many years of my professional life being overawed and intimidated by the terminology and principles of Freud and Pavlov. I think both of them have done us a great deal of harm.

ALEXANDER: Some good too.

LIDDELL: Naturally.

WHITEHORN: I believe that the term "relevance" is the key to getting on from this controversy to more constructive points. At times we have used somewhat archaic language in formulating topics and questions; for example, in the title of the Conference appear the words "Mental Disease." As defined by the psychiatric group and thus as the official terminology, the categories now in use are in terms of reaction patterns. It is easier to speak of social pressure, motivation, or intoxication if their relevance to the patterns of reaction is considered. In this way, one of the points at issue that arises from a somewhat too rigid concept of mental disease might be dodged.

I think that we have haggled unduly about prestige. I have no expectation that we will ever get completely away from it, but I wish we could proceed beyond it. Dr. Jasper's statement of the organic position carries the implication: "I am a scientist; therefore, if someone speaks terms which I do not understand, what he says is not scientific. If we would deserve the prestige of being scientific, it is up to him to put his statements in terms which I can grasp and act upon." In other documents distributed to the group, one encounters such phrases as, "for scientific advance the material 'must be' or 'should be' formulated so-and-so." Here again there is overgrown prestige, the attitude of the individual who insists that the game must be played his way. Nor are we psychiatrists without guilt on this score. For I have already pointed out that we have delineated the field in terms of re-action patterns. But I do think that we waste much effort in struggling over pres-tige. If we would focus now on relevance, I think we might make progress.

HOLLINGSHEAD: Part of the problem of the types of behavioral or reaction pat-terns confronting the psychiatrist, which are broadly termed mental disease, is that essen-tially they are defined as intolerable in a so-ciety. Society says that when persons are behaving in certain ways, they are dangerous to themselves or to society and something should be done about it. Also in the cultural system of our society, the individual who handles such persons is sometimes the psy-chiatrist and sometimes the jailer. We have not completely delineated in our society what types of reaction are appropriately within the province of the psychiatrist and what types are a responsibility for the jailer. Sometimes the reacting individuals are switched from one domain to the other. The social control system is in operation, and the reaction of the individual is within this system. Whether or not reaction patterns are disease is a cultural definition rather than a definition in the traditional sense of organization.

WHITEHORN: Because behavior is quite objective or can be so regarded, we are tempted to reduce everything to behavior and control. Clinically the psychiatrist deals with people in distress. To help somehow to reduce distress is one of the motivations in clinical operations. If behavior disorders that are socially unacceptable are regarded as disturbances, they then have three aspects: distress, disability, and disturbance. We have to consider all three; we cannot focus altogether on disturbance.

HOLLINGSHEAD: Actually I was pointing out the ambiguity of abnormal reactions or behavior which may be regarded as mental disease, maladaptation, or delinquency. I would agree that something should be done about the distress and inner feelings of an affected individual. Perhaps he may never do anything which would be regarded by society as indicative of mental disease in the traditional sense or of delinquency, and which might place him in a hospital or a jail. But he is so distressed in his interper-sonal relations that he seeks help. Clearly the problem does have three dimensions: distress, disability, and disturbance.

GRINKER: This turn in the discussion leads us back to the problem of values. I am sorry that we have to harp on it continually; but it seems necessary since it is, I think, the most important problem to straighten out in interdisciplinary groups. I have al-ready mentioned that systems might be con-sidered as part of the entire field; this point brings in the concept of hierarchical values. Later a statement was made which seemed to be logical; but analysis of it indicates that the concept of value is not clearly under-stood. Dr. Mettler stated that each disci-pline makes a validation in terms of its own frame of reference. He also cited the ex-ample of facts worth ten cents; that is a value. What we have to ask is that each discipline establish its concepts of reliabil-ity; that is what a scientific discipline can and must do.

But the validation and the relevance of what is determined by a particular discipline is by no means justifiably determined by the operators in that discipline. It is at that point in terms of the values and relevance that multidisciplinary activities come into play. Let us use the sociologist's point of view as an example. He says that mental diseases or abnormal mental reactions are those processes that become intolerable to society and threaten social control. This be-havioristic concept of mental disease from a social point of view would be completely unacceptable to me as a total definition. It would give a partial description or explana-tion. It would help in understanding, for example, that the Communist in this coun-try who is threatened by society's control and therefore behaves intolerably to society may become in his anti-Communism just as disagreeable and as intolerable to society. Hence, in trying to figure out, in any in-stance, what is acceptable and what is not acceptable as a definition of disease, it be-comes necessary to evoke certain other proc-esses which are elicited by tools that the sociologist does not possess.

We know that a person with particular mental reactions has a tendency to repeat over and over again the same ways of behavior in spite of differences in external situations. Furthermore, we know that those who are most adapted, most adjusted to a particular social control may be those who are on their way to becoming the sickest. Indeed, we have tools by which we can determine latency or nascence of mental illness. As a consequence, there is a problem of the validation of a concept and its relevancy, which cannot be inherent in the discipline, whose reliability of observation may be fine. Thus there is a need to realize that the relevancy of all of the statements that can be made regarding validation can be determined ultimately only by bringing in all of the ten-cent facts and other processes as parts in a total field.

In using the scales by which relevancy is measured, there is, of course, the need to have some kind of communicable discourse. It is here that we often fail. But over and above that—particularly since we are talking about the medical field—is the concept that those people who set themselves up as having the greatest relevancy in their operations with a particular phenomenon, let us say the mental reactions, have nothing much to do with the representatives of physiology.

The group with which I am associated has worked a long time on the subject of anxiety. My psychodynamic methods are often unsuccessful. Hence, my purpose in determining the neurophysiological or endocrinological concomitants of anxiety is to find the processes by which I can attack it, not by psychodynamic but by pharmacological means. As for the man who is standing in the street of Shanghai raising his voice, there may be, in the future, a method of dealing with him that has nothing to do with psychodynamics. Therefore relevancy and validation become a time-bound matter. We should be very humble about them at this time.

SPIEGEL: Along with the problems of hierarchy and prestige, another of the bogies that gets in our way is the concept of causation. If our task is to find a linear causal explanation in just one system—and I may be misinterpreting what Dr. Skinner said about this—, if the problem in psychology is to study behavior which is labeled mental disease, to find out the antecedents and con-

sequences of events, and to single out the villain in a linear series of events picked out of the total concept, it becomes a question of relevance. The worker in any one field is dealing with only a part of a process as a contribution to the whole. In clinical work the psychiatrist is always faced with certain choices so far as the disturbed behavior is concerned. Is he going to deal with the inner resources of the individual which play a part in the behavior, or with the environment of the individual which plays another part, or with some other aspect of the situation which plays a part? All these aspects are in continuous interaction and modifying each other so that actually there is no linear series of antecedent consequent episodes which can be plucked out of the total complex field and held to be the mechanism which one can manipulate in order to "cure" the situation. Rather one is always dealing with a complex of part-processes. It seems to me that the search for a cause or the dominance of a linear causal model is one of the things that gives us a great deal of difficulty.

METTLER: Is it the responsibility and obligation of the person who is bringing forth an idea or point of view to make himself intelligible to workers in other disciplines or is it the responsibility of others to find out what he is talking about?

ALEXANDER: Both.

METTLER: It would be fine if everybody did make himself intelligible to others; it would be equally fine if everybody did make an effort to find out what others were trying to say. But then comes a practical point. The sorry fact is that all of us are largely uninformed even in our own fields, for we do not have sufficient time. Science goes on. It puts a tremendous amount of material on our desks with every mail. We have had a plea for humility towards other disciplines; I already have it in my own science. I wish I could keep up with it. Who is responsible?

WHITEHORN: It might be useful to ask, not Whose responsibility is it? but What is the reward for doing it? I think the reward possibly comes from the return communication; if this can be made fruitful, then it will be sought.

METTLER: How is it done?

WHITEHORN: By cultivating collaboration. By sitting down together, exchanging points of view, outlining plans jointly for special study, and working together. This is a time-honored method.

GERARD: The objective of this Conference is to explore the possibilities of having the different disciplines focus their efforts together on mental disease. On the question of viewpoints, it is worth while to consider the difference between the biological, the psychodynamic, and the sociological approaches. The really significant difference in the way of thought of the biologically or organically oriented scientist and of the psychosocially oriented scientist is that the former has been approaching the problems in behavior and functioning of the nervous system primarily in terms of energy relations. That is what he carried over from physics and chemistry. The psychosocial scientist, on the other hand, has been concerned primarily with functioning in terms of communication. For the problems of normal behavior as well as of mental disease are interpersonal and therefore become matters of communication. The nerve impulse is really of interest in the functioning of the whole organism because it is a transmitted signal, not because it is associated with the breakdown of creatine phosphate. This is not to say, however, that when one looks at the problems in terms of communication, one therefore gets outside the kind of scientific mode that applies to simplified neurons. For the behavior of the total organism is again a matter of communication, now between the neurons, and involves "interpersonal" relations of neurons. This mode can be spread up and down the levels; it is still the scientific mode.

Dr. Alexander made the particular point that there are four approaches to the incident of two Chinese in Shanghai having a violent argument. Obviously each of these approaches to the phenomenon is perfectly valid and can be pursued with the aid of specific technical knowledge. But if we say each of these is an approach and stop there, why are we talking together? Then let the historian, the psychiatrist, the cultural anthropologist, and the physiologist go their separate ways rather than come together to talk to one another. But presumably we have some hope and faith that if we do talk together, we will find that these viewpoints, though equally valid, are not completely isolated; that they do grade into one another; and that something from one will help interpret a point in another. This, I take it, is our purpose. These approaches are not, however, equipotential; there is a directionalism. The biologist hopes ultimately to explain the behavior of humans in terms of the behavior of atoms. That is how the biologist holds nature to be organized.

We speak entirely as if science and interdisciplinary action were a matter of ideas, whereas we know that the reality is the interaction of human beings who have ideas and emotions. The question of interdisciplinary functioning will, therefore, depend on very human attributes, such as prestige, respect, and dependability. There is a hierarchy of disciplines in terms of maturity, not in terms of inherent difficulty or of wisdom of the practitioners of the different branches of knowledge. Because he is dealing with a much richer and better organized body of data than is the biologist, the physicist certainly is a more mature person scientifically. In turn, the biologist is a more mature scientist than the social scientist by virtue of a longer background in an easier subject. It has nothing to do necessarily with wisdom or skill or intelligence of the person; it is a matter of historical accident of time. Later physics may be a dull, outworn subject; whereas social science may then be the most precise, alert, and active field.

Because there is this difference now, it brings the problem of prestige into the minds of those in the different disciplines. The biologist ordinarily does not worry about this prestige. The psychiatrist, psychologist, the social scientist, rightly or wrongly, feel sufficiently secure in their bodies of materials. But there is a lack of reciprocity. Admittedly the biologist is often guilty of promoting insecurity feelings on the part of colleagues in these other areas, probably because he is ignorant and intolerant of their subject matter. He is inclined to be scornful and critical without fair knowledge of what is going on or understanding of what is available with which to work. He is often reluctant to accept a colleague in the psychosocial field as equally intelligent and capable, as doing his best, and therefore as entitled to the same kind of scientific respect that he would give to a physicist, a chemist, or another biologist. This kind of intolerance has been harmful; and it has been greater on the side of the biologist and organicist than it has been on the side of the social scientist. I was distressed when I read the statement made in a team meeting: A biologist is just not interested in social problems. I hope this is not universally true. So, prestige *is* a problem. But the solution lies on both sides; it requires the willingness and ability of the one to demonstrate the degree of precision or validity of the concepts and facts of his discipline, and of the other to learn these and accept them realistically.

A final comment on multicausality. We all say that there is no one cause for mental disease. It is multiple because there is a multiple-antecedent and a multiple-consequent situation. The old point-to-point cause and effect is nineteenth century science from which modern knowledge has emancipated us. Multiple-factor causation raises two points. First, it is not enough that we recognize all the factors; we begin to be useful only when we can quantify them. The situation then becomes reproducible and meaningful. This kind of causality we all can work with. In my opinion this is the direction in which analytic understanding of the problems before us is going to progress.

Furthermore, many phenomena are interrelated, feed back upon one another, and give a system which changes as a totality; but this does not mean that the system and the separate components cannot be analyzed. When carbon monoxide enters the blood or carbon dioxide leaves, the other quantity is also changed; they are interrelated. But Lawrence Henderson made a tremendous contribution by reducing the complex relations of many blood variables to a series of nomograms which show the exact changes in all other components as any are deliberately altered. It is not necessary to retreat to a more mystic attitude, that the whole field mishmashes into itself as an unresolvable whole.

chapter 26

From the Abstract
to the Concrete

❖ ❖

GERARD: It has been suggested that at this point we adopt the procedure of going from the general to the particular, with enumeration and exemplification. It might be a very useful maneuver.

RENNIE: In the present stage of knowledge it is obvious that no one discipline is going to give the answer to all the problems presented in human behavior, both normal and aberrant. Hence, I am interested in seeing whether we can come concretely nearer the point in defining in what way the knowledge of the different disciplines can be brought together to enlarge our understanding of certain behavioral problems.

The statement on the psychosocial position which I prepared, I now find very diffuse and generalized. I shall therefore try to make it a little more concrete because within the area of psychosocial contribution to the understanding of mental disorder, one can obviously hew out many variables and phenomena which one chooses to study. I am convinced that if one chooses a phenomenon and looks at it, one has to hew his tools to the task of that which he sees and to draw widely and often from outside his own discipline in getting help in forging tools which will help to master the specific task. I am engaged in just such a task in the Yorkville district of New York City.

The problem was to study a community and the social stresses existing in it, and to see whether those stresses had any demonstrable pertinence or relevance to the behavior of human beings living within that society. Almost at once I was faced with a great variety of variables which would have to be tested. For working purposes those variables may be roughly considered as follows: There are certain independent variables which come to play on everybody's life. They are subsumed under such items as a person's age, sex, socioeconomic status or level, and ethnic background, and the peculiar aspects of urban living. Then there are dependent variables which we take into account when we attempt to assay the adjustment or the mental health status of persons within this social environment. Another large group of variables which certainly have to be considered, the so-called intervening variables, would be enumerated as some of the salient items of the psychodynamicist: the parent-child relation, the intrafamily dynamics, the relationship to peers, the educational process, the occupational development of the individual, his religious affiliation, and the inadvertent illnesses, traumas, and physical impacts that come to bear. Here spelled out is a series of variables.

Can any one discipline at the present time encompass or provide tools for the study of all these variables? I think not. Clearly the psychodynamicist alone is not prepared by training or by experience to throw light on some of these very important independent variables. Certainly the social scientist needs help from the psychodynamicist in the understanding of what this impact is within the person to whom it is happening. It should be remembered also that the psychologist has very specific tools for the assaying of behavior and personality which have an important bearing on this particular task. The organicist might well throw light on psychosomatic disorders by showing how the impact of forces brought about the specific end reaction in a given organism.

All this is presented as a problem because in my judgment it can only be met adequately by an interdisciplinary approach. To that end a group of persons drawn from various disciplines did indeed sit down to have a look at the problem and to map out and plan the specific tools by which it could be studied.

Was there mumbo jumbo? Yes, for about two months. I soon very clearly realized that nothing in my medical preparation had helped me to understand some of the words that the social scientists were using, and I certainly was using words which they did not understand. But when people meet in a common purpose to effect a common end point, they are willing to listen to each other. I see nothing wrong with the fact that a science has its own language which may be esoteric for others. But if the latter want something from that science, they have an obligation to learn what the words mean. When persons from different disciplines have talked to each other long enough, sometimes two months, sometimes a year, the mumbo jumbo begins to disappear because they begin really to know what the other person is talking about. It should not be assumed that a person from one discipline can impart information easily and readily to a person from another discipline who has never been exposed to it. The process requires working together before the mumbo jumbo begins to make sense to everybody concerned.

It is a conviction on my part that human behavior has multiple variables. I do not believe in a single etiology. Nor do I believe

that any one discipline at this moment of scientific development is going to give the total answer to what is going on in the very complex experiment; namely, the study of human beings. As representatives of different disciplines, I think that we have a right to ask each other, "What don't you understand in what I say, and what have you that is pertinent to a problem such as I have enumerated?" It may put to a concrete test some of the differences of opinion.

SOLOMON: I find that the high and abstract level on which the discussion has proceeded is somewhat less than satisfying. I had begun to fear that none of us would hear anything except what we had heard before many times.

I surmise that points of disagreement or unacceptance are best revealed by the remarks uttered in the practical, operating, multidisciplinary research situation. After the psychologist has conducted an experiment on perception with human subjects, the social scientist may challenge him with the statement. "You do not know the social class from which the subjects came. How do you know that you do not have to take into account social class in describing the variables?" Obviously, from the remarks of the social scientist, the variables which he thinks are important in the experiment relate a change in the environment to the perceptual reaction of the subject.

One way to become concrete and to educate each other would be to express such annoyances. Representing four different areas, we do touch each other at several sensitive points. When we get into a controversy, it is usually when one becomes exasperated with another because the latter has not paid attention to factors which the former thinks are important. In most instances this disregard is readily excusable because the worker in one discipline does not appreciate the significance of the factors in another discipline. Persons in two different areas know different things. The one is relatively ignorant in areas of knowledge in which the other is relatively wise. This is bound to lead to difficulty. What is it, then, that the psychodynamicist does which irritates me, an experimental psychologist, the most? He may overlook certain variables which I think are extremely important. I might then raise the question, "Why don't I also have the privilege of overlooking variables? What am I losing?"

I wish that we here would air our annoyances. Each of us might appropriately address to those of other disciplines the question: "Why don't you take into account this factor which I think is so important?" I believe that it would emphasize how interdisciplinary awareness can influence the way in which the individual worker formulates his own research.

SPENCE: I think that there is a hierarchy of knowledge in the sense of the more fundamental—I do not mean to put any value judgment on that statement—phenomena of physics, such as electrons and molecules on up through neurons, to the more complex biological behavior. This is the structure whether we like it or not. I would be inclined to the view that it cannot be legislated out of existence. It is going to exist.

Dr. Liddell made a statement which puts me in an ambivalent position. I thought I detected an attack on theory. I am wholly a behaviorist; but my particular interest in psychology has been that of a theorist. It puts me in the position of a theorist having to defend theorists, Freud and Pavlov, whose theories I do not regard highly. Despite my lukewarm opinion of their theories, I would defend the position that each of these men played an extremely important role in the development of knowledge in biological and behavioral sciences, particularly the psychopathology, where I think Freud's influence is outstanding. Whether or not his theory was right, he certainly has been responsible for a considerable amount of research.

The major contribution of the experimental psychologist is in the field of more complex behavior, namely, precise control and quantification of phenomena. This has included the study, in the laboratory, of fairly simple behavior phenomena: human eyelid closure, or the rat pressing a bar. By such an approach the psychologists have worked out a fairly complete set of laws in the field of learning and motivation, much of which is ready to be translated into psychodynamic thinking. In fact, I thought I detected a little of it in Dr. Alexander's paper. I have already expressed surprise that the psychoanalysts had heard of the learning theory. However, I see very little evidence that the details of it are accurately understood. Some of the words are in there, but from their connotation I can only conclude that there is very little understanding of them. If psychologists and psychoanalysts were to work closely together, much might be added, I believe, to knowledge about learning and motivation, two of the most important aspects of human behavior.

FINESINGER: In order to bring out our differences and agreements more sharply, Dr. Alexander has proposed that a hypothetical case, with its history and findings, be presented for discussion. He suggested that it be a type of case which had factors within the four areas represented here. Dr. Mettler thought that a patient with Korsakoff's syndrome might be an appropriate case.

ALEXANDER: I would be against the choice of Korsakoff's syndrome for discussion for the reason that the psychodynamic contribution would be very scanty. On the other hand, I would not want to propose a case like a phobia where the neurophysiological contribution would be negligible. I would suggest a case where the biological, sociological, neurophysiological, biochemical, and psychodynamic contributions would be considerable. I had thought of alcoholism because it comprises observable physiological, pharmacological, and biochemical components. There are also psychodynamic phenomena and many sociological factors. A case of alcoholism would be ideal to bring out the contributions from the different approaches and to consider how they may be interrelated.

GRINKER: I will give a case. Sam is an Italian-American, single, 30 years old. He was born in this country and brought up in a district of Chicago where the Italians were somewhat isolated. Nevertheless, he went to public school and learned something of what the American boys wanted to be; he liked to play baseball and wanted to get ahead in the world. His was a very close family circle. His father, who is a barber, had always wanted him to follow in his occupational footsteps. Sam tried very hard to get away from his father. He succeeded once during military service. But he came back home and found that in order to maintain a good relationship with his father, whom he adored and respected but nevertheless feared, he had to work in his father's barber shop.

From standing long hours on his feet, Sam developed varicose veins for which a surgeon decided to operate. Before the operation Sam was in a very serious condition. He developed an intense anxiety. His heart beat fast so that the family doctor was called in to determine whether he had heart disease. His blood pressure went up; his skin was wet; he trembled all over. He had to be treated with sedatives and given many reassurances before he was able to submit to the operation. Postoperatively the wound did not seem to heal as well as might be expected from the type of operation. Nevertheless, eventually Sam found himself back at work in the barber shop. Then began a series of episodes which would occur while he was shaving or giving a haircut to a customer in the chair next to his father's. Sam would become overwhelmed with panic and dread, would rush out of the shop with a razor in his hand without knowing where he was, and would end up at home or in a doctor's office.

He went from doctor to doctor, and none could find anything physically wrong with him. His cardiovascular system seemed to be in good shape, and his veins were all right by that time. Finally he came into a mental hospital for observation of the attacks of panic and for diagnosis. While in the hospital, his panics diminished to the point where he became completely free of them. After a time he was discharged, but every time he went home to his father he developed another panic. Yet he could not find another job. He could not get away from his father; he felt compelled to go back to him. This man, under treatment over a long period of time, gradually was able to take the step of being away from his father and to work in somebody else's barber shop. Then his attacks decreased in intensity. I cite this case because it demonstrates sociological, psychodynamic, and physiological processes. There are also behavioral patterns which are characteristic of the patient in his premorbid and in his sick state.

METTLER: This particular type of case is one which anyone with my background should keep his hands off. A medical scientist who does not have information in certain areas should realize it and not intrude there. Why this patient was not having healing of his operative wound, and why he was developing the panic reactions are very interesting physiological phenomena. But they are not of particular moment for his treatment or cure. Comment should come from somebody who understands this particular kind of mechanism.

FINESINGER: Suppose this patient has hyperactive knee jerks?

METTLER: He probably would have hyperactive knee jerks. My reaction would be not so much one of disinterest as one of a feeling that I should have a disinterest.

GRINKER: I would be disappointed if you told me that, because I think that you have a place in the study of this patient.

METTLER: I would feel at a disadvantage in it. I have no business in it, and in all likelihood I would add only confusion. However, the psychiatrist might want to consult about particular symptoms. For example, he might inquire about the patient's overactive reflexes. Additional observations would then have to be gathered. It would be helpful to know whether the overactive reflexes are persistent all the time under all circumstances or whether they are related to his tension phenomena. The chances are that during the time he was in the mental hospital, he did not have overreactive reflexes; but that when he was examined in doctors' offices, he did have them. It could then be concluded that this particular physiological phenomena is a manifestation of a situational stress under which he has been. This is an adequate, complete explanation for it.

GRINKER: Isn't it possible that some difference in this man's central excitatory state made him susceptible to these particular uncontrolled outbursts? I would ask whether you would be willing to study his brain waves. Also, can you conduct determinations on the amount of adrenal cortical hormone to ascertain whether it is related to the excitatory state?

METTLER: I would refer your requests to the laboratory. Organicists are not completely ignorant of these phenomena. The tests which you request could, of course, be run. I refuse to make any comment about electroencephalographic findings in this case when such an authority as Dr. Jasper is available.

JASPER: I do not feel, as Dr. Mettler does, about this type of cooperation. In studying the reactions of a patient, is a neurophysiologist not to go into his history and the stimulus pattern to which he has been exposed and conditioned? To me these are all part of the biological problem, and I do not keep aloof from them. I want to learn all that I can about them; to refuse to concern myself with them would be, I think, a great mistake.

METTLER: My statement implied that the neurophysiologist recognizes the existence of these phenomena. The difference between you and me in this respect is that I would immediately withdraw from the situation personally. You would not. I would say it is not my area of competence.

FINESINGER: Would you think it is the concern of the physiologist to try to provide whatever information he has, to explain phenomena of this kind?

METTLER: Yes. But I would say that the direction of this activity should be under a person with appropriate training and experience. This problem in electroencephalography is in Dr. Jasper's province, not mine.

ALEXANDER: Suppose we make a specific request: We would like to know what happens neurophysiologically and biochemically in the organism of this patient who has violent anxiety attacks and panic states.

JASPER: Two studies now going on in Montreal may be pertinent. One, which is being conducted in the Allan Memorial Institute of Psychiatry by Dr. Shagass, has to do with anxiety and electroencephalographic concomitants. It is aimed to test in different types of patients the level of barbiturate injection which produces a change in the electrical activity of the brain. The level of barbiturate injection at which the response occurs has a definite end point. The response is objectively recorded in the electroencephalogram in the form of a measurable change in the character of the electrical activity of the cortex. It is related to clinical observations, such as a change in speech. The end point varies with the type of patient. The acutely anxious person requires much more barbiturate. On the other hand, curiously enough an agitated psychotic patient who appears to have a lot of tension in this particular situation gives a normal, not an anxiety, reaction. Also, hysterical patients do not differ from normals.

Neurophysiologists are beginning to study the basis for these reactions and the general mechanisms of arousal in the brain. Much has been learned about them in the last few years, not only of their anatomical, but also of their endocrine and biochemical, relationships. It has been shown that different systems of neurons seem to mediate predominantly this arousal mechanism, and that it is particularly susceptible to barbiturates before any of the specific pathways are markedly affected. This is of course a very incomplete picture, but it is contributory to understanding the patient's anxiety.

The second study is on the stimulus patterns which set off this arousal mechanism in animals. Dr. Sharpless, who is conducting these experiments, has discovered that animals can be trained to ignore a certain stimulus by simple habituation and also to be aroused by only a specific stimulus. This learning persists for days. The arousal reaction can be measured by electrophysiological methods. This habituation introduces a difficult physiological problem as to what such learning represents in neurophysiological terms. But at least we now have laboratory methods for studying learned habituation to situations which may have potentialities for "panic" reactions in animals. We can study the animals' adaptation to the stimulus-response situation, and we can condition them to "panic" responses.

From investigation into the physiology of this process, some of the circuits in the brain stem that have undergone habituation have been located. For certain types of habituation, namely, that of specific tones or visual patterns, it has been found that the cerebral cortex is not needed. Habituation still occurs after it is removed. But when animals deprived of the cortex are placed in a situation which requires habituation to a stimulus pattern, the elements of which are constant, such differential habituation cannot occur without the cortex.

METTLER: I wish to point out that an interesting thing has now happened. We have left the patient and moved to the general area of anxiety and stressing situations as an abstract problem. This is a development which is disconcerting to my clinical colleagues in the Neurological Institute. They bring a concrete problem to the laboratory, and very shortly it has become an investigation into an abstract situation which seems to have no particular bearing or relationship. It is abstract to the clinician; it is not to the medical scientist. It was also because of the likelihood of just this development that I did not enter into the discussion of the case.

GRINKER: Dr. Mettler's reaction leads me to review our steps. We agreed that we had been talking too abstractly and at too high a level, so it was suggested that we discuss a patient.

The history of a patient was presented. Essentially and ordinarily, the clinicians among us would be concerned about treatment of the patient; but for present purposes, he represents an experiment. He exhibits an interesting background; he has a variety of things happening to him; and he shows a number of symptoms. As an experiment in nature he represents a challenge to this multidisciplinary group whose members are supposed to bring all their tools to bear upon his disorder. Indeed, I sense that all here who are not clinicians have suddenly faded away with the polite excuse: "Doctor, this is your problem." It is the clinicians' problem, but they cannot cope with all the facets of it. The nonclinical scientists assert that they have information which would help the clinicians in coping with the case. The clinicians agree and request that help; then all of a sudden they find themselves alone.

FINESINGER: Dr. Jasper, in the experimental work which you reported, what about the specificity? Is that critical or is there a broad range of stimuli which will bring it about?

JASPER: An animal can be habituated to a 200-cycle tone while still retaining normal responses to a tone of 100 cycles or 400 cycles, or to a tactile stimulus.

WHITEHORN: That item has to do with arousal aspects in general. It has pertinence.

LIDDELL: It is called vigilance.

SOLOMON: I do not want to duck away from this problem. The patient is said to have adored and respected his father but nevertheless feared him. To a psychologist who has run experiments on behavior of animals in which they approach objects and in which they avoid them, this statement, from one point of view, is nonsense; from another point of view, it is very important. From one point of view, it is impossible that this person could adore and respect his father and at the same time fear him. What this statement indicates to me is a lack of specification of the stimulating conditions for setting up these two types of emotional reaction. What the psychodynamicist has done is to sample the behavior of this individual over a period of time; he finds that in the presence of the father, sometimes the son acts adoringly and respectfully but at other times he is fearful. Then comes the statement that the patient adores and respects his father, but nevertheless fears him. This fits in nicely with Freud and the conception of ambivalence. However, from the point of view of experimentation devised to ascertain some of the very important conditions necessary for producing panic states, I do not believe that any such statement is allowable. What can be said is: Under conditions A, B, and C, the father, as an idea or a stimulus, leads to a certain type of emotional arousal of the patient. Under conditions D, E, and F, or maybe some overlapping condition, the father leads to some other state. The conditions have to be defined, for an important clue is that sometimes one thing happens and sometimes another. I find it impossible to believe that both things happen at the same time.

ALEXANDER: I will not try to give a complete psychodynamic reconstruction of the case. Rather I should like to explain what is probably the nature of this problem. But mainly I should like to show the limitations of the psychodynamic approach and therefore the need for assistance from other disciplines.

Let me review the patient's history. I understand that he is 30 years old, and that the home environment was representative of Italian cultural tradition. He lived in a closed family circle in which the family had a great influence on him. But he was exposed to American culture; he went to public school. He went into military service; but when he came back, he followed his father's desire, which was somehow conveyed to him, probably directly, and became a barber. The patient developed varicose veins; then, probably in connection with the pending operation, exhibited palpitation and other manifestations of anxiety; got sedatives and reassurance; went through the operation. The wound healed slowly. He continued to work after that and developed severe anxiety; while shaving customers, he had real panic states in which he ran out of the shop. He was hospitalized. The panic states disappeared in the hospital, but reappeared whenever he went back to his father.

This would be my interpretation: This man was exposed to two major influences: (1) the home influence with loyalty towards and reverence for the father, and (2) fear of the father. These are not contradictory feelings; they cannot be isolated as sometimes has been attempted. Like sensory perceptions, his feelings are extremely complex states in which all kinds of contradictory elements may be together in one unit. Whether that makes such phenomena easy for experimentation or not, it does not change the following two facts: these are the phenomena; and the phenomena must be investigated by appropriate methods, and not be selected or modified to fit the methods available. For the phenomena cannot be changed; any modification must be in the methods.

SOLOMON: There is a real disagreement here because what you call fact is theory.

ALEXANDER: Description of emotional state.

SOLOMON: I do not think it is a description because you have to specify to me the conditions under which this person acts reverent and respectful as well as the conditions under which he appears frightened.

ALEXANDER: I agree.

SOLOMON: Tell me the difference between the two.

ALEXANDER: I agree. The description must be accurate and not general.

SOLOMON: To say that the person feels afraid and respectful at the same time toward his father is really a theoretical statement. It represents a highly prejudiced view of the situation.

ALEXANDER: I will let that remark go for the moment since it is not pertinent.

I assume that there is a complex feeling toward the father, contradictory feelings. Under certain conditions, one element appears; under other conditions, the other element appears.

SOLOMON: Now we don't disagree.

ALEXANDER: We don't disagree?

WHITEHORN: Prescriptive language has been used that certain things are permissible, and other things not permissible. That leads to difficulty. Whether his viewpoints be right or wrong, I would very strongly object to a worker from one discipline telling a worker in another discipline what statements are permissible.

GERARD: I disagree with Dr. Whitehorn that it is improper to use the word "permissible." The implications of permissible, at least as I interpreted them, were different than he took them to be. This point is highly relevant to the problem because, perhaps for the first time, I believe, we are dealing with the issues in a very specific manner. As Dr. Solomon used the term "permissible," he was saying: "In order for me to accept as valid the things that you are setting forth, you must give me your evidence at a different level; therefore it is not permissible in the sense of interdisciplinary communication." If he was using it in that sense, he had a perfect right to do it. This is a matter of laying down the rules of co-understanding.

WHITEHORN: If we could lay them down.

GERARD: Eventually each of the arguers will have to agree that certain things are acceptable to both.

WHITEHORN: Instead of laying down rules for communication here, even if we could, would it not be better to assert, "I do not know what you say?"

ALEXANDER: That is much better.

WITTKOWER: I should like to take up a point which brings out a conceptual difficulty. Dr. Solomon wants us to think along Aristotelian principles by which things have to be black and white. Yet, in the unconscious contradictions exist.

SOLOMON: I used the word "permissible" in exactly the way that you were using it. I think in terms of logic. If you say that the man both feared and respected his father, that is either a logical contradiction or your definitions of fear and respect overlap one another to a great extent. Suppose we do have these composite feelings, these contradictory feelings, they are not the same then or must be distinguishable from fear and respect. Perhaps there is a third state which an individual can be in. That is a possibility.

GRINKER: I know that the behaviorists here accept the fact that verbal communication is a part of behavior and that what the patient says to me and how he behaves can be used independently as a reference of behavior. The patient says to me, "Doctor, I dearly love my father." And he gives me evidence. "I live with him. I work with him. I do what he tells me to. I dearly love my father." What happens in the patient's total behavior? He reports, "When I am standing in the shop with my father, I run away from him in fright although I say I dearly love him." I see two manifestations of behavior. What the patient does not know is why he runs away in fear from his father. The patient can say to me verbally, "I love my father. He has been good to me. He has given me an education, has never beaten me, and has done many nice things for me." But what the patient cannot say is, "Al-though I know that I love my father, all the time I am standing there with him I am so afraid of him that I have to run out." That is the problem, isn't it?

ALEXANDER: Verbal communication has been said to be considered as a part of behavior which can be utilized in the behavioristic approach. I should like to have the opportunity during this Conference to take up this basic question: namely, the nature of psychological understanding of another person's motivation; the validity of psychological interpretation of another person's feelings, thoughts, and behavior; how this type of statement derives; and whether it is hypothesis, theory, or fact.

GERARD: That is exactly what should come out at this stage.

ALEXANDER: I should like to discuss that, not now, but some time during this Conference apart from this case, as one of the topics. What is the validity of the psychodynamic type of statement? What is the method by which we derive it? Because my contention is that it is just as factual as the behavioristic description.

GERARD: If you can convince Dr. Solomon of that statement, we will have made a great step forward this afternoon.

SKINNER: We have had a new bit of information given about the patient. He reported that his father had not beaten him as a child. However, his father was in some way an adversary; so he tried to escape from him.

GRINKER: That you cannot say. That is interpretation.

SKINNER: The father is going to hurt his son; the latter is afraid.

GRINKER: People who do not punish corporally work out subtle ways: one is a threat to withhold love. The father may have applied the constant threat of how badly he will feel if the son is not a barber. Thus the barbershop is an adversary. It means that the father is using love to punish, and that the escape is behavioral.

ALEXANDER: I do not think that you need to go so fast. I can see certain constructions being made which are not necessary. I should like to show that this case— and I will not interpret it in detail—would allow the psychodynamicist to draw certain conclusions. I will demonstrate the type of conclusions that he could make on such material, provided he has the information which has been mentioned and maybe a little more.

We see that the patient obviously has two attitudes: He wants to and does follow his father's example. He yields to the pressure, whatever way it may exist, by love, by fear. He knows that his father would like him to be a barber, and he gratifies that desire. Then the patient develops varicose veins. They were probably interpreted to be an occupational condition, from his having to stand so much. I would conclude that when he developed them, his antagonism against the father increased since probably he felt, "Because father desires that I should become a barber, I must stay on my feet, develop varicose veins, and suffer." That created a greater anger against the father because the patient obviously did only half-heartedly what his father desired, namely, that he follow the paternal tradition and become a barber. Having been exposed to public school and other influences which probably were in opposition to following the family pattern, he really would have liked to do something else. Thus he became very angry with the father; this hostility against the father has something to do with his anxiety. Why do I say that? If people become very angry and have hostility, particularly towards persons whom at the same time they love, that is a specific situation in which anxiety is apt to increase because aggression means, "I will attack a person whom I love." It is not just, "If I attack him, he will attack me." Anxiety and fear, as well as anxiety and rage or anger, are couplets. The one precipitates the other. If I hate you, I am afraid of you and I will attack you. If I want to attack you, there is already the expectation, the fear, that I will suffer at the same time, particularly if I also love you and this hostility is repressed. Then what we call the introjected images of the parents increase the anxiety, because now I am about to do something wrong. I want to hurt somebody whom I otherwise love. It is not only retaliation of fear but a kind of guilt which also creates guilt. It means that I want to do something which

is wrong and against the principles which I accept. This is reasoning based on the well-known logic of emotions and substantiated by simple empirical evidence that in such situations people do develop anxiety.

In the patient the fear of the operation became so extraordinary because he had the other anxieties which had nothing to do with the operation but came from his ambivalent attitude towards the father. That made him susceptible to fear of the operation; otherwise, the fear would not have been so great.

METTLER: Although Dr. Alexander's explanation is interpretative, it could be used in my approach as a design for an experimental situation. Such a hypothesis could be worked into a very specific experimental situation and tested. Here I would be willing to make certain suggestions as to what might be done.

SOLOMON: It is interesting that some of us seem to be bent on explaining this case, while others seem to be bent on setting up logical categories which would lead to research, especially testing other hypotheses about this patient. It seems to me that with both physiological and behavioral tests now available, we could begin to develop several additional possibilities rather than jump into the immediate interpretative scheme which leaves us with self-satisfaction.

FINESINGER: Dr. Solomon characterized the attitude of the psychodynamicist as complete acceptance of Dr. Alexander's interpretation as the explanation, and unconcern about finding another hypothesis. He then brought in the word "self-complacency." That was significant in revealing a barrier, but I doubt that the characterization was accurate. The way most of us operate in life is to put forward theories, but we do not feel self-complacent about them.

WHITEHORN: There is a reason why clinicians are more likely to appear complacent than other workers. They try to help the patients; and like all clinicians, they have to do something. They like to believe in the theory on the basis of which they do it. The experimentalist does not have such an incentive. It is not so necessary for him to feel that he is doing the right thing. This situation imposes upon the clinicians a little extra edge of a need at least to appear to be certain of themselves. It does not necessarily mean that they feel complacent; but it makes them look that way and *sometimes* it induces them to feel complacent.

GERARD: I should like to point out that a really critical issue has been raised. Following Dr. Alexander's explanation of the patient's feelings and behavior, Dr. Solomon replied that it was not an interpretation which he could accept as the answer. It has the beginnings of a working hypothesis which Dr. Solomon would like to put up against other working hypotheses and test. Dr. Alexander responded by indicating how much of his explanation he regarded as essentially certain as a statement of fact. He further indicated that his background of psychiatric knowledge and experience enabled him to present his interpretation as the answer, not as a hypothesis. Dr. Solomon, as a psychologist, was unconvinced. He regarded it as a possible hypothesis; he could think of others. He would like to see it tested.

ALEXANDER: I want to come to the points of uncertainty. I would mention one more thing about the facts which we know. The patient's wound healed slowly. I have no answer for that on the basis of psychodynamic explanation. This slow healing has something to do with his emotional state. I do not know what the correlation is, how it comes about, what mechanism is involved, or whether there is a constitutional factor which accounts for slow healing of the wound. Here is one limitation.

The patient's anxiety became very strong when he was shaving customers. He had an instrument of aggression in his hand. The explanation is clear. He could unconsciously slit his father's throat; instead, the feeling was displaced to the customers. He was afraid of his own aggressive feelings; therefore, he ran away from the place of his contemplated crime. In the hospital his fears disappeared. There he did not have to follow his father's tacit desire or command that he should become a barber. He was away from the acute stress situation which would have induced anxiety. But when he returned home and had to face his father,

he was reminded that he was expected to do what his father wanted of him. He did not want to do it. The conflict was revived, the hostility mobilized, and the anxiety followed. Something like that probably happened.

The psychodynamic approach has its limitations at present; hence, I should like to raise the question, Why didn't this man use another psychodynamic defense mechanism when the hostility against the father was aroused so strongly? We see patients in such situations who do not develop anxiety; they develop a depression. Instead of wanting to attack or kill their fathers, they attack themselves or maybe commit suicide. They indulge in all kinds of self-accusation, e.g., that they are criminals or worthless people; then they go into deep depression. Even if there were more facts. I could not explain why one defense mechanism is used, and not another. I am unable to say why this patient did not choose the depressive outcome for this type of dilemma and why instead he developed an anxiety state.

The answer which I would expect would be that one component probably is constitutional. What this constitutional factor represents, whether it carries inherent qualities of the total organism, how it should be investigated, whether there is a factor which predisposes a person to anxiety instead of depressive attack, all these are important questions. Why didn't the young barber develop hypertension? Very often patients who cannot express this type of hostility develop hypertension. Only a certain percentage in such a situation develop a mixture of fear and hostility.

WITTKOWER: We have been told that the patient is 30 years old, unmarried, and has difficulties with his father. My prediction is that the patient has difficulties in the sexual sphere. It has also been stated that the anxiety attacks occur in the presence of his father. My prediction is that the patient has homosexual conflicts. Are these assumptions correct?

GRINKER: I should like to keep out of this area, except to say that I think you have valid hypotheses. The patient does have sexual troubles. He does not have a girl friend; indeed, he does not mingle with girls. He has not made any overtures to get married; he has a very strong loving attachment to his father. That is all I will say at this time; otherwise, I will become involved in the interpretation.

SCOTT: Concerning the remarks about constitutional factors in this case, I should like to make some general comment on the genetic factor in relation to behavior. All the classical studies on neuroses in animals, such as those of Pavlov, Liddell, Masserman, Maier, and others, seem to have three common factors: One is confinement so that the animal cannot escape from the situation. Another is a kind of situation to which the animal cannot possibly adapt or adjust. The third factor is hypermotivation or hyperexcitement. Of these three factors, hyperexcitement or hypermotivation can obviously be importantly modified by heredity. The capability of the animal to adjust might be limited by genetic factors as might his ability to escape.

There is some evidence from animals to back up the genetic theory in audiogenic seizures in mice. In one strain of mice placed in a tub, 95 per cent will go into audiogenic seizures when a bell is rung. In another strain, none will show seizures—a clearly demonstrable hereditary difference in the degree of excitability aroused by a standard stimulus. Different breeds of dogs also show different degrees of emotional excitability and motivation.

There is a need to study such genetic problems in human subjects. However, they cannot be studied in just one person. Furthermore, the subjects should be studied as early as possible in human development, by the age of two or even before if possible. One reason is that by this age there still has been no great modification by the environment. The other is that if the aim is to do something about differences by altering the environment or by differential treatment, the earlier the procedure is started, the better. This points to a need in human research which has not yet been met. I would suggest that the most promising place to look for differences early in life would be in emotional arousal and forms of excitement.

As a further remark on the patient with the anxiety state, it should be pointed out that more than one thing might be causing his excitement. According to the physiological principle of summation of stimuli, it is possible that the effects of several of the factors that have been mentioned, such as sexual frustration and fear of hospitalization, might be summated and so produce an unbearably high state of excitement.

SKINNER: If we were inquiring into an explosion of an aircraft carrier in Boston Harbor, what would we as highly disciplined scientists be able to say about it? We could not say what happened. There was an explosion; we would assume that something ignited. There would be theories about what it was that exploded, and what possibly ignited it. Many of these theories would be perfectly acceptable. In our approach to an explanation of the explosion, what would come out would be the kinds of processes with which we are familiar and which would be relevant. It was my impression that here we were only trying to bring up the kinds of processes that might have some bearing or application in shedding light. Dr. Solomon's work with lower organisms on punishment, the effect of avoidance and escape, is relevant. Where are we to get beyond this?

GRINKER: In dealing with a problem of illness, it is true that much of the relevant information comes from observations on many individuals who are not categorized as ill. The explosion in human beings, the sudden onset of the disease process, the so-called natural experiment, conveys an idea of the disintegration that may occur. It also provides a tremendous amount of impetus to the study of healthy people for the purpose of understanding integration in a human being.

RENNIE: The psychiatrists could set forth other dynamics about the behavior of the barber; and they would, I believe, have a right to put considerable credence in them. For these dynamics are arrived at from observation that this set of forces operates in this way in a number of people. The psychiatrists have studied enough of them to have some confidence in believing that this is so. Nonetheless, the psychologists have a perfect right to challenge how the psychiatrists come by their belief or conviction that this is so to the extent that they can make categorical statements. I should like to ask the experimentalists whether they would feel more certain about this behavioral reaction if it could be regularly reproduced in the patient and if his blood pressure could also be observed to rise every time a specific topic were introduced.

SPIEGEL: I should like to challenge a statement by Dr. Alexander about the psychodynamics as a part of his hypothesis. He said that the patient's difficulty was rather general: A person who loves another cannot attack him.

ALEXANDER: I did not want to generalize. One pattern is that a person who loves another usually finds it more difficult to attack. I could imagine instances in which it does not follow.

SPIEGEL: Whether it is usual or not must depend upon circumstances. In this connection the kind of question that Dr. Solomon brings up is pertinent: How do you know this, and at what level of generalization and relevance is it correct? Expressing love and hatred toward a parent image might vary greatly with the family and the culture of the family. If, in the culture of a particular family, love takes the expression of aggression, the expression of hatred toward someone that one loves is very much punished. Then, of course, the difficulties will be increased. Or if love is used as an instrument of manipulation and punishment, then the tie between expression of aggression and the expression of love might be different. Hence, the ignorance of the psychodynamic analysis here is precisely at the point where the individual meets the society and the family.

ALEXANDER: I fully accept what you have said. But I do not want to be misunderstood. I brought up the point only to illustrate to the non-psychodynamicist that type of psychological conflict in which a person who loves another might find it difficult to express hostility because it is directed against the person whom he loves. It need not always be that way. Certainly I did not intend to explain in this specific case why it was so difficult to express hostility. I fully agree that in order to explain

or account for it, the family atmosphere, the cultural pattern which is true in the family must be known. Without it, the premise and the word "usually" are inaccurate. I withdraw them.

GRINKER: I am somewhat disappointed that we have not obtained more information from the biologists as to the ways in which they would study this problem. We have heard sociological, psychological, and psychodynamic hypotheses, and criticisms of each. But there are a whole host of biological, endocrinological processes going on in this individual that are different from those of people who do not have this kind of anxiety. Actually this patient was one of our favorite subjects because we could put him back in the father situation and get an increase in anxiety; thereby we had a very good method of replicate observations of certain biochemical phenomena. What is the relationship between the two systems? Does he experience stress reactions which affect the pituitary-adrenocortical system; and certain endocrine peripheral effects which evoke anxiety? What are the relationships among the various biochemical phenomena that are stirred up with the anxiety, either before or after? For there are whole series of observations that could be made to indicate time and cyclic relationships. Here is a man who represents a highly usable, pure experimental culture, and every one of us could work on him for months and even years toward an understanding of his anxiety. Whether we begin with the nature of his particular pattern, his stress response, or his cultural milieu, we are concerned with the problem of a man in action who is anxious to the point of disintegration. Whereas anxiety as a function in the human being should be signal, facilitative, and constructive, in his case it is destructive. How all the approaches are brought together is also highly important.

METTLER: Dismay has just been expressed because the organicists have not participated to a greater degree in suggesting items for study in a patient with an anxiety state. The organicists are, of course, interested in this patient. Many biological methods might be suggested for application. In actuality, what would the organicist do about it? Nothing. Why? Because, there are practical operational obstacles. When such a case appears, it presents real difficulties for study. First, it arrives *de novo,* without advance notice. Second, when a similar case will come is never known; it may be two or three years later. Preparations for study of such an isolated case, appearing out of the blue, present serious problems. The experimental design has to be laid out; the number and kind of personnel have to be planned and obtained; space has to be arranged, and funds have to be sought. All of these arrangements have to be started long in advance of the study, sometimes a year ahead. Perhaps in such an idealistic atmosphere I should not bring up these practical matters, but they do impede spur-of-the-moment cooperation in the study of a single isolated case.

POPE: Perhaps the organicist's lack of enthusiasm for the biological study of this patient has in part also a theoretical basis. Granted that this patient is interesting and admirably adapted to be the subject of any number of different physiological, pharmacological, biochemical, and endocrinological studies, part of the biologist's reluctance in undertaking them may arise from his feeling, not that the resulting observations and data would not be interesting, important, and relevant, but that despite their value, they represent secondary phenomena. The evidence presented indicates that the basic problem is much more at the level of the psychodynamic and social situation, and that the biological aspects are not at the heart of the matter. This assertion cannot be averred with certainty, but it seems to be an overwhelming probability.

GRINKER: I object to the statement that the biological phenomena are secondary. It makes me feel that I am in Humpty-Dumpty land. I hear the comments that the psychodynamicists have pre-empted the field; they talk in mumbo jumbo; their concepts are not understandable. So they present the biologists with an opportunity to participate in a collaborative research problem to which the biologists presumably would be amenable. But the biologists say, "No. The biological stuff is secondary." If

I should tell the biologists that long anxiety is conducive to premature aging and many endocrinological and physiological changes which lead to early death, would it help them to attach some kind of primacy to it? But they should not need that kind of practical incentive. Here is a patient who presents all aspects: culture, motivation, psychodynamics, physiology, sex, endocrines, everything that is concerned in this total problem of anxiety. Nevertheless, the biologists bow out while commenting, "We won't come along with you. Whatever you do shows that you monopolize everything and talk in mumbo jumbo."

SPIEGEL: Biological inferiority!

ALEXANDER: I should like to add a few words in reply to Dr. Pope's comment that the biological factors in the anxiety of the patient are obviously secondary. "Secondary" is an ambiguous word. If different variables influence natural events, none of the variables is secondary. Either they must or must not be there to produce their effect.

POPE: I shall be glad to discuss the question of the primary versus the secondary properties of the barber with the anxiety state. Apparently use of the word "secondary" was something of an incitant. Perhaps it is not wise to use terms like primary and secondary in relation to the variables in such a situation. In calling the biological properties secondary, I believe that I did qualify that statement a little by saying that *a priori,* there is no way of knowing which are primary and which are secondary. My point was that the things that can be studied in a patient at the present time by the biologically oriented investigator would be more apt to reveal consequences of this individual's illness than facts directly related to its genesis. And I would challenge Dr. Grinker to refute that at the present level of knowledge.

Dr. Spiegel has accused me of a biological inferiority complex. That brings out a curious observation: A number of people in this group have tended to uphold viewpoints which were the opposite of what would be expected of them. I surmise that on the part of the biologist it reflects a kind of superiority complex and a desire to be in on the kill. He does not want to be concerned with the things that are epiphenomena. He wants to work with things that get right to the heart of whatever the problem is. I cannot flatly say that he could not do so with the patient having the anxiety state, but it would be my guess that at the present moment it is unlikely. Moreover, perhaps the biological problem which that patient presents does not happen to fire the imagination of the particular people around this table who represent the biological point of view; there might be others in the biological field who would feel very differently.

GERARD: I had a friend who used to catch whales and make them available for scientific study. He would ask many investigators, "What do you want from the whale?" Some would want the pituitary, some would want the brain, some would want other parts. That they were all getting a part of the same beast was a pragmatic use of the situation, or whale; it was not collaborative research. Our research group would be delighted to have your patient available because we are also engaged in a stress program. We are interested in following the activation of the adrenal medullary system. We are trying to get anxiety or stress states in animals and man and then follow the liberation of the medullary hormones. But this would not be interdisciplinary research.

Only when representatives of the different disciplines have a sufficient understanding of a basic problem which requires for its answer data from the various sources, and when they are all interested in answering the problem, does it begin to be interdisciplinary research. Cooperation has to be at the level of hypotheses, not at the level of observations. Nothing that was suggested in your case or in the subsequent discussion reached the level of a hypothesis which transcends the different disciplines. I think this is why Dr. Mettler responded negatively. I would have done the same. Dr. Jasper gave a remarkably good positive response to the challenge by citing the differential sensitivity to narcotics of the interlaminar and the reticular systems, the well-known activating systems. This was a physiological hypothesis meant to parallel

the psychodynamic hypothesis; but, unfortunately, the two still have nothing to do with one another. In my opinion, each is an independent statement of a hypothetical interpretation. It is only when the two are put together that an answer will be forthcoming. The problem there, I think is methodological.

I should like to point out how methodological differences in the several disciplines can impede, if not thwart, collaboration. For many tests and determinations the physiologist has methods available or can develop them easily and quickly. What is more, he can safely entrust a capable technician to use them. Experimental psychology has a series of objective methods which a technician can also apply. But the experimenter begins to be a little less willing to trust their application entirely to a technician; there is a more subjective element in evaluation. Then there is the evaluation of the psychiatric state. What, for example, is the level of anxiety or of fear? Here the psychiatrist has to do the job himself; he cannot delegate any of this to someone else. This means many hours of direct observation for him, and he cannot describe what he observes or does in objective terms so that another psychiatrist could replace him. Yet he can demonstrate validity by self-checking or by having others rate from the interview. I once asked Dr. Grinker, "How do you measure anxiety?" He replied, "I am the measure of anxiety. I have to titrate it against myself." These are real disciplinary differences.

KING: Dr. Gerard has declared that interdisciplinary cooperation should be at the level of the hypothesis. I agree; but, in my opinion, we should not ignore the opportunity for study afforded by such a case as Dr. Grinker presented, even if we do not start with an organized hypothesis. For those concerned with the clinical care of a patient usually conduct their own activities and only occasionally ask for help; they do not ordinarily put forward clinical material on which the biological scientist and psychologist may make fundamental observations. Perhaps it is because the organicists are not used to having such material offered to them, that they have not responded with overpowering enthusiasm. In my opinion we should seize such opportunities for the experimental investigation of patients.

GRINKER: I should like to indicate what I had in mind in presenting the case as the subject of an experiment, assuming that this group was theoretically going to be engaged in the study of whatever this patient represented. We were pretending to form a collaborative research group. It is ridiculous to say that; for in reality it would take this group a year or two to become collaborators.

GERARD: It was my impression that what we were really trying to do, and the basis on which a case was presented, was not to plan a joint research project, but to bring up, in concrete instances, some of the issues about which we had been debating theoretically.

chapter *27*

The Quest for Hypotheses from the Various Disciplines and Their Influence on the Stimulation of Multidisciplinary Research

◆ ◆

ALEXANDER: I proposed the psychodynamic hypothesis, not to explain the case of anxiety in detail, but to give an idea of what type of approach the dynamicist would choose and how he would explain such a thing. It is not important that it be exactly correct. We do not have all the data. Many other psychological factors which we do not know about may be present and would modify the formula. The hypothesis which I proposed does not explain the case. It only explains the psychological stress situation, not the response of the patient to it.

I would emphasize that this man, with the same psychodynamic situation, could have different responses. He could develop depression, or a paranoid condition, or arterial hypertension. Without any major psychological insight, we can infer that his symptomatology represents a different response. Hence, there is not one, but a category of variables which we do not know, but which are necessary to explain why this particular patient developed anxiety and not something else. Our Chairman asked for a hypothesis. Even a wrong one is better than none in order to induce the biologists to join in the discussion. We proposed a hypothesis which might be entirely wrong but is worth testing.

To explain the patient's reaction, we should know something about his biological structure. We might venture the hypothesis that he has a particularly vulnerable corticoadrenal system, which has been in that state since birth. It could have been tested in his first reaction to any emotional stress situation. If he did not have this type of physiological constitutional equipment, perhaps he would have developed some other condition. That is a hypothesis. Let us study such cases with regard not only to the psychological stress situation but also to the biological make-up of the patient, and see how this latter variable influences the outcome of the relationship.

I have heard the word "experiment" again and again. Twenty-five years ago I gave a lecture about psychoanalysis to the medical faculty at the University of Chicago. After the lecture somebody asked: "Does psychoanalysis prove its statements by experiment? Are they based on experiment?"

I replied, "Mostly not."

"Then I am not interested in hearing the rest because it is not a science."

336

I wrote Sigmund Freud about this episode, and got from him the following answer, "I would suggest that at the next seminar you ask the medical faculty members whether they consider astronomy a science or not?" Obviously astronomy is a much more advanced science than biology or physiology. Astronomers cannot experiment with the stars, but they take advantage of the experiments of nature. Like the astronomers, psychodynamicists utilize experiments of nature. Just as astronomers observe a star, psychodynamicists study a case in different situations. Both take advantage of the spontaneous and natural occurrences in the cosmos.

I am very much in favor of experimentation, and I expect valuable results from it. But to consider that the psychological experiment is the only approach which will yield scientific results and that the clinical comparison of different cases will not produce equally valid information is wrong. Clinical observation is just as good methodologically as an experiment. In psychiatry it has one advantage over experimentation because the latter usually cannot reproduce the natural events. In the field of behavior so many variables in the situation are overlooked or unwittingly introduced by the experimentalist that he fools himself when he believes that he controls the variables much more than does the clinician. I still am for psychological experimentation; I think many problems of quantification never will be answered without psychological experiments. But I should like the psychologists to have an equal respect for our method of taking advantage of the experiments of nature by making systematic clinical observations.

GERARD: A word about observation, with astronomy as the example. Two circumstances make astronomy a science beyond what would be implied by sheer observation. In the first place, the astronomer has extremely precise and elaborate tools of observation, so he can obtain evidence way beyond what the layman could see by looking at the same phenomena. Secondly, although the astronomer does not manipulate the universe, it is sufficiently rich in facts to be observed at one time or another so

that he could more than exhaust the total observational capacity of humanity over eons. Therefore he has to select the things he is going to observe, and the selection is on the basis of hypotheses. The observations have all the earmarks of complete experimentation, only with fewer degrees of freedom than the biologist has in his experimental designs. The astronomer's operation is really experimental in the important meaning of the word. He even has a choice within this one universe. He develops a theory about galaxies or about star clusters and then proceeds to turn his telescope on selected individuals.

In the realm of research in psychoanalysis, the analyst would maintain, probably justly, that he also has highly precise instruments of observation which enable him to look at the ordinary phenomena of human behavior and see things that the laymen cannot see. I am willing to accept that, partly on faith; but it remains incumbent upon the analyst to prove that his technics of observation are indeed as precise and dependable as the spectrophototelescope. Again, it is true that the analyst has the same opportunity as does the astronomer of selecting from the universe of instances, and that he makes a selection by hypothesis. For these reasons, I cannot agree that experimentation is not possible in psychoanalysis. In fact, if I did believe that it is impossible, I would be most discouraged.

HOLLINGSHEAD: Dr. Grinker said of the patient with anxiety, "Here is a man in action." Speaking as a sociologist, I would say, "Here is a man in interaction." There is action, yes; but there is interaction.

GERARD: Good; I see no need for "transaction."

HOLLINGSHEAD: But in sociological terms, it is interaction between the patient and his father. There are probably also interactions between the patient and his siblings. There are also other dynamics that have not been touched upon: the patient is a second-generation Italian; he was born presumably in an Italian neighborhood; he grew up, I presume, in this neighborhood; he went to a public school, where he learned other values and attitudes that are associated with the generalized American culture. The American culture patterns are different from the first-generation Italian culture patterns. Also to be taken into consideration is the fact that he went off to war and did not start having any difficulties with his father until the return from war.

ALEXANDER: And followed father's footsteps.

HOLLINGSHEAD: The rearing in the first-generation Italian culture, partly in the home and partly in the neighborhood; the early experience in the generalized American culture obtained in school; the going off to the Army, where a new set of interactions take place with cultural and social stimuli—all of these are not a unique pattern. We can duplicate this situation in a number of cases we are studying. If we were to set up a research design, we would have to specify all of these factors.

ALEXANDER: It is interesting that a Japanese in Hawaii developed anxiety attacks in a situation similar to that of the Italo-American barber in Chicago. The Japanese father wanted the son to follow his footsteps and go into business, which the son did. However, the son wanted very much to become a musician, a band leader, following the American pattern. When he was subjected to his father's will and went into his father's business, he developed anxiety attacks. There were many differences between the Japanese and Italian examples, but this was one common factor: Two cultural influences were working the one—the old tradition represented by the father; and the other, the impact of the social environment to which the son was exposed—and under this conflict the anxiety attacks were precipitated. I fully agree that it is a common picture. It is a stress situation in which a person is exposed to two major directive forces.

HOLLINGSHEAD: We have had cited interaction in stress situations in the two cultures, the Italian and the Japanese, in both of which there are strong elements of familism. A third group with strong familism and anxiety attacks are second-generation Jewish. The dynamic potentiality is not a question of second generation but of the types in the second generation.

SPENCE: If I were a member of the hypothetical interdisciplinary team, I would be less interested in trying to explain the barber patient's behavior than in an opportunity to experiment with him. I would be particularly interested in using him as a subject in a variety of learning situations at different times; one time when he was in an anxiety state exhibiting high emotional activity, and another time when he was not. This would be a study of certain theories which we in psychology have concerning the relation of emotional activity to the general level of drive. We have theories that drive level will produce quite opposite effects in different kinds of learning situations, in the simple learning situation as well as the classical conditioning. I would predict that this individual, if he were conditioned when he is in an anxiety state—this is possible to do in the not too severe form—would show a high level of performance; whereas, if I were to test him in a period when he was not in an anxiety state, he would exhibit a low level of response. On the other hand, if I took him into simple competitive learning, I would make the prediction of an opposite outcome, that the performance would be low when he was in the emotional state and relatively better when in the nonemotional state.

WITTKOWER: We have been conducting studies on the biological concomitants of anxiety. We have tested Hempel and Reiss' assumption that there are changes in the radioactive iodine uptake in patients suffering from anxiety states. Examination of 71 psychiatric patients failed to show a positive correlation between the degree of anxiety (whether rated by the intensity of the subjective feeling or by physiological concomitants) and the rate of thyroid secretion, as judged from the duration of the biological half-life. Taking another tack, we abstracted from the literature psychological features described as typical of the premorbid personality of patients suffering from Graves' disease, applied the criteria abstracted to our experimental subjects, and predicted their biological decay curve on the basis of the psychodynamic formulations. In 34 out of 44 patients in whom predictions had been made, the prediction proved correct. Statistical analysis using the chi-square test indicated these predictions were significantly valid $(0.11 < pQ < 0.001)$.

SKINNER: During the past year Dr. Harry Solomon and I, with the assistance of O. R. Lindsley, have been conducting experiments at the Metropolitan State Hospital on the behavior of the psychotic in dealing with the environment about him. We are trying to obtain a quantifiable continuous record of a level of activity on the part of psychotic subjects. We are not turning to the clinician for data, and we are not controlling the study with regard to the environment from which the patients came. Nor are we controlling their daily lives. Once a day each psychotic subject is taken to a small pleasant room, and left for an hour or two. The room contains a vending machine which pays off with candy or cigarettes. (In a similar room, pressing a button projects a calendar-art picture on a screen.) We have found that a large percentage of the patients will stay in the room for an hour or two and continue to operate such a device at significant rates.

We have been experimenting with various "schedules of reinforcement." The machine does not always pay off, or always project a picture. In lower organisms the scheduling of reward has an important influence on the rate of responding. In catatonics and paranoids who have been in the hospital from twelve to fifteen years, we get rates varying from 100 to 10,000 responses per hour for periods up to 150 days. Many records are like those obtained with rats, dogs, pigeons, and monkeys. The results serve as a base line of an organism's level of interest in a task performed day after day. This procedure also provides a quantifiable measure which responds to various types of therapy. With lower organisms the procedure is used to study the effects of drugs. We can suppress the rate during periods of anxiety. By changing the level of motivation, we can watch these rates go up and down. We can move on to much more complex behavior, including practically all of psychophysics without verbal instruction, and complex interrelationships among response systems which resemble some of the dynamisms of psychodynamics. It is a direct experiment on the behavior of the organism adjusting to a simplified but nevertheless real environment.

FINESINGER: In Dr. Alexander's formulation of the patient with the anxiety state, he set forth a limited hypothesis. What is the trouble with that kind of a hypothesis? It might be said that it is not testable. It is true that testing it either experimentally or clinically would be very difficult, if not impossible. Perhaps the hypothesis may be regarded as either too complex or imprecise to be tested, or as not being clearly enough formulated in some respect so that it can be visualized in operation. Other hypotheses seem to be at the other extreme—simple, obvious, or meaningless. Would it not be wise therefore to consider what is the trouble with the limited hypothesis of Dr. Alexander from the points of view of the other disciplines? What do the psychologists feel about such a hypothesis? If we could clarify this area, we would get along much further.

GERARD: I feel very strongly that this is at the heart of what we should be doing.

METTLER: My mind works along practical lines on the design of the experiment. One problem in the designed experiment is that one variable has to be correlated with another. There can be an infinite number of variables, but they have to be correlated. In this particular case the essential correlaton from the biological point of view is between those phenomena which are related to the person experiencing anxiety and the biological manifestations of his anxiety. Unfortunately we do not have good measures of subjective anxiety. We can use an instrument like the strain gauge galvanometer, for instance, to arrive at a biological measure. We could then correlate it with other biological phenomena. But when the experimental situation is set up and correlated with the hospital diagnosis, such a diagnosis too often turns out to be of little value. Some method has to be found by which all of the biological phenomena can be correlated with a fixed point in psychiatric nomenclature. The only mechanism available now is that which has already been mentioned. Data are collected and submitted to a psychiatrist. He returns reams and reams of paper with a description of the case. What can be done with it? How can this very careful and astute analysis of a patient's behavior be put into a quantitative figure? How can the experimenter tell whether the patient is better or worse, or in what direction he has changed? This is a major problem for the biologist. He is trying to correlate concrete data or observations with something intangible. We are now studying psychotic patients in an institution. But we do not expect to correlate their changes with a diagnosis. We suspect that we are going to have to use a rating scale or factorial analysis of the patient's symptomatological state. We are aware of the limitations, but we know nothing better. This is a major problem in the attempt of the biologists and psychiatrists to make contact.

GRINKER: Bridging the gap is not your problem. It is the psychiatrist's problem. It can be attacked, but certainly not in terms of diagnosis. The scales of measurement are quite different. Changes will have to be devised so that the two scales can be correlated. However, such a phenomenon as anxiety can be rated. It was encouraging to find that in our replicate ratings of anxiety, there was a high degree of reliability. Furthermore, the self-ratings of paratroopers in the field, which were based on specific sentences given to indicate seven points of rating, were very close to our own objective observations. Certain types of performance, depressions, and combinations of symptoms can be rated too. Appraising the psychiatric state quantitatively is not an insurmountable obstacle. But the biologist cannot make correlations of his data with an affect, emotion, or symptom, measured in another frame of reference. He has to have a psychological or psychiatric rating. That is a problem for the psychiatrist.

METTLER: We have used anxiety rating scales. But you must remember that there are psychiatrists who do not feel too happy about rating scales.

SOLOMON: It seems to me that there is a real problem in crossing interdisciplinary lines and that the main responsibility is often on the individual who is formulating theory. I should like to try out a different line of procedure with our biologically oriented colleagues. Suppose, when the case of anxiety had been described, that Dr. Alexander had not interpreted it in terms of psychodynamic principles, and I had said, "I have a theory. I think that when individuals are angry, the emotional response constellation contains many of the same elements as when they are hungry." I am not saying that this hypothesis has any chance of being right. What I want to exemplify is the kind of hypothetical reasoning that immediately pulls together representatives from various disciplines in pondering over a problem. Suppose I had continued: "I think that this patient, when he was young, displayed much aggression and hostility, was angry much of the time, and may have been punished quite a bit for it. The cultural conflict might have led him to spend more of his time as a child being angry, especially at his parents, than do other children. Thus, anger is a problem for him. Being hungry is like being angry; both states have autonomic response pattern, visceral response pattern components that are somewhat similar." Suppose I had said further, "Dr. Grinker, you left out some information that is very valuable to me at this point. What you forgot to tell me is that this patient very often has mild hypoglycemia when he works for long periods between meals. When there are customers in the barber shop, he sometimes has to wait a long time before meals and he gets very hungry. Being very hungry makes a person irritable. In this extremely hungry state the patient begins to recapitulate some of the components that enter into the normal anger pattern. His skeletal response impulses tend to be aroused in incipient fashion in this situation, and he finds himself wanting to give the customer, not his father, a good swat. The father is not so important in this case."

This hypothesis would be partly *ad hoc* and partly predictive. You could easily refute my statements by the appropriate observations. But notice who has to make these observations. I cannot do it. Some more biologically oriented investigator would have to make them. But in order to make him feel that what he can contribute to this study is important, I have to make a strong case about how biological observations would be basic to the theory of emotion and how it is that when people are very hungry, they can be partly angry too, or at least that the responses which often accompany the emotional reaction of anger tend to accompany the motivational pattern of being hungry. This is one way to go about arousing the biologist's interest.

Moreover, by modifying the presentation, I could get the psychodynamicists interested in cooperation. I would cite the animal experiments in which it has been shown that in avoidance conditioning under the impetus of extremely intense shock, the interval between the danger signal and the delivery of shock controls, to some extent, the qualitative aspects of the emotional pattern. When the animal becomes conditioned, it will show, with very short intervals between signal and shock, that the signal elicits an emotional pattern containing lower intestinal activity, with defecation and urination. However, if the time interval is long, this particular manifestation will not be as common. Instead, retching and vomiting will often appear during the time interval between the signal and the shock.

Next, I am going to bring out another item which you did not mention; that is, the patient's mother never did any punishing. She always waited until father came home and left it to him. Hence, there were long time intervals between danger signals of impending punishment and the actual occurrence of punishment. I would then predict that this patient has digestive upsets quite frequently, and that they occur at times when he expects disapproval from his father. A specialist in psychosomatic medicine might well become interested in such a problem because the prediction does not come out of psychosomatic medicine, but from experimental studies with animals. It is truly interdisciplinary.

I have taken a circuitous course in an attempt to state a theoretical problem in a way calculated to entice investigators in the fields of biology, psychodynamics, and psychosomatic medicine to join in cooperation. However, even the approach of adopting their language and concepts in formulating the problem may not be successful in enlisting their help. Nevertheless, if we had started with such a presentation as I have given instead of Dr. Alexander's, the outcome might possibly have been different with regard to the participation of the biologists.

JASPER: Various hypotheses can be formulated, but their value depends upon what can be done with them, what they enable the psychiatrist to do with the patient. The validity of a hypothesis is tested by the effect it has in the treatment situation. It is a type of therapeutic testing in which the psychiatrist engages daily. Whether it provides firm validation from the scientific point of view is another question. Certainly this therapeutic test on the patient has nothing to do with laboratory biological experimentation. To biological experimenters like Dr. Mettler and myself, what is disturbing is to encounter hypotheses which we do not understand and cannot subject to experimental testing. I am pleased to note that Dr. Alexander is very anxious to formulate hypotheses in terms that we will understand so that we may design experimental tests of their validity. But take the statement that "repression impoverishes the dynamic reservoir of the ego." What is the meaning of this type of hypothesis? Does it mean something that can be tested therapeutically, and that can be understood and subjected to experimental test in the laboratory or in any other setting? It is not that we do not believe it is a valid statement. Rather it is a statement that we would like to understand; otherwise it is very hard for us to put it to test or to apply it to design of meaningful experiments on the nervous system.

ALEXANDER: Repression is a defense mechanism. A person who represses submerges his aggressive feelings. When he is challenged, he is silent or withdraws instead of manifesting opposition. We advance the hypothesis that this man has these feelings; but having become intimidated through early conditions, he eliminates them from his consciousness and builds up certain defense reactions, overcompensatory reactions. Instead of being aggressive, he is humble; instead of being active, he is passive; instead of taking the initiative, he becomes a follower. What I meant by the statement which you quoted was that this type of repression depletes the person of some kind of psychological resource which we call aggressiveness, initiative, self-assertion.

This hypothesis can be validated by experiment. If the psychiatrist succeeds, through a therapeutic process, in reconditioning the repressed person and in making him able to express his feelings, then his psychological reservoir with regard to this type of faculty is enriched, whereas before it was impoverished. In the therapeutic situation this person begins to answer the psychiatrist and contradict him, then begins to do the same with his boss; and this happens when certain memories which caused his repression and inhibitions are revived. If the observations can be repeated, it may be said that the hypothesis can be tested.

GRINKER: The barber with an anxiety state has been a rather stimulating subject. But if this group had gone into actual operation with some of the conceptions, attitudes, hypotheses, and procedures which came out in the discussion, the time devoted to him would have been costly.

For one thing, what is meant by the transactional approach should be clarified because it has been misconceived that we should take every single possible variable in a mishmash and spend time seeing what the relationships are to each other.

The second thing that would cause us to waste our time would be a pessimism, as brought out by Dr. Pope, that up to now no biological data that have been significant for the problem of mental disease have been evolved. The reason is that the methods of observation, the methods of handling the data, and the relationship of the various systems have not been clarified. However, I am very optimistic that much can be learned about mental disease through biological studies.

The third point which I think would have been costly in time—costly if it were presented in that fashion—would have been the hypothesis that Dr. Solomon brought up. I had hoped that representatives from the various disciplines besides psychodynamics would offer empirically derived hypotheses which were logical and drawn from previous experimentation in their sphere of operation, but which were not directly refuted by observations on man. We certainly want hypotheses from biology and psychology to be presented because in working with human beings, our tools and our approaches are strictly limited; and any new hypothesis should be advanced for us to consider in our total work. But it should also be tested in light of its logicalness and past empirical experience with man. We already have experience in man with anger in relation to hunger, and with anxiety in relation to low blood sugar and hunger. Unfortunately we have observed just the opposite from what Dr. Solomon postulated.

In talking over clinical data with representatives from the biological and psychosocial fields, I have had the startling experience that all of a sudden they have said something to me which immediately indicates a certain area which I have neglected, but which is interesting and fits in logically with what I know about human beings. Such an occurrence has a stimulating effect in a multidisciplinary group, but it does not mean that every proposed hypothesis or every possible function needs to be tested by that group.

chapter *28*

Pyschoanalytic Technic of Observation and Validation of Hypotheses

• •

WHITEHORN: In the interim between sessions we took a step forward in a discussion which centered on the questions: What degree of validity is to be attached to different people's statements? Where does straightforward factual reporting come to its margin and interpretation begin? What is the range of such widely accepted interpretation that it has almost the impact of fact within a group? Where are the systematized theories coming in? The discussion indicates that it would be desirable to have some means of indicating the margin of probable error in a statement, or the range of phenomena over which the statement is presumed to have such-or-such a degree of validation. When a member of one discipline talks with those outside his daily sphere of conversation, these considerations are differently delineated and give rise, therefore, to difficulty. In these interdisciplinary conversations it is necessary for him to draw the lines differently than when he talks to his own group. Within his special group there is a fairly general understanding of how much conjecture and how much fact there are in a statement; they are automatically taken into account. But when he talks to another group, the members are likely to be very suspicious because they see the amount of conjecture. But they do not know whether he sees it.

In a field in which I used to work, biochemical analysis, it is possible to state with some degree of certainty within what limits a value is reliable. The results of determinations can be expressed in terms of a value, plus or minus such-and-such amount. It is a very convenient device by which to compare measurements, so that the degree of probability that a difference between them is significant can be known. In a clinical judgment it is oftentimes very difficult to derive a figure representing the probability that it is true, or has just a 50 per cent chance of being true, or is perhaps just a shot in the dark with one chance in ten of its being true. Nevertheless, in their work clinicians have to act on probabilities, sometimes even on a one to ten chance. That creates a special problem for them.

Many of the controversies occurring among multidisciplinary groups arise from misunderstandings about what is the probable truth of statements, and what is the allowance for error. To that, may be added the likelihood that the modes of speaking in shorthand to each other magnify these misconceptions. It is a matter of how much conjecture and how much clear-cut factual observation enter into remarks.

Perhaps some clarification of communication could be achieved if this topic were to be discussed further. It is likely that most controversy will revolve around the psychoanalytic method of interpretation. On the program it is included within what is called the psychodynamic view. As Dr. Kruse knows, all through the preparation of the program I quarreled with him on the use of certain words. One was about going back to the concept of mental disease. I would have preferred to have reaction patterns. Another word to which I objected was "causation." As many of us have indicated, into the causation, so to speak, of a given reaction pattern goes everything that determines what kind of a person is doing the reacting, so that John Jones becomes one of the causes of John Jones' behavior. And what is the cause of John Jones? That illustrates the absurdity of speaking about cause as the logical approach, for talking about the cause of John Jones sounds like nonsense.

The psychoanalytic school has pushed itself forward into a dominating position among those who have concerned themselves with psychodynamic principles; hence, I think it is appropriate to begin the discussion by considering the problem of validating or determining probable errors, or distinguishing between hypothesis and observation in the operations of the psychoanalytic school and psychodynamics. I should like to ask Dr. Alexander to speak on this general topic.

ALEXANDER: I shall not speak for any school, for what I say could very well be rejected by many other psychoanalysts. I should like to concentrate on the main issue: What is the epistomological principle and technic whereby the analyst obtains information? How does he reach formulations or interpretations? On what psychological processes are these based and what is their validity? Every science can use only natural faculties for getting information, but these are improved upon by common-sense knowledge. Physics is based upon improved methods of observation by microscope, telescope, and fine scales; and upon improved methods of reasoning by which these data of sense perception are interpreted. Thus, the basis is sense perceptions improved by instruments and logical common-sense reasoning, that is, in methodical fashion, making the conclusions more precise.

My next statement will, I am sure, arouse some contradiction. In psychology there is also a common-sense faculty upon which science improves. Everybody uses this faculty. It is peculiar that since psychology emancipated itself from philosophy, starting with Weber and Fechner and their disciples and continuing today in the scientifically minded experimentalists, there has been a tendency, which I can historically analyze but cannot understand, to disregard the basic natural faculty to understand another human being and rather to introduce into psychology other methods which are really somewhat alien to it since they are borrowed from other sciences. The psychologist who disregards this natural faculty, or does not want to use it because he considers it subjective or not reliable, is like a physicist who says, "I want to develop a physics without using the visual sense. I shall use only hearing, touching, and smelling; seeing is out of bounds." To operate under such a self-imposed restriction is a real handicap; that is exactly what experimental psychology has sometimes tried to do.

What is this natural faculty? The ability to communicate with each other. Everyone possesses it. Without it social life would not be possible. If they speak the same language, one person can communicate to another what is going on in his mind. Since they use the same symbols to express their internal psychological state, they can convey to each other what they feel, what they want, what they hope, and what they think. It is by this process that the psychoanalyst obtains information about a patient's motivations. From this information he can draw inferences.

WHITEHORN: Would you tolerate an interruption at this point?

ALEXANDER: I should prefer not to be interrupted until I have completed my exposition.

Everyone uses this natural faculty. We are all using it at this moment when we communicate with each other. Undoubtedly you have very definite ideas about my mental state at this moment, which probably have great validity. You surmise that I want to make my point. You infer that maybe I am a little bit on the defensive in being the exponent of a controversial position. Thus, you have made inferences about my mental state. They may be very precise if you have a first-class intuitive faculty. Perhaps your inferences are partially or even entirely wrong. I fully agree it is not a magic power. It is a very complex faculty, more complex than simple sense perception. Science here, as in every field, consists of improving this common-sense faculty.

There are four sources of error in this common-sense psychological understanding of another person's motivation. The *first* is that we do not tell each other what really goes on in our minds. As a matter of fact, we try to deceive each other. As Talleyrand said, speech is the best way to hide one's thoughts. We use speech to communicate with others; but often to tell them only as much as we want them to know, or even to deceive them. Therefore that one fact alone makes this common-sense psychological understanding not a precise scientific instrument. *Second,* even if we wanted to tell our motivations to another person, we now know that we cannot tell them because we do not know them completely ourselves.

The *third* source of error is that the identity between observer and observed is not complete. There is a difference between them. The natural faculty of communication is based on the simple fact that we are similar. It is this similarity in expressing what is going on in our minds that makes communication possible. But the similarity is not always there. If I were to use different word symbols than you, we could not communicate. If I were to have an entirely different way of gesturing than you, we would misunderstand each other. When I first saw the natives of Southern Italy using a gesture, I did not know what it meant. Until I learned that it meant "no," gesturing was a barrier. It has been said that only a schizophrenic can communicate with a schizophrenic. There is some truth to that. If you would study a Chinese, you must learn his language and become similar in method of expression.

The *fourth* source of error is our own blind spots. I do not see and interpret you correctly if I see in you something which I do not want to see in myself. Again, a man becomes a judge because very often he wants to be very righteous. With him it is an important issue; and since he has to overcome his natural criminal tendencies, he will be very intolerant toward the criminal. For he fights on two fronts: he fights his own criminal tendency; hence, he must punish the guilty prisoner very severely in order to set an example for his internal audience. If he lets the prisoner get off, he himself then runs the risk of temptation of doing something wrong. In this manner our own blind spots, our own disinclination to see our own motivation, interfere with our understanding others.

It is my contention that Freud's introduction of the psychoanalytic technic was a real scientific achievement. He developed it, not by logical reasoning but by groping trial and error and some intuition. By means of four devices it minimizes the four sources of error inherent in common-sense understanding. It brings about an improved common sense which everyone uses every day. First, the therapeutic situation is one of the few in which a person really wants to show, as much as he can, what his internal feelings are because he is suffering. It is almost impossible to analyze a person without this motivation. Accordingly, the therapeutic situation eliminates the source of error arising from our not wanting to show each other our internal processes.

What with his repressions, how can a patient tell something that he does not know? This is probably the most controversial issue. This repression can be overcome by the method of free association within a permissive interpersonal atmosphere. It results in the gradual loosening up of the resistances of the patient to see himself. The psychiatrist can get out of the patient more than he knows. For example, at the beginning of the procedure he says to the psychiatrist, "I cannot kill a fly." Two months later he relates that as a little child he had the greatest pleasure in killing every little animal against which he could take out his rancor. In consequence he developed guilt, pity, overcompensations. The psychiatrist has now learned that the patient has struggled against very cruel tendencies. This knowledge was obtained by the methodical procedure of free association in an interpersonal climate which is permissive. It tends to minimize the second source of error; namely, that a person is unaware of his motivations.

It will be recalled that the third source of error was that the identity between observer and observed is not complete. The difference between observer and observed makes intuitive firsthand understanding very difficult. The only way to overcome it is by long contact. After all, the elements of emotional reactions in the two are the same, only they are in a different configuration. If the observer and observed are together long enough, the former begins to understand the latter. Hence the time element becomes very important.

It is not unlike coming to understand a country's customs and habits by spending time there. When I came to this country, I experienced this. How difficult it was for me to analyze and understand a person from another cultural setting! My most impressive memory is one of my first cases who always had a mid-morning appointment. One day he asked, "Can I come an hour earlier?"

I said, "Yes, but why?"

He was a rich man who had nothing to do. He replied, "I must be in my office at an earlier hour."

"But why? You don't do anything."

He said, "I have an office with two secretaries."

"But you don't have any business!"

"I manage my charities."

"But that is not sufficient reason."

"I have to keep full-time hours because my wife's family are very austere and industrious; they would regard me as a loafer. I must make believe that I am working hard."

I could not understand. I thought he was odd; after all, he came for psychoanalysis. I had come from Budapest, where everyone pretends that he does not have to work. At twelve o'clock everyone, whether he is a busy lawyer, physician, or whatever

his occupation, comes to the fashionable spot of the city to walk up and down on the shores of the Danube. Everyone imitates a gentleman of leisure with an income. That is the custom and tradition there. In that urban civilization people keep up the front of not having to work. Thus the patient's pretense of work to conceal leisure was totally different from what I was accustomed to in Budapest; namely, simulation of leisure to conceal work. In time, as the observer meets with the observed, the source of error due to their dissimilarity is overcome.

Psychoanalysis is grounded on the premise that the analyst, through knowledge of himself, understands the patient. But the fourth source of error creeps in because the observer, unless he is trained, is unaware of his own blind spots; consequently, what he does not want to see in himself, he will not discover in a patient. This gap in the untutored observer can be remedied only by his coming to know himself. That makes his training analysis very important. It is really the same preparation that an astronomer undergoes. He must find out the peculiarities and distortions of his own optical apparatus in order to correct his readings with the telescope.

By these four devices the psychoanalytic approach, the common-sense understanding of another person, is improved. Critics may say that it is not trustworthy, that it is not scientific. But we find it reliable for prediction. Indeed, we can make very precise predictions in our everyday psychology. We know whether a person will blow up and punch another in the nose or pass a compliment. That, we can predict if we do not deal with insane or neurotic persons. My main contention is that psychology starts with common sense as a base line, which is high; and that science has brought a little improvement. We now know something about the unconscious motivations. We have more or less reliable ways to reconstruct material which a person does not know, but which later he will know; hence, we have proof that what we say is correct. In contrast the natural sciences started with a very low base line, but the improvement has been tremendous. Common-sense understanding of nature and modern atomic physics are very far apart, over a tremendous range. There has been improvement in what is observed and in mathematical reasoning. Science has made a big step. It started three hundred years ago when Galileo first introduced the scientific method.

If we take our present knowledge of psychology or psychoanalysis and compare it with, let us say, what Shakespeare knew about human beings, we must admit that we have not made a very great advancement. But we are on the right road. At least we now have certain technical equipment: the therapeutic confidential situation, the free association method, the nonevaluative study of other human beings, the prolonged contact with other persons, and the training analysis. All this makes for the beginning of a science. I am not cocky about it. I do not think that our scientific structure is very reliable or goes far beyond common sense. But it goes a little further.

WHITEHORN: In speaking about the use of common sense, Dr. Alexander compared a psychologist who does not employ that particular kind of common sense which enables him to understand more or less another person's motivation, to a physicist who might specify that in the study of physical phenomena all senses could be used except sight. I think that an interruption to stop one's train of thought might be very useful at this point. I should like to interject that this common-sense faculty is a double affair. It involves not only the ability to sense certain cues but also a scheme of interpretation to understand their meaning. This, I would submit, is a different kind of thing than the faculty of sight. This is partly a theoretical proposition, a motivational theory, and partly a use of faculties of perception. In going further with the development of psychodynamic knowledge, it will be useful to distinguish carefully the theories of motivation per se and the methods by which the cues are perceived and utilized.

By this unwillingness to be interrupted until he had finished his discourse, Dr. Alexander illustrated one of the phenomena which I think has characterized much of the analytic presentations. It has an annoying effect upon others, and I think I can put my finger on one of the reasons.

ALEXANDER: I do not wish to answer your comment on the analogy which I drew. Rather I want to explain why I did not agree to an interruption. The point to be discussed during the interruption was of such significance that it would have required an extensive period of time and would therefore have constituted a digression that would have broken the thread of continuity of my presentation. My subject, the methodological view of psychological understanding, was complex; hence, I wanted to present it as a whole so that it might be more readily and clearly comprehended. An interruption that would lead to digression was undesirable. Under the circumstances I really feel that I was justified in opposing an interruption.

WHITEHORN: In commenting upon the interruption I merely wanted to illustrate that psychoanalysis, more than any other discipline here represented, presents itself in a package. One either buys the package or does not buy it. It seemed to me that your resistance to interruption provided a neat demonstration of the package sale of psychoanalysis.

ALEXANDER: I do not believe that you read my mind correctly. My reaction was not due to the cultural mode of the psychoanalyst, but simply to the desire to present a complex view so that it could be understood.

WHITEHORN: It would probably be unfair of me to select what may be a personal characteristic of yours or a logical organization of material as any proof that psychoanalysis has this characteristic.

ALEXANDER: That is true. That is its characteristic, but I do not think that it motivated me.

LIDDELL: I once asked several students of psychoanalysis in what respect a training analysis was distinguishable from therapeutic analysis. One of them said, "Every analysis turns out to be therapeutic." Is this true or false? I understand that Freud's own self-analysis was really therapeutic.

ALEXANDER: Very much so. In the complex world of today, everybody has problems. Consequently, if a person begins to pour out his troubles, the difference between his and another person's is only a matter of quantity. He may come in with a severe compulsion neurosis anxiety, or he may have concerns which are common to everyone about his future, or his wife, or his children.

Take the case of the violin player who says, "Doctor, I cannot play anymore. When I go up on the podium, I have a cramp in the left hand; and I cannot play the violin. If you cannot help me, I am through." That is a strong motivation. This man I helped in three months, in spite of the view of the American Psychoanalytic Association which does not recognize that anybody can be analyzed within that period. I do not know whether I analyzed him, but he was helped; not because I am a great therapist, but because he wanted to be helped and took everything that I could give him. If another person comes in and says, "Doctor, I must be analyzed; otherwise I cannot become a member of the American Psychoanalytic Association," that does not have the same motivational force.

LIDDELL: The students said it turned out to be a therapeutic affair.

ALEXANDER: To some degree. The candidates are selected and should have only a mild disturbance at the most. To that extent the analysis might be regarded as therapeutic. But primarily and preponderantly the purpose is to allow the student to learn about himself.

FINESINGER: There are difficulties in the analytic setting which block communication between many analysts and members of other disciplines. These are inherent, not in the material, but rather in the way the group behaves. I can recall that when I began working in analysis, I had to come to terms with myself. If I asked questions, or brought up basic issues for discussion, I soon found that my analytic colleagues— this was in Vienna—would have little to do with me. This behavior of the psychoanalytic group has been one of the difficulties which has discouraged other scientists in their attempt to understand. It has finally led some of them to give up entirely. In consequence, it has barred communication between the analytic and other disciplinary groups.

ALEXANDER: I am not here to defend psychoanalysis as a sect. I feel just the same way about these things as you. The package theory, I reject. I do not think that the libido theory or any of the theoretical superstructures should be bought as a package. They are no more than very crude holistic hypotheses. Some of them already have been proved weak or unusable; yet the psychoanalytical world sticks to them as if they were the cornerstones. Thus, I do not defend these weaknesses of psychoanalysis. I know them and fight them myself. It is still partially a sect and partially a scientific group. What I believe in is the method of observation. That is all.

FINESINGER: Either resulting from or associated with impaired interdisciplinary communication, very strange reactions about psychoanalysis are manifested by persons outside the analytic group. For example, the analytic students whom Dr. Liddell interrogated were probably young and inexperienced. They made a statement. Apparently he attached much credence to it; he would not have if they had been graduate psychology students. I find that members of other disciplines pick up strange, often ridiculous, remarks about psychoanalysis which usually come from persons who are not too important in the field, or who have not had too much experience, or who are expressing their own personal bias. Indeed, highly intelligent scientists are often heard repeating the most amazing nonsense about psychoanalysis. This fact demonstrates that the attitude of scientists toward analysis and toward those who speak about it is anything but discriminating and critical. This creates an obstacle in bringing together the psychodynamicist and representatives of other disciplines.

GERARD: I am quite prepared to buy the package which Dr. Alexander has displayed. My only quarrel with it is that it is too small, not too large, a package. He drew very succinctly and effectively a picture of the observational technics of psychoanalysis, but there was no discussion of the technics of hypothesis formation. Certainly there has been no dearth of them. The really critical issue has nothing to do with the validity of the analyst's observations, although such a plethora of information is obtained that it does become distorted during codification. The issue is: How does the analyst use the data to test, to validate, or to exclude, his hypothesis? This phase is still the great weakness in the technic of the analytical school. It is, I believe, one of the reasons why so many people say that research is not done in psychoanalysis, and why so many analysts say they cannot do research.

I want to object to considering common sense as a different kind of awareness of the universe than any other sense. Insight and sight are really not so different as it would seem if one thinks of the work of Rieson and others on perception after congenital blindness. It is fantastic how much experience and general learning go into the ability to recognize a triangle or circle. It is exactly the same process that the analyst uses in interpreting by Eingefühl, the symbols, gestures, and phenomena obtained from other persons. The internal and external, the public and private, are not so sharply different as we think because we are all part of a common epiorganism. Therefore, what seems to be private to the individual is really only partly private to the total culture, and the analyst does have this direct access to it.

ALEXANDER: Not perception but apperception. The American psychological literature in particular now uses the expression "perception" for the original Wundtian term "apperception."

GERARD: Whitehead uses it that way.

WHITEHORN: Dr. Gerard accepts the package offered as a description of observational technic, but would like an exposition illustrating how it is used in the validation of hypothesis.

GERARD: What technics are used in validation?

WHITEHORN: I should like to suspend momentarily this request, and to indicate a challenge to the interpretation that Dr. Gerard has put upon the presentation. I have already indicated that this exposition

of technic involves hypothesis formation, more particularly in regard to the extent to which hypothesis of motivation enters into the system.

GERARD: I agree with that. But the query that my ilk of scientist would raise regarding results of psychoanalysis would not be at the level that has been presented so far. In science we are used to the difficulty which arises from observations being selected in terms of a hypothesis and from reading into them. But the difference between science and art is that in looking upon an object of creative art, the artist says "beautiful"; but in examining an imaginative construct, the scientist asks, "Is it true or not? How am I going to prove it?" The latter is what I am asking.

WHITEHORN: It is the proper method of proceeding with the data in the checking and validation of the theory. This may not be what all the others are asking for.

ALEXANDER: It is difficult to answer Dr. Gerard's question about the technics of validation. I fully agree with his viewpoint. No matter how much we improve the exactness and precision of our observations, the analytic situation is always, as it has been in the past, a two-man affair, the patient and the doctor who reports, usually very inadequately, what he observes, and says, "I found that, and that is that." This question of validation presents a very great difficulty. After maintaining that a psychiatrist's observation is better than common sense, I must say that many problems of validation still remain unsolved.

METTLER: I should like to point out that Dr. Alexander's approach deals with a selected sample of people who are said to be mentally ill. This selected sample is not representative of the total area of human behavior; rather, it is restricted as a consequence of the exclusion of several large groups for one reason or another. First, there are many people who are referred to the psychoanalyst but who never reach him because they will not go. Another group of persons seen by a psychoanalyst comprise a type who are soon rejected by him with the explanation, "Look here, I can't deal with this person because he will not come at the time I want him to come." Incidentally, the patient's difficult manner in social relations is a manifestation of his disturbance. Third, there is a type of patient who, upon referral, will see the psychoanalyst and arrive on time but is completely uncommunicative. This raises the very serious question whether the data which are presented are not extremely restricted. Of course it will be argued that the laws and principles which were established on the type of people who were studied would hold true for the entire group of mentally ill. But it is questionable whether the sample was in fact representative of the group and whether the methodology does not select certain types of people and reject other large groups or segments of the mentally ill who may be subjected to a different set of etiological circumstances which are operative in their particular situation.

ALEXANDER: In somatic medicine observations come from both autopsy and surgery. In contrast, psychoanalysis is limited to the same source of information as is surgery, i.e., it can study only live human beings. There is no autopsy in psychoanalysis. After a person is dead, the analyst cannot verify what he had been talking about previous to death.

To use this analogy between psychoanalysis and surgery in considering the representative character of a sample of subjects, let us assume that all knowledge about the inside functioning of the human body has to come from surgery. It is obvious that surgeons operate on a selected group of patients. All the persons needing surgery do not come to operation. Some will not consult a surgeon; others will come to him for an opinion, but will not submit to an operation. On the other hand, some who need surgery and are willing to undergo it, the surgeon rejects. For one reason or another —it may be that the patient is extremely obese with a cardiac condition, or is too old, or came too late—the surgeon regards them as inoperable.

To be concrete, suppose that the anatomy of the vena porta could be revealed only through surgery. Since only a proportion of persons needing surgery come to operation, the anatomy of the vena porta would become known only through operation on a

sample that might be said not to be representative. Certainly all the inoperable persons have a vena porta. Therefore it might be said that observations on the vena porta were true only for that segment of the population which underwent operation. In my opinion such a selection would not negate or depreciate the principal information about the vena porta. It can be reasoned very logically that both groups, the inoperable as well as the operated, have a similar constellation, and that the blood supply of the liver is about the same in both. Likewise, I do not believe that there is an entirely different type of psychodynamics in the sick than in the so-called normal.

METTLER: I do not accept the analogy.

Another point concerns the constancy and uniformity of the frame of reference. Description involves interpretation; there is a frame of reference in which a thing is described. In science the frame of reference is usually constant with major points upon which there may be disagreement but which at least are generally known. In psychoanalytic literature, however, different frames of reference are apparently used and oftentimes material is not put down in a descriptive manner. This is true of other disciplines, for example, neurology. One frequently notes that the reflexes are said to be overactive. This I submit is completely meaningless as a statement. Reflexes have amplitude, threshold, and spread; they should be described in these terms. When I read or hear a statement that such and such has happened to the ego, I am uncertain about its meaning. I am no more sure what it means than when I hear the statement that the reflexes are overactive. This is a troublesome point. I should like to ask whether there is not some methodology, within the dynamic literature, of rendering uniform the frame of reference. This is a question, not merely of validation of data, which has already been raised, but also of whether the data which are reported are the same from person to person.

RENNIE: Dr. Mettler knows full well that psychoanalytic or dynamic observational theory is not at present fixed and immutable, now and forever. He knows that it is constantly being re-examined, and new hypotheses are being formed. Although very rightly he may be confused by the numbers of hypotheses or the numbers of schools represented in the research investigations, he will have to use some criterion of judgment of his own as to which one he prefers or which one strikes him as being more valid, until that day arrives when further prediction and refinement can be stated. We are not at that point at present.

In a curious way the observations by psychodynamicists are obtained by a very uncommon sense. It is as uncommon sense as that employed in auscultation. A second-year student listening for the first time through a stethoscope hears a bewildering number of sounds. He has to learn what these sounds really mean. Likewise, the observers in psychoanalysis have to have training and experience to learn what sounds—that is, words and communications—really mean. Many analysts have come up through the biological and medical sciences. They are not without experience in observation. But they believe that their powers of observation have been refined by training to exclude their own emotional biases, and that in consequence they observe with more directness and accuracy than the observer who has not had his emotional biases examined and removed.

How does the analyst validate what he finds? There are several ways that represent reliability and validity. The analyst studies a phenomenon in a person and draws certain hypotheses. After he has examined a sufficient number of persons with the same phenomenon and has applied his hypotheses, he will be either reasonably certain or dubious of their validity, according to the outcome.

Is this procedure reliable? One test of it is to see whether other observers using the same tools and examining the same phenomena come out with the same observations and roughly the same kinds of hypotheses. This test has been applied often enough in dynamic studies to show that multiple observers using the analytic method come out with roughly the same observational data and the same formulation in terms of hypotheses. In another test the analyst asks himself, Is this phenomenon which I see in this context characteristic only for this behavioral disturbance and not for others? This test too has been applied in analytic investigations. It has been found in not a few instances that constellations of dynamics and forces which operated in one did not necessarily or frequently operate in exactly the same way in other behavioral disorders. This is also a test of reliability of the analyst's observational method.

When a phenomenon under observation is seen regularly repeated under certain circumstances or can be regularly reproduced by creating a situation, that is a demonstration of its validity. You may recall Dr. Grinker's reporting that when the barber-patient was put in a certain situation, he regularly repeated a behavioral pattern. Over and over Harold Wolff has reproduced in subjects any one of a number of indices of physiological response of the human organism. By introduction of appropriate stimulus material for discussion, and with changes in the mucosa or some other manifestation as an index, the same phenomenon can be observed to occur regularly. It can be reproduced week after week. I consider that this is a kind of validity.

It is also true that many of the early hypotheses were derived from the retrospective accounts of adult human beings, recreating in memory certain things that had happened earlier in their lives. Objective observers have seen in the infant and the child, normal and sick, the same phenomena taking place which had been reported retrospectively by adult people. This is another evidence of validity.

Moreover, when an analyst is observing and working with a phenomenon in a patient, when by virtue of interpersonal action the patterns are changed within that period of association, when the patient finds new avenues of solution for his problems or loses an investment of high affect in an object that has been very important for him, and when in this process a substantial shift takes place in his behavior, this is *ipso facto* evidence that something of psychodynamic significance has been touched and altered and a new behavioral pattern has resulted. This is a pragmatic test of validity.

Dr. Alexander has said that psychoanalysis has nothing comparable to an autopsy. That is true. However, the analyst may make observations which lead him to believe that a person has potentials for future serious difficulties. Six months later this person may be seen in a psychiatric hospital in a flamboyant, full-blown psychotic episode. This is not unlike the pathological procedure. It is not an autopsy, but it is an advanced pathological observation.

Do all of these lines of evidence add up to a representation of reliability? Will this psychoanalytical observational technic regularly do what it is supposed to do? Will it identify regularly and accurately that group of people which it is designed to select, and not identify those in another group? I submit that the validity of observations and hypotheses can be tested, and that the psychoanalytic technic exhibits reliability. This is of course an over-all framework; these basic points should be studied.

The psychodynamicist has had some experience in the methodology of the organicist, particularly in neurophysiology and biochemistry. Unhappily, representatives from these latter disciplines have had no experience in psychodynamics. It is difficult, therefore, to expect them to understand psychodynamic methodology when they have never had the opportunity to use it. I would wish that some day they might attempt to use the observational technics which the psychodynamicist has found so valuable, and to test for themselves whether they think it gathers data that are significant.

chapter 29

The Search for New Technics to Verify Observations and Validate Hypotheses in Psychoanalysis

• •

SPIEGEL: I want to take the position which is more in sympathy with Dr. Mettler's and Dr. Gerard's point of view, because there is a tendency for us in psychoanalysis to become defensive, to try in the face of an attack to defend what we do as scientific, when actually the criticisms seem to be valid. We operate always in an area of doubt and indecision about the phenomena which are taking place before our eyes at the moment. This occurs to a much greater extent in psychoanalysis than in most other scientific areas. We would probably be better off if we could admit the vastness of the area of doubt and indecision, and if we would spend more time searching for methods to increase our precision and ability to find reliable data and to reach reliable interpretations that can be verified.

However, there is great difficulty in designing procedures for this purpose. In the more common scientific situations the observer is ostensibly in a detached relationship with the subject, and the design of the study is simplified. Contrastingly, in psychoanalysis the observer is himself a part of the field that he is studying, and the field is extremely complex and changing all the time. Even if it were not so complex, the mere fact that the observer is a part of the field and has both to participate in it and

observe his own participation makes for a great difficulty in being specific and objective about what is taking place. To add to the complexity, the analyst as both participant and observer is playing his role in a larger field of action or transaction. For whether he is conducting his sessions as a private practitioner or as a member of a hospital staff, what he does is markedly influenced by many other things which are happening in this larger field and which he may not be aware of.

I should like to take as an example the barber-patient whom Dr. Grinker described. What I am going to say about him now is entirely hypothetical; I am making it up only for purposes of illustration. Let us say that he is in the hospital on second admission, having been previously discharged with improvement, but having returned with more anxiety when he went back to the barber shop. Let us say further that he has been in the hospital about two months under the care of a third-year resident, under the supervision of a member of the hospital staff; that in this situation his anxiety has died down again; and that the resident and his supervisor both have the feeling that they are making much progress with him. The patient has been talking about his family background. He has been remembering how his mother encouraged him to be a little more independent, but how his father always seemed to be reproachful and angry with him whenever he made any attempt in that direction. All this seems to be extremely relevant to the situation that he is in, and he is now without anxiety and seemingly doing very well.

At this point the superintendent of the hospital calls in the resident. The superintendent states that he has observed that the resident keeps his patients in the hospital a very long time. He wonders aloud whether the resident is not being much too reactive to the patients' dependent needs. After all, the superintendent reminds the resident, the hospital is an institution; it has to serve the public; beds are being occupied; patients have to be discharged; the hospital has to have a turnover. What is not told the resident is that the superintendent has just had a hard time with the Board of the hospital which has reached the conclusion that the institution is not earning enough money, and that too many beds are being occupied by part-paying patients. In conclusion, the superintendent recommends to the resident that he get busy in arranging the discharge of some of his patients.

In general the impression that the resident takes from this conference is that he has not been an objective and satisfactory doctor, and that he has not been successful as a staff member of the hospital. In short, it appears that he has failed in both respects. He is so very much disturbed by the outcome of the conference that he decides that perhaps the barber-patient has been in the hospital too long and should be discharged. But the resident is not quite certain that the superintendent's criticism of him is valid on scientific grounds; nevertheless, he is still disturbed by it.

Upon seeing the barber-patient that day, he decides that he will not say anything about discharging him because in any event that would need preparation. Accordingly, the resident carries on with a pattern that he has established of going into the patient's background. What he does not notice is that in talking to the patient his voice and his manner, usually so sympathetic, are now somewhat cold, more distant, and a little reproachful. He does not hear the

sound of reproach in his own voice. However, the patient hears it, becomes more anxious than he has been in weeks while in the hospital, notices the signs of anxiety increasing throughout the day and into the night, and decides that he needs some medication for sleep. So the patient goes to the nurse for a soporific.

But all during the patient's stay in the hospital, the nurse has felt that the resident has been treating him with too much sympathy and indulging him too much. Furthermore, she has heard some repercussions of the resident's interview that day with the superintendent of the hospital. She gives the patient the medication but at the same time advises him with some asperity in her voice that he should try to wean himself from this kind of treatment. After all, she tells the patient, he is not going to be in the hospital all his life and is not going to be able to have sleeping tablets forever. That night the patient does not sleep. The next morning he has one of his typical panic attacks. The effect of this attack is to make the resident conclude that the superintendent of the hospital is right. He thinks to himself: "I believed that I was making progress with the patient; now I see that I have achieved nothing. I have just been indulging him; because of it, he only seemed to make some improvement."

None of these happenings, remarks, and thoughts would have appeared in the record, or would have been a part of the scientific data on the basis of which interpretations and hypotheses were being drawn, unless an anthropologist or sociologist uninvolved in the association had been observing the total field and had had an opportunity to interview the superintendent, the resident, the patient, and the nurse. Those who are principally responsible for the care of the patient and the scientific evidence on which it is based do not usually take into account the type of material which I have described. It is not organized in their minds.

This set of interactions, I like to call transactions because the interaction of any two people in such a situation is being influenced all the time by the wider field. It is not just a question of A acting on B and B reacting to A, but of A and B playing roles in the situation, all the while their actions being modified by the wider situation, and the wider situation in turn being modified by what they are doing. The result is that a system of events is going on which transcends what any individual is doing. For this reason it seems wise to use the term "transaction," which indicates the spread and reciprocal nature of the system.

In this kind of situation the psychodynamic conclusions that are usually drawn have some lack of validity because they do not incorporate enough and are based on the real dimensions of the transactional field that is occurring. In actuality, episode A is not really comparable with episode B. This, I think, is the main difficulty so far as the reproducibility and validity of psychodynamic observations are concerned. What we need are concepts and methods that will enable us to get really comparable episodes, the kind that can be reproduced in a laboratory. We can never reproduce the same situation, but we can develop concepts which will allow us to pinpoint some of the transactions in such a way as to make them more comparable.

If the social roles of the doctor, the patient, and all of the others transacting in the situation are specified and characterized in such a way that they will include the total field, and if probable role constellations or configurations are sought in the situations of treatment, this procedure would present a possibility of developing the kind of principles in this area which has been lacking in the past. It would seem to be a promising method of obtaining repeatable observations which could be subjected to verification.

WHITEHORN: Dr. Mettler pointed up the limited segment of the population which has been subjected to the psychoanalytic method of study. Then the question was raised as to the pertinence of that for psychodynamic hypotheses and observations. An attempt to attach a plus or minus whatever per cent to the validity of such ideas prompts a point that requires consideration. The ways of dealing with psychoanalytic methods, concepts, or studies have not been actually limited to specific psychoanalytics such as Dr. Alexander presented. For instance, Dr. Adolf Meyer for many years assiduously cultivated methods of studying personality development by the biographical approach to understanding a person, and by consideration of the situation in which reaction patterns occurred as part of the problem, not by relying specifically on methods of dream analysis or other approaches to the unconscious. Others, too, approached psychotic patients with some curiosity and intuitive appreciation of the meaningfulness of their behavior, gathered data, and developed ideas which, I think, would properly be called psychodynamic. There is a body of knowledge, supposition, and theory which should be included in the general discussion of psychodynamics and its pertinence for the large population that Dr. Mettler is most concerned about.

I believe that it was Dr. Paul Schilder who used to say that the psychoanalytic method was a special therapeutic method for upper middle-class Jews. The material gathered was largely from that segment; hence, I think that it is pertinent to suggest that the emphasis on insight, as a feature of therapy, probably has something to do with the general intellectualistic aspirations of the types of patients who were at one time the stock in trade of the analyst. Here were people for whom it was personally important to understand or to have the feeling of understanding. So their uneasiness was in some measure appeased by a pseudo-insight.

In the Department of Psychiatry of The Johns Hopkins University School Medicine, my associates and I have been conducting a study over a number of years on the variable kinds of results obtained by the staff with the patients through the use of various formulations. Some of the members of the staff are simultaneously in the process of psychoanalysis themselves; many of them are not being analyzed and are somewhat defensive and anti-analytic; but most of them are oriented to the study of their patients as persons, and wish to arrive at a personalistic basis of understanding. This study provides material which can be studied from the standpoint of the question: Does the hypothesis of motivation constitute a frame of reference for interpretation independent of some of the other features of the psychoanalytic package? This, I take it, is where the broader meaning of psychodynamics exceeds the special limits of psychoanalysis. It is not merely a theoretical point of whether theories are alike. It also covers Dr. Mettler's point that observers, in trying to comprehend motivation, have scrutinized and studied a wider range of patients than the group to whom the psychoanalytic method in its pure state has been applied.

We have not, so far as I can see, attempted systematically to cover in this Conference the various schools of thought concerned with psychodynamics. Representatives here have mostly been trained in the psychoanalytic points of view. We are all aware, I am sure, that on the issue of the role of insight in therapy, Dr. Alexander has taken a position somewhat at variance with that of what might be called the classical orthodox school. Dr. Mettler's point concerning what should be included in a discussion of psychodynamics should be taken intô account in assessing the existing literature because there are different views.

SCOTT: I have already commented upon phylogenetic development in relation to the problem of mental disease in human beings. I pointed out that animals obviously can learn things and solve problems without the use of language, and that probably in the course of human development language was added to this earlier ability. This creates a situation in human beings which is not likely to occur in animals; namely, that man can have one kind of learning which is verbal and another which is nonverbal, and the two can be in conflict. In most of the discussion about the psychodynamic school and its methods of therapy, the emphasis has been on resolving a possible conflict between verbal ideas and nonverbal learning. The patient says one thing, but something else is really troubling him. It is assumed that if he comes to know what is troubling him and gains insight, he will be improved. This points to a limitation of the psychodynamic method. It is known that neuroses can be produced in animals which do not have the power of words. Hence, it is very likely that in certain instances of be-

havioral disorders, the difficulty is not the result of a conflict between verbal and nonverbal learnings. Cases of that type would probably not be susceptible to improvement by the psychoanalytic method. Further, it is also possible that even if a patient does have insight and knows what is troubling him, that would not help him.

An example might be drawn from the field of combat. If a soldier in a very dangerous situation keeps under cover and his head down, he will be reasonably safe, according to the military manuals. This is a verbal type of learning. On the other hand, it is very likely that the nonverbal portion of his brain will be telling him at the same time, particularly if a high explosive shell lands a few feet away and kills one of his friends, that it is really a very dangerous situation and that he had best flee. It is therefore a conflict situation. Suppose the soldier realizes verbally that it is a very dangerous situation, is it going to help him? He says to himself: This is extremely dangerous. If I stay here, I am going to be killed. If I go back, I will be shot. Will this verbalization be of help to him? It may not.

The problem presented by the different schools of clinical thought is that each tends to have its limitations. Therefore, the best possible way to go about the solution of practical problems of human beings should be on a basis of group action. That is to say, since practical problems differ in type, each might be referred to an appropriate specialist. It would be important to be able to recognize the type of behavior problem and the particular kind of therapy which would be helpful; this is a type of diagnostic method which still needs to be developed by research. Above all, it would be necessary to have a sufficient number of various types of specialists.

WHITEHORN: Dr. Scott has done a service by pointing out a misunderstanding; correction of it is long overdue. It has been a prevalent misconception that psychodynamic ways of studying or theorizing are necessarily bound up with the idea that insight is the paramount instrument. Many psychodynamicists would promptly say that insight and verbalization have very little to do with either psychodynamic theory or practice of therapy, and that the roles attributed to them have been vastly overrated.

ALEXANDER: I agree with Dr. Spiegel on his thesis. The transactional concept has finally reached psychology and the behavioral sciences; a similar idea has been recognized in the natural sciences. In any book of theoretical physics will be found statements like the following: Modern physics is characterized by the fact that the observer himself enters into the equations. Methods of observation stir up much dust which obscures the observed phenomena. The whole relativity concept comes from the recognition that the observer's position changes during the observation. Hence the same difficulties which prevail in psychodynamics also obtain in physics, particularly in the study of the very distant and the very large or very small dimensions. Newtonian physics did not concern itself too much with such matters because the objects observed were not at either extreme in magnitude. But in atomic or astral physics all the considerations of transactional philosophy come into play.

I am less than satisfied with the methods of validation in psychoanalysis. At the time of my entrance into this field more than thirty years ago, the difficulty of validation was my greatest concern. Because of it I often wondered whether I should leave this field. Although the difficulties are extreme, I now think that the problems can be coped with.

Psychoanalysis, like the natural sciences, should have its observations and interpretations checked and verified. Those of one analyst should be re-examined and reviewed not only by other analysts but also by observers trained in other disciplines. As a first step, obviously the analytic material of one observer must be made accessible to others. In some way it must be recorded. The excuse that recording would interfere with therapy is understandable, but it is not a decisive factor. Observers in other disciplines particularly should know how and why the analyst reaches his interpretations. In order to re-examine and review properly the analytical material, specialists trained in other disciplines must learn the

analytic technic, just as a biochemist wishing to verify a histological observation must learn to look through the microscope. As for interpretation, it appears in every science; out of it come differences of opinion. Even in histology, a discipline of lesser complexity because objects are seen directly under a microscope, there are differences of opinion and interpretation. I grew up in a time when histologists were divided into two groups: the neuron theorists and the fiber theorists. In one lecture room I heard arguments for the neuron theory; in the next room I heard attacks against it. In this respect psychoanalysis is no different from histology. Ways and means must be devised to subject to verification both observations and interpretations in psychoanalysis. Recording of material is therefore the first prerequisite.

GERARD: I approve of your comments, but you have not quite come to grips with the essential difficulty of validation.

ALEXANDER: You are quite right. There is one kind of evidence for validation that to me is most convincing. Let me use a concrete example.

In Berlin I treated a kleptomaniac who was an actress and mistress of a playboy. She stole many things. Usually after she stole them, if they were of value, she went at night to the bridge over the Spree River and dumped them in. Of the stolen articles, she kept only pictures of the Madonna and Child. That was her predilection.

She was caught several times. I started her treatment when a trial was pending. When the trial came up, the prosecutor had me invited as an expert witness. I proposed to the judge that this woman was sick. The judge asked me, "Why does she steal silverware?"

I replied, "She does not know. It is a question of motivational validation. Obviously she did not steal to obtain money. She is not an ordinary thief because she throws away most of what she steals."

Then the judge said, "But she stole a little volume of Goethe's *Faust,* and that she did not throw away. That was found."

I answered, "That is true, but it was not for gain because it was a fifty-cent copy, which she could have bought. She was not in financial stress. The act of stealing meant something for her."

So it went, until finally I saw that there was no way out of giving a full explanation. I told the court that she is an orphan, that she is in love with a playboy, that he cannot marry her. She has a compelling desire which she does not know. At this point I gave my interpretation, "She wants a child from this man. He gave her everything else, money and security; but not marriage and therefore no child. As an orphan she had tremendous resentment against her stepmother. When she stole from her, it was out of revenge; for she was taking by force what she never got voluntarily from her stepmother. She also stole from the landlady," I explained, "just as a man angry at his boss kicks a dog." Finally the judge—imagine a Prussian judge, very cold, very precise—becoming very interested said, "Doctor, I have a niece—" He suddenly discovered the use of common sense. Although he was not trained in psychoanalysis, he could very well understand that unfulfilled desire may take a devious way.

Then came the court psychiatrist who said, "It is not a case of kleptomania because in kleptomania there is tremor of the hands and sweating of the palms. That was not found in this case." He had looked up "kleptomania" in some old textbook and had found, perhaps, a paragraph stating that these were the characteristic clinical symptoms. This is typical of the objective approach in psychiatry. Instead of finding out why a person steals, the objective psychiatrist puts down only the observable manifestations—sweating of the palms and tremor of the hands—which might be incidental; he goes into nothing. Finally the judge gave the girl a suspended sentence and recommended that she continue her psychoanalysis.

You may ask: "How do you really know that this girl stole the pictures of the Madonna as a symbolic outlet for having a child? She collected those pictures; the rest of the stolen articles she threw away." She had an unconscious desire. If this desire were to become conscious, insight would manifest itself. Through becoming conscious, the desire could be gratified in its original form by at least the hope of having a real child, and the symptoms would disappear. Recognition of this desire had been repressed in the patient. After becoming conscious of it, she was just as much aware of it as of hunger. This communication of the patient is a source of validation.

You may say that the patient was influenced by me by suggestion, that she is really not conscious of the desire. I can only say that by talking with a patient, the analyst, on the basis of common sense, gains a very definite impression of her and of whether she gives lip service to please the analyst, or whether she means what she says. There are so many checks on the patient's general behavior. In this instance, resentments vanished; a more hopeful attitude appeared; and she discussed the possibilities of having even an illegitimate child with the lover. It is obvious that the girl was now conscious of the desire and that her behavior had changed. These evidences prove the validity of the interpretation that it was an unconscious desire which motivated the stealing.

When a patient is not conscious of a desire or motivation, it is a source of trouble for her and of ill repute for the attending psychoanalyst. He is regarded as a culprit who uses preposterous fantasies, constructs a neat but improbable theory, and considers that it is the truth. Actually he does not consider it true until the unconscious becomes the conscious. But if it becomes conscious, and if certain changes occur in the person's behavior, it is proof that a new motivational force has appeared which accounts for the new pattern of behavior. When a clogged-up carburetor in an automobile is cleaned and the engine begins to run properly again, a cause and effect relationship is unquestionably accepted. With the change in a patient following psychoanalysis, the evidence and proof is just as convincing.

SKINNER: Dr. Alexander has developed a theory of knowledge with the intention, I think, of justifying analytic practices and theories. It is a theory of knowledge which has very deep historical and traditional philosophical roots. He seems to be willing to base the matter eventually on a pragmatic test. We cannot ask any more than that. I am perfectly willing to let him or anyone who so desires use that conception of knowledge to show how useful it is. However, he does seem to imply that it is the only theory or interpretation of human knowledge, and that alternative views will necessarily miss something which is fundamental and particularly important.

The notion that knowledge consists of sense impressions and concepts derived from sense impressions was, of course, the view of British empiricism, and is still held by many people. But others, including myself, believe that it is incapable of representing human knowledge adequately. Even a simple idea is not, as Locke supposed, an assemblage of sensory materials in response to stimulation. To suppose that physical knowledge exists in the mind of a physicist as psychic or mental material—as the way he looks at the world—seems to me quite absurd. At no time is a physical theory a psychic event in the sense of an image or sensation.

To say that physics always gets back to sense impression is simply to say that the organism is in contact with the environment only through its sense organs—a very obvious axiom. But the organism does more than soak up the environment. It reacts with respect to the environment, and throughout its lifetime it learns more and more varied ways of reacting. An alternative conception of knowledge, which many of us hold, is that knowledge is action rather than sensing, and that a formulation of knowledge should be in terms of behavior. It is true that we may be aware of our own behavior in the sense that we can see ourselves seeing something. Some of the time we know when we are reacting to the world around us, but, as Freud pointed out, at other times we do not know. When we do know, we are reacting to ourselves as we react to the world about us.

The notion of knowledge as response is useful in enabling us to formulate the assembled knowledge of physics in terms of the equations and laws which comprise the verbal behavior of the scientist, rather than his mental states. It also gives a much more plausible view of the insight which is apparently so useful to the analyst. We acquire the vocabulary which describes our own behavior under great difficulty. The verbal community which can easily teach a child to distinguish colors, for example, cannot with the same technics teach him to distinguish aches, pains, feelings, and emotions. As physical states in the individual, those are a part of the physical world, but the individual himself has a special connection with them. My aching tooth is mine in a very real sense because none of you can possibly get nerves into it, but that does not make it different in nature from the ceiling light which we all react to in more or less the same way. As a result of this physical privacy, the subjective vocabulary such as was used by introspective psychology and seems to be used today by some analysts has limitations in precision which no one has been able to surmount.

When the analyst states that he can predict what a patient is going to do, I accept the fact that he can make that prediction. But I challenge the statement that he does it by experiencing the same sensations or feelings. I do not see any distinction between predicting what an individual is going to do and predicting what, let us say, a sailboat is going to do. A person who is familiar with a sailboat and knows how it will take the waves has a high predictive knowledge of how to handle the tiller. That seems to me to be parallel to what the skilled analyst does in knowing what to expect and what to do next in the course of an analysis. We do not need to assume that the skillful sailor must be experiencing something which the boat is experiencing. It is obvious that he is not. The analysts have tended to conceptualize certain ways of dealing with the behavior of themselves and their patients which may be convenient or inconvenient, but need not be evaluated accordingly.

Those of us who work with verbal behavior per se, rather than with expression of meanings, become suspicious of efforts to improve vocabularies for talking about what is going on inside the individual. It will be recalled that the old introspective psychologist had a trained observer, but it is now clear that in training him the psychologist was definitely shaping the way in which the observer reacted to stimuli and was to some extent creating the very data which he was trying to collect. Something of the same sort may very well happen in the training analysis. It is necessary to be on guard lest the interchange between the patient and the therapist results in building up a very particular vocabulary which will lead to quite spurious results.

Several experiments are now in the literature in which an interviewer has skillfully shaped, by very slight reinforcements and punishments, the verbal behavior of the person being interviewed. It is fairly easy to get another person onto an arbitrarily chosen topic during a conversation by showing attention when the topic is being approached and inattention when it is being left. The same process could generate a misleading community of vocabulary in the personal interaction between two particular people.

SPIEGEL: In the epistemological theory which you expounded, you sounded as if you were excluding the sensory area and observing only actions.

SKINNER: No.

SPIEGEL: Were you including the sensory area and action taken with respect to it?

SKINNER: That is it exactly. Most of the work on perception can be included if perception can be conceived, not as soaking up the stimulus, but as action on the stimulus.

GRINKER: Use of the word "common sense" in relation to psychoanalysis always makes me a little uncertain because common sense has an implication of universality. I naturally ask myself, "What composes the universe that is characterized by this commonness in a particular kind of sense?" I think that there is less commonness to the sense that analysts use than has been indicated. Furthermore, what is common sense today, tomorrow is not common sense, but nonsense.

Because the analyst is involved with the patient and is therefore a participant-observer, and because of his own biases, the psychoanalytic method has been said to be lacking in objectivity. This I contend is a universal criticism applicable to all scientists because everyone approaches a scientific experiment with some degree of bias. Even though the analyst himself has had certain emotional blind spots removed, he still has about as much bias as any other observer. However, his involvement with his patient has been shown to be no greater than the Pavlovian experimentalist's involvement with his dogs or the physicist's admiration of his particular instrument.

In the problem of validation of hypothesis in the dynamic field, no reliance can be put on any aspect of therapeutic results. That applies not only to the general field of psychoanalysis as a therapy but also to treatment by whatever method, either successful or not. By this time it should be recognized by the other participants that the psychoanalysts present are perhaps even more critical of their own field than anyone else could be, and that they are by no means subscribers to any set of beliefs in a package. The analysts also know that psychoanalysis has until now been practiced on a limited, selected material; that information came out recently in a survey made by the American Psychoanalytic Association. But this limited material has been increasingly broadened by the establishment of free clinics and also by the utilization of the fundamental principles of psychoanalysis in the field of psychodynamic psychiatry. For the kind of validation which I am about to propose, it is not necessary to draw a distinction between psychoanalysis and psychodynamics as research procedures.

Dr. Spiegel outlined a field within which the many variables concerned in the problems of sick or healthy human beings are related and in interaction. But validation of transactional studies *in toto* raises a knotty point because of the many data that have to be handled. Even the statistical methods for the determination of sequential processes are extremely difficult. The transactional *method* is ideal, however, for the purpose of bringing psychoanalysis or psychodynamic psychiatry into the same level of discourse as experiments involving other disciplines.

For purposes of validation it is possible to utilize a very small fraction of a trans-

NEW TECHNICS FOR PSYCHOANALYTIC VALIDATION 361

action between two people, which is perhaps a counterpart of the experimental psychologist and his animal. In this very narrow segment of time, which Dr. Thomas French has called a therapeutic unit, with knowledge of what variables are thereby excluded, it can be said that the statements made to the patient represent stimuli that are imposed upon him, and that his responses are of the same character as any response to interference with a human or animal in a specific situation. The responses are expressed in behavior; sometimes motor, sometimes verbal, sometimes indirectly verbal, often first pictorial in the nature of a dream and then verbally communicated. The single observer who is transacting with a patient makes certain conclusions about the relationship between the stimulus and the response. But replication becomes impossible because it cannot be achieved with the same subject.

Nevertheless, if the same procedures were applied often to large groups of similar subjects, enough data should be provided on which to make statistics similar to those of the experimentalists. What we really require is an added observer who would not be as directly involved in such an experiment as an experimentalist usually is. I recognize that in this transactional experiment, the living human being has been rudely separated from his total transactional field, which I agree is more representative of life than the segment is. Yet for the purpose of experimentation it is often advantageous to slice behavior into a narrow segment.

Leaving out all the therapeutic implications, what is this faculty of understanding others which is distilled from common sense by the procedures of psychoanalysis? The patient responds to interference with a certain fragment of behavior. What criteria do the psychodynamicists use to judge the significance of the response? To me this is the crux of validation in psychodynamics, as it is in all other experimental fields, I think. This is not some highly theoretical concept; rather, it concerns practical, day-by-day estimation of significance of responses to a particular stimulus.

Perhaps it can be said that the analysts have a certain patterned consistency among the criteria which they use; that is, they have not a single criterion but multiple criteria of responses. There is a better opportunity today of placing some reliance on workers in other disciplines, who from their own perspectives can observe several variables during the processes of a temporal sequence of changes from a particular stimulus. This approach constitutes the multidisciplinary concept, but it requires an implementation which we have not yet been able to produce. I myself am very interested in establishing methods to take advantage of multidisciplinary help in validation of psychodynamic concepts. I think that we have to develop processes of mensuration which need not be as precise as the pH of the blood, but should be sufficiently accurate so that quantities of change can be reliably correlated with measured phenomena in other systems. To me this problem of validation has been lightly passed by in the expression of the term "knowing" or intuition. The crucial problem is how can we determine how much of what we "know" is correct at the level of knowing, inherent in other disciplines which are making simultaneous observations.

There is another equally important problem. Since psychodynamicists are dependent upon the study of the effects of the stimulus, namely, their interpretation, and since they attempt to make some prediction or hypothesis as to what a specific interpretation or stimulus will bring out in a patient, we find ourselves dissatisfied with only the total behavioral responses of the person. We need to have some verbal expression of the patient's knowing that something is happening to him and what it is. Knowing is not communicated by words of the subject which repeat the stimulus, namely, the interpretation, or by repeating some intellectual concept related to theory, but by the observer's recognizing that a change is occurring in temporal and quantitative relationships to the stimulus imposed. How are we able to determine the knowing within the observer and within the subject? It is a problem which we are confronted with in all behavioral sciences, not only in psychoanalysis. It is unfortunate that we have attempted to avoid this particular problem in psychoanalysis by taking refuge in less satisfactory evidence of change.

We have to develop newer methods and experimentation in the strictest sense of the word; namely, the utilization of different stimuli to see whether they produce a similar response in different or the same subjects, and the development of alternative hypotheses. These are constantly used but in a poorly organized way. If this multidisciplinary Conference could do anything, it could recognize that the technics used by other sciences have become so important to each of us.

JASPER: In the early days of electroencephalography it was naïvely thought that alpha waves perhaps had a relationship with personality. The characteristic patterns of electrical activity of the brain were established in a group of patients. A number of psychoanalysts then studied the patients. They came out with an initial conclusion that there seemed to be a reliable correlation between the amount of alpha rhythm and the tendency of individuals to be sexually aggressive or passive, or to have homosexual tendencies. This was a rather startling correlation; hence, we immediately began to try to test it. Two subjects in whom the alpha-waves were predominant were selected for the test. According to the psychoanalysts' conclusion, they should have been of a passive nature. Actually, they were known to be extraordinarily aggressive characters. The comment of the analysts was that the outcome of this comparison really did not refute their proposition. They explained that the two men were fundamentally very submissive, and that their aggressive behavior was merely a manifestation of their compensatory reaction to their submissive tendency. This is a type of material which an experimenter in a discipline other than psychoanalysis finds difficult to validate. The circular argument leaves the experimenter nonplused as to how to proceed in validation.

ALEXANDER: This study was never published because I was not convinced that the correlations were adequately proved. But the argument which you find difficult to believe is not necessarily wrong. There is such a thing as compensating for basic tendencies and it can be demonstrated.

For example, a man came late to the interview. I asked him why?

He replied, "Because I could not walk on the street. I saw a driver of a delivery wagon mercilessly whipping his horse because it could not pull the wagon out of the mire. I could not move; I was rooted to the spot. As I watched, I became so angry that I attacked the driver. He told me that I should mind my own business. There was a big row. A crowd gathered, and the police came. That is why I am late."

I then asked, "Why were you so fascinated by the beating of the horse?"

He replied, "Doctor, I cannot kill a fly."

"What do you mean you cannot kill a fly?"

"I cannot see suffering of animals."

In the same interview during the free associations he succeeded in going back to his childhood. He told me the most gruesome stories of his torturing animals in his youth—of putting a straw into a frog's belly and blowing it up until it exploded. From that I concluded that this man had developed very strong sadistic, aggressive feelings against animals. I found that these feelings were directed also against helpless creatures, including younger siblings. It was mainly a reaction to having been bullied by his parents. He used the same technic as that of the German sergeant who is tyrannized by the lieutenant and takes it out on an underling. In Germany it is called the bicycle psychology: to bow upwards and push downwards. This reaction originated in him as a means to vent his pent-up rage and fury which were aimed at his parents and others over him; hence, he tortured others who were weaker than he.

During his growth process he developed a defense against this hostile and sadistic tendency; it was pity. When a person manifests a character tendency, such as extreme pity for animals, it is usually possible to go back into its origin and to show that previously there was an opposite attitude. On account of internal conflict this earlier attitude became overcompensated by an opposing characteristic. When repeatedly it is shown that a tendency manifested in an adult can be traced back to an opposite attitude in the past and that the circumstances which occasioned the repression of the original tendency can be brought out, that evidence is sufficient to demonstrate compensated behavior.

WHITEHORN: This view can be substantiated in terms of time sequence in biographical study, and also in terms of the material in contiguity. I might point out that there are people so devoted to peace that they are willing to fight at the drop of the hat to maintain peace.

Dr. Gerard had a question related to this issue: Considering the plethora of material that comes to the attention of a psychoanalyst, how does he discriminate what material to use for what constructions?

GERARD: This matter of validation has led the discussion from validity of the data to validity of the interpretation. Scientists have several methods available for establishing the validity of their conclusions and the correctness of their hypotheses. One is simply the ability to predict phenomena. I recall that after a student analyst had had her first interview with her first control patient, she was told by her supervisor what the contents of the reports for the next several interviews were going to be. She did not believe it, clearly was not prejudiced favorably, and was very much impressed when later interviews came out as forecast. This is prediction. I witnessed an analyst receiving a description of the symptoms and phenomena of a psychotic patient in a distant city, whom he had never seen. The analyst said that the past of this patient should have been so-and-so. Upon looking into the record of the patient's background, the attending psychiatrist found that this "prediction" was confirmed. This is the kind of validating evidence that all of us will accept.

A second type of validating procedure is experimentation, in which the variables are manipulated and the results observed. There is an excellent summary of experimental approaches to psychoanalysis by Hilgard* in the Hixon Symposium entitled *Psychoanalysis as a Science*. A minor induced conflict was symptomatized by the inability to recall a word recently memorized, and the effectiveness of two counseling technics in overcoming it could be tested quantitatively. Another experimental approach was in relation to the study of dreams. A naïve subject under hypnosis was told she had wet the bed, was dreaming, and was to report the dream. The "dream" contained the universal symbols recognized by psychoanalysts. When it was told to a second hypnotized subject, who was asked to interpret it, the report was, "It means bed-wetting." Evidence from such experimentation is convincing, but it is rarely offered. It takes considerable imaginative and experimental skill to devise these approaches, and most psychoanalysts by virtue of their situation are not in a position to do this kind of research.

They must rely on the third method of validation: amassing data, correlating them, and trying whether this or that interpretation fits. For example, eight or ten analysts, all unquestionably competent, were given a transcript of several interviews with a patient, from which had been expurgated direct clues to the actual psychosomatic disease present. They attempted, from the interview material and their psychodynamic interpretations, to diagnose the particular case. The success or failure is immaterial in this particular instance; what is impressive is that each picked from the material different items on which to base his conclusions. This means that much of psychoanalytic operation at the experimental level is still no more than the anecdotal type of approach.*

I now come to what I had in mind in raising my original question, namely, to point out and emphasize the difficulties of validation in psychoanalysis. Take into account further problems that Dr. Mettler raised, that the sample must be sufficiently wide and representative; add to that the technic that Dr. Shakow is introducing, of obtaining not merely the analyst's notes and a verbal recording but also a complete animated cinematographic record of the inter-

---

* Hilgard, E. "Experimental Approaches to Psychoanalysis," in *Psychoanalysis as a Science*. Stanford, Calif.: Hixon Fund Symposium, Stanford Univ. Press, 1952. pp. 3–45.

* I recently suggested having the interviews judged by untrained persons on the basis of keyed criteria. The success in diagnosis by secretaries so operating seems to be at least as great as that of psychiatrists under the other conditions.

view (which takes just as long to run off and review as it took to record it); add to that the additional fringe transactional variables which Dr. Spiegel has cited; and you will recognize that the limits of magnitude, multiplicity, and complexity are being approached. There is such a plethora of data pouring in, that the more precise the collection of data, the more impossible it is, with current procedures, to sample with any assurance of having selected wisely.

This is what I mean by the dilemma of the historian. A distinguished historian looks at the entire array of human experience, from it picks out hundreds or thousands of facts, and makes a beautiful, well-supported hypothesis—which another equally competent historian says is nonsense because he can bring together another thousand facts which fit *his* hypothesis and not the original historian's. This, I think, is the dilemma. As I have sensed it, this is the reason for the basic query and reservations in the minds of those biologists who remain uncertain of how far they dare accept the current theorizing in psychoanalysis. The selection of data is a very serious problem.

The histologist has a problem comparable to that of the historian. The histologist looks at an infinitude of details; which ones he chooses to recognize and report are subjectively selected. Thus, Sherrington and Cajal, each looking at the other's set of slides, saw in them what he had seen in his own slides; so their different views on what the synapse is like remained unsolved.

The same problem occurs again in the interpretation of brain waves. The performance of a skilled observer is quite good; without any measurements, he can look at a record, interpret it, and be right in a high percentage of instances. But this skill cannot be communicated to another, except by comparable practice and experience, until a series of objective, codified measurements has been established.

The needs for advance in psychoanalysis and psychoanalytic experimentation are not for improvement of the collection of data, the enrichment of the field by the kind of data taken, or spreading of the area to get better sampling. These are all valuable; but, if pursued too much at this stage, they may simply glut the investigator with an unassimilable mass of data. It is much more important to push in the direction of codification, of scaling, of better technics of interview analysis, of devising entirely new procedures of study, and of applying methods which come from other areas of science. These, I think, are what psychoanalysis really needs in order to get on with its research, and to make completely convincing, to those who still remain somewhat unsure, the validity of its data, interpretations, conclusions, and hypotheses. Dr. Whitehorn struck the motif in his comment that what is wanted is the probable error. Dr. Grinker made the same point in emphasizing the need for mensuration. It can be done.

ALEXANDER: I agree completely.

chapter 30

Collection of Observations and Validation of Hypotheses in the Sociological Approach

WHITEHORN: Dr. Spiegel has referred to a wider range of psychodynamic factors than those intimately personal in the patient. It is appropriate, I believe, to ask Dr. Hollingshead to indicate the approach and methods of validation of the social scientist in studying the milieu.

HOLLINGSHEAD: On the question of validation, the sociologist is no different from other investigators. He has sensory equipment, common to all investigators. However, his professional orientation differs from that of the psychoanalyst. The sociologist's basic equipment is an awareness of the cultural and social components in the organization and control of human behavior. Sensitizing the sociologist to the social milieu by systematic training and experiences in different cultural environments makes him aware of motivations from a cultural point of view. This aspect of the training of sociologists might be regarded as comparable to the sensitizing of the psychoanalyst to unconscious motivations through a training analysis.

The sociologist is trained in the use of specific methods such as participant observation, sampling, and statistics. In participant observation the sociologist participates in social situations and systematically records what he observes.

The sociologist utilizes principles of sampling to help him understand the social situations he studies. He is concerned with whether or not he has a sample of observations representative of the population functioning in the universe he is studying. *The sociologist differs from the psychoanalyst on this point in validation.* The latter is concerned primarily with people who come to him and (*a*) are willing to participate in the psychoanalytic process, and (*b*) are able to afford the expense and time involved. These people may be "normals" who want to undergo a training analysis to become psychoanalysts, or they may be disturbed individuals who come to the psychiatrist for help. The sociologist usually does not work with situations or "cases" of this type. He is concerned with getting a cross-section of both the individuals and the social situation in which they participate, that is, a representative sample of the universe appropriate to his study. If his research problem required the sampling of persons involved in the psychoanalytic process, he would be prepared to gather data from this universe. However, he would be concerned with studying the psychoanalysts and the patients as functional parts of a larger cultural milieu. He would also attempt to obtain a representative sample, so that he could generalize to the larger universe from which the analysts and the patients were drawn.

The sociologist is concerned with methods to control observations from one individual to another in a sample. The same questions need to be asked of every person in the sample, ideally in the same order and in the same way from person to person. However, this is not always possible, and differences in questioning may produce a certain measure of variance in the results. Whether or not a specific set of questions is put to every person in the sample in the same way is of minor importance compared to the question, Are the questions asked, the ones that need to be asked? The answer depends upon the problem under investigation. The questions have to be appropriate to the problem under study or they will not elucidate the working hypothesis of the study. Thus, all questions should be pretested for their clarity and appropriateness before they are used in the study.

Many studies are of such magnitude as to require the services of interviewers. When interviewers are used, the study director must be sure they are thoroughly familiar with the protocol of the study. They need to be trained so that they will ask the questions and record the answers in appropriate ways. Reliability in field procedures can only be achieved by careful training of interviewers and continued supervision. Then too, the work of each interviewer needs to be tested for reliability by retake interviews made by the supervisor or some other staff person. Training, supervision, and rechecks will indicate whether the interviewer recorded the response correctly, or whether he allowed his own blind spots, motivations, predilections, and idiosyncrasies of interpretation to enter into the record. This is a difficult problem to control. To obviate or minimize these sources of error, I stress to interviewers the necessity to record the exact response, or in previously categorized questions, to check the category the respondent selects.

What does the sociologist do with the collected data? There is no simple answer. What is done depends upon the nature of the investigation. In sample studies, the sociologist generally uses statistical technics. But he faces definite limitations in applying statistical formulae to social data, because most statistical procedures have been developed for metric data, that is, data of equal intervals. The sociologist is handicapped by the paucity of nonparametric tests, that is, statistical tests that do not make assumptions of equal intervals within a matrix. Some have been developed, but many more are required. Quantitative analysis of social and cultural data is restricted severely by the nonavailability of suitable statistical technics. This area needs development before we can cope fully with the question of validity.

With these limitations facing him, how does the sociologist determine validity? Like other scientists, he turns to the theory and method of probability for his standard. In short, he relies upon tests of significance; e.g., the probability, expressed in percentage form, that a given result would occur by chance, one time in 20, 100, or 1,000. The quantitatively oriented sociologist asks: Is the relationship between independent and dependent variables significant? The level of significance is stated; and on the basis of it, the hypothesis under investigation is judged to be tenable or untenable.

To summarize, although the sociologist follows the funded canons of the scientific method, he is handicapped in the determination of validity by the very material with which he works; namely, human beings operating within social systems.

I will give an illustration of what I have in mind. It would be very naïve to think that everyone drawn in a sample is eager to be interviewed, wants to answer questions, and is going to give reliable and valid answers. This problem is particularly acute in the field of mental illness. It would be extremely difficult, I am convinced, to make a probability sample study of the distribution of various types of psychiatric reactions in a population. It has never been done, and I am not sure it is going to be done in the immediate future.

We have not solved the problem of the intervening social variable, namely, that people are afraid of mental illness and psychiatrists. There are good and sufficient reasons why they should be; but until we can overcome this fear, we are going to experience extreme difficulty in interviewing a representative sample with enough depth to enable us to make a valid estimate of the prevalence of mental illness in a defined population.

GRINKER: The problems in the analysis of data seem to be somewhat similar for the sociologist and the psychodynamic psychiatrist who wishes to include the larger field. Probability statements with relationship between independent and dependent variables were mentioned. How many variables can be covered at the same time in such statements?

HOLLINGSHEAD: Ordinarily two variables can be dealt with at a time, but four, five, or even six variables can be controlled by holding constant selected factors. For instance, psychiatric diagnosis, age, sex, race, religion, and size of the family can be held constant. Six are about as many variables as can be held constant statistically in trying to study the relationship between an assumed independent variable and an observed dependent behavior, because so many cases are lost by the addition of variables to the control procedure.

GRINKER: Those items that are being held constant are by their very nature constant. They do not have to be held.

HOLLINGSHEAD: They have to be isolated so as to yield homogeneity and to determine whether or not a particular variable is confounding an apparent relationship between the assumed independent and dependent variables.

GRINKER: They are constant and are used as constants. But suppose you had to work with a number of variables that could not be held constant and were moving, or suppose there were changes in the social structure, how would you deal with them?

HOLLINGSHEAD: Dr. Grinker has posed a difficult question, because not all dimensions of a social structure change, and the changing dimensions may not be changing at the same rate. One aspect of the problem is to isolate the changing variables from the stable ones. Then those variables that are changing slowly need to be isolated from those that are changing rapidly. In addition, we face the question: What factors are conditioning the changes, as well as the stability? What interactional variables are at work? The investigator must make assumptions, and he must postulate the effects of some variables on others. If he is able to control his variables experimentally, observationally, or statistically, he may solve the problem posed; but in most sociological research this is impossible with the methods now available to the investigator.

SPIEGEL: The distinction between the manifest and latent structure in the social process is a highly important point. In our studies of families and their impact upon the development of the individual, we found this to be a continually intriguing factor and also a methodological problem. Both the manifest and latent structures and functions are found at many different levels in the social system. This phenomenon seems to have a fascinating parallel in the psychiatrist's observations. For example, during an interview the common statement that the Irish family would make about itself had to do with the independence and initiative of the Irish. It would be expressed in such formulations as, "You can't push the Irishman around." We were interviewing high school boys who were very bright, who were in upper IQ levels in their class, but who had decided not to go to college. My interest was in the motivation of the boy. But I was collaborating with social scientists who were studying the impact of the culture and neighborhood upon the family with respect to this decision. The statement was frequently made by the family, "We don't try to tell our boy what to do. He has to make up his mind himself."

Actually, when one examined the way the family was operating, this hands-off policy did not take place at all. The boy was continually being defined by the parents in such a way that he had very little freedom of choice. He was told that he was lazy, or he was not suited to go to college, or he had no particular intellectual propensity. In many different ways the unwitting, the unconscious proscription of the boy by the parents was of such a nature that he would have had to have had a tremendous amount of emotional strength to be able to overcome this type of identification on the part of his parents. So actually the way the Irish family operated was to constrict the individual greatly. There are parallels to this at levels of national structure. We like to think, for example, that we are all very independent, that democracy means the freedom of the individual; but we all know that when we get below this manifest and apparent level of behavior, we have great problems with respect to conformity.

In such an institution as a hospital can be found exactly the same divergence between the manifest and assumed principles on which the hospital asserts that it is operating and the way that it really functions. It is common knowledge that when a person comes to a new institution, he really has to learn the ropes. Learning the ropes means that he has to learn the latent structure because the manifest structure takes him only so far.

This contrast between manifest and latent structure is a methodological problem in social science, for the social structure does not impinge in a straightforward way upon the individual. It is one of the issues at stake when the validity of interview material is under consideration. It is also a methodological problem to anyone interested in the disturbed behavior of the individual, because a disordered person reports to a large extent what the manifest social structure is and has great difficulty in reporting latent social structure, which is nevertheless influencing him.

HOLLINGSHEAD: Dr. Spiegel's point is well taken. Sociologists struggle with it constantly in their studies of social behavior. Manifest and latent structure proliferate throughout society. Furthermore, as Dr. Spiegel pointed out, many of the problems the psychiatrist encounters in handling his data also abound in social science. Lazarsfeld at Columbia has developed a quantitative method, a model of calculus, to measure relationships between the manifest and the latent dimension of social structures.

ALEXANDER: In ordinary language it is what we call hypocrisy.

HOLLINGSHEAD: It is what is publicly professed and privately practiced.

SPIEGEL: More unconscious than conscious hypocrisy.

SCOTT: In the use of interviews or questionnaires in the study of human behavior, we have to consider both what people say they do and what they actually do. If an investigator wants to find out what people actually do, their replies to questions may give him a rough and inaccurate answer. However, the questionnaire or the interview method would seem to be a sound and valid way to ascertain what people think they ought to do. It is an excellent measure of verbal culture.

HOLLINGSHEAD: I take a skeptical view of the questionnaire technic because it seldom yields representative data, but what is more important in the present discussion, there is no way to get at latent structure material from questionnaires. Contrastingly, in the interview situation, if the interviewer is perceptive, he can often obtain simultaneously the latent with the manifest structural material. Also, if the interview is structured with a protocol of questions, and the respondent is under the impression that the interview is over, but the interviewer continues the interview in an unstructured way, then the interviewer can gather data on crucial points about the latent social structure. Inasmuch as the questions during this period are not prestructured, the data from them are not as precise as those from the formal protocol. However, if the interviewers are trained to follow this procedure systematically, it will reveal how much parallelism there is between manifest and latent material.

METTLER: Dr. Grinker, was your question about fluctuating variables with specific regard to the sociologic situation or were you also interested in it with regard to biological data?

GRINKER: I wanted information in general.

METTLER: For biological data there is now available a method for handling any number of variables which change continually. In order to arrive at an estimate of variation, the data are fed into a remote derivative machine and a factor is obtained. The values for a variety of functions, such as muscle tension, blood pressure, respiration, can be introduced in the machine and the desired answer is produced. It is applicable to biological data.

HOLLINGSHEAD: There is no such machine to process social data.

WITTKOWER: To my mind one point indicates a difference in outlook between the sociologist and the psychoanalyst. The sociologist is descriptive in his approach; the analyst thinks in terms of motivation. One describes what he sees; the other person asks himself, why. This difference creates an obstacle. The two have difficulties in communication with each other because they speak to each other from different levels.

Furthermore, the sociologist is predominantly observation-minded; whereas the psychiatrist, as a doctor, is action-minded. In our project the sociologist says, "Under no circumstances must you disturb the experiment by taking action." But the experimental subjects want something in return for their participation. They give us something; so they say, "Give us something in return." The group of sociologists with whom we work look rather disdainfully on any social engineering; whereas we psychiatrists are apt to think in terms of therapy, change, and improvement.

HOLLINGSHEAD: The sociologist is oriented descriptively. There was a period in the development of sociology when he was dynamically philosophical; he thought he had a frame of reference that explained the dynamics of history. That was the social evolutionary approach of seventy-five years ago. When a new generation of more scientifically oriented men matured, the ideal constructs tumbled; hence, the sociologist of today leans over backwards to be descriptive and empirical.

Difficulties in communication between the sociologist and the psychoanalyst are a continuous source of friction in interdisciplinary discussion, but this can be overcome if representatives of each discipline respect the viewpoints of their particular frames of reference, and then take enough time to work through their communication and motivational problems. By this process each is going to be modified somewhat in his point of view; the psychoanalyst will have become oriented more toward description, and the sociologist more toward motivation. Ultimately they will reach a point where they find themselves communicating with one another. If the sociologist is to continue to be a fruitful member of an interdisciplinary group cooperating with psychiatrists, psychologists, and organicists, he will have to learn more about the theory and methods of these disciplines; but for the interaction to be a success, the other disciplines must also seriously attempt to learn sociology. In brief, all members of an interdisciplinary team need mutual education.

When the sociologist admonishes the psychiatrist not to give anything in return to patients in the study group because it disturbs the experiment, he is taking a puristic position. Theoretically the sociologist has justification for his stand; but practically he disturbs the situation by his study. Some psychiatrists believe they cannot carry on a study of patients in a clinic without giving them service. Parenthetically, I may say that in interviewing there is a current practice to which I do not subscribe, that of giving something in return, namely, paying informants. In my opinion it is not necessary to pay them. When there is a monetary consideration, the informant may fashion material for the interview.

WITTKOWER: By and large, the psychiatrist can carry out an experiment without giving service. But specific situations may arise where the mother says, "I realize that there is something wrong in this family. What should we do about it?" What should the psychiatrist do?

HOLLINGSHEAD: When a mother reaches the point of realizing that something is wrong, that is part of the reality situation at that time in that family. Something should be done about it.

WITTKOWER: Who should do it?

HOLLINGSHEAD: It would be preferable to have a psychiatrist unassociated with the study provide the service rather than to assign a member of the research team to it.

BINGER: Does not the process of interview disturb the situation and in that sense is not the sociologist in the same category as the psychiatrist?

HOLLINGSHEAD: Yes, but I do not know the solution. The effect of the participant-observer on a situation may be minimized by having him live with the situation being studied. He may develop a role that is accepted in the situation. All the while, he is making observations. But this procedure has a certain element of artificiality associated with it. For if the participant-observer is engaged in research full time in a community, for example, he has to establish the role of a researcher there. The community, in turn, has to accept the role which the researcher has set for himself, and it has to accept the researcher personally in that role. After a short period of time, members of a community tend to forget that the participant-observer is a researcher and look upon him as a person, a fellow citizen, and one of them. This approach yields data that are not too heavily distorted.

However, the role of a social researcher is not a part of the established social structure in an American or Canadian community. The researcher, in his efforts to play a role acceptable to the members of a community, may give service to people without being aware of what he is doing. Every community has many needs in public service, and community leaders are always looking for persons who are able and willing to help share the burden. The researcher may participate in community life in an accepted way by assuming some of these responsibilities. However, the researcher soon is consuming a large amount of his time in community affairs. Furthermore, if he has a sympathetic ear for persons in difficulty, he may expend much time listening to their stories. In the process he may obtain valuable information on social processes in the community; but he gains it at a tremendous cost in time, and biases are built into what he receives. In short, although he is not paying the members of the community for their time, and he is not giving them recognized psychiatric service, he is nevertheless paying his way in the community by the service he gives.

WHITEHORN: The interchange focused rather sharply on money as an incentive, but as the discussion went on, other incentives were recognized. One of them obviously operative in the interview situation of a sociologist has to do with what value the informant attributes to the attention given by the interviewer. In the significance of the information which the interview yields, this is a consideration which clinically often outweighs the supposedly advantageous position of the doctor in his usual role. Establishing empathy with the patient by being a person interested in him seems to elicit more significant information than appearing in the obvious role of the physician who is going to help him get over his aches and pains.

HOLLINGSHEAD: It is well known to perceptive field workers that when they play a participant-observer role, certain types of individuals will devote much time to them and give them valuable information about the community, their families, friends, enemies, and themselves. These subjects may be in need of psychotherapy and may unconsciously use the participant-observer for this purpose. This is why I advise a combination of participant-observation and sampling in a study. If a random sample, or other type of sampling, is not being used, it is very likely that masses of depth data will be obtained from a relatively few people who may not be representative of the social life in the community.

Empathy is of extreme importance in conducting interviews with individuals. If I may use a metaphor, the interviewer can tune his personality to certain individuals in the situation, or they will tune to him; as a consequence, he can communicate with them better than he can with others. This may create biases in the choice of people who give data and in the kind of data obtained.

WHITEHORN: You have already pointed out that if the interviewer is perceptive, he can sense and distinguish the latent structure as contrasted with the manifest structure of the social situation. If he is not perceptive, the distinction may not be made. This introduces the concept of the perceptivity of the interviewer.

HOLLINGSHEAD: The perceptivity of some interviewers comes out best in repeated interviews with the same respondent by different interviewers. For example, let us assume that five interviews, which involve data on the manifest and latent dimensions of a social structure, are held with a person over a period of a year by five different interviewers. The first interviewer, A, gathers his data and makes his assessment of points that indicate latent structure. Interviewer B, who may be socially different from interviewer A, but close culturally to the respondent, may elicit in his interaction with the respondent many latent factors not evoked or recognized by interviewer A. Subliminal cues may facilitate communication between interviewer B and the respondent. An unverbalized "empathetic" state may unite interviewer B and the respondent; hence, he will obtain information not given to interviewer A. Moreover, A may not have perceived latent factors if they were present. Interviewers C and D also may not make any observations about the latent structure pertinent to the situation; but interviewer E, who is of the same social and cultural group as interviewer B and the respondent, may gather the same types of data as interviewer B, and interpret them as B does. An explanation of such similarities and differences appears to lie in the background of experiences interviewer B and interviewer E share with the respondent. Insofar as the manifest statement of the situation is concerned, all interviewers may have obtained essentially the same data. But interviewers B and E detected nuances essential in understanding the latent structure.

WHITEHORN: A similar situation very frequently occurs when two clinical clerks work with a patient; quite different stories of his illness come out. It then becomes necessary to try to ascertain probable correctness. How do you overcome or compensate for the variable of different interviewers?

HOLLINGSHEAD: The collection of data on a manifest structure is relatively objective and not too difficult. When the latent dimensions of a social structure are studied, the problem becomes complex; for a sensi-tive, perceptive interviewer, who is very effective in one type of social situation, may fail miserably in the one at hand. The researcher needs to recognize this problem, and to attempt to overcome it by matching his interviewer to the reality of the situation he is studying. The most effective interviewer is a person who is most like his respondents, but still a good interviewer. That is, he is professionaly competent, while he is also a particular social type.

An interesting observation concerning psychiatrists has come out of one of our studies. If a psychiatrist is upward mobile, a second- or third-generation American, and he is given freedom of choice of patients in a clinic, he selects patients who are also upward mobile, second- or third-generation Americans, and are troubled by their social mobility and cultural marginality. Obviously empathy is in operation. The tentative evidence indicates that such psychiatrists are more successful in their therapy with patients who are socially and culturally similar to themselves than they are with patients who are culturally divergent.

GERARD: In your operations in a community, to what extent do you play the role of a medicine man? Does this create hostility because you are infringing upon another person's prerogatives or propensities?

HOLLINGSHEAD: I suspect your metaphor has relevancy, particularly in communities of three to ten thousand population. In a small community, the local physicians are practically always general practitioners. Usually they are so busy that they do not have the time to listen to persons who need to unburden their troubles to a sympathetic ear. If the inhabitants realize that the researcher is willing to be a listener, they are encouraged to talk; and if they think they can tell the researcher what is troubling them and it will not be passed on, and if they are not told that the researcher is recording what they are unburdening, he can obtain the most intimate types of material. The speakers will enter into free association; the researcher may even probe for material in the latent structure. When this occurs, the researcher may well be playing the role of medicine man.

This aspect of community research does not generate hostility in the local physicians; rather, they may be happy to be relieved of the burdens of a few petulant patients. By the field worker's listening too long to some people, hostility is generated in those who want to receive his time and attention. The field worker may infringe on the role of the customary confidant, because the latter may feel threatened by the attention the interviewer is giving to his friends.

ALEXANDER: You mentioned that traditionally the sociologist has been descriptively oriented. You also commented on the early theoretical formulations which later collapsed. That, of course, happens in the history of every science. Further, you described how the sociologist carries on his observations. In science it is always found that even if theories collapse, new theories are built because observations without hypotheses, whether good or bad, ultimately become meaningless. Sociology appears to have an abundance of data. It is always theory which puts them together. If the theory does not fit the data, it must be modified.

Are there any modern substitutes for the earlier theorists? Is there a sociodynamic theory which imparts sense and meaning to the sociologist's detailed observations? What do his data mean from the viewpoint of sociodynamics? To be more specific, I have been impressed by Kluckhohn's reference to the functional theory which appears to be an immediate and real advance in the interpretation of ethnic observations. His proposition is that the functionalist considers that social institutions develop as adaptations to a general structure of society, which is responsible for what Ruth Benedict called the "ethos" of the society. Thus, social institutions are an adaptive mechanism to a total situation, just as character trends are in an individual. Even if the sociologist does not have a grandiose theory, what kind of theoretical guide does he have today in making his observations?

HOLLINGSHEAD: The interplay between theory and observable facts in sociology is the same as it is in other sciences. All the sciences have grown out of man's long quest to understand and control the world he experiences. In this process some men have used their imaginations to develop "explanations" of how one phenomenon or event is linked with another. These "explanations" are verbalized, systematized, and related one to another. The process of explaining or understanding is theory. The phenomena explained are the facts.

Sociology, like other sciences, in its early history was characterized by too much theorizing. Comprehensive theories were formulated by such men as Auguste Comte and Lester F. Ward. The pioneer sociologists were system-makers in the philosophical tradition. To them, the idea was the primary consideration. Facts were used merely to illustrate broad, loosely formulated concepts. The next generation attempted to test some of the system-makers' broad generalizations in a disciplined way; and the systems collapsed, for the most part. This phase of sociological development was followed by a generation concerned mainly with fact-gathering rather than the rebuilding of the theoretical side of sociology. Thus, sociology may be criticized for describing observable phenomena, and for ignoring theory. However, the critics should be aware that these charges are contradictory, and they are applicable only to particular phases of the history of sociology.

With these preliminary remarks I will try to answer Dr. Alexander's first question, "Are there modern substitutes for the earlier theorists?" The answer to this question is difficult, because the interests of sociological theorists have shifted in the last thirty years from the formulation of comprehensive "theories" to "explain" both the structure and dynamics of all human societies, to the development of limited theories tested by empirical research in some delimited area of the sociocultural whole.

Pitirim Sorokin is an outstanding example of a distinguished sociologist who has developed an all-inclusive general theory of social and cultural dynamics in the grand tradition of the late nineteenth century Talcott Parsons is representative of a different kind of theorist. Parsons is concerned with the formulation of a general theory of the properties of social systems. He relies heavily upon logic and introspective insight for his understanding of the properties of the social system. He views social phenomena from the perspective of the actor. Parsons' formulations are logically developed, but a heavy emphasis is placed upon the classification of the parts of the social system as he perceives it. Less attention is given to the interplay between the actors and the system in which the actors play their roles. Parsons has been criticized because he has not tested his theory either in whole or in part with empirical data. Some critics have charged that his theory is stated in such a way that his propositions cannot be tested empirically. Parsons has made a distinct contribution to the development of sociology. His emphasis upon theory came at a time when sociology was snarled in a plethora of "facts"; his work has given our thinking a different focus in a desirable direction.

The second question Dr. Alexander asked was: "Is there a sociodynamic theory which imparts sense and meaning to the sociologist's detailed observations?" Sociologists are convinced they do have a sociocultural theory to explain their observations. Briefly, most sociologists are interested in the formulation of a limited theory that will help them understand the complexities and contradictions they observe in the behavior of individuals and groups in a society.

From my viewpoint, a meaningful sociodynamic theory needs to consider three principles. These may be stated briefly as follows:

1. Social behavior is learned by individuals through their interaction, or association with other members of their society.

2. The content of what individuals learn is provided by their society's culture.

3. What individuals learn is determined by participation in a society's culture.

These three principles are interdependent, and any sociodynamic theory needs to build upon them. They help the sociologist explain uniformities, as well as differences, in social behavior. Thus, to understand the dynamics of social behavior, we need to (a) analyze the structure of a society's culture, and (b) study very carefully the way an individual participates in his society. Detailed knowledge of the participation process is crucial to an understanding of the dynamics of social behavior, because it is in the participation process that individuals learn what they may, may not, can, or cannot do within the effective social structure that impinges upon them. It is here that meaning and motive become associated with social acts and social structures.

WHITEHORN: Your earlier reference to roles implied a limited concept with hypothetical and theoretical implications that there is some function which a person performs, more or less recognized by him or by others or both, to which you apply the term "role." This would appear to be an example of an *ad hoc* hypothesis which is used in sociological operations.

HOLLINGSHEAD: Role is a recognized concept in sociology. It may be applied to a particular social situation, and in this sense it may be an *ad hoc* hypothesis. However, it is a general concept used by theorists to explain a particular kind of social behavior in a defined social structure. The structures which interest the sociologist are made by men as members of society. That is, they are cultural in origin and social in function. Mental hospitals are a familiar example of a type of social institution. They are characterized by a structure; and definite kinds of social roles are played by the persons who are connected with them. For example, the psychiatrist has a role in the social structure of the mental hospital. In playing his professional role, he performs a definite function in the maintenance of the institution's social structure. The sociologist is interested in roles because they operate as bridges between structures and functions in social processes. The way that a role is played may determine how the function is performed.

WHITEHORN: In my experience it seems to be an extremely important matter to gain understanding of a patient's conception of his roles. How does he behave with others in the family? What is the general expectation of him? How does he manage to deviate from it?

HOLLINGSHEAD: A role is a social structure with definite meanings for individuals, whether they are in the family or functioning in some other institution. Role may be defined as the way society structures the activities expected of an individual who performs particular functions. For instance, the role defined for a surgeon is determined both by the structuring of medical education, and the values and expectancies associated with the function which the surgeon performs. The surgeon's role is circumscribed by an elaborate subculture which includes, among other things, norms of professional conduct, the training he receives, his expectancies of his patient, and what the patient's family expects of the surgeon when he performs an operation. Role involves action, and expectancies of action, as well as rewards or punishments for actions taken in the performance of the functions ascribed to the role.

JASPER: Are there any groups who are studying the social problem which concerns all of us perhaps more than any other, the structure of national societies and their conflicts?

HOLLINGSHEAD: A number of cooperative interdisciplinary studies on the subject are being carried on by social psychologists, sociologists, social anthropologists, political scientists, and psychiatrists. The Russian Research Center at Harvard and the Institute of International Politics at Princeton are conducting such research.

SPIEGEL: Would Professor Hollingshead comment on the current research on behavior in the small group? A cursory review of it indicates that perhaps something of benefit to mental ill health will be derived from it. Hospitals function mainly on the basis of small groups: small teams on the ward and in occupational therapy. How could we think of this area as being of significance to our concern with mental disorder?

HOLLINGSHEAD: Systematic study of social interaction, social roles, and the structuring of social relations in small groups is one of the most promising postwar developments in social science research. The study of social interaction in small groups is particularly pertinent in the mental health field because personality development is found largely in the family. The family is an institutionalized small group, with rather definite manifest and latent structures, and well-structured roles for adults and children. However, little of the small-group research is focused on the family. Much of the current research in this area is concerned with game theory in *ad hoc* groups, the solution of an artificial problem of interest to the investigator, or how juries reach decisions. These studies are worthwhile, but they are not focused on the study of personality development in the continuing, natural small group of paramount importance, the family.

Research on behavior in the small group may contribute to the understanding of the psychotherapeutic process. Clearly the therapeutic aspects of psychoanalysis is a group product because it involves two human beings sharing and interacting. It is tutorial education.

There is a need for carefully defined studies of the therapeutic process by persons competent in the analysis of small-group interactions. Such studies might investigate the psychoanalytic process in a small series of representative cases. The dialogue of the analysis from the beginning to the terminal interview might be recorded; motion pictures might be taken at the same time; and the systematic observation of the psychoanalyst and the patient through one-way windows might be arranged. Some studies should throw new light upon the therapy process. Psychoanalysis and other psychotherapeutic procedures need to be carefully studied both for purposes of validation of their theoretical principles, and for their effects on patients.

chapter *31*

The Role of the Basic Scientist in Multidisciplinary Research

WHITEHORN: In many areas of medicine it has become almost routine practice to examine a clinical situation, to consider the hypotheses that seem pertinent to it, and to abstract from them a theoretical problem which can be attacked at the laboratory level. To some extent this has been occurring in psychiatry, too. Both human and animal experimentation has been oriented toward the problems related to psychiatry. It would be appropriate to consider the assumptions and modes of operation in animal experimentation.

SCOTT: It is obvious that much research in psychiatry will perforce have to be done with animals. There are limitations to research on human beings. Deliberately to induce a mental disorder in a normal human subject is a matter not to be undertaken without serious consideration and adequate safeguards. To run the risk of aggravating an existing disturbance in a patient likewise gives us pause; for his welfare must be our first concern. In animal research the investigator is not so limited. He can conduct more drastic experiments, and derive information which he might not otherwise obtain. In addition, he should carry out all legitimate studies that are desirable, proper, and permissible on human beings because the results from them will be more meaningful and valid than those from animals.

Mental health seems to pose fundamentally a social problem. However, it embraces many scientific disciplines which are not ordinarily labeled as social. These disciplines range from genetics and biochemistry to biology, and each of them has something different to contribute. I do not believe that biology, for instance, will give the complete, final solution by itself, but it has its own particular and significant contribution.

I should like to list a number of topics for research in which the use of human beings as subjects would be considered difficult, unfeasible, or fruitless, but in which the use of animals would be practicable and promising. I have already mentioned genetic differences. Research on this point could be done in part on human beings but much better on animals because pure stocks could be used.

Clinicians frequently report studies in which conditions were almost perfectly controlled, yet a few subjects reacted differently than all others. Presumably the difference is caused by some genetic or constitutional factor. However, with most human material this explanation remains only a hypothesis. There is still a need for critical and decisive experiments on animals which will show that one genetic variety of animal is more susceptible to a particular stress than is another. In my opinion this has not as yet been demonstrated.

Rival hypotheses on the causation of

mental disorders could be tested on animals. Psychiatrists have sometimes assumed that a physiological upset, a trauma or shock unrelated to learning, which occurs early in life is the possible origin of later disturbance. An alternative explanation is provided by learning theory, i.e., that the individual learned from this experience.

Experimentation on the physiological causes of various types of behavior could also be conducted with animals. This, of course, is basic to the studies of motivation in psychiatry. The psychodynamicists tend to mention only a few types of motivation, usually fear or sex. On the other hand, the type of motivation which has been most thoroughly studied physiologically and psychologically is that which lies behind eating behavior. Perhaps this point is not too important in psychiatric research. Still, there must be many types of motivation which are significant for the mental health of man.

SPIEGEL: Therese Benedek conducted a study on alterations in attitudes of mothers toward their children. She attempted to correlate the psychodynamic situation with the physiological status.

SCOTT: A type of behavior observed quite widely in animals is the tendency for one to do what the other does. This "allelo-mimetic behavior" is characteristic of sheep, flocks of birds, most primates, and of human beings. Its particular type of physiology and the motivation underlying it have been virtually unstudied.

One promising field of research at the present time is that of investigatory behavior, or exploratory drive as some psychologists call it. Harlow has found that monkeys will work a long time just for the privilege of looking out a little window. For these primates, curiosity is an important source of motivation. Extensive study of it may have been previously neglected because it may not have seemed important in clinical experience. But prejudgments can be wrong. An accumulation of background information on any subject may later prove valuable.

Another area of research in which experiments on animals would be productive is that of the effects of early experience, especially of differential experience. This area includes the problem of early learning. When does an animal begin to learn and how well does he learn? In our studies of the development of a dog, we found that no real learning or conditioning occurred until approximately three weeks after birth. That means that the animal's experience prior to that time has a very different effect than later experience. This is not characteristic of all animals. But it does raise the question whether the human infant at birth and shortly after can learn as well as an adult, whether this faculty develops suddenly at some later date, or whether it develops gradually.

SPIEGEL: Do you mean that if a puppy is removed from its mother before it is three weeks old, the separation will not make any difference to its subsequent development?

SCOTT: If a puppy is removed from its mother and is then put back with its mother before it is three weeks old, the separation will not make any difference in later development. Of course, if it is taken away from its mother and never brought back, its development will be affected because it will have an entirely different environment later in life.

HOLLINGSHEAD: The puppy does not start to learn until it is three weeks old?

SCOTT: That is exactly the point. It is based on two lines of evidence. The first is observational: the puppy placed in a situation to which it might adapt, behaves the same way each time; it does not adapt to the situation according to previous experience. The second is from studies on conditioning: until the puppy is approximately three weeks of age, permanent conditioning cannot be obtained.

LIDDELL: We have obtained conditioning in a lamb four hours old. Of course, it is a different species.

SCOTT: Examination of the brains of puppies reveals that the myelination correlates with the observations on behavior. Electroencephalographic records of the puppies show very little activity up to about three weeks of age. After that point, differentiation between sleeping and waking states appears. This occurs simultaneously with the first appearance of conditioning.

All of these observations raise a question about human development. Maybe human beings, like lambs, learn at birth. Maybe, on the other hand, like dogs, they learn later. The evidence on the human infant is quite contradictory. The studies of Spitz would indicate that the human infant learns to discriminate visually at a rather late age, at five or six months. Other studies, however, would indicate that the infant can be conditioned before it is born. Fundamental to understanding the effects of early experience is the question, When does the human infant start to learn and how well can he learn at different ages?

Indeed, too little is known about the physiology of the learning process. This is a gap in our knowledge which animal experimentation could help to fill. The majority of studies on learning have been based upon eating behavior, and generalizations from them have been extended to include all behavior. But when an animal is put in situations other than eating, different results are obtained. For example, in a conditioning experiment Dr. Solomon taught dogs to jump at the sound of a buzzer by giving them an electric shock. He found that he had to give the shock only once or twice; then the dogs would react indefinitely to the buzzer although the primary or reinforcing stimulus was never repeated. This result contrasts with that of the usual experiment in which a response is rewarded or reinforced with food. If the food reward is discontinued, the animal soon quits and the response is extinguished.

In an experiment with fighting mice, we found that animals which were badly defeated would not fight back. When we tried to train them to fight, they showed two trends in behavior. The reflex behavior that they had learned in jumping away from other mice disappeared rather rapidly. But the avoidance behavior continued over a very long period of weeks and even months without the animal's having been defeated again. The learning process differs with the kind of behavior.

Hale, at Pennsylvania State College, has used sex behavior in experiments on motivation. He found that a bull presented with a teaser cow would repeatedly mount for about three or four hours. When Hale switched the stimulus object by introducing new cows, the bull kept mounting intermittently over a stretch of twelve or thirteen hours, long after all semen was exhausted. At this point the investigator got tired and stopped the experiment. This kind of motivation is different from that in other types of behavior. It may also be quite different in bulls from what it is in primates.

Socialization in animals, which I think is closely related to identification and therefore to psychoanalysis, is another topic for animal experimentation. Animals seem to have some mechanism by which they learn to accept the individuals with which they grew up and to reject individuals in other species which are strange to them.

Animal experimentation can also be useful in the study of symptomatology. This topic raises the questions: What symptoms are related to particular situations? Can certain kinds of abnormal behavior be repeatedly produced under certain conditions? The use of animals in such a study is especially suitable because the predisposing situation can be closely controlled.

WHITEHORN: I should like to explore the implications of your views. The process of learning in animals has obvious clinical implications since people apparently learn their symptoms and also go through a process of unlearning or learning something else. This is a concept which you believe links the two fields?

SCOTT: Learning is surely involved in functional neuroses.

WHITEHORN: A role seems to be something that is learned. One learns to perform certain functions. Dr. Gantt has a dog which is of interest in this connection. When Dr. Gantt opens the cage, the dog comes out, takes three steps to the right, turns around, walks about ten feet down a corridor, enters a room, and becomes immobile. He remains immobile sometimes for as long as thirty minutes, until Dr. Gantt inserts a hypodermic needle in him, whereupon he becomes a lively dog, chases around, and has a good time. I do not know whether this is a role which the dog is enacting in the sense that he has learned it. Is it just a series of motor mechanisms which he has learned? When animals are trained, we do not ordinarily think of them as enacting roles. But conceivably there may be an element of role-performance in it. We do have experimental monkey colonies where a hierarchical system is developed, which seems to be a matter of roles. This we know from Roswold's work at Yale, that lobotomy or surgical destruction of parts of the brain interrupts this playing of roles; it may not show otherwise in the behavior of the animal. It would appear that if one can bring about role behavior in animals and then study the modes for its distortion, he might have something more nearly approximating human mental disorders.

SCOTT: It is only fair to say that animal experiments also have their limitations. Clinical reports on human mental disorders indicate that they are the product of a social situation. Most of the animal experiments so far have been conducted in such a way that it is very difficult to ascertain the actual social implications.

For instance, when Pavlov taught dogs to respond first to a circle and then to a square, and then kept squaring the circle and rounding the square until the dogs could not tell the difference, they became neurotic. It is very difficult to see the social parallel in that study, except that the dogs might be regarded as being placed in a situation comparable to that of a child with a parent who is expecting him to do more than he can do.

WHITEHORN: There are data on the differential behavior of the dog toward the person. There is that type of evidence.

LIDDELL: The evidence is fully corroborated.

SCOTT: Animal studies can be connected with the social situation in terms of social relationships, by which is meant regular and repeatable behavior between two individuals. When two animals meet each other for the first time, they tend to react to each other. For a time their behavior is quite variable, but they eventually come to an adjustment. Then they form the habit of reacting to each other in a particular way and so develop a stable social relationship. Perhaps the early stage of this relationship in which mutual adjustments are made corresponds to what has been called a transaction.

GRINKER: We are all well aware that for many reasons there is a limit to the research that can be done with human beings. Hence, I appreciate the importance of suggesting topics for study in animals in the laboratory to further our knowledge of mental illness. In truth, the individual working in the laboratory develops a huge body of data that are possibly significant for man. The problem, however, is the transcription of observations made in the animals into concepts and methods that are valid in man. More than that, there is a possibility that the psychiatrist who develops a large body of empirical knowledge from his clinical sessions with patients can communicate to the laboratorian the problems of significance that are possibly open to attack in the laboratory. This need not be multidisciplinary or cooperative research. It requires, however, a communication of the central problems.

So many of the activities going on in the laboratory and the clinic have been independent of each other; therefore communication of significance is missing. Those laboratories which have been set up in psychiatric institutes have been too often without connection or contact with the clinic. Oppositely, only with reluctance have the clinicians gone into the laboratory to converse with the animal experimenter who in his way has been attempting to further knowledge about man. This segregation has been costly; for information relayed back and forth, and interaction are extraordinarily valuable. However, one word of caution: the direct translation of results from animal to man must be avoided unless there is a valid, empirical evidence from clinical sources.

SCOTT: The aim and hope of animal research is to obtain information on a sufficient variety of animals with different kinds of behavior so that general biological laws may be formulated, which may hold for human beings. Thus, the animal experimenter and clinician may furnish each other with facts and ideas. But it is always difficult to draw an exact conclusion from an animal and apply it to human data because what is true of animals is not necessarily true of human beings.

METTLER: There are a number of reasons for the present unsatisfactory communication between disciplines in the world of medicine and science. One arises from the practical exigencies of living. Programs are prepared for scientific meetings with foremost authorities as speakers, yet audiences are often embarrassingly small. Dwindling attendance at medical and scientific meetings is said to be both common and nationwide. It is a reflection of the times. Society is so highly organized with a plethora of meetings, many of them highly specialized in nature and often requiring attendance, that in this intense competition the meetings which are designed for their broadening influence and depend on voluntary attendance suffer in attracting an audience. Clinicians and scientists alike have so many commitments, some of them compulsory, that little time is left for voluntary quest of knowledge in the lecture hall. It is therefore very difficult to have scientists from different disciplines avail themselves of an opportunity to exchange views.

In view of the decline in attendance at meetings, a scientist such as an organicist might be expected to put down his thoughts and suggestions for publication for the benefit of those in other disciplines. But truth to tell he may be gun-shy. Recently Dr. Whitehorn directed a question very pointedly at me.

WHITEHORN: A physiologist experimenting on a purely physiological problem greeted me with the comment that we are working in the same field. Actually he meant it as a compliment. He envisioned that I was a scientific worker and that we shared the scientific approach. At that time it startled me that he would equate the experimental and the clinical and feel, therefore, a member of a partnership by virtue of the practical effects that might flow from experimental work. I suppose that every scientist imbued with curiosity needs support at times for the feeling of significance of his work, and gains satis-faction and stimulation by conceiving of the consequences that might ensue from it.

METTLER: Dr. Whitehorn asked me whether I thought this attitude was typical of physiologists. That is a delicate question. In order to conduct research the investigator has to submit applications for financial support of the project. There is always a question on the application blank which reads, "What practical relationship does this project have to medicine or public health?" This puts the applicant in a dilemma. By one course, he is tempted to intellectual dishonesty. If he is a geneticist studying chromosomes, for example, he may toy with the idea of saying that he is working on cancer. The alternative course is only less uninviting. Actually the average basic scientist is interested in basic science per se. He is glad to cooperate and share his knowledge with scientists in other fields; but he is so constituted as to be interested primarily in fundamental work, not in its application. He believes that when he says that he is interested in the broad application of his experimental results, he is stepping out of his field and is liable to be tripped. Therefore he becomes exceedingly cautious.

Any organicist could make a catalogue of 1,000 items which he believes have relationship to mental diseases. He could start with molecular phenomena and proceed to biochemistry, electrophysiology and genetics and then into psychology and sociology; but I doubt that much would be gained by making such a catalogue. There are important points to be clarified and settled before that.

WHITEHORN: Dr. Mettler has raised the issue of how to determine pertinence for the purpose of communication.

GRINKER: During the war some soldiers were subjected to great anxiety over long periods of time. Associated with the anxiety were profound somatic changes which persisted long after it had ceased. For a conference on the subject the most distinguished talent was assembled. The chief performer was a distinguished professor who catalogued from A to Z all the possible tests that should be conducted on the subjects with anxiety. Actually what we wanted were hunches that were pertinent to the problem.

SCOTT: The only effective way to plan and conduct research is by systematic procedure. The investigator settles upon an area in which the facts are missing and then tries to gather the facts. The primary need in science is facts; the systematic gathering of facts is the basis of science. This is quite different from the clinical approach. If the investigator sets up an animal experiment by following a hunch from clinical practice, the results are apt to be unsatisfactory. They either do not support the hunch or cannot be confirmed in other hands. This approach does not lead to the accumulation of background information; instead it contributes confusion.

POPE: We have come back to the role of the basic scientist in interdisciplinary research on human beings. I should like to relate my experience in trying to conduct studies on brain tissues from patients classified in various psychiatric categories. Using biopsy specimens of cerebral cortex excised during frontal lobotomy, we have studied the quantitative microchemistry of enzymes in the cortical architectonic layers. Neuropathological examinations were likewise made, mainly for purposes of control. I must confess that my main motivation has been to obtain and study specimens of human brain under conditions suitable for biochemical analyses. At the same time we have tried to take advantage of the opportunity for recording certain facts concerning the patients for possible future correlations between laboratory findings and clinical status. The problem is: What kind of questions should the psychiatrists be asked about these patients that would be relevant and logically defensible? I do not believe anybody will quarrel with the possibility of making valid correlations between observations made with the method of physical science and behavioristic descriptions of these patients, nor with the likelihood that such correlations would be accepted without question. The hitch comes in deciding whether one is to record, in addition, simple formulations of psychodynamics. The point at issue is whether it is possible to correlate statements of physical fact with statements having to do with motivation and meaning without getting into logical difficulties; that is, whether an attempt at correlating statements between the two language systems does not mean mixing different universes of discourse and therefore making questions which would violate syntactical rules and be "nonsensical" in the logician's sense. I have had great difficulty in getting psychiatrists to think about this problem; to try to understand its nature; after taking it into account, to figure out what one might or might not be able to learn by such interdisciplinary study. The basic scientist who studies individuals with mental disease runs into the problem of being leader of the project and encountering inertia from the psychiatrist in thinking about its significance, just as the psychiatrist often encounters it when he tries to associate the basic scientist in a project primarily his own.

JASPER: Having been continually frustrated for the past twenty years in trying to make progress in collaborative research and having gone through a defeatist point of view, I can sympathize with Dr. Mettler. But I now refuse to accept that viewpoint as necessary. Moreover, I believe that at the moment the situation is not as dismal as Dr. Mettler would make out; for neuroanatomists and neurophysiologists are actually interested in mental disease, as well as in their own little curiosities in the laboratory. Indeed, when one sees a physiologist absorbed in a narrow, specific, seemingly isolated problem in the laboratory, it is sobering to realize that his motivation may reach back very far. Actually he may be very much interested in how his problem can fit into others of greater significance. Sometimes I wonder whether anyone would continue being interested in what a spike is in an oscilloscope if it were not for the motivation in the background.

The next step is the choice of areas that are fruitful for cooperation. That innumerable topics for study can be listed is not an exclusive characteristic of mental disease. In neurophysiology a list of 500 problems for investigation can be prepared, but those which seem likely to be rich in results are selected. From cooperation with men of experience in the psychiatric field, the neurophysiologist expects expert opinion on which of the numerous topics are most promising for study. I hope that a group like this will carefully select or propose only three or four topics worth intensive study rather than an indiscriminate list. Such hunches would be received with much confidence.

For example, we are conducting a series of studies on functions of the temporal lobe in man. We have found that stimulating electrodes will bring out in great detail long-lost memories that the patient is otherwise unable to recover. That they are memories can, of course, be validated. How are we going to make use of the constant flow of data on the subjective responses of patients to electrical stimulation of the temporal lobe? At this point the psychiatrist who wants to understand the mechanism of repression, memory, and recall in certain circumstances should step in and indicate how the studies might be adapted to reveal information on these phenomena.

WHITEHORN: Dr. Scott used the significant phrase, "facts that are missing." That raises a fascinating question of how one's attention is directed to the possible existence of a fact that one does not have. Presumably it is because one becomes aware of a vacant spot in a conception of things and recognizes that something ought to fill this void. To have a notion that the fact is missing implies some structuring of the field of inquiry. In a way Dr. Jasper's request is to cultivate an awareness of the missing links between the different areas of work.

ALEXANDER: Not long ago I read an article by a Professor of Chemistry at Manchester on this subject. He emphasized that particularly in the nineteenth century and the beginning of this century the development of science could be better compared with growth than progress by planned blueprinted procedure. For example, a scientist in New York City working on a problem reaches a conclusion. In the course of his work it comes to his attention that in Berlin ten years ago an investigator made observations pertinent to the same problem. Then searching further, the New York scientist finds that forty years ago in a French journal a mathematical theorem was proposed which is applicable to this particular problem. Thus the Professor emphasized that science is a collaborative enterprise which is loosely organized but not blueprinted and planned. I was therefore much interested in the suggestion that lists of topics for investigation should be prepared. That is how science is not made. A scientist does not work out a plan that he will investigate a particular problem for information, and that he will assign one part to a worker and turn over another part to a colleague. That is how factory work is done; there, what is to be achieved is known. It is not research. It is application of knowledge to a goal-directed purpose. Because we live now in an industrial civilization, we are beginning to model inquiry, the quest for new knowledge, after the pattern of industrial production. Investigative science is not industrial production.

In contrast to the industrial approach, an investigator comes across a problem and then he sets about to find pertinent information that has been contributed previously by others. As was just asked, how can gaps be filled? A search in scientific journals is one means. But to go through the bibliographic indices is a tedious task. Hence, a conference on one topic, bringing together persons whose contributions might be pertinent, is a desirable arrangement; for it facilitates intercommunication and thus conduces to an exchange of ideas. Furthermore, if the investigator needs information, advice, and technical assistance outside his field, he should come to know where to obtain it.

POPE: Tremendously large research projects, which are essentially along developmental lines, will lead nowhere. They are fine, once the primary crucial observation has been made. But all the money in the world would not necessarily, for example, have brought about the discovery of uranium fission. Once the latter was established, then the developmental project could make the fission bomb.

In the interdisciplinary type of research, the establishment of new outposts is more than doubly difficult because it almost invariably means the coming together of two people who happen to have the right type of information and interest to interlock and form a proper research project. This is short of the ideal person who knows all about two fields. Such events are rather unlikely to occur just at random. Meetings like the present Conference are excellent for the very purpose of catalyzing cross-knowledge, which might lead investigators in different areas to get together and have an idea among them that leads to the establishment of such new outposts.

METTLER: I evidently created an impression which is totally erroneous, namely, that I am discouraged and feel defeatist about collaborative research on mental disease. Nothing is further from the fact. If I were discouraged, I would not be currently engaged in collaborative research through organizations which we have set up in three psychiatric institutions, where we have teams of 30 in one place, 42 in another, and 16 in another. We are in fact actually engaged in collaborative research on a very extensive scale. Neither do I think that there is any dearth of things which might be done. Indeed that explains my attitude. There are so many things that need to be done that an afternoon could not possibly exhaust the number.

What I want to emphasize is the fact that multidisciplinary research, like the investigation of the individual, must be on the basis of totality. It is not just a question of investigating the social pattern of the individual. That is fine, but it is not a basic phenomenon. Of course, it should be studied. But it may very well be that as one proceeds, one will find that there are whole groups of people in the area of mental illness in whom the activities occurring in their environment had absolutely nothing whatsoever to do with what happened to them as mental patients. On the other hand, there are individuals in whom the activities of the social environment are primary factors. Probably in the great majority of the mentally ill, several factors are interacting. Whether one problem is more important than another, is the kind of comparison which is out of place here. To judge whether one piece of research is more significant than another is often a difficult decision.

I am perfectly willing to play hunches, and I do play them. I agree that the important thing is the research which gets results and gives knowledge.

BINGER: In a historical vein, I should like to recall the origin of the Rockefeller Institute and the Rockefeller Hospital, when medicine was still in an undeveloped and unsophisticated state in this country. Dr. William H. Welch and Dr. Simon Flexner, in starting the Institute at the beginning of the century, gathered men around them like S. J. Meltzer, Jacques Loeb, P. A. Levine, pure scientists devoted to physiological and clinical sciences. Later they brought in men like Noguchi and Peyton Rous in parasitology and cancer research.

Ten years after the founding of Rockefeller Institute, the Hospital of the Institute was established. Scientists at the Institute said, "This is a magnificent opportunity. Now we will apply our pure research to clinical phenomena in the hospital." Dr. Rufus Cole, the director of the Hospital, was a very farsighted man. He replied, "Absolutely no. This is going to be a clinical research hospital where the doctors will do the research."

He set up an ideal institution for the study of diseases. It was decided to study pneumonia and heart disease; research on degenerative diseases was added later. The whole hospital was organized around the research program; the chiefs of the various departments were well-trained clinicians who also were grounded in fundamental science. There was cross-fertilization between the Institute and the Hospital; but the clinicians formulated and studied the clinical problems.

I believe that psychiatry is now in the state that medicine was then. Until psychiatrists take the responsibility for defining the problems, planning the research, and then seeking assistance from experts in other disciplines as needed, I do not believe that research on mental disease will make much headway. I doubt very much whether collaborative research is possible unless there is leadership. That is the psychiatrists' job.

One of the reasons why we seem to be at cross-purposes is that the psychiatrists themselves have not assumed this job.

SCOTT: In our laboratory we have a system for carrying on interdisciplinary research that has worked well for a number of years. The principles on which we set it up are (1) The group should be small, not more than four or five people. (2) The group should like each other. Members are not chosen at random and told to work together. Rather, the original members of the group have a chance to choose their colleagues. (3) The group is constituted so that each individual has a specialty in which he is supreme in the particular group. Each is interested in the other's work; each has a reason for respecting the other. But members do not compete with each other. This situation is both highly pleasant and stimulating. In such a group there is a need for leadership and direction so that the members adhere to important work and do not digress into side lines. Someone in the group, preferably more than one person, should know what problems are important.

In presenting a list of research problems here, I was not implying that anyone present ought to undertake all of them. In trying to orient research, I have several different frames of reference. From them, certain problems appear to be important. I wanted to show missing areas and to indicate my hunches in these areas. I gave the list as examples. There is enough evidence behind them to indicate that any future research along those lines might be relevant.

In applying this approach, it would not do to tell a colleague to work on a partic-ular problem. I know from experience that a problem can be brought to a creative scientist without necessarily kindling an interest for it in him. What can be done is to encourage him if he shows an interest.

WHITEHORN: We might perhaps have benefited if we had focused on particular problems which in clinical psychiatry are now extremely important; they might have served for possible exchange of concepts and formulation of research to further our understanding. For example, the use of electroconvulsive therapy might profitably have been considered. What is the rationale? How does it work? What are its shortcomings? What is the explanation for its failures? What are the possibilities for more effective use? The same questions might have been put concerning the varieties of insulin therapy. We have had a number of references about lobotomy in recent years; there is still probably much to be done with this technic. A new drug, chlorpromazine, has aroused an enormous interest. What dynamic interpretations would bring an understanding of how it works in apparent reduction of overactivity? That also holds for the Rauwolfia alkaloids. Any of these topics might serve to bring out the possibility of contributions for the enlargement of knowledge in the fields in which we have experts present. I am sure that we do not come to the end of our session with lack of material or ideas. We are all eager, I am sure, that the proceedings of the two Conferences be preserved to serve as reminders to us and as possible stimuli to others. Then the views and procedures might be shared on a larger scale.

Index

Set in Intertype Baskerville

Format by Norma Stahl

Manufactured by The Haddon Craftsmen, Inc.

Published by PAUL B. HOEBER, INC., *New York*

Medical Book Department of HARPER & BROTHERS